DEATHWATCH
THE JERICHO REACH

ROLEPLAYING IN THE GRIM
DARKNESS OF THE 41ST MILLENNIUM

CREDITS

LEAD DEVELOPER
Andrew Fischer

WRITTEN AND DEVELOPED BY
Owen Barnes, Nathan Dowdell, John Dunn, Jordan Goldfarb, Andy Hoare, Charles May, Eric Sarlin, Sam Stewart, and Ross Watson

EDITING
Graham Davey

PROOFREADING
Mark Pollard

GRAPHIC DESIGN
Evan Simonet

COVER ART
Michael Phillippi

INTERIOR ART
Jacob Atienza, Matt Bradbury, Christopher Burdett, Victor P. Corbella, Zach Graves, Nikolaus Ingeneri, Jason Juta, Ameen Naksewee, David Auden Nash, and Sept13

MANAGING ART DIRECTOR
Andrew Navaro

ART DIRECTION
Andy Christensen

PRODUCTION MANAGER
Eric Knight

LICENSING AND DEVELOPMENT COORDINATOR
Deb Beck

EXECUTIVE GAME DESIGNER
Corey Konieczka

EXECUTIVE PRODUCER
Michael Hurley

PUBLISHER
Christian T. Petersen

Games Workshop

LICENSING MANAGERS
John French and Owen Rees

HEAD OF LICENSING
Jon Gillard

HEAD OF INTELLECTUAL PROPERTY
Alan Merrett

HEAD OF LICENSING, LEGAL AND STRATEGIC PROJECTS
Andy Jones

SPECIAL THANKS
Playtest Coordinator Ron DeValk, "The Bolter and Chainsword Playtest Group" Ryan Powell with Matt Bogart, Jon Cox, Max Hardenbrook, Matt Hunt, Steve Koelzer, Anders Lang, and Richard Sanders, "No Guts, No Glory" Sean Connor with Adam Lloyd, Aaron McManus-Wood, Stephen Pitson, Mark Smith, and Simon Tierney, "The Librarians" Pim Mauve with Keesjan Kleef, Jan-Cees Voogd, Joris Voogd, and Gerlof Woudstra, "Roll Perils" Matt Eustace with Sean Kelly, Rob Lord, Stuart Lord, and Mike Madani, "Veterans of a Psychic War" Benn Williams with Chris Lancaster, Scott Philips, John Ross, Rebecca Williams, and Eric Young, "You Bid Babies?!?" Jordan Millward with Keri Harthoorn, Kyle Harthoorn-Burton, Kieren Smith, and Julia Smith, "Unrepentant" Lachlan "Raith" Conley with Jordan Dixon, Mark McLaughlin, and Brad Twaddell

FANTASY FLIGHT GAMES

Fantasy Flight Games
1975 West County Road B2
Roseville, MN 55113
USA

ISBN: 978-1-58994-785-6 Product Code: DW08 Print ID: 1214FEB12

Printed in China

For more information about the DEATHWATCH line, free downloads, answers to rule queries, or just to pass on greetings, visit us online at
www.FantasyFlightGames.com

CONTENTS

INTRODUCTION

As the Achilus Crusade raged through the Jericho Reach, it redefined system after system, forging a new Imperial sector from the ashes. But now, the Crusade has faltered; the devouring Tyranids, cunning Tau, and fiendish armies of Chaos have proved a worthy match for the forces of Lord Militant Tetrarchus, and the Crusade now teeters upon the brink of disaster.

The Space Marines of the Deathwatch stand as the unseen defense that protects the Achilus Crusade from its looming demise. Acting behind the scenes, unbeknownst to the majority of the Imperium, the Deathwatch holds back and counters xenos threats from every side. Their treacherous missions bring them to every corner of the Reach, and the veterans of Watch Fortress Erioch know the stars of the Jericho Reach like the backs of their hands.

WHAT'S IN THIS BOOK?

The previous DEATHWATCH sourcebook THE ACHILUS ASSAULT took a comprehensive look at the history of Jericho Reach, and explored the tumultuous unfolding of the Achilus Crusade. THE JERICHO REACH explores elements of the setting not discussed in THE ACHILUS ASSAULT, delving into detail on allies, adversaries, and worlds that define the struggles of Kill-teams currently operating throughout the Reach. Each chapter of this book examines the personalities, planets, and themes of a specific salient, as well as providing players and GMs alike with important resources for integrating the setting more deeply in their campaign.

CHAPTER I: THE NIGHTMARE SALIENT

The Space Marines of the Deathwatch have mastered the art of fighting the countless xenos of the galaxy. However, missions often bring Kill-teams deep into the Hadex Anomaly and, despite their speciality, the Battle-Brothers must contend with the forces of Chaos that control the systems there. This chapter explores the centre of the Reach, providing players and GMs resources for their campaign in the Acheros Salient. It also delves into the war that consumes the Cellebos Warzone, outlining rules for simulating the full scale planetary battles that rage there.

CHAPTER II: THE GREATER GOOD

The Velkhan'Sept started as the primary target for the Achilus in the beginning years of his crusade. But as the decades stretched on, much greater threats have reared their heads, leaving the Canis Salient stagnating, lead by the increasing unstable Commander Ebongrave. This chapter is an invaluable resource for Kill-teams operating in the unpredictable battleground of the Canis Salient, providing background and tools for navigating not just the hostile Tau systems, but the turbulent political landscape of Crusade leadership in the salient.

CHAPTER III: THE GREAT DEVOURER

The ravening hordes of Hive Fleet Dagon continue to gather momentum as they swarm over the hapless star of the Orpheus Salient. This chapter delves into the worlds that now fight for their lives against the Great Devourer. It also presents a host of Tyranid creatures new to the Deathwatch setting, including the massive Heirophant Bio-Titan!

CHAPTER IV: FALL INTO DARKNESS

Finally, this book also includes an adventure set on the world of Khnum. Deep within the Orpheus Salient, this planet is in the final stages of being consumed by the Tyranids of Hive Fleet Dagon. When the Deathwatch receives an astropathic distress signal from inside the planet, the Kill-team is immediately dispatched to investigate. The Battle-Brothers will have to fight their way through monstrous Tyranid adversaries as they work to uncover the source of the mysterious message.

THE NIGHTMARE SALIENT

CHAPTER 1: THE NIGHTMARE SALIENT

"Death and glory, horror and bravery, loyalty and corruption—all these can be found here. But mostly death."

–Lord General Ovidius

Of the three Salients that divide the Jericho Reach, the Acheros Salient is the smallest in total number of planets, but it has also been the most fiercely contested. Every time the Imperial forces drive further towards the Hadex Anomaly, the Chaos-worshipping Stigmartus push back with twice as much fervour. This back and forth has turned the small stretch of stars now known as the Cellebos Warzone into a bloody meat-grinder, consuming the lives of the millions of Imperial soldiers committed there every year.

The bloody stalemate between the two forces has been a constant drain on the rest of the Achilus Crusade. It has pulled untold amounts of materiel from the other two salients to fuel the endless war against the Stigmartus, and, many commanders believe, left the other Imperial forces unprepared to deal with the arrival of Hive Fleet Dagon.

OVERVIEW OF THE ACHEROS SALIENT

Before the Age of Shadow fell over the Jericho Reach, the area now known as the Acheros Salient was known as the Calitar subsector, and was the political and spiritual centre of the entire Jericho Sector. The capital of Verronus stood at the centre of the Sub-Sector as a shining example of Imperial culture, the Sector Lord himself ruling from one of its monolithic hive cities. The Calitar subsector was a bustling centre of trade and production, and Verronus was its beating heart.

What little has been recovered from the ruined archives now consumed by the Hadex Anomaly indicates that the Age of Shadow had a rapid and devastating effect on Verronus and the surrounding systems. As the warp storms tightened their grip on the sector, trade dwindled and the sprawling hive cities that covered the surface of Verronus began to starve. Rebellion started quickly, and by the time the first Rogue Traders braved the warp storms to determine the Sector's fate, the entire region was in total anarchy.

As the sector plunged even deeper into darkness, small pockets of humanity still loyal to the Imperium remained, clinging to the light of the Emperor. However, with limited resources, and assailed from every side by ambitious warlords and the worshippers of the Ruinous Powers, they inevitably fell. Within a matter of generations, the subsector that had been the crown jewel of the Jericho Sector became a debased hive of murderers and thieves who aligned themselves with the Dark Powers of the warp.

There are many theories throughout the Imperial Forces in the Reach regarding the formation of the Hadex Anomaly, but the only true evidence of its genesis now lies deep in the record halls of Watch Fortress Erioch. While the Jericho Sector descended into anarchy, the Deathwatch could only observe from their Watch Stations, incapable of saving humanity from its own treachery. So as the Space Marines on the Long Watch waited out the dark millennia of the Age of Shadow, they stayed ever vigilant to the movements of the enemies of the Imperium, even as the worlds of the Reach lay in ruins. As the years stretched on, the Deathwatch viewed the Calitar subsector with little concern. They were more concerned with the machinations of xenos races than the actions of Chaos-worshippers and traitors. However in 656. M40, all this changed.

Records stored in the massive halls of Watch Fortress Erioch indicate that the Hadex Anomaly came into being during a planetary alignment late in that year. What little can be gleaned from these documents indicates that a vortex of warp energies burst into real space, consuming the entirety of the Calitar subsector and some surrounding systems, and leaving a permanent tear in reality marring the middle of the Reach. The records state that the vortex was the result of a sacrificial ritual of horrific proportion performed by cults in the Verronus system worshipping the Ruinous Powers, but no real evidence remains that can substantiate these accounts.

Since the time of its formation, the Hadex Anomaly has haunted the Jericho Reach, casting out its malign radiation and corrupting hundreds of different worlds. Measurements performed over the centuries in Watch Fortress Ormasim indicate that, since its creation, the Anomaly has continued to grow fractionally every year, slowly pulling the worlds of the Reach into its dark grasp.

EARLY ADVANCES

After coming through the warp gate, Lord Militant Tiber Achilus' first priority was to establish a solid foothold in the Jericho Reach, so he set his eyes on the planet of Karlack. The planet had been of little note before the Age of Shadow, and this insignificance had kept it relatively safe from the roving bands of marauders and warlords of Khazant that had ravaged the Reach over the past millennia. The populace still clung to derivations of the ancient rituals of the Imperium, and welcomed the forces of the Crusade with open arms.

A beachhead was quickly established on Karlack as the Crusade forces spread out and secured the other systems around the warp gate. One of the primary objectives of the Crusade from its outset was the world of Khazant. Its warlords were a persistent threat to the rest of the Reach, and the corrupted inhabitants of the world were anathema to everything the Imperium stands for. Unfortunately, the looming threat of the Tau presence in the coreward edge of the Reach was too great a threat to ignore, and Lord Militant Achilus redeployed the majority of the troops in the Reach to Operation Hammerfall—a multi-planet offensive to drive the Tau back towards the Black Reef.

As Operation Hammerfall forced the Tau to fall back, the remaining battlegroups began reclaiming the worlds around the Iron Collar. The battlegroup charged with reclaiming the area towards the centre of the Reach was under the command of Lord General Ovidius, a veteran commander who had served alongside Achilus in countless campaigns across his career. His task was not only to establish a perimeter around the Iron Collar, but also to scout out enemy resistance on the world of Khazant, which still remained a primary target for the Crusade.

Ovidius' initial scouting reports painted Khazant as a valuable world to the Crusade. Centuries of plunder had left the many warlords that now controlled the planet in control of incredible resources and manpower, and the infighting among them left the world open to attack. Meanwhile, Operation Hammerfall had succumbed to catastrophe. Necessary reinforcements never arrived, and worlds that had been left in the wake of the advancing troops and thought compliant began to rise up. Seeing that the Crusade needed a new direction to give the troops a sense of progress, Achilus left the battle against the Tau in the hands of Lorgath Maclir and the Imperial Commanders. He thenheaded to the centre of the Reach to wage a campaign against the world of Khazant.

THE HISTORY OF THE ACHILUS CRUSADE

This section provides an overview of the Achilus Crusade, specifically as it relates to the Acheros Salient. A broader look at the history of the Crusade can be found in THE ACHILUS ASSAULT.

The campaign to take Khazant stretched over a bloody year, costing Imperial forces greatly as the warlords fought back with an unexpected fervour. Finally, the Imperial forces triumphed from sheer strength of numbers, and the remaining warlords fled back towards the Charon Stars. Instead of pursuing his fleeing adversaries, Achilus had Ovidius consolidate his forces in the area to prepare for future operations. They could not have expected that letting these warlords live would create the most dangerous foe the Achilus Crusade would face.

NEW RESOLVE

The unexpected loss of Tiber Achilus to the warp and the appointment of Tetrarchus brought about a complete change in the structure of the Crusade. Tetrarchus' plan to break the Crusade into three separate Salients saw a political battle for leadership of these three different fronts, and many of the commanders who had become comfortably favoured by the old Lord Militant found themselves completely out of the running.

As Tetrarchus began reforming the Crusade, his primary concern was to take the worlds near the centre of the Reach. Not only had they been the former seats of power in the Jericho Sector, but the forces of Chaos that now dwelled there posed a significant risk to the Crusade in all areas of the Reach. Not trusting the monumental task of pushing into the Hadex Anomaly to any other commander, Tetrarchus personally took command of the newly christened "Acheros Salient."

Although this change of leadership frustrated Ovidius, he was not forgotten like so many other commanders under the new leadership. Even though the Lord General had gained his position due to his history with Achilus, he was a wise commander, and Tetrarchus greatly valued his advice. Because of this, Ovidius kept a significant amount of command over the new Salient, acting as Tetrarchus' right hand as the battlegroup began moving deeper into the Reach.

Still fresh from Achilus' victory in the campaign on Khazant, both commanders felt confident in the battlegroup's superiority over the rag tag forces of Chaos scattered amongst the stars around the Hadex Anomaly. At the advice of the Lord General, Tetrarchus spread the battlegroup's forces out across multiple systems, and began a steady advance towards the borders of the Anomaly, sure that even dispersed, their forces would be more than a match for the scattered renegades. This strategy saw rapid results as forces claimed dozens of planets, including Vanity and the Blood Trinity, but left the battlegroup woefully unprepared for the organised counterattack that was bearing down on them.

With remarkable speed and coordination, forces from deep inside the Hadex Anomaly struck out against the advancing

Imperial battlegroup. Consisting of elements of the Khazantian warlords vanquished five years prior, this cult of zealous worshippers (who were to become known as the Stigmartus) struck a devastating blow against the Imperial forces. Ovidius' cruiser was lost in the first strike, leaving Tetrarchus reeling without the advice of his closest counsellor in the Salient. As the Imperial forces desperately tried to consolidate their forces and recover, the Stigmartus warriors reclaimed nearly all the systems near the Hadex Anomaly—giving birth to the Cellebos Warzone.

THE CELLEBOS WARZONE

After the Stigmartus' initial attack, Tetrarchus quickly organised the battlegroup to counterattack, realising that a quick response was the only way to prevent the Stigmartus from fortifying their hold on the Cellebos Warzone. But as the fleet began to move back into the Warzone, it became obvious that these were not the same scattered warlords they had vanquished five years prior. The Stigmartus were a well organised war machine that seemed to have near unlimited resources as they poured out of the Hadex Anomaly into the Cellebos Warzone.

To compensate for the Stigmartus' unnatural amount of resources, Tetrarchus began pulling more forces from the Callixis Sector through the warp gate, and also began relocating materiel from other Salients to aid in the fierce battle for the Cellebos Warzone. Years began to stretch on and little progress was made; Imperial forces would take a planet, only to lose it to a fresh wave of Stigmartus streaming out of the Anomaly. The planets of the Cellebos Warzone quickly became charred battlefields, barely hospitable to life after decades of constant war.

As the years passed, the situation began to destabilise in the other Salients. The Tyranids relentlessly devoured the rimward edge of the Reach, while the Tau fought back with pernicious tactics that confounded Imperial commanders. Tetrarchus' attention was required in far too many places for the Lord Militant to continue devoting all of his attention to the bloody stalemate against the Stigmartus.

Tetrarchus assigned command of the Acheros Salient to Lord Admiral Gorvus Xant of the Imperial Navy, a man who had been instrumental in preventing the Stigmartus fleet from completely overrunning Imperial forces in the Salient. Aboard his flagship, the *Sword of Macharius*, Xant oversaw some of the boldest manoeuvres seen in the Salient in decades. However, his daring tactics were only rewarded with disaster, as he was continuously defeated in ground battles. Under his leadership, the Salient saw a significant loss of ground in the Cellebos Warzone, and many called for him to be replaced.

As the Salient dramatically lost ground, Xant organised a massive push far beyond the Cellebos Warzone, into Stigmartus controlled systems. His plan was to lay siege to the planet of Vespasia and disrupt the flow of Stigmartus troops to the Warzone, giving the battlegroup some respite from the relentless onslaught. This time, Xant's daring plan was successful, but he would pay the ultimate price. During the siege, the bridge of the *Sword of Macharius* was struck by

an orbital defence platform, killing the Lord-Admiral and the majority of his command staff. This turn of events left the strike force directionless as they assaulted the well defended Stigmartus world.

In the void left by the leadership's sudden loss, Magratha von Karlack, then a young Adjutant, stepped forward to lead the remainder of the Imperial forces. From a young age she had been trained to be a figurehead and a leader for the troops of the Achilus Crusade, and she saw this as the perfect opportunity to fulfil her destiny. She gathered together all the Guardsmen still aboard the *Sword of Macharius*, and launched towards the planet with every available drop pod on board the ship. Her bold actions paid off, and the Imperial Guard forces managed to take the keeps of Vespasia, securing a great advantage for the Imperium in the Acheros Salient.

After her decisive victory, Magratha demanded that Tetrarchus put her in charge of the Acheros Salient. The Lord-Commander did not refuse; Magratha had proven herself in battle, and was extremely popular amongst the Guardsmen of the Salient. Since she has taken command of the Salient, it has seen more success than in decades, her bold leadership inspiring the men to new levels of determination and bravery in the battle against the vile Stigmartus.

WORLDS OF THE ACHEROS SALIENT

"The sickly light of the Hadex Anomaly lights our night sky, the looming threat of Chaos is always at our doorstep, but we shall not despair, for the Emperor Protects!"

–General Helga Vastorpoole

Aseemingly endless conflict rages on through the stars of the Cellebos Warzone, consuming dozens of worlds in the fires of war. But behind the battle lines many Imperial worlds thrive, standing as bastions against the corrupting influence of Chaos and the Hadex Anomaly.

PYRATHAS

"A less likely place for life, I have never seen."

–Captain Dominique Valduris of the *Omnissiah's Dispatch*

In a galaxy plagued with oddities and anomalies, Pyrathas nevertheless deserves mention. Although ignored by the humans of the ancient Jericho Sector, this world was set to become a lynchpin in the Iron Collar and a vital resource to the Acheros Salient.

Pyrathas was discovered almost by accident, in the second year of the Crusade. As the Crusade fleets advanced into what would become the Iron Collar, Explorator ships ranged ahead, cataloguing new worlds for conquest. When the frigate *Omnissiah's Dispatch* dropped out of warp on the edges of System Designate 018-9J0-5B, they found a system dominated by a fierce blue-white supergiant star. The fury of the star's heat had long ago blasted every planet to half-molten cinders—save one. An immense jovian world, Pyrathas Majorus (itself a smouldering brown dwarf star) whipped around the supergiant in a tidally locked orbit. Tucked safely in its penumbra, a single moon was likewise tidally locked, heated by the embers of its planet, and containing a breathable atmosphere. The captain decided to investigate.

The moon that would become known as Pyrathas was a harsh, inhospitable place. Low gravity had created a world of towering cliffs, high mountains, and deep fjords. The constant gravitational stresses generated massive volcanoes, leaving the atmosphere a grey haze, and life had not evolved past hardy lichens and mosses. At first glance, Pyrathas had nothing useful to offer the Crusade. However, Lord Militant Achilus and his staff saw an opportunity in Pyrathas—a shielded anchorage, protected by the fury of its sun, and ideally placed between the fortress-worlds of Karlack and Hethgard.

On Achilus' command, Pyrathas became the latest link in the rapidly forming Iron Collar. The rough terrain proved ideally suited for fortifications. Legions of Munitorium convict-labourers capped the mountains with adamantium bastions and dug extensive launch bays for Lightning and Thunderbolt fighters into the cliffs. In areas of active vulcanism, they sank deep geothermal shunts to power concealed defence laser batteries. Meanwhile, the Mechanicus constructed large orbital docks around the moon to service the needs of the myriad warships that would soon come. In one short decade, Pyrathas was the Iron Collar's second largest anchorage for the Imperial Navy, surpassed only by Karlack itself.

Unlike the majority of the other fortress-worlds, the Navy took some pains to conceal Pyrathas' exact location from its adversaries. Pyrathas' coordinates are considered a Magenta level secret, and the signs and counter-signs to enter gun range are only possessed by the pilots of system defence monitors who wait on the edges of the star system to escort arriving vessels. Of course, the Navy realised that it could not maintain Pyrathas' location as a secret forever, and also installed scores of orbital laser and torpedo batteries.

In the years since, Pyrathas has become a valuable fortress in the Iron Collar. When the Orpheus Salient succeeded well beyond the Crusade's plans, Pyrathas served as a transit centre for Guard regiments and military supplies retasked to the nearby Acheros Salient. Then, when the tendrils of Hive Fleet Dagon began to curl around the Crusade forces in the Orpheus Salient, Pyrathas saw its role reappraised. It remained a transit centre, but the flow of men and materials reversed to staunch the dangers of Dagon.

Certain Crusade commanders (Pyrathas' Captain Skor among them) have privately voiced the opinion that should the Tyranid hive fleet defeat the Crusade and consume the Jericho Reach, Pyrathas may prove a final refuge against the swarm. The furious glare of the blue supergiant makes approaching the anchorage without the protection of void shields suicidal, and thus far the Tyranid hive ships encountered do not have a suitable alternative. These commanders argue (amongst themselves, where their thoughts may not be labelled sedition by the Commissariat) that should the Crusade falter and fail, what Imperial Guard and Fleet elements that could not be evacuated through the warp gate should be pulled back to Pyrathas, where they can wait for an Imperial counter-offensive.

Some even more pessimistic voices argue that the more likely outcome is that the Imperium would attempt to destroy the warp gate. Although this would strand the forces remaining within the Jericho reach, they postulate that the Tyranids would wipe out the Chaos and Tau-held worlds, leaving Imperial forces free to "pick up the scraps" after they passed.

What none of these individuals speak of, but all fear, is that the supreme adaptability of the Tyranids may lead to some new way for them to endure Pyrathas' glare, and consume the world anyway.

KEY LOCATIONS

Due to the unique stellar architecture of Pyrathas, many of the fortress-world's installations are concentrated in orbit. However, the Imperial Guard still maintains substantial fortifications on the surface, along with Munitorium supply depots, sustenance-mills, and mining installations.

Adamant Station

Pyrathas' primary orbital installation, Adamant Station looms over the moon like a vast, ironwork spiderweb. Adamant is an orbital warehouse, the void-dock for dozens of ships at any one time. Stretching many hundreds of kilometres across the sky, this mid-orbit installation is so large that it is easily visible from the surface.

Scores of defence laser batteries comprise the outermost sections of Adamant Station, linked together with massive adamantium chains and straining grav-links. Together, these stations provide an interlinking field of lance fire covering many of the approaches to the station—with free-orbiting batteries on the far side of the moon defending against the rest.

Further inward, the station becomes a maze of docking bays, loading stations, and orbital cargo vaults. These facilities allow the flow of vital supplies between two Crusade salients. Naval anchorages are segregated from the transport docks, though most of the Navy warships prefer independent orbital anchorages high above Adamant.

The centre of the station hosts its command basilica, as well as vast gaping launch bays for flights of Furies, Starhawks, and other attack craft. In the centre is a massive orbital tower, capable of ferrying large quantities of men and supplies to the surface installations.

Since the crisis of the Orpheus Salient, Adamant's facilities have been working triple-shifts to accommodate the increased movement of supplies. In the perpetual darkness of Pyrathas' Majorus' shadow, arc-welders, manoeuvring thrusters, and stab-lights illuminate the facility in an inconstant, actinic glare. In such conditions, accidents are quite common, and the rate of fatalities amongst the indentured workers and even able voidmen has steadily increased.

To maintain the urgent work pace, the Navy has begun searching far afield for warm bodies to replace Adamant's losses. This is no easy task, however. In these desperate times, manpower has become a valuable commodity in the Crusade. Many Imperial Navy voidships have suffered heavy losses in the battles against the Tyranids. Too many vessels struggled back to port as half-gutted hulks, their crews decimated by the horrific monsters used by the Tyranids as boarders. Not only does repairing these vessels require far too much time and effort from Adamant's facilities, the ships' captains demand facilities like Adamant give up their best trained crews to replace their losses.

All this means that Adamant is severely understaffed. Captain Skor continues to place ever more tersely worded requests to Commodore Hemelschot about the manpower situation, however the Commodore has his own concerns and may not be able to help.

The situation is desperate enough that some senior Bosuns have taken to ambushing isolated groups of Guardsmen passing through the station and press-ganging them into the Navy. In response, the Commissariat and senior sergeants of the Imperial Guard have taken to escorting their men en masse from transports to the surface installations (which are under Imperial Guard control), even releasing small arms to their men to defend themselves. Needless to say, this has only increased tensions on the station, and already several reports of isolated skirmishes have arrived on Skor's desk.

Some senior warrant officers whisper that the Captain is considering another means of solving his problem. They say he's been in constant talks with Lieutenant-Commander Alaxis McKale about leading an expedition off-station in order to find additional personnel somewhere else.

Pyrathas Surface

The surface of Pyrathas is a hellish, inhospitable place; a craggy world of jutting peaks, sharp ridges, and deep fjords, with little life beyond hardy algae and lichens. The climate is exacerbated by the world's unique stellar geometry. As it is tidally locked with Pyrathas Majorus, half the world has never seen the sun. On this side of Pyrathas, the fjords fill with glaciers and every peak is covered with a cap of snow that has not melted in millions of years. At the far point, the very air is so cold that it can freeze a man's lungs the moment he inhales.

On the other side, the baleful but muted glare of Pyrathas Majorus warms the world like hands held close to a smouldering ember. Here life is possible, but only just. The constant glow from the brown dwarf keeps its moon above freezing, but the world is constantly lit by a deep red glow. Those stationed here find this so psychologically unsettling that the thick shutters covering most of the structures' windows remain permanently sealed.

Even so, the installations on Pyrathas have grown to an impressive size, even larger than Adamant Station above it. Scattered along the rocky cliffs of one of Pyrathas' larger oceans, the fortifications have been dubbed Fortress Illium, and they have capped the cliffs and ridges in steel and adamantium.

Illium is centred around the base of the orbital tower that links it to Adamant Station. Through it flows a constant torrent of supplies and Imperial Guardsmen—the former destined for the vast supply caverns cut into the bedrock below the base, the latter to wait inside the labyrinthine stretches of barracks surrounding the central bastion.

Most of Illium's installations—supply caverns, barracks, sustenance processors, hab-farms, laboritoriums, medicae facilities, repair and maintenance depots, and even a small forge maintained by the Adeptus Mechanicus—exist within the miles of caverns carved under the surface. The population of a major city lives, works, and prepares to fight under the ground.

Above their heads, thousands of kilometres of trenches, bastions, fortifications, walls, and razor wire stretch out from the central bastion. Every sector has overlapping artillery emplacements, supported by shorter ranged mortar positions and buttressed with air defence emplacements. Every cliff along the ocean has hangers cut into the very rock for Thunderbolt, Lightning, and Marauder aircraft. In the five years since she

Planetary Datafax: Pyrathas

Population: Estimated 57 Million

Tithe Grade: Aptus Non

Special Notation: Second largest Imperial Navy anchorage in the Iron Collar.

Geography/Demography: 65% nominal gravity. The planet mainly consists of craggy, mountainous terrain, much of which has been utilised for housing fortress structures, hanger bays, and other Imperial Navy structures. Atmosphere stays at a consistent 25% visibility due to volcanic ash.

Government Type: Departmento Munitorum-appointed Commander/standard military hierarchy.

Imperial Commander: Captain Sylas Skor, commander of Adamant Station

Adept Presence: High; Pyrathas acts as one of the main points through which Imperial Navy forces are reassigned throughout the Crusade. High Adeptus Administratum presence monitors the flow of personnel and resources, and a contingency of Adeptus Mechanicus operates out of Ice Station Zeta.

Military: Extensive; due to the difficulty to reach the planet, nearly all of Pyrathas's population is involved in the operation of the large fortress complexes that cover the planet.

Trade/Economy/Addendum: Pyrathas has no exports, and requires a large supply of munitions and food usually brought in through the warp gate. Its primary purpose is in the management and distribution of Imperial Forces. The harsh atmosphere and craggy, barren landscape leaves little in the way of planetary resources.

A Shielded World

The system's primary star is fierce blue-white supergiant. This star is orbited by a second brown dwarf in a tidally locked orbit. Inside this brown dwarf's penumbra, Pyrathas also hangs in a tidally locked orbit, shielded from the fury of the supergiant. This unique location affords Pyrathas a distinct defence against outside incursion, making it an advantageous location for an Imperial fortress-world.

first took command of Illium, General Helga Vastorpoole has kept the Imperial Guard regiments transferring through Illium constantly busy. Under the philosophy that idle hands can only cause trouble, she keeps those staying in her fortress busy constructing new and improved fortifications.

Any enemy foolish enough to attack Illium would come under fire from Hydra autocannon emplacements and Icarus lascannons upon entering the atmosphere. The mountains around the fortress contained many cunningly disguised air defences, supported by long-range Manticore launchers and their deadly Storm Eagle missiles. Once on the ground, enemies would still have to contend with constant airstrikes from Marauder bombers, and long range shelling from the base's Earthshaker cannons. Then, when they finally launched their attack, they would have to chew through kilometres of interlinked defences, trenches, bunkers, block-houses, and underground sally ports—all the while under fire from heavy bolters, Colossus siege mortars, and the lasguns of tens of thousands of veteran Guardsmen.

The defences seem impregnable, and Vastorpoole certainly believes they are. However, they have yet to be tested by either the Tyranids or the Stigmartus, and both are incredibly dangerous foes.

Ice Station Zeta

On the far side of Pyrathas from Illium is Ice Station Zeta. Laid atop one of the largest glaciers on Pyrathas, Zeta is a Phaeton Pattern research complex with a single landing pad, spartan living quarters, several extremely advanced research facilities, and a permanent defence detachment of two squads of Storm Troopers.

Zeta is operated by the Biologis branch of the Adeptus Mechanicus. Here, several gene-magos frantically research possible biological weapons or defences against the Tyranids. The station takes every precaution with the volatile and dangerous materials they are utilizing, but its biggest safeguard is being a world away from any other humans on the planet. Even so, its presence is kept secret from the Imperial Guard and Navy commanders of Pyrathas. Instead, the Mechanicus has maintained ties with the Ordo Xenos and the Deathwatch Librarian Zadkiel, who secretly sponsor their endeavours.

Penumbra Outpost

At the tip of the shadow cast by Pyrathas, the Navy maintains an observatory station to watch for approaching enemies. A tiny disk only three hundred metres across, Penumbra Outpost maintains a crew of slightly less than two hundred malcontents, failures, and washed-up junior officers.

The station is lightly defended, and Captain Skor's feeling is that it is completely expendable in the case of a major attack. Because of this, he consciously sends his worst to crew it, so they will be out of his way.

This plan may backfire, however. Unknown to his superiors, the current commander of Penumbra Outpost, Lieutenant Vance Ulderhoff, is a traitor to the Imperium. Captured by the Stigmartus during one of the Salient's battles five years ago, Ulderhoff survived when the rest of his unit was executed by giving up valuable Imperial secrets. The Stigmartus decided to return him to Imperial lines, hoping he would prove some use as a double agent.

Ulderhoff eventually ended up on Pyrathas, and then on Penumbra Outpost when his malingering ways earned him one too many official reprimands. He is eager to let his true masters know about Pyrathas' location, but as of yet has no way to dispatch any message. Until he finds one, he waits, doing just enough of his duty to ensure he won't be executed for complete failure.

NOTABLE PERSONS

There are several individuals a Kill-team may encounter while operating on Pyrathas:

Captain Sylas Skor

Captain Skor is the commander of Adamant Station, and in practice is in charge of all Imperial Navy forces within the Pyrathas system. Like many station-bound Navy officers, Skor is looked down on slightly by other Navy Captains, earning equal parts pity and contempt that he does not command a warship. Skor's resentment at his posting and his peers' judgement is tempered by his own nature. A naturally cautious man, he has taken well to Pyrathas, a defensive posting that does not require much in the way of proactive thinking.

Skor is a whip-thin man of late middle years, with his fair share of scars from leading boarding parties as a young midshipman. These days, his conflicts are mainly of a more bureaucratic nature, as he struggles to direct the actions of the hundreds of thousands (perhaps millions) of men and women under his command. The price of these efforts show in the nervous tic in his hands, the ever-growing collection of wrinkles, and the spectacles he vainly avoids wearing around his subordinates.

Due to Skor's cautious nature, it is unsurprising that he has become one of the primary proponents of the "withdraw and endure" battle plan for coping with the Tyranid threat. In truth, Skor sees the Crusade as an eventual failure. He is terrified that as the Tau, the Tyranids, and the forces of Chaos press in from all sides, the Crusade will collapse and the last half century of blood will be for naught.

General Helga Vastorpoole

Commander of the Imperial Guard on Pyrathas, Vastorpoole is a young, ambitious leader who sees her star on the ascent. Promoted from the ranks of the first Scintillian Guard regiments to make the assault through the gate, she has served in the Crusade since its inception. Now she serves on Pyrathas. The Crusade Command's intention is to give her ample experience in bureaucratic organisation, then send her back through the gate to take command of a newly mustered Guard regiment. Her veteran leadership should have the regiment well prepared when they enter the Jericho Reach.

Vastorpoole was one of a young crop of officers promoted after the disastrous first conflicts with the Stigmartus killed so many senior staff. Her entire military career has seen her fighting the minions of Chaos, and Vastorpoole has become quite good at it. In fact, she sees the transferring of men and materials from the Acheros Salient to the Orpheus Salient as a mistake. Better to crush the true enemy, the Stigmartus, quickly and decisively. Then, with the centre secure, focus the combined military forces of two salients on eliminating the Tyranid threat.

Lieutenant-Commander Alaxis McKale

McKale is in command of the Navy warships permanently stationed in the Pyrathas system, reporting to Captain Skor. In practice, this consists of the light cruiser *Misadventure*—an Endeavour class warship—plus a picket force of half a dozen Cobra destroyers retrofitted with long range augur arrays, and a dozen intersystem defence monitors.

Although technically these forces fall under the command of Captain Skor, his constant preoccupation with the base means that more and more of the responsibility for commanding the flotilla has fallen on McKale. Thus far she's born the responsibility well, although she is still unsure of herself when it comes to what is effectively a squadron command. For that reason, she almost always defers to Skor when the senior officer makes his opinions known.

ADVENTURE SEED

Ice Station Zeta has failed to report in. The station was due to receive a dangerous shipment, a live Tyranid vanguard organism—a Lictor or several Genestealers. With this test subject, the Magos Biologis on site feel they can come up with a way to redirect the attack vectors of the Hive Fleets, perhaps leading them into ambushes, or even the heart of the Hadex Anomaly. Initial reports were promising, but now no reports have been sent via astropath for two days. The Deathwatch Librarian Zadkiel orders the Kill-team to investigate the Ice Station, eliminate the vanguard organism, and recover the research data. However, when they arrive the Battle-Brothers find that the Magos on site was conducting other, more heretical research as well, and the presence of the vanguard organisms may ultimately draw the Hive Fleet straight to Pyrathas.

THE WICKED SISTERS

"There is something off about this place, the people here revel in laxity and debauchery. I am going to send out a formal petition for an investigation on both of these systems... I just have to make a stop first... well, maybe I'll get to it tomorrow..."

—Overheard Imperial Guard Commander

Located dangerously close to the heavily contested Cellebos Warzone, the Wicked Sisters are twin pleasure worlds that are markedly bizarre. The two systems they are each located in, Delphos and Iatos, are completely identical, and the planets themselves are nearly indistinguishable from each other except for the Imperial structures that have been built there. Located very close to the same warp route, the two systems have the same number of planets that orbit identical stars and the exact same frequency. In fact, they are so similar that the Imperium has established a vox beacon in each system, perpetually broadcasting the system's designation to avoid confusion for ships just dropping out of the warp.

After the conquest of these two systems by Lord General Ovidius, there were many members of the Administratum who opposed establishing an Imperial presence on the worlds due to their bizarre nature. However, after seeing the verdant and beautiful terrain for themselves, they could not let such worlds go unused. Since then, the planets have acted as the main retreat for ranking members of the Imperium from both the Acheros and Orpheus Salients. In practice this has left them relatively deserted of any military personnel, as time for rest and recreation is severely limited given the current state of the Crusade.

Both the systems are in close proximity to the Hadex Anomaly; its glowing presence in the sky tinges every night on the planets with a sickly red glow. There are many Inquisitors operating in the Reach that believe that the influence of the Anomaly has tainted these worlds, infecting those who stay there with the subtle taint of the warp. However, with many more pressing concerns bearing down from all sides, no Inquisitor has been able to spare resources long enough to launch a full investigation. The suspicions of these Inquisitors are even more accurate than they could imagine; underground cults dedicated to Slaanesh have sprung up in both the systems, and the subtle influence of Chaos can be felt by any who stay on the surface for an extended period of time. In the decades since the worlds' reclamation they have garnered a reputation for laxity and the pleasures of the flesh, giving them the name "The Wicked Sisters" amongst Imperial citizens.

HISTORY

Before the Age of Shadow, both Delphos and Iatos appeared completely different to now. They were arid wastelands that barely managed to sustain life, with windswept plains stretching on as far as the eye could see, broken up by hive cities dotting the horizon. The only reason the Imperium continued to cling to the surface of these inhospitable planets was a rare metal that was mined from deep under the surface. This jet black metal was fabled to be capable of repairing itself, seeming to almost spring to life in the holder's hands.

All reference to this metal, however, has been completely stripped from Imperial records, even those in the halls of Watch Fortress Erioch.

In their prime, the Wicked Sisters—known by their system names at the time—were immensely wealthy thanks to their mining operations. They had a working partnership that, paired with their proximity to the Jericho Sector capital world, ensured their power within the region.

When the Age of Shadow fell upon the Jericho Sector and plunged the worlds into anarchy, Iatos and Delphos not only stayed safe, but prospered. The working partnership between the two systems help protect them from the bands of roving marauders that prowled the warp, and the population's constant toil in the mines kept them too distracted to fall to the seduction of Chaos. They began trading their rare metal with surrounding systems, supporting the various warlords that had risen from the ashes of the former Jericho Sector in exchange for food, supplies, and protection.

Deathwatch records indicate that Iatos and Delphos continued to grow in power throughout the Age of Shadow, becoming one of the most powerful forces in the entire Reach until 655.M40 and the eruption of the vortex that created the Hadex Anomaly. This marks a large gap in the records of Watch Fortress Erioch—due to warp disturbances from the Anomaly no reliable data was gathered for nearly a millennium.

The next reliable data on the systems was collected by the Deathwatch frigate *Eye of Retribution* in 523.M41 when it had to make an emergency drop out of the warp while en route to the rimward edge of the Reach. The navigator insisted that they had dropped out on the edge of the Delphos system, but upon analysis of the planets they found no sign of life, or even civilisation. Upon approach to Delphos they found, not the desert hive world that had been there a millennium ago, but a verdant paradise covered in lush jungle. After a full survey of the planet, the *Eye* could not even identify any sign of human ruins anywhere on the planet.

A stop by the Iatos system found that the same transformation had occurred there as well; where previously there had been a wasteland, there was now a garden. Although this metamorphosis concerned the Deathwatch, it was not an event that fell directly into their purview. The *Eye of Retribution* took note of the events and then continued on its previous mission.

With the arrival of the Achilus Crusade, the advancing forces quickly added the systems to their tally, claiming the lush planets as the glorious spoils of the Crusade. Some members of the Administratum spoke out in protest to settling these worlds, contesting that the strange nature of the twin systems warranted a full investigation before proceeding. However, with the Crusade in desperate need of a good turn of events, the cries of opposition were ignored and the planets were immediately settled.

PLANETARY DATAFAX: IATOS AND DELPHOS

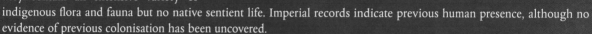

Population: Estimated 3 Million

Tithe Grade: Aptus Non; world designated for Administratum and Ecclesiarchal use.

Geography/Demography: Temperate/wet climate, both Iatos and Delphos are extremely verdant worlds, they contain an extensive variety of indigenous flora and fauna but no native sentient life. Imperial records indicate previous human presence, although no evidence of previous colonisation has been uncovered.

Government Type: Dual Planetary Governor appointed by the Adeptus Terra.

Imperial Commander: Lord-Governor Pashrar Vel Darganse

Adept Presence: High—although present on the planets for recreational purposes, the vast majority of each populace serves the Imperium.

Military: High—although it is not inside the area designated the Cellebos Warzone, there is a significant military garrison present at both planets to protect the important Imperial personnel present.

Trade/Economy/Addendum: Geographic analysis by Adeptus Mechanicus agents has uncovered the presence of [REDACTED BY INQUISITORIAL ORDER] under all major continents on both Iatos and Delphos, but no other materials of worth to the Crusade.

STRANGE SYMMETRY

Since the discovery of the two identical systems there have been many attempts to ascertain the nature of these bizarre twins. Dozens of Adeptus Mechanicus installations are scattered throughout each system, each dedicated to collecting specific subsets of data. This information is then astopathically transmitted back to a central station on Delphos for in depth analysis with powerful and ancient cogitators that have been shipped in with the Crusade.

Thus far the collected information has netted no useful clues in determining the origin of Iatos and Delphos. All analysis has shown that, besides the alterations caused by Imperial forces, the system are completely identical. Investigation has been further hampered by constant Inquisitorial intrusion—an entire Adeptus Mechanicus installation dedicated to geological analysis was completely shut down under strict orders from the Ordo Xenos, and all information gathered was destroyed.

A STARK CONTRAST

Despite being identical for all intents and purposes, Delphos and Iatos have developed very differently. Since its reclamation, Delphos has maintained itself as a typical pleasure world of the Imperium; the Ecclesiarchal presence keeping everyone strong in their faith to the Emperor. Iatos, on the other hand, has strayed far from the Emperor's light. The damaging presence of Charsilith's Den has allowed the insidious influence of Chaos to affect the populace and turn them away from the Emperor. Without swift Inquisitorial action, the populace of Iatos could be in danger of straying too far for the Imperium to tolerate and drastic action may have to be taken.

A COMPLETE TRANSFORMATION

With the complete transformation of the Wicked Sisters after the creation of the Hadex Anomaly, any shreds of Imperial records left on the planets vanished. The only reliable information that has been recovered from elsewhere in the Reach are simple planetary datafaxes recording the Imperial geographic analysis of the planets' original surfaces. Although Administratum agents found it bizarre that both planets had undergone such a dramatic shift during the Age of Shadow, they attributed it to a changing orbital pattern or other natural causes. Only the records of the Deathwatch, who observed the Reach all through the Age of Shadow, indicate that the metamorphosis occurred in conjunction with the creation of the Hadex Anomaly, and that there may be a more sinister cause behind it.

Key Locations

The following section contains details of a number of significant locations on the worlds of The Wicked Sisters.

Verdure Basilica

Upon the reclamation of the twin systems, the Ecclesiarchy planned to build a monolithic cathedral on both of the pleasure worlds to act as the centre of religion on the planets. They began construction first on Delphos, but the process was plagued by problems from the beginning. Machine spirits failed, workers died, materials were faulty, and what was meant to be a simple construction dragged out for decades.

Eventually the construction was finished, and the Verdure Basilica stood as a monument to the Emperor's will, resplendent amongst the towering forest in which it was built. The Basilica now acts as the spiritual heart of Delphos, keeping the population pure in the Emperor's light.

The main section of the building is constructed from a grey and green speckled stone, its towering walls blending in with the forest around it. Vinelike plants grow over every facet of the structure, up its columns and buttresses, and covering most of the ornate windows.

If a Kill-team operating on Delphos is going to meet with a member of the Administratum or the Ecclesiarchy, it would likely be within the walls of the Verdure Basilica. The towering building is the centralised meeting place for people from all across the planet. There is a constant flow of citizens and off-worlders milling throughout the grounds, each talking in quiet whispers to each other. For a Kill-team who would prefer to stay out of the sight of the public, the cathedral has multiple wings that stretch out into the forest. These dark and often abandoned areas would work perfectly for a quiet, low profile meeting with an important contact.

Charsilith's Den

While the Ecclesiarchy constructed the Basilica on Delphos to act as the centre for all culture on the planet, the people of Iatos had no centralised location in which to congregate. Charsilith's Den rose up to fill this void on the planet. Since then it has become a giant complex of excess and debauchery, a powerful influence on the entire planet that is—unbeknownst to most of the planet's inhabitants—driving Iatos closer and closer to the Ruinous powers.

Initially Charsilith's Den was no more than a small establishment in which the artists and Administratum members of the pleasure world could come to gamble and unwind. But with no central location in which to congregate, more and more people began spending their nights there, and it started to expand rapidly. As the Den grew, and other buildings were erected around it, the area began to resemble more of a tiny hive than a single building. Many people began spending their entire days wrapped in the pleasures that the Den offers, being gently corrupted by temptation.

The Den is a dark, imposing presence that can easily be seen on the approach to the planet. It is a jumble of rockcrete and adamantium buildings, clustered in the middle of a huge cleared section of forest. Between the different buildings are small, cramped streets filled with people intent on gambling or darker deals. The chaotic and quick expansion of the complex has led to these dark streets being nearly labyrinthine in layout, perfect for secret meetings and illicit activities.

The debauchery hidden deep within the walls of Charsilith's Den has been a perfect vessel for the Ruinous Powers to extend their influence, especially Slaanesh. Multiple cults secretly operate deep inside the walls of the Den, spreading their influence far beyond to the rest of the planet. Many Inquisitors have investigated the establishment, suspecting the corruption within, but mysteriously no action has ever been taken to shut down or destroy it. Whether the Inquisitor and his retinue meet a mysterious fate, a more pressing matter materialises in the area, or they broker a secretive deal with a member of the Administratum, inevitably each Inquisitor ceases his investigation of the Den.

The difference between Iatos and Delphos is noticeable. Anyone who spends much time at either can see the effect that the presence of the Basilica and the Den have had on the two planets—one desperately fighting off the malign influence of Chaos, the other giving into the call of the dark powers.

Gollard Mountains

Since the Gollard Mountains are a geographic feature, they are present on both Delphos and Iatos. Named by Lord General Ovidius, they (confusingly) both share the same name. Whether he did so out of humour or lack of creativity, no one will ever know.

The mountains are made up of a jet-black rock that shimmers in the light of the sun. The range sticks out in stark contrast to the lush greenery of the rest of the planet, cutting a swath across the main continent like a dark scar. Weather has not worn down the peaks, which are pointed with sharp, jagged edges as if they had just been created yesterday.

Anyone trying to navigate the mountain range on foot would have a difficult time. The sheer rock faces are steep and slick, and the endless peaks leave very few landmarks to guide the way. This has prompted a number of Imperial nobles to build their extravagant properties on the peaks of the Gollard Mountains. These giant structures are only accessible via a flying craft, allowing the nobles to enjoy solitude and privacy away from prying eyes.

WATCH STATION IOBEL

Located deep in the storm-wracked mountain range of Iobel II, Watch Station Iobel is less of a Watch Station and more of a fortress. Its winding halls are carved out of the very mountain itself, and its facilities are large enough to house and train multiple Kill-teams simultaneously. Iobel has acted as the primary launch point for all operations into the Hadex Anomaly, and contains various ancient devices for monitoring and observing the movements of xenos in and around the warp rift.

HISTORY

For the long millennia of the Age of Shadow, Watch Station Iobel was no more than a lonely tower perched atop a storm-wracked mountain range. The dark halls were all but empty save for a few serfs and servitors and the two Battle-Brothers whose task it was to stay ever vigilant for the rise of whatever unknown threat the desolate planet posed.

The Watch Station originally housed no equipment for monitoring the rest of the system it inhabited. From what the Deathwatch could ascertain, its original purpose was to watch over the valleys far below the mountain on which it stands. A grand network of pict-feeds had been assembled and maintained across the surrounding area of the planet, though the images they transmit back to the Watch Station are commonly blurry and distorted from the massive electrical interference within the planet's atmosphere.

There was little evidence as to why the architects of the Watch Station desired the barren valleys to be observed. Year after year the pict feeds would return nothing but grey, static images of a barren landscape. Fanciful tales were passed down amongst the serfs, tales of mechanical horrors that stalked the valleys during the worst of the storms. But this was always dismissed as nothing more than the superstitious legends of mortals.

However, there are some Battle-Brothers amongst those who have served at Watch Station Iobel that believe the tales of the serfs. Scattered through the archives are different grainy picts, saved from the feeds, that depict looming silhouettes of mechanical spiders, a faint green glow emanating from lines on their bodies through the distortion in the storm. Each time one of these picts was taken, the Battle-Brothers would leave to investigate after the storm subsided, but would find no evidence that any such being ever existed. This has led to the Watch Station getting a strong reputation for ghost stories and tall tales.

Since the Achilus Crusade came to the Jericho Reach, Watch Station Iobel has seen a radical transformation. As the Hadex Anomaly expands, it has begun to consume the systems around it. One such lost world housed Watch Station Midael, the closest Deathwatch outpost to the Anomaly. With the loss of Midael, Iobel became the closest, and it began housing all Kill-teams operating in the area.

This increase in traffic was far larger than the small tower could possibly house, and as more and more Kill-teams passed through, it became a necessity to expand the Watch Station. Techmarines and serfs under the supervision of Harl Greyweaver began construction to enlarge the Watch Station, hollowing out the very mountain it stood on. Intricate networks of passages were carved out, a giant hanger was created, and ancient equipment was shipped in. Within the course of a decade, the Watch Station turned from a lonely tower to a veritable Space Marine fortress.

Now, the hallways of Watch Station Iobel bustle with activity. Banks of cogitators process information on xenos activity in and around the Hadex Anomaly, Kill-teams prep for missions, and Ordo Xenos Inquisitors commonly make use of all the facility has to offer.

With the explosion of activity within Watch Station Iobel, its original purpose has been pushed to the background, all but forgotten. The network of picters and cogitators continues to monitor the valleys, but all its fuzzy data is stored away and forgotten. But as the Deathwatch focuses on the Anomaly, something has begun to awaken deep beneath the planet's surface.

USING WATCH STATION IOBEL

With its new status as the primary Watch Station for all operations around the Hadex Anomaly, it is highly likely that a Kill-team operation within the Acheros Salient would be stationed at Iobel at some point. Due to its recent additions, its size, and its close proximity to Watch Fortress Erioch, Iobel contains an extensive armoury as well as many large vehicles to which other Watch Stations do not have access.

This wide access to supplies is a great boon to Kill-teams, but it doesn't come without its difficulties. Because of the number of Kill-teams operating out of the Watch Station, a Battle-Brother may find the wargear he wants has already been requisitioned by a different Kill-team. The GM can use this to introduce roleplaying opportunities wherein two Kill-teams vie over which one gets the materiel for their mission, highlighting rivalries or loyalties between different Chapters.

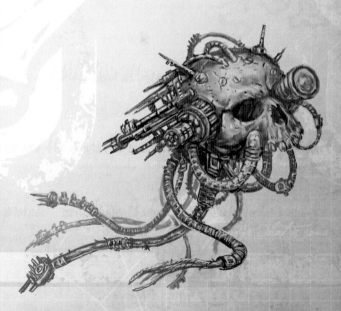

HEROES OF THE SALIENT

"Xant, my predecessor, said this war would take centuries. Well then, we had best get started!"

–Magratha von Karlack

Against the seemingly endless forces of the Stigmartus, few men live long enough to rise in rank; fewer still maintain their sanity. These heroes have all proved their worth in battle, fighting the terrifying forces of the warp and living to talk about it. Without them, the Acheros Salient would crumble, leaving the Jericho Reach defenceless against the tide of Stigmartus soldiers.

LORD GENERAL MAGRATHA VON KARLACK

Magratha is one of the only commanders in the Crusade who was actually born on a planet in the Jericho Reach. From House Orphel, her family was one of the only noble lines to successfully make it through the Age of Shadow. Cherry-picked by the Administratum, Magratha was taken from her home and brought to the Calixis Sector for officer training. As she trained, Imperial agents in the Achilus Crusade began spreading propaganda that heralded her as the champion of the Crusade; she adorned every poster and every pict that was distributed to the masses. Their goal was to make an icon for the people to rally behind and to justify the bloody war that rages on in the Cellebos Warzone.

Upon her return to the Crusade, Magratha was placed in a token position as Adjutant to Lord Admiral Gorvus Xant,

USING MAGRATHA VON KARLACK

Lord General Magratha von Karlack is a ruthless and confident woman, who never hesitates or second guesses her decisions. However, this does not make her a harsh person to talk to—her years of officer training and her esteemed reputation have made her a skilled conversationalist. She seems calm and assured, even in the most strenuous situations, and if she is taken aback by dealing with the Battle-Brothers of the Deathwatch, they will never be able to tell.

A Kill-team operating within the Acheros Salient will almost inevitably deal with Magratha, for she seems to be almost everywhere at once. If they meet with her, she is never at rest—whether briefing her officers, prepping an assault, or fighting on the battlefield, she seems almost perpetually in motion. Similarly, she is not one for small talk, especially in front of Space Marines. She will be polite and friendly, but straight to the point, wanting to move on to more important things.

safely out of harm's way, to continue as a symbol to the men and women fighting on the front lines. But the Administratum was not prepared for the consequences of their actions. In an operation deep beyond the Cellebos Warzone at the planet of Vespia, a chance strike crippled the Salient Flagship *Sword of Macharius*, and killed Lord Admiral Xant. In the ensuing confusion Magratha took charge, rallying the troops and leading an all out assault on the planet's surface.

Coupled with her already sweeping fame, news of the victory spread through the Crusade with astonishing speed. When Tetrarchus returned to Karlack to appoint a new commander to lead the Acheros Salient, Magratha was already there waiting for him. She demanded that he place her in charge of the Salient; in her mind she had not only earned the position, but it was her birthright. Impressed by her abilities, and her confidence, Tetrarchus promoted the brash young commander to the position of Lord General and placed her in charge of the Salient.

The commanders of the other two Salients were taken aback by the Lord Militant's choice, however they would quickly have to eat their words. Magratha took no time to prove her worth as the Acheros Salient's new commander. She has begun attacking the Stigmartus forces with ruthless precision, striking faster than even the forces of the Hadex Anomaly can respond. Despite her slight frame, the Lord General personally leads her forces into battle, seeming almost invincible as she wades amongst the carnage.

COMMODORE HEMELSCHOT

"The Imperium demands that every man to do his duty unto death."

—Commodore Stefan Hemelschot

In the aftermath of the Council of Ashes, Lord Militant Tetrarchus desired a sturdy and competent commander to prosecute an aggressive space campaign in the Acheros Salient. Solar Admiral Ram Thoen grudgingly appointed Commodore Stefan Hemelschot command of a considerable Imperial Navy flotilla in the region in order to do just that. The Commodore fought a series of bitter engagements with heretic fleets across the Cellebos Warzone, most notably in the First Battle of Vanity and the Accursed Blockade.

To the Solar Admiral's surprise, Hemelschot proved himself a most able fleet commander. It is largely due to the Commodore's efforts that the majority of the ships under his command remain intact after a punishing series of battles fought in the Acheros Salient.

Hemelschot himself arose from humble beginnings in the Imperial Navy, having been merely an Ensign when an Ork boarding assault slaughtered many of the senior officers aboard his first voidship. Then-Ensign Hemelschot rallied the survivors and led a surprise attack upon the greenskins in order to reclaim the vessel in the Emperor's name. Fast-tracked for command since that time, Hemelschot has always made a habit of working closely with the Fleet Commissars assigned to his vessels, and he demands nothing but the very best from both his ship and his men. Morale amongst the Commodore's fleet is generally very high, and he is well known as one of the strongest supporters of Lord General von Karlack.

Commodore Hemelschot silenced even his most virulent critics at the Second Battle of Vanity in 811.M41. The Commodore's fleet encountered a strong presence of Stigmartus-crewed vessels, including a pair of heavy cruisers. The Commodore flanked the heretic ships with a squadron of Dauntless-class light cruisers, while he sent his main cruiser line in a slingshot manoeuvre around one of Vanity's larger moons. The two forces caught the Stigmartus voidships in a deadly crossfire of torpedoes, followed by heavy bomber wings. These strikes kept the enemy damaged and off-balance until the Imperial ships broke the line and blasted the heretic ships into scrap with close-range broadsides.

The Commodore has recently had some dealings with the mysterious Eldar Ranger known as Shandyr the Traveller (see page 141 of THE ACHILUS ASSAULT) and there have been some scattered reports of Eldar ships shadowing the movements of Hemelschot's fleet in the Cellebos Warzone. This has drawn the attention of Ordo Xenos Inquisitors throughout the Salient, concerned that alien involvement in the already unstable Cellebos Warzone could only further weaken the Crusade's hold in the area.

USING COMMODORE HEMELSCHOT

Commodore Stefan Hemelschot possesses a keen understanding of the complex nature of interstellar warfare in the Acheros Salient, and has more battle experience than many of his peers in the Crusade. These assets make him an invaluable ally to a Deathwatch Kill-team planning any operations in the Cellebos Warzone, particularly if their mission has anything to do with voidships, orbital stations, bombardment, or insertion via drop pod. Hemelschot has no trouble lending his assistance to the formidable Space Marines of the Deathwatch, and his tactical and strategic expertise is noted in his Inquisitional records.

The Commodore's contacts with Lord General von Karlack and Shandyr the Traveller are also useful to a Kill-team seeking additional allies in the region, and his obsession with the possibility of a Blackstone Fortress in orbit around Magog provides a ready-made adventure seed for the Deathwatch.

Hemelschot can share his insight into void battle operations with the Kill-team. This assistance grants a +20 bonus to all Tactics (Void Combat) Tests and access to the Imperial Navy Assets (see page 214 of RITES OF BATTLE), reducing the Requisition Costs for all such Assets by 10.

WATCH CAPTAIN KAIL VIBIUS (MARINES ERRANT)

"Come, xenos scum or corrupt heretic, come and face a mighty son of the Marines Errant and wither under the gaze of the Golden Throne!"

—Watch Captain Kail Vibius

A Battle-Brother of the Marines Errant Chapter and a newcomer to the Acheros Salient, Watch Captain Vibius has a burning desire for vengeance against the xenos, which has marked him out even amongst the alien-hunting ranks of the Deathwatch.

An otherwise unremarkable skirmish during the Corinth Crusade between the Marines Errant and a raiding force of Dark Eldar ended with a squad of Space Marines—Vibius amongst them—captured and taken away to the dark realm of Commorragh. Stripped of his power armour and weapons, Vibius and his Battle-Brothers were forced to do battle in savage gladiatorial contests against other slaves, xenos beasts, and Dark Eldar Wyches. More than a few of the Marines Errant did not survive these trials, but every fallen Space Marine stoked the fire of Vibius' rage. In time, the Dark Eldar turned their attentions to newer playthings, and Vibius seized the opportunity. Stirring his fellow captives into action, the Marines Errant led a small but determined slave uprising that caught their languid Dark Eldar captors by surprise. The embattled Space Marines fought their way to freedom, and returned to the Imperium.

Vibius bears a badge of honour marking him as one of the Marines Errant Chapter's Dark Void Elite for his accomplishments, and he was swiftly nominated for the honour of representing his Chapter in the Deathwatch. Vibius impressed his commander, Watch Captain Bron of the Dark Sons Chapter, and it was not long before the Marines Errant Battle-Brother was leading his own Kill-team. When Bron was mortally wounded during a confrontation with a Slaugth Overseer in the Black Reef, he recommended that Vibius be promoted to the rank of Watch Captain, a role he has held ever since.

The Marines Errant have sworn ancient oaths that link them closely to the Rogue Trader House of Ecale, and it is known that Vibius has taken advantage of these links during his secondment to the Deathwatch. From time to time, voidships bearing the heraldry of Rogue Trader Ecale have docked at Watch Stations throughout the Acheros Salient. These voidships bear scrupulously correct Inquisitional codes, and it is said that many times Vibius went aboard to confer with the vessels' mysterious passengers. There are few that know any further details about the link between the Watch Captain and the Rogue Trader, but many Deathwatch operations put into motion by Vibius after one of these meetings have been uncommonly successful.

Vibius has personally led a number of Kill-teams into battle against the Stigmartus in the region with great relish. There are many in the Deathwatch of the Jericho Reach who consider him uncommonly reckless and aggressive, particularly towards the corrupt soldiers of Cult-General Elak Sarda. Some whisper that Vibius' unusual zeal is merely disguised pragmatism—that Vibius believes the sooner the threat of the Stigmartus is eliminated, the sooner the Watch Captain can resume his own quest for revenge against the Dark Eldar.

Watch Captain Kail Vibius

WS	BS	S	T	Ag	Int	Per	WP	Fel
65	40	62 (12)	45 (8)	47	50	51	55	60

Movement: 5/10/15/30   **Wounds:** 23

Distinctions: Crux terminatus

Skills: Awareness, Charm +20, Ciphers (Chapter runes), Climb, Dodge +10, Command +20, Common lore (Adeptus Astartes, Imperium, War), Common lore +20 (Jericho Reach, Koronus Expanse), Concealment +20, Drive (Ground Vehicle), Forbidden Lore (Adeptus astartes, Deathwatch, Xenos), Intimidate +10, Literacy, Navigation (Surface) +10, Scrutiny +10, Scholastic Lore (Codex Astartes, Tactica Imperialis), Silent Move +20, Speak Language (High gothic, Low gothic, Eldar), Tactics (Recon and Stealth), Tracking

Talents: Air of Authority, Ambidextrous, Astartes Weapon Training, Bulging Biceps, Call to Vengeance, Combat Formation, Combat Sense, Hatred (Dark Eldar), Hardy, Heightened Senses (Hearing, Sight). Hunter of Aliens, Into the Jaws of Hell, Iron Discipline, Killing strike, Nerves of Steel, Quick Draw, Resistance (Psychic Powers), Rapid Reaction, Signature Wargear (Power axe), Signature Wargear (Master: Power axe), Slayer of Daemons, Swift Attack, True Grit, Unarmed Master, Unbowed and Unbroken

Traits: Unnatural Strength(x2), Unnatural Toughness (x2); Touched by the Fates (2)

Weapons: Master crafted Power Axe (1d10+20 E, Pen 6, Unbalanced, Power Field, signature wargear) Storm Shield (1d10+12 I, Pen 0, Defensive, -20 to hit)

Armour: Power Armour (10 body, 8 arms, legs, head) Storm Shield (Force field 55%, 01-10 overload, +4 to arm and body, Guarded attack at half action)

Special Ability: Connected due to the long standing pact between the Marines Errant and Rogue trader house Ecale, Captain Vibius has access to a much wider range of resources than the average Watch Captain in the Jericho Reach. Any Kill-team operating under Watch Captain Vibius gains access to an additional 5 Requisition per Primary Objective on their mission.

USING WATCH CAPTAIN KAIL VIBIUS

Watch Captain Vibius is a courageous and honourable warrior who seethes with a desperate hatred of the Dark Eldar. He often wishes he were deployed elsewhere in the Crusade, where he might turn his prodigious zeal against alien foes rather than the degenerate heretics of the Acheros Salient. However, Vibius is bound to his duty, and strikes all the more fiercely against the Stigmartus and Chaos Space Marines he encounters in the Cellebos Warzone.

Any Kill-teams that fall under Vibius' purview can benefit from his veteran experience and unusual connections.

The ancient pact between the Marines Errant and the Rogue Trader house of Ecale is a perfect tool for a GM seeking to provide further adventure hooks, particularly for any stories that link operations between the Deathwatch and the Rogue Traders of the Koronus Expanse. At the GM's discretion, this assistance can take the form of additional Requisition points to represent the unusual items that the Rogue Traders come across, one free Imperial Navy Asset (representing the Rogue Trader's fleet, see page 214 in RITES OF BATTLE), or a +10 bonus to all Common Lore (Jericho Reach or Koronus Expanse) Tests attempted by the Kill-team. Naturally, Rogue Traders rarely give anything away for nothing in return, so there may be a favour that the Kill-team is expected to perform on the behalf of the Ecale dynasty as well.

In addition, there are those who whisper that Vibius' escape from Commorragh was arranged with the help of an unusual ally; a Grey Knight Techmarine, long separated from his glorious Chapter. Given that Vibius' Kill-teams operate in the region of the Jericho Reach most often beset by the forces of Chaos, it is possible that a group of Grey Knights (see pages 103-138 in DAEMON HUNTER) may wish to call in this favour by working with Vibius in a joint operation against a daemon prince... the foul presence of Mephidast the Plaguereaver (see page 95 in the ACHILUS ASSAULT).

Lastly, any missions that the Kill-team undertakes against the forces of the Dark Eldar (although a rare and extremely unusual sight in the Acheros Salient!) would gain the undivided attention of Watch Captain Vibius, and he would spare no effort towards achieving total success. Such missions would gain double normal Kill Markers and provide an additional 3 points of Renown per Primary Objective.

EPISTOLARY ZADKIEL (DARK ANGELS)

Epistolary Zadkiel is a powerful and honoured librarian of the Dark Angels Chapter, seconded to the Deathwatch and a prominent leader in the Acheros Salient. His potent psychic abilities have banished daemons without number, shrieking back into the warp, and his force staff has reaped a bloody tally against the heretic hordes of the Cellebos Warzone.

Zadkiel's history is oft speculated upon amongst the halls of Watch Fortress Erioch. Known to possess an aloof and proud mien, Zadkiel is rarely forthcoming on his past, but there are a few facts known to his Battle-Brothers in the Deathwatch. As a young Lexicanium, Zadkiel studied under the Dark Angels Grand Master of Librarians, no less a personage than Ezekiel himself. Zadkiel proved himself under his tutor's strict training, and swiftly ascended the ranks of the Librarium. In time, Zadkiel earned the right to be examined by Ezekiel for induction into the mysterious Inner Circle of the Dark Angels.

The trials that one must overcome in order to be worthy for such an honour are not spoken of outside the Chapter, but there can be no doubt that they are rigorous and exhaustive in nature. For Zadkiel, the strength of will and determination needed to pass these tests wrought a change within him, and upon his induction into the Inner Circle, his demeanour had entirely changed. Where once the young Librarian had jested and spoke easily with his Battle-Brothers, Zadkiel had become withdrawn and silent. Where once he sought battle eagerly, Zadkiel turned bloody-minded and recalcitrant.

Ezekiel dispatched his former student to fight alongside the elite 1st Company of the Deathwing for a number of years. Zadkiel once more excelled, honing his own battle skills and developing a talent not unlike that of his teacher–an ability to read the tides of war and predict the flow of strategy with uncanny precision. Once, Zadkiel even crossed blades with the enigmatic Cypher during the Battle of Screams, an encounter that left the Librarian with a bionic eye and a bitter heart.

On the nightmare world of Quiette, Zadkiel and the Deathwing fought a savage engagement against a serried tide of bloodthirsty aliens known as the Khrave. Many Battle-Brothers fell, their minds devoured by the xenos foe. When the aliens massed for a final assault, Zadkiel marshalled his will and held the line, his psychic powers and force sword barring the way until the battle-barge in orbit could fix upon the Deathwing's coordinates. In a matter of moments, Deathwing reinforcements teleported directly into the fray, assisted by pin-point barrage blasts from the orbiting vessel. Zadkiel's accomplishments that day earned him a special honour, and the Grand Master of the Deathwing himself granted Zadkiel the right to bear Deathwing heraldry upon his armour from that moment forward.

Inquisitor Ghraile has assembled a considerable file on Zadkiel, and she fervently believes that the Librarian's history is entirely fabricated—a clever cover story, she asserts, for Zadkiel's placement in the Acheros Salient. Whilst Ghraile has many theories about the truth of the matter, even she is reluctant to endorse any single explanation without further evidence.

Using Epistolary Zadkiel

Zadkiel's knowledge of psychic powers and the warp are of great value to Kill-teams operating in the Acheros Salient. The Librarian possesses an ancient tome that purports to contain lore and secrets within its passages relating to the Hadex Anomaly and how to successfully navigate through its bizarre radiance.

However, Zadkiel nurses a deep-seated grudge against the Space Wolves Chapter, and he has little patience for any Sons of Russ, particularly Erioch's Master of the Forge, Harl Greyweaver (see page 25 in the **Deathwatch Game Master's Toolkit**). Kill-teams that contain a Space Wolves Battle-Brother must first pass a **Challenging (+0) Charm or Command Test** in order to secure Zadkiel's assistance. Kill-teams that benefit from Zadkiel's knowledge and ability to read the ways of war gain a bonus of +10 to any Forbidden Lore (Psychic Powers) or (Warp) Tests and +5 Kill Markers for any three objectives during a mission.

Despite these doubts, even Inquisitor Ghraile has no complaints about Zadkiel's service to the Deathwatch. The Librarian regularly assists Kill-teams with strategic and tactical planning for missions in the Acheros Salient, and Zadkiel has led a number of assaults upon key Chaos Space Marine leaders in the Blood Trinity region. Zadkiel regularly meets with Space Marines seconded to the Deathwatch from Successor Chapters of the Dark Angels, and he has built a rapport with many of these Space Marines who are so far from familiar surroundings.

In the last five years, Zadkiel's attention has sharpened upon a particular world in the Acheros Salient, a foully polluted fortress-world known as Malehi. A battle force of Dark Angels Space Marines were cut down upon that world by a Stigmartus ambush. There are some reports that claim the Stigmartus General Elak Sarda has taken a meteorite-forged sword from the fallen Dark Angels Captain, possibly one of the famed "heavenfall blades" prized by the Dark Angels Chapter.

Epistolary Zadkiel

WS	BS	S	T	Ag	Int	Per	WP	Fel
49	56	(8) 46	(8) 42	34	52	47	67	42

Movement: 4/8/12/24 **Wounds:** 24

Skills: Awareness, Ciphers (Chapter runes), Climb, Deceive +20, Dodge, Common lore (Adeptus Astartes, Imperium, War), Concealment, Drive (Ground Vehicle), Forbidden lore +20 (Warp, Psykers), Forbidden lore (traitor legions), Intimidate, Literacy, Navigation (Surface), Psyniscience +20, Scholastic Lore (Codex Astartes), Silent Move, Speak Language (High gothic, Low gothic), Survival, Tactics (Defensive doctrine), Tracking.

Talents: Ambidextrous, Astartes Weapon Training, Bulging Biceps, Hardy, Hatred (Chaos Marines), Heightened Senses (Hearing, Sight), Killing strike, Nerves of Steel, Quick Draw, Resistance (Psychic Powers), True Grit, Unarmed Master, Warp Conduit.

Traits: Psy Rating 7, Touched by the Fates (1), Unnatural Strength(x2), Unnatural Toughness (x2)

Weapons: Force Sword (1d10+10 E, Pen 2, Balanced, Special)

Armour: Astartes Power Armour (10 body, 8 arms, legs, head)

Psychic Powers: Avenger, Bonds of Brotherhood, Compel, Force Dome, Inspire, Possibility Shield, Reading, Vortex of Doom.

ACHEROS SALIENT SPECIAL ABILITIES

"Take not the time to know the heretic. For in knowing the foe, thou might become the foe."

—Inquisitor Tellemain

Service within the Acheros Salient can be a series of unending conflicts against the devotees of the Ruinous Powers. The most common opponents include members of the Traitor Legions, well equipped Imperial Renegades, and even nightmares spawned from the warp itself. These sorts of conflicts can begin to have an effect upon even the well honed personality and abilities of a Space Marine serving within the Deathwatch. Some may come to develop new abilities that can enhance their combat effectiveness against these foes. Others instead undergo personality changes as a direct consequence of the foes that they engage on a daily basis.

ACHEROS DEMEANOURS

Continued exposure to the forces of Chaos, especially to those Space Marines who have turned from the light of the God-Emperor, can have a profound effect. The knowledge that the traitors they oppose were once brothers in arms can begin to sap the fortitude of even a Deathwatch Space Marine. In spite of their constant training, prayer, and study, the Battle-Brothers may begin to reconsider their outlook. These moments of doubt may even trigger a change in the character's Personal Demeanour.

Of course, different individuals can respond to the same conflict in very different ways. This section suggests a few alternatives for Battle-Brothers who begin to adapt their core values to the situation. Note that any change in a character's Personal Demeanour should be a consequence of actions undertaken through the course of the campaign. Players may freely enact such a change, but are encouraged to strongly consider the motivations and consequences associated with the adjustment. Their new demeanour may have also change how they interact with the enemy and with their Battle-Brothers. Players are encouraged to seriously consider all of these consequences before selecting one of these alternative Personal Demeanours.

BITTER

Constant exposure to those who have lost faith with the Emperor and chosen to side with the forces of the Ruinous Powers wears on the Battle-Brother's very soul. These servants of the Dark Gods were once brothers in arms. They bear the very essence of their Primarchs and the Emperor within their bodies. By committing these tools to a use against the empire that created them, they are committing the worst kind of sacrilege imaginable. Even further, they have foresworn the vows that they made when they were first inducted into the orders of the Adeptus Astartes.

Instead of bearing their responsibilities, the traitors have chosen to flee from those duties into the arms of the warp itself. Not only have their actions benefited the Great Enemy, they have also gone so far as to deplete the resources of the Imperium; the same resources that the Battle-Brother must use and depend upon to fulfil his responsibilities of defending mankind. The Space Marine's ire towards these fallen brothers grows ever hotter, as he encounters further difficulties in his day-to-day life. Each challenge faced—whether it be an ammunition shortage, a loss of troops, or the death of an innocent citizen of the Imperium—reminds him that this might not have happened if his fallen brothers had remained loyal.

ACQUIRING SALIENT ABILITIES

The Salient specific abilities presented in this volume are available for purchase only by Space Marines who have served the Deathwatch within specific fronts of the Achilus Crusade. These abilities are not specific to their chapters, nor are they tied in to codex-specific traditions. Instead, these are techniques that are learned through endless conflict against specific types of opponents. Some of these may be new methods developed within the Salients, while others are abilities that a Battle-Brother shared with his fellows during shared service.

These different Solo Modes, Squad Modes, and Oaths grant the Space Marine techniques which are particularly effective against a particular type of opponent. Learning these techniques is not a swift process. Rather, it takes extensive practice and training; the sort of training that only comes through surviving countless battles against foes that use a consistent set of tactics. They are generally shared only among those who have fought within the different Salients of the Achilus Crusade for an extended period of time.

Player characters may only select a Salient Ability after having served at least two Missions within a specific Salient. At that time, they may choose to purchase any of the abilities associated with that Salient using XP earned during those missions. An additional Salient Ability may be purchased after each additional two missions served within that salient of the Achilus Crusade. Choosing one of these abilities as an Advance does not constitute an Elite Advance.

Cold-Hearted

The onerous battle against forces contaminated by the warp has begun to change the Space Marine's perspective. Continuous exposure to the armies of the Ruinous Powers has convinced him that faith in the Chaos gods may be virulent, for there is no other possible explanation for the speed with which these blasphemies have spread. No matter how quickly the heathens are eliminated from a region, within days a new cult seems to appear among those who seemed loyal. These heretical beliefs and the abilities that accompany them spread far too quickly for them to be entirely dependent upon a mundane religion. Rather, the blasphemers must somehow be able to transfer their heretical ways to newcomers with little more than their physical presence.

There is only one effectively solution to curing a disease so infectious. The offending organs must be cut out and cleansed with flame, so that no others might be harmed. As a loyal representative of the Imperium, you have accepted the challenge that the Emperor has placed before you. You remain true to your duty and have hardened your heart before the distasteful actions that must be taken. There can be no mercy for the unbeliever. The heretic shall have no opportunity for redemption. There can be no sympathy for those who have fallen. Instead, all must be eliminated as quickly and thoroughly as possible. Any who might bear the taint of the warp must be cleansed, so that the Imperium may be purged of these unholy beliefs.

Devout

Watching the activities of the endless streams of heretics has begun to affect the Space Marine's judgement. As he slays countless foes, he also realises that some of these were once truly loyal to the teachings of the Ecclesiarchy. The Battle-Brother realises that descending to the paths of heresy is not always due to a simple decision. Often, it is a gradual process. The fallen might have begun their descent with minor transgressions—when they complained of the hardships of their duties or made light of an inconvenience with the Administratum. Years of these small blasphemies soon made more severe ones seem acceptable. The avalanche of heresy began with a single pebble.

To prevent any such fall, the Space Marine has embraced the guidance of the Imperium and the Codex in all things. He now focuses all of his attention upon his study of Imperial traditions and meditation upon their values. He stubbornly refuses to stray from the words dictated by the sacred tomes, as any such action might be the first step towards heresy. Instead, he takes care to ensure that every step he takes is in keeping with the one true Imperial Path. As he embraces this way with total fervour, he also lets his Battle-Brothers know each and every time that they stray from the path set out by the Codex.

Inspired

The forces of Chaos are endless and vile, and as varied as the warp that spawned them. Each day offers a new battle against a wildly different opponent. Though the very essence of Chaos is an affront to the Imperium and all of humanity, the conflict with its forces offers a disciplined Space Marine an amazing opportunity to develop all of his talents and abilities. As new foes are constantly encountered, alternative tactics and techniques must be employed. Because many of these opponents use strategies very different from anything ever considered by the Codex, the Battle-Brother must think and react with lightning speed to have any chance of success.

The Space Marine revels in the excitement of these boundless challenges. He sees combat with the forces of Chaos, particularly the members of the Traitor Legions, as the ultimate test of his abilities. He never feels exhaustion, because the continuous conflict inspires and energises him. The Battle-Brother looks forward to encountering and overcoming each new conflict. He knows that his faith in the Emperor preserves him and that his every test is nothing more than a chance to identify a novel way to defeat a hated foe.

Vengeful

Those who have turned against the Imperium must be stopped before their actions might cause a grave harm to those who remain loyal. The endless conflict within the Acheros Salient is a constant reminder of the dangers that may arise if heresy is given ample time to fester. World after world may soon fall to the Ruinous Powers, leaving behind mere animals who are barely recognisable as descendants of humanity. Those who triggered such a downfall are to blame for the existence of these wretches and the continued loss of additional worlds.

It is never enough to simply find and eliminate the monstrosities responsible for these crimes. Instead, they must be punished for the actions that they have taken. These betrayers are responsible for not just their own fall, but for the demise of everyone that they have led down these false paths. The Battle-Brother is determined to see that these traitors pay the necessary price tenfold. Their deaths must be slow and the word of their defeat must be spread far and wide. Others must learn from their failure so that none might ever fall again. The Space Marine is determined to be a manifestation of the Emperor's vengeance, setting an example that could live for generations.

ACHEROS SOLO MODES

Not only are the servants of the Ruinous Powers bloodthirsty, they also often have armaments that are capable of penetrating power armour and grievously wounding even a Space Marine. This has led to many situations in which a Battle-Brother's comrades have fallen, and he must exploit special techniques to complete an essential mission. Those members of the Deathwatch that serve within the Acheros Salient have accepted this fact and embraced a number of specialised techniques to improve their odds in such situations.

This section provides a few such techniques that can offer a veteran of the Deathwatch new methods to overcome the servants of Chaos. Battle-Brothers who have served within the Acheros Salient carefully developed these techniques, enhancing them often at great personal risk. Only those who are true veterans of this battlefront have an opportunity to learn these abilities from those who developed them. Once learned, these Solo Mode abilities function for the Space Marines that know them in the same fashion as Chapter abilities. Refer to page 215 of the DEATHWATCH Rulebook for more information on Solo Mode abilities.

DISDAIN THE DAEMON

Cost: 250 XP
Type: Active
Required Rank: 2
Effects: Though no two daemons are quite identical, they are not native to the physical realm. Spawned from the warp, their physical manifestations and the mundane laws of physics are completely foreign to their sense of being. These various creatures of the warp fight with an unnatural skill and fury that tests the might of even the best Space Marine. Those that have met a daemon in battle and lived are markedly better warriors for it, learning and developing new techniques to combat these horrors of the warp.

A Space Marine who develops this technique has become intimately familiar with daemonic tactics. As a consequence, he is particularly adept at avoiding them. Any time the Battle-Brother fails a Reaction against a daemonic attack, the player may re-roll the failed test. Treat this just as if a Fate Point had been spent. Note that there is no limit to the number of times that this ability may be used within a game session.

Improvement: By Rank 4, characters with this Solo Mode ability have become particularly experienced in dealing with daemonic attacks. When facing daemons, they may take a Dodge or Parry Reaction against every attack they suffer. There is no upper limit to the number of these actions that they take. Note, however, that they may only use their re-roll on the first Reaction attempt failed each turn. Further, no additional special abilities may be combined with these extra Reactions.

DENY THE CALL

Cost: 250 XP
Type: Passive
Required Rank: 1
Effects: Within the Acheros Salient, Chaos forces constantly attempt to undermine Crusade and Deathwatch forces. Though their unholy sponsors crave the blood and souls of the righteous, they also hunger for the devotion of new servants. The heretics constantly attempt to seduce loyalists to the ways of the Ruinous Powers. Their siren calls take a broad range of approaches, but all of them are founded in the ways of the most unholy. Space Marines' minds are steeled against such mortal temptations, but the corrupting influence of chaos can still creep into their minds, confusing and tricking even the most righteous Battle-Brother into unwittingly compromising the mission.

A Space Marine that has mastered this Solo Mode ability has focussed his will to ignore these unholy messages. Constant penance, meditation, and focus serve to silence the base human emotions and desires that the Chaos forces target with their persuasive efforts. The Battle-Brother isolates and silences this portion of his soul so that it cannot fall prey to the ways of these blasphemous deceptions. Any time an agent of Chaos uses an Interaction skill against a character that has this ability, the test suffers a –20 penalty. This applies to any test that adheres to an Interaction skill mechanic, no matter the basis for the skill roll.

Improvement: At Rank 5, the character's soul is completely hardened against the call of heresy. A character using this ability is completely immune to any Interaction skills employed by agents of the Ruinous Powers. Note that this resistance applies even if the Space Marine is unaware that the opponent is an agent of Chaos.

PURGE THE BETRAYER

Cost: 250 XP
Type: Active
Required Rank: 3
Effects: Members of the Traitor Legions possess the same enhanced physiology and are equipped with power armour that is very nearly as effective as that used by those who have remained loyal to the Imperium. As such, these traitors are capable opponents who can shrug off many of the attacks within a Space Marine's arsenal. Though Deathwatch Space Marines train against one another regularly, their practice bouts are seldom focussed on delivering a killing blow to one of their fellows. Battle-Brothers who continuously engage the Traitor Legions must learn to overcome the innate defences of a Space Marine so that they can eliminate the threat of these fierce opponents.

To better defeat their fallen brethren, some Space Marines choose to carefully study the weak points on the various Marks of Space Marine power armour. This highly specialised training requires intense study of the finer points of the armour, and many hours of meditation upon schematics borrowed from their Techmarine brethren. Once the ability is mastered, a character using this ability may halve the armour value of any power armour location targeted with a Called Shot.

Battle-Brother is in the presence of an artefact that a human has used in the service of Chaos, he may make a **Challenging (+0) Awareness Test** to immediately sense its presence.

Improvement: When a Battle-Brother with this ability reaches Rank 6, he becomes even more aware of the subtle cues that accompany the Chaos taint. Any time that he socially interacts with a human character, he may choose to make a Scrutiny Test with a +20 bonus against the target's Deceive. On success, he immediately becomes aware if the target has any sympathies towards the Ruinous Powers.

SLAUGHTER THE UNCLEAN

Cost: 250 XP
Type: Active
Required Rank: 1
Effects: While there are vast numbers of daemons and a substantial presence of Chaos Space Marines within the Acheros Salient, the greatest threat that the Space Marines face are the massive hordes of human renegades. The Ruinous Powers have accrued planets full of human followers devoted to their path over the millennia since the Jericho Reach was separated from the Imperium. Even without considering their resources and training, the heretical humans pose a substantial combat threat solely on the merit of the sheer numbers that they can bring to any conflict.

A few Space Marines have embraced the notion of defeating these purely human opponents. As they are well versed in the frailties of the human form, they are readily capable of inflicting vast damage quickly. Any time that they engage a horde of purely human opponents, all of their attacks count as Explosive Damage. If their weapons already inflict Explosive Damage then each counts as inflicting two additional Hits.

Improvement: At Rank 3, the Battle-Brother also increases his Toughness bonus by +4 to resist attacks made by human hordes.

STEEL THY MIND

Cost: 200 XP
Type: Passive
Required Rank: 4
Effects: Those who continue to battle within the Acheros Salient are exposed to the dangers of the warp on a continuous basis. For mortals, this can shatter their minds and their souls. Even for a Space Marine, the presence of these abominations may diminish his combat effectiveness.

Fortunately, continuous exposure to the most common dangers of the warp has hardened this Battle-Brother's resistance to some of its effects. Though these horrors may be unknowable, the Space Marine has concluded that they are certainly survivable. This simple knowledge has begun to lessen their impact upon his psyche. A Space Marine with this ability always treats the Degree of Fear posed by a daemon as one degree lower. See **DEATHWATCH** page 277.

Improvement: At Rank 6, the Space Marine becomes further hardened, and reduces the Degree of Fear by two degrees. At Rank 8, this reduction increases to three degrees.

Improvement: At Rank 6, characters may expand the types of armour that they affect with this ability. In addition to working against the standard iterations of power armour, the technique is also effective against Artificer and even Terminator Armour.

SENSE CORRUPTION

Cost: 250 XP
Type: Passive
Required Rank: 3
Effects: Space Marines active within the Acheros Salient must continuously deal with human forces that are exposed to the taint of Chaos. The vast majority of these humans have no inherent resistance to deal with the horrors that they encounter during the ongoing conflict. Because of this, it is tragically common for them to fall prey to the corruption of the warp. There have been numerous instances in which Space Marines unexpectedly fell prey to attack from allies who had been turned to the path of the Ruinous Powers.

Some Battle-Brothers choose to devote time to studying the effects of corruption upon the mortal form. They closely examine Inquisition records and even participate in the interrogation of heretics taken as prisoners. This extended study and exposure can grant them an additional ability to detect those mortals who have taken their first steps upon the path towards Chaos. A Space Marine with this ability gains +30 to detect falsehoods and untruths, as well as deliberate attempts to conceal allegiance. Furthermore, any time the

ACHEROS SQUAD MODES

When Space Marines encounter the forces of Chaos, their discipline and cooperation serves as a tremendous advantage. These blasphemous creatures are incapable of working together to recognise a greater vision, such as the glory of the Emperor. Rather, they overvalue their individual worth and accomplishments in the eyes of the Chaos Gods. Many of the Battle-Brothers within the Acheros Salient have pioneered Squad Modes that can specifically exploit the divisive nature of their foes.

Though Deathwatch Kill-teams are hardly focussed towards eliminating the agents of Chaos, their members are nevertheless highly skilled to this task. These novel techniques often take methods learned through fighting xenos forces and apply them directly towards the task of overcoming heretics. When in battle with forces that include Daemons, these specialties often become even more valuable.

See the Using Salient Squad Modes sidebar on pgae 84 for more information on how these Modes may be integrated with Oaths.

ATTACK PATTERNS

These techniques are specifically designed to quickly eliminate targets, drawing on the Space Marines' faith in Emperor and Primarch to overcome the blasphemies of the Dark Gods.

Cleanse the Traitors

Cost: 300 XP
Action: Half Action
Activation Cost: 2
Sustained: Yes
Effects: Space Marines fighting actively within the Acheros Salient are well aware of the foes they face. These devout warriors realise the danger imposed by the presence of their warp-tainted opponents. The gruelling battles against the dark forces have begun to sap the Crusade's resources to the point that every life and every unit of ammunition is a precious commodity. Because of this, the Battle-Brothers must take ever greater care with each shot fired, trying to save Crusade resources and make every bolter round count as an instrument that might channel the full fury of the Emperor.

Through the power of meditation and the strength of their divine faith, some Space Marines have mastered new techniques that offer additional accuracy to shots taken against the forces of the warp. In much the same way that Deathwatch members identify the weaknesses of xenos foes, these characters analyse the physiology of these unholy spawn. With this understanding comes an ever greater focus.

While this power is in effect, all Battle-Brothers automatically confirm Righteous Fury when fighting daemons and Chaos Space Marines. This effect counts for both ranged and melee combat attacks.

Improvement: If the Battle-Brother is Rank 5 or more, then both he and his Kill-team may re-roll a single damage die on each successful attack while this power is in effect. The value on the re-roll stands, even if it is lower than the initial roll.

Overlapping Fire

Cost: 250 XP
Action: Full Action
Activation Cost: 2
Sustained: No
Effects: Chaos Space Marines are equipped with armour that is capable of dramatically reducing the efficacy of the standard Astartes Bolter, while some of the daemons of the warp are so preternaturally tough that even a well aimed shot may have little effect. While Deathwatch Kill-teams are often equipped with specialised rounds designed for such foes, the supply of these unusual rounds are finite. As the brutal combats within the Acheros Salient continue, Battle-Brothers have been forced to adapt their techniques so that they can effectively use whatever types of ammunition are at hand.

Through careful expansion of their battlefield cants, some Space Marines have begun to carefully coordinate their fire. The language has become so precise that when using it, trained squad members are capable of not only simultaneously targeting the same individual, but also firing upon the same visible portion of that target. In this way, multiple rounds can strike home at the same time, often weakening the foe's defences in that location.

When a Space Marine activates this ability, all squad members within Support range may make an immediate Called Shot upon a single target with a Pistol or Basic Class weapon. All of the Battle-Brothers who choose to make this attack must make their called shot against the same location. The first successful attack is treated normally. All additional attacks made during the action halve the target's Armour and Toughness Bonuses for reducing damage.

Improvement: If the Battle-Brother is Rank 4 or higher, all characters receive a +10 bonus to their Called Shot Action.

Perdition's Hand

Cost: 250 XP
Action: Free Action
Activation Cost: 1
Sustained: No
Effects: The forces of the Achilus Crusade within the Acheros Salient face dread blasphemies manifested from the unholy warp itself. These creatures are anathema to the very fabric of reality. Their very existence spreads corruption and the instability of the warp wherever they travel. Exposure to these horrors is more than enough to increase the fervour of those who survive their first encounter without being swayed to the cause of these entities. Many gladly give their lives to the cause of eliminating such foes from the universe for the glory of the Imperium.

Such devotion extends to the Adeptus Astartes as well. While not subject to the guidance of the Ecclesiarchy, these warriors hold true to their core tenets in the wrath they feel towards the forces of the powers of Chaos. Space Marines firmly believe that sacrifices must be made to overcome these abominations, as well as those humans who have fallen to the warp's corruption.

When a Space Marine activates this ability, all squad members within Support Range may immediately sacrifice their next Reaction to gain an additional 1d10 damage on their next successful melee attack against a Chaos-aligned foe.

Improvement: If the Battle-Brother is Rank 3 or higher, the bonus damage increases to 2d10. If the Battle-Brother is Rank 6 or higher, all squad members within Support Range may make an extra melee attack, which counts as a free action, the moment the ability is activated.

DEFENSIVE STANCES

The forces of Chaos are capable of channelling the power of the warp to twist reality against the forces loyal to the Emperor. Within the Acheros Salient, Deathwatch Kill-teams have identified specific squad tactics that provide them some measure of defence against these manipulations.

Fury Preserves Us

Cost: 300 XP
Action: Free Action
Activation Cost: 1
Sustained: Yes
Effects: Everywhere that the followers of Chaos venture, they sow corruption, deceit, and treachery. Interacting with these heretical wretches, even if only through violence, runs the risk of both physical and spiritual contamination. For the forces of a Deathwatch Kill-team, the very notion of these foes' betrayal can instigate a blinding rage.

As physical manifestations of Imperial vengeance, Space Marines may rely upon their anger to preserve them. Within the Acheros Salient, there have been several documented instances in which Battle-Brothers emerged from the cauldron of battle against the corruption of the warp with little evidence of damage.

When a Space Marine activates this ability, all squad members within Support Range immediately gain the protection of their rage. This counts as a Force Field (see **DEATHWATCH**, page 166) with a Protection Rating equal to each character's Willpower minus 10 and an Overload Roll of 01–10. Each field remains in effect for as long as the Squad ability is sustained or until any one of the fields becomes overloaded.

Improvement: If the Battle-Brother is Rank 4 or higher, the Protection Rating becomes equal to Willpower. At Rank 6 or higher, the Overload Roll is reduced to 01–05.

Closed Minds

Cost: 200 XP
Action: Full Action
Activation Cost: 1
Sustained: Yes

Effects: Many of the worlds within the Acheros Salient are contaminated by the infections that spill forth from the depths of the Hadex Anomaly. On these planets, the very laws of physics seem altered. Seemingly innocuous objects may suddenly turn deadly. Known foods can spontaneously turn toxic. Reality is subject to sudden, inexplicable transformations that are inimical to life.

Deathwatch Kill-teams are at times dispatched to these treacherous places. Fortunately, many of these missions are brief, and require little interaction with the planet's environment. In these instances, the Space Marines may complete their assignment with little fear of extended interaction with the contamination of Chaos. Other missions, particularly those focussed upon observation, require a squad to spend an extended period of time under the influence of the Hadex Anomaly. On these assignments, simple survival among the environs of Chaos can be a substantial challenge. Some Space Marines have learned to cope with this twisting reality by a stubborn and intense denial that anything untoward is even occurring. Consciously closing their minds to the unnatural phenomena, the force of their disbelief actually seems to calm and dissipate the warping effects around them.

When a Battle-Brother activates this ability, he and all squad members within Support Range may immediately make a **Challenging (+0) Willpower Test**. On success, those characters manage to overcome the influence of Chaos and stabilise a region around them that extends for 20 metres from the location of the most central character in the squad. This area becomes a mundane portion of the physical galaxy for as long as the ability is sustained. For the duration, the air becomes breathable, the environs become more natural, and any penalties for anomalies or attacks inherent in the environs are eliminated.

Improvement: If the Battle-Brother is Rank 3 of higher, the stabilization continues for one hour after the squad stops sustaining the ability. At Rank 6 or higher, the duration increases to one day after the squad stops sustaining it.

Vengeance of the True

Cost: 250 XP
Action: Reaction
Activation Cost: 2
Sustained: Yes

Effects: The worlds of the Acheros Salient are littered with Chaos Space Marines. More than any other opponent, these traitors stir a cry for justice among those Battle-Brothers who remain true to the ways of the Imperium. There can be no understanding or reconciliation with these traitors. Death is the only possible resolution to a conflict that has spanned millennia.

These opponents are treacherous foes, many of whom remain intimately familiar with the techniques of the Adeptus Astartes. Because of this, loyalist marines are often compelled to innovate new techniques that the traitors may not have a

means to counter. Unless such actions are taken, Space Marines may feel that they are fighting before a dark mirror, destined to mimic and counter their every move. As a consequence of this expertise, it is not uncommon for a Space Marine to be seriously wounded in these conflicts.

When a squad member suffers a wound due to a Chaos Space Marine action, the squad leader may choose to activate Vengeance of the True. At that time, the squad leader and any members within Support Range may immediately use an available Reaction to make a Standard Attack.

Improvement: If the Battle-Brother is Rank 4 or higher, the Standard Attack action does not require the expenditure of an available Reaction.

ACHEROS OATHS

When facing the threats of Chaos, Space Marines frequently choose to swear Oaths that are focussed on these traitors. This section provides a sampling of those that have been developed within Acheros Salient for that express purpose. These Oaths provide the Kill-team with a balance of Codex Squad abilities and techniques that have been refined within the Acheros Salient. Space Marines active in other regions may choose to swear these same Oaths, but they must first learn them after embarking upon Missions within this Salient.

OATH OF PURITY

Chaos represents a threat that once overcame some of the most devout Space Marines in the history of the Imperium. Those who allow its subtle influences to affect them will likely be damned to just as catastrophic a fall from grace. Even the subtle sin of pride or the cleansing fire of pure wrath against the Imperium's foes could represent the first step if these emotions are allowed to take control. Every emotion and motive must be carefully examined so that a warrior can be certain they are in keeping with the ways of the Codex Astartes.

The forces of Chaos are a constant reminder that mankind must remain always vigilant against the Ruinous Powers. The ways of the unholy are always manipulative and their cunning is boundless. With this Oath, the Battle-Brothers renew their dedication to fulfil their sacred duties without succumbing to the forces of darkness.

Cost: 250 XP

Prerequisite: Librarian or Apothecary

Effect: When a squad swears the Oath of Purity, its members must first cleanse their minds and bodies of contamination through rituals of meditation and fasting. These are enhanced by rituals that focus their minds into immutable patterns and re-establish the rhythms of all their biological systems. In this fashion, they are able to identify any contamination to their core essence and purge it from their bodies and souls. Once cleansed, their resistance to such forces is completely renewed. All members of the Kill-team receive a +10 bonus to Willpower for resisting applicable psychic powers and a +1 Toughness Bonus to reduce damage caused by any entity with the Daemonic Trait.

Squad Mode Abilities: Tactical Spacing, Faith is Our Shield, Vengeance of the True

OATH OF VENGEANCE

Virtually every Chapter has its own legends that have been passed down since the time of the Horus Heresy, recounting the foul deeds performed by the vile Traitor Legions. All of these legends have one central tenet: those who betrayed the ways of the Imperium must be punished for their actions. Only by thoroughly eradicating these ancient foes can their stain be cleansed from the honour of the Adeptus Astartes and their memory allowed to fade from history. This Oath is devoted to accomplishing that goal with extreme prejudice. The Battle-Brothers renew their devotion to specifically eliminating the most hated of all their foes: the Chaos Space Marines.

Cost: 250 XP

Prerequisite: Devastator Marine or Tactical Marine

Effect: When the Kill-team prepares for their mission, the members recount ancient tales of heresy. In a tradition originating amongst the Watch Stations of Acheros Salient, each story is told and an act of treason remembered, a scroll bearing a traitor's name is hurled onto a brazier. All of the Battle-Brothers inhale the smoke from the flame and swear to slay the foe with increasingly graphic detail. With each legend told and each scroll burned, the flames of their anger kindle ever higher and the brutality of their promises heightens. Any time a member of the Kill-team successfully attacks a Chaos Space Marine, all of the Battle-Brothers' weapons gain the Tearing quality until the end of combat. If the weapon is already Tearing, it gains an addition 3 Pen until the end of combat instead.

Squad Mode Abilities: Cleanse the Traitors, Holy Vengeance, Overlapping Fire

OATH OF THE WATCHGUARD

The Hadex Anomaly within the Acheros Salient is a blight upon the galaxy. It represents a place where the warp and the physical realm interface in a manner that enables daemons to freely enter reality. This hideous manifestation must not be allowed to continue. Unless the Imperium discovers a way to seal this massive portal, the forces of Chaos can continue to corrupt reality. Some Inquisitors believe that as more daemons pour through the gap, the Anomaly grows in size, spreading its taint ever further. The only possible response for the Adeptus Astartes is to violently eliminate the daemons responsible for this incursion, with the hope that as they fall the gateway might

TABLE 1-1: ACHEROS OATHS

Oath	Prerequisite	Benefit	Squad Mode Abilities
Oath of Purity	Librarian or Apothecary	+20 to resist psychic powers; +1 Toughness bonus against Daemons	Tactical Spacing, Faith is Our Shield, Vengeance of the True
Oath of Vengeance	Devastator Marine or Tactical Marine	All successful attacks against Chaos Space Marines count as Tearing	Cleanse the Traitors, Holy Vengeance, Overlapping Fire
Oath of the Watchguard	Techmarine or Tactical Marine	+10 Bonus BS against daemons, no Cohesion loss	Bolter Assault, Stalwart Survivors, Soak Fire
Oath of Zeal	Tactical Marine or Assault Marine	Hordes become more likely to break when reduced in size	Furious Charge, Perdition's Hand, Squad Advance

begin to shrink. This Oath represents a devotion to the long-term goal of cleansing the Hadex Anomaly from the galaxy.

Cost: 250 XP

Prerequisite: Techmarine or Tactical Marine

Effect: During their mission preparations, the Battle-Brothers perform an extended process of cleansing and blessing all of their armaments. With each sacred prayer, their focus increases and their senses sharpen. As these prayers and dreams are recounted to their Battle-Brothers, all gain an added focus and devotion to the cause of defeating the Ruinous Powers. All of the Kill-team's members grow in their devotion to protecting the Imperium from the taint of the warp. Each Space Marine receives a +10 bonus to Ballistic Skill for any attack actions taken against creatures with the Daemonic trait. Space Marines squads facing creatures which cause Fear suffer no Cohesion loss when they swear this Oath.

Squad Mode Abilities: Bolter Assault, Stalwart Survivors, Soak Fire

OATH OF ZEAL

When the Jericho Reach was divided from the Imperium, many of its worlds lost all understanding of the Imperial Cult. With time, new heresies emerged upon these worlds. As their technological base collapsed, the slide away from the purity of Imperial teaching accelerated. Since the arrival of the Achilus Crusade, agents of the Ecclesiarchy and the Inquisition have discovered that this fall was often far more severe than initially suspected. The discovery of the Hadex Anomaly offered proof-positive that many of these cultists were more than misdirected heretics; they were actually adherents of the ways of Chaos.

Identification of the Stigmartus initially spurred Crusade forces to new levels of zeal against the foe. However, as the battles intensified and Imperial resources were exhausted, the battles ground to a standstill. With every passing day, the Ecclesiarchy struggles to reaffirm that zeal in the Imperial warriors so that they gladly make whatever sacrifices are required to overcome the devotees of the Dark Gods.

Cost: 250 XP

Prerequisite: Tactical Marine or Assault Marine

Effect: When the Kill-team swears an Oath of Zeal, they begin with an intense regimen of physical exercises. These serve as a reminder both of their superhuman capabilities and of the limitations inherent in the unmodified human form. As their enhanced metabolisms reach the peak of efficiency, their minds embrace the notion of punishing those who have turned from the glory of the Emperor. Once this idea has been grasped, it burns in their very souls as they prepare to slay the traitors. In the heat of battle, they enthusiastically deliver the just punishment to those humans who have embraced Chaos. When the Battle-Brothers defeat enough members of a Chaos-aligned Horde that it must make a break test, the Willpower Test suffers a −10 penalty at 25% losses and a −20 penalty at 50% losses. The Space Marines also receive a +10 bonus to Weapon Skill when attacking a Chaos-aligned Horde.

Squad Mode Abilities: Furious Charge, Perdition's Hand, Squad Advance

CRUSADE FORCES

"Ah! There it is! There it is! So faint, so faint, but I still feel it. You brutes are lucky you have me to guide you. Bulging muscles and bolter shells mean nothing in the crushing red glow of Hadex!"

–Lord-Scion Navigatus Vectris-Vectrix Vor'cle

The Acheros Salient is a particularly brutal front in the Achilus Crusade. As it advances the designs of Watch Fortress Erioch and metes out the Emperor's justice, a Kill-team operating in this region of the Jericho Reach is often called on to face overwhelming odds. By coordinating efforts with the Imperial Guard and Navy, or calling on their allies in the other Ordos, a Kill-team can bring the full might of the Imperium to bear on their enemies, greatly improving the likelihood of success in even the most perilous of missions.

Due to the nature of the threat the Imperium faces in the Acheros Salient, notably the ever-present menace posed by the warp and the forces of Chaos, the Salient is home to numerous Crusade forces that would normally fall under the authority of the Ecclesiarchy or one of the Holy Ordos of the Inquisition. Unlike in other salients, where the vast majority of the forces at hand can be manipulated and utilised by a well connected Kill-team with relatively little in the way of political ramifications, the Acheros Salient is home to a great deal of activity from Inquisitors from both Ordo Malleus and Ordo Hereticus. As such there is always the potential for internecine Inquisitorial posturing and infighting, as individual Inquisitors jockeys for control over the Salient's resources.

At the GM's discretion he can allow players to acquire assets for their missions from Table 1-2: Acheros Salient Assets. These assets represent allies and specialised equipment which the Kill-team may call on, using Requisition in the same way they would select weapons and armour from the Deathwatch. Furthermore, each asset that the players call on represents a potential NPC that the GM can add to the dramatis personae of the campaign. These assets have their own descriptions and game effects as detailed below, and each has a set Requisition cost and Renown requirement. For more details on Requisition and Renown see page 138-129 of the **Deathwatch** rulebook.

HADEX-PRACTISED NAVIGATOR

Navigation in the Acheros Salient is often made difficult or impossible due to the baleful presence of the Hadex Anomaly, as its sickening red light drowns out the Astronomicon. Those chosen of the Navis Nobilite who have braved the Anomaly's glow, who have learned to navigate in spite of it and not been driven mad by the attempt, are highly prized by the forces of the Imperium within the Salient. When a Kill-team must travel near, into, or through the Anomaly, the assistance of one of these masters of the warp is invaluable. A Kill-team that has a Hadex-Practised Navigator present may negate a single complication on any of the Hadex Complications Tables (see page 53) per mission.

Those vessels fortunate enough to have on board a Navigator experienced with the perils of the Hadex Anomaly have an easier time passing through the section of the Anomaly known as "the Drop", the Anomaly's only known semi-stable warp route. This can easily shave weeks off of any journey a Kill-team might make to the outer regions of the Jericho Reach, or allow them to travel to one of the Charon Stars unscathed, if that is their destination. There is a danger in using this route, however. It is guarded by the Cyclopean Confederation, a group of rogue Navigators who are known to demand tribute for the use of "their" warp lanes (see pages 83-87 of **The Achilus Assault** for more information). Any Navigator a Kill-team takes into the Hadex Anomaly will likely want assurances that he will be well protected from his mad cousins.

SISTERS OF BATTLE SQUAD

Thousands of the stern-faced sisters of the Adepta Sororitas have been dispatched to fight in the Achilus Crusade, to aid the forces of the Ecclesiarchy in prosecuting the enemies of the God-Emperor in the Jericho Reach. The incorruptible Battle-Sisters are an inspiration to behold and have helped turned the tide in numerous engagements on the Acheros front, purging the enemies of the Imperium with holy bolter and flame. There is no greater joy for these loyal servants of the God-Emperor of Mankind than to cleanse the heretic and mutant. In times of great need they have been known to fight shoulder-to-shoulder with the Deathwatch.

A Kill-team may call on a squad of the Adepta Sororitas to cleanse heretics from the battlefield, countering one Horde of Chaos-followers (subject to the GM's discretion) per mission. Additionally, the fury and unshakable faith of the Sisters of Battle can be used as a rallying point for faithful servants of the Emperor. When battling the forces of Chaos, the Sisters of Battle may add +15 to any Command Test the Kill-team is required to make to strengthen the morale of flagging Imperial forces.

TABLE 1-2: ACHEROS SALIENT ASSETS

Asset	Requisition Cost	Renown
Hadex-Practised Navigator	15	Respected
Sisters of Battle Squad	25	—
Experienced Banisher	15	Distinguished
Explorator Attachment	20	Respected
Grey Knights	40	Famed

EXPERIENCED BANISHER

The few Banishers active in the Jericho Reach are from a mysterious subsect of Calixian clergymen, under the direct control of the Ordo Malleus. They have been hand-picked from the best their sect has to offer, and each one has survived multiple encounters with the daemonic. These wizened, robed figures are often festooned with all manner of charms and warding amulets, while tomes filled with ancient and proscribed knowledge, gathered throughout the centuries of their sect's ancient war against warp spawn, hang from their belts. They have studied, at length, esoteric lore regarding the fighting and banishing of daemons and are privy to secret warding rituals and rites. A Banisher is a wealth of arcane knowledge regarding warp entities, giving any member of the Kill-team a +10 to any Forbidden Lore (Daemonology) Tests they may be required to make. Additionally, using his esoteric rituals, the Banisher may negate the Daemonic trait from an enemy or Horde unit the Kill-team is facing.

EXPLORATOR ATTACHMENT

An Explorator is one of the Machine Cult's elite, usually ranging far ahead of the rest of the Mechanicus to uncover ancient and archaic technologies from the Dark Age of Mankind. The Explorators active in the Acheros Salient, however, have an additional mission. They have been tasked with using any and all means necessary to combat the hereteks of the traitor forge-world of Samech, and to counter their influence wherever it is found. An Explorator Attachment may provide a Kill-team with a +20 to any Tech-Use or Common Lore (Tech) Tests they may be required to make during the course of the mission. Additionally, the Explorator is capable of sharing his expertise with the Kill-team, giving them the opportunity to re-roll any Dodge Tests made as a result of being attacked by any automated defence system they may face.

GREY KNIGHTS

It is currently unknown how many Grey Knights there are active in the Acheros Salient, or if there are even any such forces in the Jericho Reach at all. Their mere existence is a myth to all but the most knowledgeable Battle-Brothers and highest-ranked Inquisitors. They are the chamber militant of the Ordo Malleus, and their warded armour, nemesis force weaponry, and psychic powers make them a fearsome foe to any creature of the warp. The exact benefit the Grey Knights can bring to the Kill-team is up to the GM, but these are the pre-eminent daemon hunters of the galaxy. A squad or even a single veteran Grey Knight can slay hordes of lesser daemons, should be a match even for a greater daemon, and goes a long way in helping the Kill-team take out a daemon prince.

Calling on the Grey Knights is not without its risk, however. They have been known to slay any allied Imperial forces that have witnessed their daemonic foes, to guard against the possibility of corruption and to prevent the dangerous knowledge of the existence of daemons spreading to the wider Imperial population. They have even, on occasions, mindwiped the Battle-Brothers of the Adeptus Astartes that have fought by their side. Whether they would be willing to make an exception for the Deathwatch, none can say.

RUNNING ACHEROS SALIENT CAMPAIGNS

"Though the gates that stand between the mortal world and the immortal Realm of Chaos are now closed to me, still I would rather die having glimpsed eternity than never to have stirred from the cold furrow of mortal life."

—Telros the Ever-Changing, follower of Tzeentch

The warfare in the Acheros Salient, more than anywhere else in the Jericho Reach, is constant and vicious. While the Orpheus Salient is a place of encroaching dread and grim finality, and the Canis Salient is a chess game of tactical manoeuvring, politicking, feint, and counter-feint, the Acheros Salient is charnel meat-grinder, a warzone of ceaseless and unending brutality. Every inch of victory in this salient is purchased at great price, and there is no reprieve from the constant struggle, for a moment of distraction is all it takes to see all the Crusade's hard-fought gains in the Acheros Salient vanish.

In addition, there are all the hallmarks of humanity's ancient and implacable foe, the forces of Chaos. The power of Chaos is born of madness and nightmare, and it twists and corrupts everything it touches. Any Kill-team willing to brave its horrors must steel their souls as well as their bodies or become a tainted mockery of everything they once held dear. While the Battle-Brothers of the Deathwatch are some of the Imperium's finest, they are far from incorruptible, a fact borne out by the very existence of the Traitor Legions.

When building campaigns that are set in the Acheros Salient, the GM should keep the following themes in mind:

A DARK MIRROR

The Acheros Salient is filled with warped reflections of Imperial culture, things that the Kill-team should find both familiar and abhorrent. For every force that the Imperium sends to the Acheros Salient, Chaos offers up its evil twin. The Imperium has its countless regiments of the Imperial Guard, the forces of Chaos have the endless legions of the Stigmartus. The Mechanicus sends its Magos and Explorators to keep the engines of its war machine humming, while the forces of Chaos have the hereteks of the fallen forge-world of Samech, brandishing forbidden weapons of unspeakable power. There are warp-witches, zealous clerics, and twisted mutants, bold Chartist Captains and depraved Chaos Raiders, and loyalists and renegades of every stripe. Finally there are the Battle-Brothers themselves, the Emperor's elite, and their dark counterparts, the Traitor Legions who so long ago swore fealty to the Ruinous Powers. Each evenly matched, each one is the sinister likeness of the other.

Beyond this duality, which itself is an important and pervasive theme of the Acheros Salient, the mirrored nature of the Salient allows the GM to portray the darkly human natures of the antagonists that assail Kill-teams active in the Acheros Salient. Every foe the players face, from the lowliest Stigmartus recruit to the most battle-hardened Chaos Marine, may have the opportunity to interact with the Kill-team in a substantial way. With the various dark epithets, threats, and invective hurled at the Kill-team, the GM is able to communicate the mindset of their enemy. The followers of Chaos have their own twisted values and logic, and their screams of triumph and dismay can convey to the players that they are fighting a war not against faceless, nameless monsters, but against people who have, for whatever reason, made a choice to eschew their claim to their own humanity. That is one of the reasons why the followers of Chaos are so hated, and why they are so feared. They are a dark reflection, reminding those who have yet to fall from grace the price of the failure to maintain an eternal vigil against corruption.

STILL HUMAN

Showcasing the inherent (albeit twisted) personality of the enemy is another benefit of having your players fighting in the Acheros Salient. While there are plenty of humans to interact with in the other salients, they usually come in two flavours. Kill-teams are mostly dealing with a loyal citizen of the Imperium or someone who has just been revealed as not being a loyal citizen of the Imperium. Either way, there is very little opportunity for the sort of open disdain and rivalry a player character group can have with an explicitly hostile, but still mostly human, enemy. Whether it is the constant vox-taunting that the Kill-team receives from a high-ranking Stigmartus commander at the end of every battle, or the out-of-context Codex Astartes quotations painstakingly and beautifully scribed in blood and left for the Kill-team by a Dark Apostle of the Word Bearers legion, this sort of back-and-forth can elevate a relatively unremarkable villain to an unforgettable arch-enemy.

ALL THINGS BEING EQUAL

Another side-effect of the all-too-human nature of the foes fought in the Acheros Salient is that it takes very little for the Kill-team's human allies to be drawn in by their false promises and turn from the light of the Emperor. Betrayal is an all-too-common occurrence in the Acheros Salient. Unlike a Tau defector in the Canis Salient (where the turning of your back on the Imperium can, while deeply heretical, at least be considered a reasoned response) treachery against the Imperium in the Acheros Salient is often the result of a slow descent into madness and corruption, the realization of some form of jealousy or power-hunger, or the result of some deep-seated character defect. More often than not it is a warping of what it means to be human that results in this type of betrayal. The forces of Chaos rarely appeal to a potential convert's reason or good nature.

Nothing breeds tension in a Kill-team like having their trusted allies turn on them at a pivotal moment. Whether it is an Imperial Commander who has succumbed to the honeyed promises of the Ruinous Powers, or an entire Imperial Guard regiment who has switched sides in the middle of a battle just to survive another day, these betrayers make some of the best antagonists in a game, and whole campaigns have been built on something as simple and pure as righteous vengeance.

HORROR AND MADNESS

Another major theme in the Acheros Salient, and in the fight against Chaos in particular, is the maddening and horrific nature of the warp. The daemonic enemies that assail the players are, in many ways, the subconscious terrors of mankind made manifest. Fighting, or even interacting, with the forces of Chaos eventually cracks the psyche of all but the most resolute. Those allies of the Kill-team without superhuman resolve or unshakeable faith in the God-Emperor eventually and inevitably falter when faced with the mind-breaking pressures of combating the Ruinous Powers.

There are a few ways for a GM to convey this theme to his players. Perhaps a Guardsman, without warning, begins to fire wildly on his fellows until put down, or the Kill-team comes across an Imperial commander with his eyes gouged out and a self-inflicted laspistol wound to his head. Among those who have finally succumbed to the horrors of the long war with Chaos, inconsolable screaming and incomprehensible babbling are quite common. This erratic and abnormal behaviour is also present in the mortal enemies a Kill-team is likely to find in the Acheros Salient: most of the Traitor Legions are known for irrational idiosyncrasy, and the Stigmartus are famed for relishing all wounds sustained in battle, even their own. Beyond these simple quirks, though, there should be the tension of knowing that, as a result of the mind-warping nature of Chaos, the player's allies could become unreliable and unpredictable at any moment.

Space Marines endure the consequences of the mind-warping power of Chaos differently from the rest of their Imperial allies. Their psycho-conditioning allows them to endure, but the stresses of the grotesque and monstrous nature of the warp still takes its toll. Those veterans of the Deathwatch who have fought the forces of Chaos in earnest in the Cellebos Warzone, or who have spent large periods of time within the Hadex Anomaly, will likely bear a few mental scars as a result. A GM can impress this upon his players by having Deathwatch and Adeptus Astartes NPCs with a history of activity within those zones display some of these quirks. For some examples of the idiosyncrasies these Battle-Brothers are likely to develop, see the Battle Trauma section on page 279 of the DEATHWATCH Core Rulebook.

UNPREDICTABILITY

One of the main themes of Chaos is that it seems to act in blatant disregard of what would otherwise be the immutable laws of the universe. One of the reasons that Chaos is so dangerous and terrifying, then, is its inherent unpredictability. How can you fight a force of nature, especially one whose only constant is that it changes the nature of all the forces around it? It seems unreasonable to expect peace and calm, or even mere survival, when at any moment gravity can be

reversed, the seas can turn to blood, or the sky may set itself ablaze with eldritch energies. When a place has been touched by the warp it is not uncommon for hulking, nightmarish abominations to rip into existence and do their daemonic best to devour every living and unliving thing in sight.

While these overt manifestations are most common in the daemon worlds of the Charon Stars, even those planets that are outside the Anomaly are not immune to the horrific changes wrought by Chaos' grasp. All it takes is the presence of one unnoticed psyker, one uncontained psychic potential left unchecked, to open a gateway into pure pandemonium. Chaos devotees are often able, through the use of foul rituals and sorcery, to bring stable warp rifts into being. Whole worlds having been consumed in such a fashion, turned overnight from idyllic and serene into a harrowing horror-scape, hellish and surreal.

A Tear in the Fabric of Space and Time

Nowhere does this unpredictability loom larger than when the Kill-team must venture into the Hadex Anomaly. There even the stalwart souls of the mighty Adeptus Astartes are tested, as the taint of the warp made manifest attempts to change them into something both more and less than human. When on a daemon world or in the Anomaly itself, the players are completely cut off from the rest of the Imperium in the Jericho Reach, deep behind enemy lines. The GM should make sure the players track their resource expenditures, as the Kill-team has little opportunity to refit and resupply, possibly having to go so far as to loot equipment from their enemies depending on how long their mission keeps them within the warp rift. There are no known, active Watch Stations remaining within the Hadex Anomaly, no safe place to rest and regroup.

An added danger is that the Anomaly itself is constantly shifting, warping both time and space. The Kill-team could be fighting for years in the Anomaly, and come out to find that only a few weeks have passed in real space. Additionally, any foray into the Anomaly, however brief, is under constant threat of attack by the warp entities that make this place their home. For more information on the dangers of the Hadex Anomaly see the Hadex Complications Tables on page 53.

THE TAINT OF CORRUPTION

The enemies of the Imperium in the Acheros Salient are fuelled by the warping power of Chaos, a power that inexorably twists the body as much as it destroys the mind. While the Battle-Brothers of the Adeptus Astartes are fortified against such contamination, the minds of many of the rest of their Imperial allies are not. Chaos is a very persuasive, seductive force, and there is always the chance that the Kill-team's previously loyal companions finally succumb to temptation and turn on them. Paradoxically, in fact, the longer one spends fighting Chaos, the more likely one is to succumb to it. The war for the Acheros Salient is not just a physical contest, but a spiritual one as well.

Honour and Duty

None are truly immune to Chaos' corrupting touch. The Space Marines of a Deathwatch Kill-team are shielded from this insidious influence by a strong sense of honour and duty, but this is a shield that Chaos knows all too well how to tear asunder. Even the mighty Adeptus Astartes feel the touch of temptation when their sense of honour and duty is conflicted. This is especially effective if events can be engineered so that a given Space Marine has to make a choice between his honour as a member of his Chapter and his duty to the Deathwatch. A Space Marine so conflicted is forced to decide if he will stay the wrath of his Chapter and complete the mission, or if he will abandon the mission and see his Chapter's ancient oaths satisfied. If the Space Marine in question chooses honour before duty, the Kill-team may begin to fracture, as the Space Marines are forced to choose between their loyalty to their Battle-Brother or their loyalty to the mission. A team so divided is that much easier to corrupt or conquer.

The Steeling of a Soul

The tug of Chaos is meant to be subtle, insidious, and deeply personal. One of the simplest ways for a GM to present the players with this kind of challenge is to use a Space Marine's own personal demeanours as the basis for his temptation. Over the course of a campaign a player will be crafting the personality of his character, likely through a liberal use of his personal demeanour. The idea, then, is for the GM to get to the heart of that character's personality and find some way to align it with the designs of Chaos. As a Space Marine's personal demeanour becomes rote, as he begins to rely on it, the GM can attempt to manoeuvre him into situations where the application of his demeanour would be a cause for corruption. This is much easier to accomplish with demeanours such as Hot-Blooded, Ambition, or Pride, but a GM should theoretically be able to devise a temptation even based on demeanours such as Stoic and Pious. It's possible the player won't realise he's done the will of the Ruinous Powers until far too late.

Often the Space Marine is faced with a choice, a choice that has been the burden of many a Battle-Brother before him: stay true to his sense of self and begin to accumulate corruption, or rely less and less on his personal identity and remain pure. Perhaps it is for this reason that so many Space Marine veterans seem so terse and are so consumed by their duty. The long weight of the centuries has made it necessary to subsume their own sense of self, their independence, and individuality, into what it means to be a Battle-Brother of the Adeptus Astartes.

GRIM DETERMINATION

The forces of the Imperium and the forces of Chaos are very evenly matched in the Acheros Salient. The fighting ability of a unit of Imperial Guard roughly equals that of an opposing number of Stigmartus warriors. Likewise, a squad of Battle-Brothers has a roughly equivalent battle potency of a squad of Chaos Space Marines. What this equivalency means is that the outcome of any given battle in the Salient is as much a matter of attrition as tactical acumen. If one side or the other attempts to gain the upper hand with a specialised unit, it is likely the other commander will simply bring an equivalent counter to bear. Because the forces of Chaos and the forces of the Imperium in the Acheros Salient are such equal adversaries, most conflicts between them are decided by whichever side has the most resources. This is how the Acheros Salient has developed its reputation as a "meat-grinder." There are very few options for an Imperial Commander to seize his objectives beyond simply buying his way through with the lives of his men. Reinforcement is the de facto currency of the Acheros Salient, more so than in any other front in the Achilus Crusade.

As a GM, a simple way to convey this to the players is to have them witness first hand the vicious nature of such a conflict. Seeing scores upon scores of Stigmartus and Guardsmen firing at each other, each side taking heavy casualties, and then witnessing the ensuing charge and carnage is a good way to invoke the sheer scale of the brutality of the Acheros Salient. For a subtler approach the GM may want to simply show the eerily quiet aftermath of such a warzone, the countless acres of dead Guard and Stigmartus littering a recent battlefield.

PYRRHIC VICTORY

In such an environment it is fitting to reflect on the great cost. The Imperium is built on sacrifice, of this there can be no doubt, and the Acheros Salient is an excellent place to impress upon the players the personal costs associated with the war effort. By all accounts, the Stigmartus have a few regions within the Hadex Anomaly where time flows far faster than it does in real space. Because of this time dilation they are able to recruit legions at an astonishing rate, as those within the Anomaly are born, grow to adulthood, are trained to fight, and are then shipped off to war in a matter of months. Without such an advantage, the Stigmartus would likely have crumbled years ago, but because of it they have a seemingly limitless supply of fresh troops.

The forces of the Imperium, of course, have no such advantage. The Imperial levies compete by recruiting on a vast scale, by the sheer numbers of worlds they can draw upon. Each Imperial Guardsmen has come to this battlefield leaving a life behind. He likely has his family in another sector, or may be from a world the players have heard of or visited. On the eve of a battle, a Guardsmen may wish to tell his story, or beg the Kill-team to take some trinket of his so that he can be remembered. The Guardsmen that the Kill-team interacts with are often unique, each platoon taken from a different part of the Imperium, each group different in dress and custom. There are bold feral world warriors next to chivalrous feudal worlders who stand shoulder-to-shoulder with jaded hive worlders, none of them likely to survive the coming engagement. It is in this fashion that the GM can impress upon the players the human cost of warfare in the Acheros Salient.

A HEAVY BURDEN

There are instances, however, when a battle is decided by the appropriate application of tactical force. A Kill-team is often just such a force. When the odds are so evenly stacked, it is often the elite units that decide the outcome of major conflicts. In this way the impact of a Kill-team far belies its small numbers. Because the battles of the Acheros Salient are so evenly matched, a single Space Marine can decide the fate of tens of thousands, a Deathwatch Kill-team hundreds of thousands.

If a Kill-team can take out or defend a fortified area, or defeat a group of Chaos Space Marines, or break a line of Stigmartus elites, this usually tips the entire combat zone in favour of the Imperium. Because a Kill-team can accomplish these goals without the commensurate casualty rate of a unit of Guardsmen, whole battle lines are shifted, and these victories have far-reaching ramifications for the Imperial forces as a whole. Likewise, if a Kill-team must retreat in the face of an enemy, it is likely that the enemy will decimate the regular Imperial forces in the area, causing widespread mayhem and destruction to the Imperial line. The GM should make sure that the full scope of the consequences of the players' victories and defeats are described to them, as the Space Marines currently fighting in the Acheros Salient are often directly responsible for Imperial souls beyond counting.

The Battle for the Cellebos Warzone

"More men. Send more men. We will choke them with victory until their victory becomes defeat."

—Lord Militant Solomon Tetrarchus

When the forces of the Imperium that controlled the Jericho Sector of old began to fall, the Deathwatch observed and waited. As the once loyal worlds around them began to collapse, first into anarchy and barbarism and then into outright blasphemy and corruption, the forces of the Deathwatch could do very little. Though it is and was the duty of the Deathwatch to ensure that xenos threats are eliminated, they began to attempt to combat the heresy and recidivism they saw springing up around them; however, there were simply not enough Battle-Brothers to keep those worlds from their inexorable descent. One by one the planets that remained devoted to the Imperium were snuffed out, until it seemed that only the Watch Fortresses remained. It was over these fallen worlds that the Deathwatch held their uninterrupted vigil.

When the Hadex Anomaly burst into being, it took those stationed at Watch Fortress Erioch by surprise. Whatever the great and secret purpose of Watch Fortress Erioch was and is, apparently preventing the formation of the Hadex Anomaly was not a part of it. If the Master of the Vigil or the Inquisitor in Chamber had any forewarning of this event, they did not breathe a word of it or lift a finger to stop it. There were a few brief forays into that dread region by the Deathwatch, but they were few and far between; for the most part the Deathwatch in the Reach was far too undermanned to risk extensive missions into the Anomaly. Instead, they watched and waited for another millennia, attempting the best they could to hold back the darkness that continued to creep in around them.

All that changed with the coming of the Achilus Crusade. The incursion of Imperial forces saw the residents of the Hadex Anomaly spring to life, amassing huge armies in relatively small amounts of time and bringing the Anomaly to a level of activity not seen in its entire history. This new life triggered and created innumerable new xenos threats, as old artefacts were unearthed, and new alliances formed. Erioch began sending more and more Kill-teams, and before long the Deathwatch found themselves completely embroiled in the conflict in the Hadex Anomaly.

THE EARLY CRUSADE

The early forays into what would later be known as the Cellebos Warzone were great victories for the advance forces of the Crusade. The armies arrayed were freshly committed to the Jericho Reach, and the combined Adeptus Astartes, Adepta Sororitas, Imperial Guard regiments, and Imperial Navy under the command of Lord Militant Achilus had little difficulty driving into the heart of the region. They took Khazant in a year-long, semi-protracted battle, steadily gaining ground and fortifying their positions until the last of the warlords who had previously laid claim to Khazant had fled. It was far from an easy conquest, but the Imperial forces had a few advantages.

First, the legions under the command of the Warlords of Khazant spent about as much time attacking each other as they did defending their planet from the Imperium. Their ragtag bands of raiders, mutants, and warp-witches were undisciplined. They would as soon make war on rival warlords as fight the Crusade, content to exact petty revenge and settle ancient and trivial blood feuds with one another. Second, it took some time for the warlords to grasp the full size and extent of the threat of a returned Imperium. To them, the vaunted God-Emperor of Mankind that Achilus' forces were fighting for was just another aspiring warlord of the Jericho Reach.

After a few defeats, and some opportunistic backstabbing, the remaining warlords banded together. This was how the warlords had dealt with newcomers to Khazant and the Cellebos region for centuries. They were a vicious lot, and wealthy in captives and plunder, but the truces that united the warlords of Khazant were uneasy at best. They would use the arrival of a hostile force as an excuse to kill some particularly hated counterparts and then the remaining warlords, now made stronger by the culling, would band together and kill the interloper, inevitably dividing up his armies, slaves, and wealth between them. If the new element was particularly resilient or charismatic, he might even be allowed to join the warlords' ranks. There simply had not been a serious threat to the power that the warlords of Khazant had held over this region of the Jericho Reach in centuries. It was also fortuitous that Lord Militant Achilus favoured such a slow and methodical approach to his conquests. If he had been more aggressive in taking Khazant, it is likely the warlords would have banded together much sooner, and the planetary invasion might have become bogged down.

Achilus' armies, however, showed no signs of slowing. The warlords began to get desperate as they started to recognise the full scope of the forces of their new enemy, but by then it was far too late. A few warlords sacrificed themselves in reckless assaults rather than suffer the shame of retreat, at some cost to the forces of the Crusade. Durak Palun, Lord High Marauder of the Bloody Hands, killed fourteen Sisters of Battle before a Palatine of the Order of the Crimson Oath finally slew him in single combat. The majority of the warlords, however, chose to flee. Unfortunately, as a drawback to Achilus' slow and steady tactical advance, there was no force in position to blockade the warlords as they absconded with what remained of their troops, thralls, and loot, escaping into the Hadex Anomaly.

In 782.M41 Khazant had been successfully claimed in the name of the Achilus Crusade, and numerous systems in the Cellebos Warzone soon followed. The Achilus Crusade had gained a strong foothold in the region, and it seemed as if the reformation of the nascent Jericho Sector under the Imperial banner had been all but achieved.

THE COUNTER-THRUST

It was a few years after the successful taking of Khazant that Lord Militant Achilus was lost in the warp, and Lord Militant Tetrarchus rose to power. Tetrarchus' plan was simple. Instead of the overly cautious, plodding pace that Achilus had charted for the sector, Tetrarchus wanted to use the reserve forces that had been built up in the Jericho Reach to prosecute a three-pronged assault, and the main thrust of that assault would strike at the heart of the Cellebos Warzone. It was an audacious and decisive plan. The new Lord Militant would pour his largest and most experienced regiments into the newly christened Acheros Salient.

What exactly happened to the warlords of Khazant while they were within the Hadex Anomaly is a mystery, but it is known what they were called when they emerged. The forces of the Imperium in the Cellebos Warzone were suddenly faced with the armies and armada of the Stigmartus, and they were completely unprepared for their numbers or their ferocity. The warlords of Khazant had been transformed from a collection of small-minded, disparate, and backstabbing warbands into a cohesive and nigh-unstoppable horde of fanatical devotees of Chaos. They had become the officer-bishops of Elak Sarda, and they had emerged from the Hadex Anomaly to do his will and to kill and die in his name.

The first true disaster that befell the Imperial forces of the Acheros Salient was a devastating series of naval battles. Expecting little in the way of resistance, Tetrarchus had ordered a dispersed naval formation to support this new offensive, so that the handful of hardscrabble Chaos Raiders believed to be in the area could be more easily and quickly rounded up and eliminated. The Stigmartus had spent their time in the Hadex Anomaly putting together a strong naval force, with Chaos-controlled Space Hulks and allied Chaos Space Marine-helmed capital ships forming the backbone of their fleet. The divided Imperial Navy quickly crumbled, and was decisively crushed again and again as the heavy core of Stigmartus ships ripped through the separated Imperial Navy patterns. It was all the Imperium could do to regroup and make a steady retreat, and even so the casualties they suffered were immense.

At this point, the allied Chaos forces moved on to reclaim Khazant. The fighting in orbit was ferocious, but it was not protracted. Without reinforcement, the Imperial orbital defences quickly fell to the invaders, leaving a whole Imperial fleet destroyed. The Stigmartus legions descended to the surface, and in spite of five solid years of fortification, Khazant was lost in a matter of weeks, the Imperial forces there slaughtered almost to a man. The year was 786.M41, the Imperium had suffered grievous casualties and had lost all the gains it had made in the Cellebos Warzone.

THE MEAT-GRINDER

Lord Militant Tetrarchus immediately launched another offensive, redoubling his efforts in the Cellebos Warzone, and the war for the Acheros Salient began in earnest. The forces of the Stigmartus on Khazant fought and died with rabid zeal, but were eventually overwhelmed and fell to the pressure of a concentrated Imperial push. The Imperial Guard who had taken the planet were then devastated weeks later by a swift counterattack, but regrouped, and the planet went back and forth under the control of these two factions numerous times before eventually stabilizing into the pitched battleground it has become today.

It is now 817.M41, thirty-five years after the first taking of Khazant by Imperial Forces and thirty-one years after the devastating counterattack that followed. For three decades, the Cellebos Warzone has been a bloodbath, with neither the regiments of the Imperium or the legions of Chaos able to get the upper hand. While the Stigmartus and their Traitor Legion allies have been unable to make any real headway into Karlack or the Iron Collar region, the Crusade forces have been unable to make any meaningful advance into the Hadex Anomaly. The two struggle tooth and nail over the Cellebos Warzone, paying a steep price in blood for the honour of stalemating one another, and Khazant is the fulcrum point over which they fight.

FIGHTING ON VANITY

Not long after the second battle for Khazant, the undisputed leader of the Stigmartus and centre of their veneration, Cult-General Elak Sarda, made his first appearance in the Cellebos Warzone. Assaulting an Adeptus Astartes emplacement on Vanity, Sarda and his elite bodyguards, the Undying, swept through a joint Storm Warden and Dark Sons bunker, killing the six Battle-Brothers stationed there and ending their stoic defence of an Imperial landing point. This was Elak Sarda's first known appearance outside the Hadex Anomaly.

His followers immediately erected a statue in Sarda's honour, and laid the defiled bodies of the dead Space Marines in front of it. Bloody fighting erupted over the new shrine as Stigmartus forces attempted to defend their new holy place and Imperial Forces sought to reclaim their honoured dead. The ruins that remain of the bunker have changed hands countless times; it is called the Shrine of the First Scar by the Stigmartus forces and is referred to as The Last Stand of Kestyr by the Imperial Forces. Long since losing all tactical significance, this site is venerated as hallowed ground by both sides of the conflict and has seen some of the fiercest fighting on the planet.

Vanity is a unique field of battle, for it is missing one of the trademark characteristics of the rest of the Cellebos Warzone. As a battleground it is relatively empty. This is because the fighting on Vanity is done almost exclusively by small groups of specialised forces. The environment on Vanity is so hostile that the main fighting forces of both the Stigmartus and the Imperium are unable to wage war there. Besides the harsh radioactive fallout that blankets the planet, any large cluster of soldiers is subject to attack by the hordes of spectral creatures that make this world their home. The fighting is left almost exclusively to Space Marines, Chaos Space Marines, a particularly tough breed of mutant, and small units of troops who having been heavily augmented (either by the Adeptus Mechanicus or by the powers of the warp). They strive for dominance among the cracked and broken remnants of the planet's empty hive spires.

Despite the hostile environment, however, taking the system of Vanity would be a great strategic victory for the Imperium. Having control over orbital facilities there would give the Imperial Forces a closer beachhead to Khazant, allowing the Imperial Naval forces a safe place to rest and regroup within the Cellebos Warzone itself, which is a luxury currently denied to them. An Imperial-garrisoned Vanity would be an excellent foothold for the forces of the Achilus Crusade, and would do much to speed up the flow of men from the Iron Collar region to the battlefields of Khazant.

COMBAT IN THE BLOOD TRINITY

Unlike many of the other planets of the Cellebos Warzone, the three remaining life-sustaining worlds of the Mataras system–collectively known as The Blood Trinity–are completely under the sway of the forces of Chaos. They are crucial recruiting grounds for the Stigmartus and, further, are rumoured to house the traitors of the Word Bearers legion in the area. Life on the surface of any of the three planets is usually cruel, violent, and fleeting, but those ships in orbit that are allied with Chaos can usually expect safe harbour.

Docking near The Blood Trinity is the closest thing to shore leave that Chaos forces can expect in the region, and a sustained assault against it would do much for the Imperial war effort. If The Blood Trinity were to fall, the forces of Chaos would likely have to fully retreat to the planets outlying the Hadex Anomaly in order to find fresh recruits and refit their ships, in much the same way most of the Imperial troop loading and retrofitting is done at Karlack. This would bog down their supply lines, and the added inconvenience would be of great benefit to the Imperial force as a whole and the battle for Khazant in particular.

All this makes The Blood Trinity a very tempting target. There are proposals to expand the war effort in the Cellebos Warzone to The Blood Trinity being worked on by numerous officers, but so far none of them have proposed a cohesive plan to the Lord Militant. While even making a dent in the defences that currently protect The Blood Trinity would easily make an officer's career, they all know that an Imperial Force attempting to take The Blood Trinity would be hard pressed.

One such plan, which is being mulled over by a handful of ambitious Inquisitors in conjunction with some elements of the Crusade hierarchy, involves a mission of sabotage and misdirection. It calls for covert Imperial forces, possibly Inquisitorial Throne Agents but most likely a Callidus Assassin, to clandestinely enter the system and begin fomenting unrest. While the various factions of the area already fight viciously among themselves, if the right warp-witches were assassinated and blame was to rest on the correct God-clan leaders, it is possible that a network of allegiances would be broken and that The Blood Trinity would be plunged into outright intrasystem war. Getting enough intelligence on the ever-shifting "political" landscape of The Blood Trinity, and preventing the Stigmartus or the Chaos Space Marines in the region from intervening and restoring what passes for order, currently remain this plan's biggest hurdles.

THE BATTLE FOR KHAZANT

Khazant is considered the most important planet in the Cellebos Warzone and is currently the most desired prize in all the Acheros Salient. It can, perhaps, even be considered the most significant strategic location in the Reach as a whole, if loss of life is any measure, for more Imperial Forces have died fighting on this planet than anywhere else within the Jericho Reach.

The surface of Khazant is a pocked and pitted landscape, lined with trenches and covered with Imperial crenellations and Stigmartus battlements. The heaviest fighting occurs at the various landing points and staging areas—these are the strategic areas in Khazant that change hands most frequently. Often a battle will be joined as soon as a group of reinforcements arrives, with troops heading directly out of their landers to defend an already besieged space port from being overrun by the enemy.

There is a pitched and near constant naval engagement in orbit above Khazant. The inner periphery of the planet's orbit is covered with the detritus of a thousand space battles, with the still-burning remnants of cracked and broken Imperial frigates floating through the thousandfold wreckages of old Stigmartus vessels. In this way, the fighting above Khazant is a grim reflection of that below it, with ship formations engaging in brutal and costly battles before receding to their side's zone of control. Blockade running is common and necessary, as both sides must desperately penetrate the other's area of influence to get troops to where they are needed most, the influx of which is, as often as not, the difference between life and death for the beleaguered combatants on the ground. When a section of the sky above is controlled by the enemy, a regiment on the surface can expect orbital bombardment and a fight against fresh troops. When it is controlled by their allies, they can expect the new reinforcements they so desperately need.

Every major faction of the Imperium is present on Khazant: numerous Imperial Guardsmen sporting an array of regimental colours and dying by the scores, the striking Space Marines of the Adeptus Astartes making spearheads deep into enemy lines, ramparts and turret defences hastily constructed by the Magos of the Mechanicus and their Skitarii bodyguards, and brave Sisters of Battle fighting with ferocity and zeal. Likewise the allied forces of Chaos all have a presence on the world: countless Stigmartus rank and file charging headlong into lasrifle lines, Chaos Space Marines tearing through Guard regiments until blunted by their loyalist opposites, disgusting, slavering mutants doing battle with shining Adepta Sororitas. Whole waves of combat, seemingly stretching from horizon line to horizon line, the rocketing explosions of artillery and orbital bombardment punctuating the fighting multitudes, with tactics and formations shifting like ocean tides until each unit meets its counterpart, and the occasional flare in the darkened skies—a not-so-gentle reminder that another vessel has met its fate in the void.

OTHER WORLDS IN THE CELLEBOS WARZONE

There are over fifty planets in the Cellebos Warzone that see semi-regular fighting. Some of the more strategically important of them are microcosms of Khazant, with Stigmartus forces and their Chaos allies fighting the Imperial Guard and whatever Space Marine or Sisters of Battle forces can manage to support them in a brutal cauldron of battle. In the grand scheme of things, though, the majority of these planets are relatively unimportant, as control passes back and forth between each side with considerable frequency. For their part, the forces on these secondary planets in the Warzone are mostly left to their own devices, and receive troops sporadically. No one wants to commit troops anywhere other than Khazant, for fear that armies deployed elsewhere will prove to be the missing momentum that might have spelled victory in that more pressing front.

Another factor that separates these outlying worlds from the rest of the Warzone, other than the relative inconsistency in the influx of fresh recruits, is that many of the Chaos armies on these planets are dedicated to one of the Ruinous Powers over the others. Because they are often fighting far away from the main chain of command, those Chaos followers fighting in the outer reaches of the Cellebos Warzone are often chosen to fight together because of their worship of the same Chaos God, ostensibly to better prevent infighting. The tactics of these various warbands usually vary based on the deity to whom they have sold their souls. There are vicious and bloodthirsty warbands of Khorne, masochistic warbands of Slaanesh, crafty and manipulative warbands of Tzeentch, and vile and corpulent warbands of Nurgle. Each fighting force is usually accompanied by their associated power's daemons, and the members of the warband usually bear the dark gifts and mutations appropriate to their chosen patron. While Imperial commanders in the area may eventually catch on to the differences between each type of force, the nuances sometimes elude the inexperienced. Knowledge of the Chaos Gods and their proclivities is proscribed, and well beyond the purview of the average Imperial Guard commander. Likewise a planet is often garrisoned by only a single regiment of Imperial Guard, if that, and so the fighting is done by forces that are, when compared to the larger fronts in the Warzone, relatively homogenous.

The end result of this is that the commanders of the forces that fight over the minor planets and systems of the Cellebos Warzone get to know both their battlefronts and their opponent's tactics quite intimately. The fighting done on these neglected worlds is guerrilla warfare and small unit tactics for the most part, as the commanders on these fronts may not be in regular contact with the rest of the Imperium and may not be resupplied for years, sometimes decades, at a time.

THE FUTURE OF THE CELLEBOS WARZONE

The Achilus Crusade cannot continue at its current pace. While the forces of the Acheros Salient were showing some signs of success, that all changed with the pressures added to the Crusade by the arrival of Hive Fleet Dagon. It has become obvious to those in command that the current rate of attrition does not favour the Imperium, and that eventually the hordes of Chaos will overwhelm them. Chaos has no such weakness; there is no other front for their war, no other enemy vies for their attention. They have but one purpose now, to break the hated Imperial forces and reclaim the Jericho Reach as their plaything once again. Once they have done so, they can go back to their petty squabbling and internal strife.

The Imperial forces in the Jericho Reach have, with their offensive, united the disparate forces of the region. If they lose their foothold at Khazant, it is possible that the followers of Chaos will fracture and resume their usual bickering and infighting. This is one possibility. The more likely scenario, however, and a prediction that has the Imperial generals of the region rightly terrified, is that the aggression of the Imperial assault has united all the necessary components of a new Black Crusade. If Khazant falls it will not just be the Jericho Reach that suffers, but entire sectors will be razed by the forces of Chaos as they go on an unstoppable rampage throughout the Segmentum.

DEATHWATCH ACTIVITY

"I do not pray for victory. I do not pray for my life. I do not pray even for the lives of my men. All I pray for is that we have bought our allies enough time."

–Colonel Clastus Deign, Maccabian 16th Janissaries

The level of Deathwatch activity within the Acheros Salient was relatively modest before the coming of the Achilus Crusade, when compared to the other salients. The numbers of the Deathwatch were comparatively small, and most Deathwatch missions in the area were focussed on fact-finding and containing threats on the other side of the Hadex Anomaly, stopping xenos activity in the worlds of the Outer Reach and the Slinnar Drift, and lightning strikes against Chaos raiding forces that the Deathwatch had decided had wandered too far afield or too close to a Watch Station. All of this changed with the arrival of the Crusade forces. The Acheros Salient then became the front line of the Crusade, and as the Imperial forces drove into the heart of the Jericho Reach they stirred up a whole new set of problems for the Deathwatch.

When the forces of the Crusade began their redeployments to concentrate on the emerging Tau threat and the appearance of Hive Fleet Dagon, the focus shifted from the Acheros Salient to these new developments. The Kill-teams who remained active in the salient began to see less and less support, even from their Deathwatch brethren, and all the while the numbers and strength of the enemy forces inexplicably swelled. The tactics of the Deathwatch, much like the tactics of the Crusade forces in the Acheros Salient as a whole, began to switch. The Deathwatch began having to contend with the ever increasing forces of Chaos and the Stigmartus. Kill-teams started to perform targeted strikes just to keep Chaos forces at bay, so that other agents of the Deathwatch could pursue their missions into the Anomaly without overwhelming resistance.

Those members of the Deathwatch that have stayed within the Salient have watched as the position of the Imperium slowly becomes more fragile and untenable with every passing battle. Whether a skirmish is won or lost hardly seems to matter; the price this theatre of war demands has become too high to sustain. With the pressures of the other salients mounting, and with the resources of the Acheros Salient slowly and inexorably dwindling, it has become obvious that decisive measures must be taken. What those measures will be, though, and whose burden they will be to bear, are yet to be decided.

OPERATIONS AND TACTICS

The types of combat missions the Deathwatch are called on to complete within the Acheros Salient are varied. Defending and extracting Imperial Guard command units that have been trapped between enemy lines, assassinating particularly

adept or particularly warp-fuelled Stigmartus fighters, and countering forays by Chaos Space Marine warbands are all responsibilities that Deathwatch Kill-teams are called to accomplish on a regular basis. Because they are so close to the front lines, Kill-teams active in the Acheros Salient can usually expect immediate support from Imperial forces in the area, as the area is heavily occupied and almost all troops in the region are at full combat readiness. Likewise, the Battle-Brothers can be expected to be asked for aid whenever they reveal themselves, for the needs of those same forces are pressing and urgent. That being said, the Kill-team's victories are often thankless, and refusal of aid is met with vitriol or pleading from the desperate commanders in the area. Only when they have ventured far from the front, usually into the Hadex Anomaly or beyond, will the Deathwatch in this region of the Jericho Reach be distanced from the masses of their Imperial brethren.

The forces of the Deathwatch often encounter tension with Inquisitors of the other Ordos in the salient. Many Inquisitors and Throne Agents of Ordo Malleus and Ordo Hereticus wonder why an organisation with such close ties to the Ordo Xenos is persecuting against such a broad spectrum of enemies. The Deathwatch of Watch Fortress Erioch, for their part, make vague reference to the timeless pact and ancient prophecies that put the Jericho Reach completely under their purview. While most of the older and more venerable Inquisitors active in the area respect this long-standing mission, remembering rumours and half-forgotten legends of this ancient accord from well before the Achilus Crusade had begun, many of the younger Inquisitors and their Acolytes in the Acheros Salient are suspicious of the Deathwatch's actions.

SEARCH AND DESTROY

Deathwatch Kill-teams are often tasked with decimating high-profile targets in the Salient. So far, numerous Imperial forces, including a few Temple Assassins and at least one Deathwatch Kill-team, have reported Elak Sarda, leader of the Stigmartus, successfully killed, though it is usually shortly thereafter that he emerges somewhere else in the Cellebos Warzone, apparently unscathed. Whether he has numerous doppelgangers or whether he has survived using other, more arcane means is unknown. The Deathwatch ceaselessly prosecutes leading members of the Stigmartus, and Kill-teams are often called on to track and face down daemons and daemon princes in the absence of more dedicated hunters of warp spawn. There is little that most members of the Deathwatch relish more, though, than hunting down and facing the many warbands of the Traitor Legions active in the area. Nearly every Chapter has a fallen Legion of Chaos Space Marines that they have a particularly undying enmity against, and many have several. Among those that actively hunt Chaos Space Marines in the Acheros Salient is Librarian Zadkiel of the Dark Angels, whose zeal is legendary and who ruthlessly seeks after the Unforgiven rumoured to be lurking in the area (see page 20 for a full profile). It will be a supreme test of will for any Dark Angels who are asked to accompany him to do anything but abandon their current duty, so great is their hatred for their long lost brethren.

Information Gathering

The Hadex Anomaly obscures everything in the Acheros Salient, and so it is often up to the Deathwatch to discover what nefarious plans the forces of Chaos have in store for the Imperium in the region. Kill-teams will often assault Chaos Raider fleets, stealing onto a ship via teleport and prying ciphered communiqués from hostile cogitators before disappearing back into the void. The Battle-Brothers may be tasked with capturing an enemy commander to bring him to the tender ministrations of a nearby Inquisitor and his retinue, and then await the subsequent revelations. The Deathwatch will often send Kill-teams to retrieve data from the various automated Watch Stations situated around the anomaly, and if the records that have been gleaned are particularly time sensitive it will often be up to the Battle-Brothers how best to interpret or disseminate the information they have received. In this way a Kill-team may arrive just ahead of a Chaos fleet, bearing news of an imminent attack and aiding the Imperial forces in their defence against it, or they may judge themselves sufficient to the task and attempt to head off the invading warband without assistance.

In the Balance

The Cellebos Warzone has seen its share of titanic, cataclysmic battles. Innumerable soldiers ceaselessly slaughter each other on the charnel fields of Khazant as mere feet of ground are taken, lost, and retaken again. The Imperial commanders of the salient constantly plead with the Deathwatch. They beg the Kill-teams to break the deadlock and spare incalculable loss of life. The duties of the Deathwatch in the Acheros Salient are varied, and a Kill-team has left Imperial Guardsmen to be slaughtered on numerous occasions in the name of duty, but this is a call they heed whenever they are able.

The test of open warfare is one of the greatest a Kill-team member can face. Battle-Brothers on the field of combat must be wary of the ever-shifting battle lines, lest they be completely cut off from the greater Imperial forces and be overwhelmed. Even the might of the legendary Adeptus Astartes can be laid low by the overwhelming press of an uncountable enemy. A Kill-team is usually well advised to keep their focus on a few goals, the destruction of an enemy fortification or the defence of a strategic pass, and to know also when the main body of an army is faltering and make its retreat. It is usually considered against orders for the Kill-teams of the Deathwatch to sacrifice themselves in any of these pitched battles; glorious though such a death might be. The duty of being seconded to the Deathwatch is more important than the honour of contributing to any one of the many final stands the Battle-Brothers will no doubt witness while active in the Acheros Salient. That is not to say that the Deathwatch may not be asked to die for their duty, it just that it is frowned upon if that death is in service to an Imperial Guard commander or Chapter Brother, instead of the integrity of a mission in support of the Deathwatch.

Areas of Interest

The main battlefronts of the Acheros Salient are the worlds of the Cellebos Warzone. So far, millions of Imperial citizens have met their end there, and millions more will die before those systems will have any chance of knowing the Emperor's peace. Much of the focus of the Deathwatch is on this handful of important worlds, as Kill-teams fight time and time again on the battlefields of Khazant, or make forays into the Charon Stars to gather vital intelligence.

The whole region falls under the blood-red shadow of the Hadex Anomaly. Nothing in the Acheros Salient escapes its scarlet gaze. As the Anomaly expands and contracts, fleets in warp transit on either side of the conflict are scattered like chaff, and entire solar systems are lost or disgorged seemingly at whim. The warp lanes of the Acheros Salient are also comparatively teeming with ships, both Imperial Navy and otherwise, most often on raiding missions or ferrying troops to and from the battlefield. It is in this salient, then, that the Deathwatch must take the greatest care that their fast-strike vessels remain undiscovered, for there is probably more warp traffic in the Acheros Salient than anywhere else in the Jericho Reach.

Chaos Cults

The taint of Chaos is a cancer that attempts to consume the Imperium from within and without. Despite the best efforts of the Holy Ordos it is undoubted that some of the troops and support staff brought to the Jericho Reach by the Achilus Crusade were already tainted by the Ruinous Powers, and that close proximity to the horrors that lie in wait in the Hadex Anomaly will likely cause the unholy conversion of many more. Worse yet, it is sometimes within the power of these cults to summon foul daemons, turning once loyal Imperial bastions into charnel-filled, warp-contaminated footholds. The Deathwatch, then, must stand ever wary, even among their erstwhile allies, for there is no knowing when the Imperial forces that fight beside them will reveal their true colours as servants to the Dark Gods and attempt to lay the Kill-team low with rank and blasphemous betrayal.

This is especially true of the many minor planets of the Cellebos Warzone. It is there that small Imperial garrisons are in a close contact and constant standoff with equal-sized Chaos forces. These units are often underequipped and undermanned, and oversight by the main Crusade is barely maintained and sometimes nonexistent. It is a recipe for corruption. There have been a few cases of Kill-teams venturing to these worlds and landing amongst the Imperial Guard there, only to be ambushed by their erstwhile allies and assaulted by mutants, daemons, or worse. A wise Kill-team commander will speak with an Imperial Guard outpost's Commissar as early as possible, as having one around is usually a good (but not fool proof) indication that the unit stationed there has remained loyal. Those regiments that claim to have lost their Commissars to attrition should be treated with suspicion, if not outright hostility. Other Kill-teams will simply avoid the Guardsmen stationed on these planets altogether, going about their business without ever revealing their presence, but while these cautious Battle-Brothers have not exposed themselves to possible betrayal, they may have missed out on vital intelligence. It is a quandary each Kill-team leader must weigh for himself.

Lost Worlds

Caches of Imperial weaponry, much of it from before the Age of Shadow, still lie scattered throughout the Jericho Reach. Whole planets that could not survive on their own without trade with the rest of the Imperium, especially those hive worlds that relied on the free flow of trade with Imperial agri-worlds for the bulk of their foodstuffs, starved en masse when warp storms cut them off from vital supply lines. Others suffered planet-wide asphyxiation when they couldn't find the technical expertise necessary to maintain their lumbering terraforming engines. While many of these worlds have since been recovered or pillaged, either by Imperial forces or Chaos raiding crews, there still stand many more undiscovered, devoid of life but brimming with equipment and manufactoria, untouched since the beginning of the Age of Shadows. Some of these long forgotten worlds may even house archaeotech and STC template fragments, holding inside their shattered spires technological marvels now vanished from the wider Imperium. Those old Imperial planets that remain unspoiled are a rich find, supplying either the machinery the flagging Imperial forces desperately need to continue to prosecute their war effort or valuable plunder that must at all costs be denied the enemy. There are even rumours of vanished Watch Stations lost deep within the Anomaly. None can say what sort of information they may have chanced to collect in their data reservoirs over the past millennium, or even if the old stations still exist at all.

Stigmartus Recruiting Planets

Somewhere within the nightmarish regions of the Charon Stars lie the Stigmartus' infamous recruiting worlds. These worlds are cut off from the proper stream of real space so that time passes much faster on them, and it is alleged the ruthless Stigmartus have set them up as breeding and training grounds for their warriors. In this way the forces of the Stigmartus keep their legions replenished at a vigorous pace, even as the armies of the Imperium are spread thinner and thinner. If the Imperium could find the recruiting worlds of the Stigmartus rumoured to be within the Hadex Anomaly, they could deal a decisive blow to the forces of Chaos in the region. Some Administratum estimates currently assert that as high as a third of the Stigmartus forces arrayed against the Imperium in the Acheros Salient are originally from these temporally displaced worlds. The ability to strike directly against them, to cut out the beating heart of the Stigmartus' sustained assault, would be a great triumph for the Imperium in the Acheros Salient.

RUNNING A BATTLE IN THE CELLEBOS WARZONE

The war against the Stigmartus has raged across the stars of the Cellebos Warzone for decades, transforming formerly gorgeous planets into smouldering battlefields and haphazard fortresses. The Space Marines of the Deathwatch in the Jericho Reach in general do not concern themselves with these battles, spending most of their attention on the other two salients and the xenos foes that bear down on the Imperium there. However, the Acheros Salient spans a large swath of the Reach, and even under the smouldering battlefields there lie ancient alien secrets just waiting to be awakened, and a Deathwatch Kill-team can easily find themselves inserted into the centre of a raging battle against Chaos, with the mission of extracting or eliminating an important xenos target.

The Imperium's battles against the forces of Chaos can act as an epic and dangerous backdrop for a mission, giving the GM an opportunity to showcase enemies the Deathwatch do not normally deal with. The pitch and sway of battle creates a dynamic background that the Kill-team must navigate around and manipulate to achieve their objective. However, the GM should stress to the players that the Deathwatch should, in general, not concern themselves with the final outcome of the battle. It is not their place to wade into the thick of combat alongside the rank-and-file of the Imperial Guard, but to fight a war of secret priorities behind the veil of the ongoing crusade.

This section gives the GM guidance on using the rules presented in **MARK OF THE XENOS** for running massed battles to create a dynamic backdrop for Kill-team missions in the Cellebos Warzone (and the rest of the Acheros Salient). This technique can be used to create a completely open, random, and exciting setting that keeps both the players and the GM on their toes.

MASSED BATTLES AS SETTINGS

The rules presented in **MARK OF THE XENOS** give the GM three different options for running a massed battle; the Abstract Method, the Detailed Method, and the Very Detailed method. This book reviews both the Abstract Method and the Detailed Method, and gives guidance for GMs on combining these two to create a dynamic battlefield for their Kill-team's mission into the Acheros Salient.

The primary elements of using a massed battle as a setting are the locations consumed in the combat. The GM should break down the battlefield the Kill-team is entering into a series of areas. This breakdown can take the form of a list or even a rough map dividing the area into sectors, each with its own defining quality. This will give the players an idea of the general area where the battle is happening, and will provide meaning and clarity when one side seizes new ground or is overrun.

The fierce battles between the Imperial Guard and the Stigmartus can stretch across an entire planet; whole continents can be consumed in the fires of war as the two sides vie for control. Because of the large scale of this combat, the overall progress of the battle as a whole cannot be tracked in terms of the structured time used for regular combat. Instead, the concept of a Strategic Phase is used to track the events of the battle. A Strategic Phase is not a fixed unit of time, and it can contain many Rounds of normal Structured Time. This abstract representation exists so the players and the GM can keep track of where different battalions of troops are moving and fighting. The passing of each Strategic Phase should represent a shift in the battle based either on the resolution of rolls using the Detailed System discussed below, or simply based on the judgement of the GM based on the narrative he wants to unfold.

At the resolution of each Strategic Phase, the GM should present the Kill-team with at least two options for Turning Points (discussed on page 47) in the battle. This will provide the Kill-team with a choice of how they want to affect the outcome of the battle. These may be an Imperial Guard regiment breaking through the Stigmartus forces, opening up an opportunity for the Kill-team to sneak in and take out the Stigmartus' command station; or a critical column of Leman Russ tanks being ambushed and requiring rescue before they are all destroyed. Having multiple turning points available at one time creates meaningful choices for the Kill-team, allowing them to shape the battle to complete their own overall mission, whether it be recovering a dangerous xenos artefact from the hands of the Stigmartus, or assassinating a xenos agent attempting to align with the forces of Chaos.

TACTICAL DISPLAYS

Massed battles can become very complicated depending on the number of units involved and the nature of the battlefield. In these instances the GM can find it useful to create a tactical display for his players to show them where units are in relation to one another and perhaps the fighting strength or condition of these units. This can be as simple as making some marks on a piece of paper or using a collection of markers, coins or other counters to provide an overview of the battle at a glance. If the GM wishes to add more detail, he could use a grid or hex map to help define distances and include the fog of war so that enemy units (or even friendly ones) disappear and reappear on the map as they fall in and out of vox or visual contact. GMs should also note that creating a tactical display is different from using a tactical map (see **Deathwatch** page 245) as it is intended to give a broad view of a battle, such as an actual commander might have, rather than an exact representation of the location of the characters and each individual enemy.

RESOLVING COMBAT

As events unfold on the battlefield, there are many military confrontations that don't directly involve the players and thus occur in the background. The GM should resolve these quickly to keep the players engaged in the action, either using the Abstract or Detailed methods. The Abstract method provides a quicker and smoother way of resolving the combat, however it lacks the degree of randomness the more detailed method provides.

ABSTRACT METHOD

The easiest way for the GM to run a battle off screen is by handling it as a narrative. This means that the GM simply uses his judgement, depending on the strength or number of allies and enemies (or as determined by the course of the plot) to work out victors and losers. This method also allows the GM to take into account things such as morale, environmental effects or the special abilities of commanders, without the need to assign additional Talents or Traits to combatants. If the GM feels an Imperial Guard regiment is of poor quality, or suffering from weeks of reduced rations and tainted water, he can have them fare badly in battle. Equally, if facing a damaged Stigmartus tank, the GM could have it break down or malfunction intermittently, describing the hereteks working desperately to repair it, dodging fire as the Imperial forces close in.

If the GM wants to add a bit more randomness to this method, he can make dice rolls, usually a single dice to keep things quick, to determine the outcome of events. For example, he may decide that a company of Imperial Guardsmen will hold if they can roll equal to or less than their Willpower. The same Imperial Guard company may come under fire from aerial bombardment, at which point the GM could roll against their Toughness and have them destroyed if they fail. Just as

with results the GM creates using purely his own judgement, this kind of quick random outcome should only be used for action between allies and foes, not for direct attacks from or against the PCs.

DETAILED METHOD

This method is slightly more involved than the abstract method, though it aims to keep things simple and fast to run and allows the GM to keep the action moving along at a good pace. The detailed method assigns each enemy or allied Horde, Elite warrior, Master warrior (see page 358 in the DEATHWATCH rulebook), or vehicle with an Attack Value (AV) and Defence Value (DV) based on the damage they can inflict and the wounds, armour or Magnitude they have. To work out these values use the following guidelines:

Working out Attack Value

- Add 1 point for each die of damage the unit inflicts with its weapons (if the unit is armed with multiple weapons use the weapon which deals the most damage)
- Add 1 point for every attack beyond the first (additional weapons and twin-linked weapons count as extra attacks)
- Add 1 point if it is using a semi-auto weapon
- Add 2 points if it is using a full-auto weapon

EXAMPLE

A Horde of Renegade Militia is armed with autoguns and has a Magnitude of 40. The damage from an autogun is 1d10+3 (adding 1 to the Attack Value for the one die of damage). Because of its Magnitude of 40, the Militia Horde inflicts an additional 2d10 damage on all its hits, adding another 2 to its Attack value. Also as a result of its Magnitude of 40, the Horde can make 3 ranged attacks (2 extra beyond the first) adding another 2. Finally an autogun can fire on full-auto adding another 2. This gives the Militia Horde an Attack Value of 7 (3 of for the number of its damage dice, 2 more for its extra attacks and 2 for being able to fire full-auto).

Working out Defence Value

- Defence is the first digit of the Horde, vehicle or warrior's wounds or Magnitude (use the highest value if the unit has multiple values). For Magnitude or wound values of less than 10 (i.e. scores of 1-9) the Defence Value counts as 0.
- If the unit has armour points, add another 1 to its Defence Value for each full 4 armour points it possesses in the body location.
- If the unit or Horde has force fields (a very rare occurrence!), add another 1 to its Defence Value for each full 10 points of the Force Field's rating (see page 166 in the DEATHWATCH rulebook).

EXAMPLE

A Magnitude 30 Horde of Renegade Militia is wearing flak armour which provides 4 Armour Points. The Militia use the first digit of their Magnitude to work out the Defence value giving them a DV of 3. They then add another point as they have 4 points of armour giving them a final DV of 4.

EXAMPLE

The Kill-team is in the forefront of an Imperial attack against a hilltop complex held by Stigmartus forces. Riding into battle within the Chimeras of a company of veteran Guardsmen, they must make the assault under fire. Deciding to run the battle as a narrative, the GM describes the roaring Chimeras speeding over the terrain as defensive fire blazes around them from Chaos positions on the approach to the complex, even having one or two of the Chimeras burst into flames and explode. The GM only makes rolls to hit the Chimeras with the Kill-team inside, however. When they reach the complex and jump out of their transports, they then immediately come under fire from several companies of Stigmartus militia (represented as Hordes) led by two Chaos Space Marines. Once again the GM describes Guardsmen being gunned down and blown apart as they breach the perimeter but only rolls for attacks directed at the Kill-team and only works out damage against the militia from their attacks. After a few rounds of furious combat, the GM then decides that the Guardsmen have broken through, though they have taken heavy casualties (this equates to reducing the Guardsmen by half and having the Stigmartus militia Hordes retreat along with the Chaos Space Marines). The Imperial forces, led by the Kill-team, then move off into the complex.

When running a combat between foes and allies during a Strategic Phase, the GM rolls 1d10 and adds the unit's Attack Value, which he then compares to the target's Defence Value, every point over this inflicting a wound or a point of Magnitude. If the GM decides to have the PCs abstract their actions across a Strategic Phase in combat against a larger force of foes, they always use their own characteristics (they never use the Attack value and Defence value method) when attacking foes, and foes always use their normal characteristics when attacking the PCs. However, it is recommended that the PCs influence the battle through playing out Turning Points in the same fashion as a normal mission, to keep the players interested and engaged. Based on the outcome of each individual Turning Point, the GM can change events as they play out over the larger Strategic Phase.

EXAMPLE

Using the same example as above, the Kill-team are part of an assault on a Stigmartus military complex. When the Guardsmen (AV 6 and DV 5) hit the beach the GM plays out the combat between them, the Militia (AV 7 and DV 5) and their Chaos Space Marine leaders (each with AV 4 and DV 4). Using all the normal rules for initiative and weapon ranges he begins with the Militia firing into the Guardsmen rolling 1d10 and adding their AV of 7, getting a total score of 13. The GM then compares this to the Guardsmen's DV of 5 reducing their Magnitude of 40 by 8 to 32 (the amount over their DV). The Guardsmen then return fire (after reducing their AV by 1 to take into account the extra ranged attack lost by their reduced Magnitude) concentrating on the Chaos Space Marines. They roll and inflict 7 wounds which are applied to one Traitor Marine. Finally the Battle-Brothers make their attacks using their normal profiles against the Traitor Marines, using their normal characteristics, inflicting another 25 wounds, which in addition to the 7 wounds caused by the Guardsmen destroys one of the Chaos Space Marines.

++A moment of laxity spawns a lifetime of heresy++

//Document Desc: Priority report to Acheros Salient command from Khazant surface//

++CLASSIFIED++

As commanding officer of the Brontian 53rd—deployed to the surface of Khazant—I was ordered to take and hold Stigmartus site designated 54:762B. Upon approach to the enemy defenses, we were met with no enemy resistance. We proceeded to breach their battlements with Basilisk bombardment and send in forward squads. They found nothing but piles of dead Stigamartus soldiers, many of which appeared to have been killed some time ago.

According to field reports, no Imperial Guard or Imperial Navy forces have been operating in the area for some time. Also, the level of efficiency with which the Stigamartus were dispatched is far beyond the work of Guardsmen. I advise a full investigation, for I fear there may be a third presence on Khazant.

These suspicions are unfounded. Site 54:762B was struck by a Deathwatch Kill-team operating under Watch Captain Kail Vibius.

— Inquisitor Galian Tolst

LARGE SCALE TURNING POINTS

The massive battles that consume the Acheros Salient stretch over continents, embroiling entire planets in the fires of war. A single Deathwatch Kill-team cannot affect the course of such an immense battle simply by charging into combat alongside the rank and file of the Imperium, nor would it serve their usually incredibly specialised mission. Instead, Kill-teams work from the shadows, striking out at high profile enemy targets, weakening their hold in the area and possibly changing the course of the entire conflict. Turning Points like these are explored in MARK OF THE XENOS as small but important moments in a battle that are played out in more detail because of their importance. In the larger scale battles of the Cellebos Warzone, Turning Points can be entire missions that eliminate an important Stigmartus facility or a shrine to the Ruinous Powers, weakening the enemy just enough to give the forces of the Imperium the advantage they need.

EXAMPLE

The GM is running a planetary invasion of a Chaos-held world on the edge of the Hadex Anomaly, in which the Kill-team is involved. Rather than playing out each stage of the combat between the Imperial forces and the Chaos forces, he creates a number of turning points. During the first battle of the campaign, the PCs land, along with a regiment of Imperial Guard and an Inquisitor and his retinue, in a blasphemous temple to the Dark Gods. While the GM plays out the battle using the mass battle rules he creates three turning points for the battle, involving toppling a huge monument that draws the power of the warp, stopping a counterattack by a squad of Chaos Space Marines during the battle and successfully killing the daemon prince before he can escape. If the Kill-team can win at least two of the three turning points, then the GM rules that the Imperial forces have shaken the enemy's fanatical zeal and can move ahead with the Chaos forces on the back foot; if not then they have merely fuelled the foe's insane belief in the power of their gods and face an influx of daemonic reinforcements.

USING TURNING POINTS

Turning Points in planetary battles are a useful tool for the GM to make a setting that shapes itself based on a Kill-team's actions and choices, putting them in control of the fate of an entire world. As the different Strategic Phases play out, and troops move and resolve combat, the GM should open up choices for different Turning Points for the Kill-team to choose between. These different missions should have obvious consequences on the conflict as a whole, and providing multiple options for the players to choose from allows them to feel like the outcome of the battle is in their hands. After the players choose a Turning Point that they wish to engage in, depending on its size the GM can quickly play it out, or alternatively run it as its own mission with objectives, arming, etc.

Below are a few examples of some large scale Turning Points. These examples represent high profile targets the Kill-team would encounter on the battlefields of the Acheros Salient. Each of them has a different structure that has serious effects on the way the battle plays out—the GM can play up the dramatic benefit the enemy forces are receiving from these assets, and maybe even have the Kill-team do recon to figure out what is causing these dramatic benefits. Once they have intel on the location, they can strike, dealing a serious blow to the forces of Chaos, and helping to secure an Imperial victory.

TURNING POINT: STIGMARTUS COMMAND STATION

Stigmartus commanders frequently direct their operations from within heavily fortified bunker complexes outfitted with heretek systems purchased from the Magi of Samech. Mistrustful of even their own troops, the command and control systems of these bunkers allow them to defend themselves with automated systems slaved to dangerously independent cogitators, all the while directing battles across half a world from inside the ferrocrete walls. It is typical that no more than half a dozen personnel will be found within such a bunker. Even if additional troops are called in to defend the complex against a determined assault, only the commander's personal support staff are allowed access to the inner chambers.

This scant handful of overseers remains sufficient to direct the ruin of even the best Imperial forces. Within the black walls of the primary structure in any Stigmartus command facility is a heretek masterpiece, dubbed a "Herald Engine" by those Imperial officers unfortunate enough to be deployed against emplacements containing one. Herald Engines use advanced cogitator technology to analyse the stratagems used by the Imperium and respond to them with frightening accuracy. Some commanders even believe enslaved daemons to be used in guiding the analysis, doubting the ability of any machine to be so precise. No matter how a given commander interprets the Tactica Imperialis, while a Herald Engine aids his foe, the Stigmartus are almost impossible to surprise, able to respond to any ambush or feint while directing counter-assaults at the weakest points in the Imperial line.

MISSION OVERVIEW

Given the advantage offered to a Stigmartus force by the blasphemous technologies inside such Command Stations, the Achilus Crusade will devote incredible resources to taking one down. The Watch Captains of Erioch have also requested independent missions against these structures at times, when they threaten Deathwatch operations within the Acheros Salient. A Kill-team deployed against such a foe must break through deadly automated defences to dismantle the Command Station as thoroughly as possible, before getting bogged down in an extended firefight with a major Stigmartus force.

PRIMARY OBJECTIVE

Destroy the Herald Engine: The danger of a Stigmartus Command Station revolves around the Herald Engine. Though it is deadliest when matched with a skilled heretic commander, the most simple-minded officer of their ranks can still cripple Imperial operations with its aid. It is also the most irreplaceable of the station's assets, as the Magi of Samech are said to become enraged with any who let their prized creations be destroyed. As such, no assault on the base can be considered complete without destroying the Herald Engine.

SECONDARY OBJECTIVES

Destroy the Command and Control array: The Magi of Samech provide more than just Herald Engines to the Stigmartus, as the advanced defence systems of the Command Stations show. Where a normal Imperial officer's bunker would have a vox array, the Stigmartus rely on advanced cogitator links to direct both the base's automated defences and deliver their orders. Destroying these systems can compound the loss of a Herald Engine, turning the tactical situation around entirely as Imperial forces gain the logistical upper hand.

Slay the Stigmartus Commanders—For all their tactical prowess, the Stigmartus are followers of the Ruinous Powers, and respect power over sophistication. The officers placed in charge of a Command Station will invariably be ruthless killers, blessed by their patrons with unnatural prowess and might. While lesser warriors die at their hands, the Kill-teams of the Deathwatch have the strength to cast them down and strike a mighty blow against the enemy's morale.

TERTIARY OBJECTIVES

Rescue Captives of the Stigmartus: The Stigmartus are not known for mercy, but they frequently take prisoners to sacrifice to the Ruinous Powers in profane rituals. Rescuing these poor souls could be as simple as granting them a clean death, or as difficult and glorious as shielding them from enemy fire in the escape from a collapsing base, and delivering the prisoners back to the hands of the Imperium.

Destroy the Defence Systems—While the automated defences of the Command Station are not a great threat to the Imperial war machine in and of themselves, few Kill-teams would simply leave the blasphemous machines intact when they could be cleansed from the face of the battlefield. Pitting the might of a Space Marine against their firepower and devilish machine intellect would also surely gain the victorious warrior great honour among his Battle-Brothers.

COMPLICATIONS

The Automated Defences: A Stigmartus Command Station could have anything from a dozen long-range automated weapons to keep attackers at bay to scores of point-defence turrets gunning down intruders and unauthorised heretics with equal readiness. They typically attack with a Ballistic Skill of 40, using the profile for any Basic or Heavy weapon in the Deathwatch Armoury. When it is necessary to make other Tests, the machine intellect will usually have a 25 in the relevant Characteristic, varying this at the GM's discretion. These emplacements typically have 9 points of Armour and 20 Wounds, and possess the Machine (3) Trait.

They Know We're Coming: Given the prodigious cognitive ability of a Herald Engine, it is quite possible that some element of the Imperial strategies it has analysed could give away the presence of the Kill-team, or even their target. At the GM's discretion, the Command Station might be reinforced by Hordes of Renegade Militia (from the Deathwatch core rulebook), or any of the Stigmartus forces described in THE ACHILUS ASSAULT.

TURNING POINT: SHRINE OF SKULLS

The Stigmartus dedicate their victories to the Dark Gods, claiming that their patrons help them in battle. Unfortunately for the Imperium, the heretic army does indeed have the favour of their gods, channelling the power of the warp through immense shrines. The Stigmartus warrior lodges dedicating themselves to the Blood God build profane reliquaries on every world they fight over, heaping the skulls of their victims in a towering mound over the blood-caked earth.

The true horror of the shrine is not mere bodily desecration, however—each skull added to the mound has profane marks of power written upon it in the blood of sacrificed warriors. These sigils are said to shackle the soul of the fallen warrior to the Skull Throne of Khorne, and to grant the slayer their victim's prowess in battle. The psyker-adepts in the service of Inquisitors are silent as to the truth of the first claim, but the second is provable enough. As the mound expands to host more victims and blood-soaked dedication rites, the warrior lodges attending it grow noticeably mightier, with corded muscle straining the frames of every warrior, and new, deadly mutations erupting from their flesh.

MISSION OVERVIEW

An established shrine to Khorne fills the Stigmartus with unholy vigour, making them capable of shrugging off grievous wounds and filling them with a terrible lust for battle. With enough sacrifices channelling this unnatural vitality into the Stigmartus troops, they become a match for even the Adeptus Astartes in raw physical power. The Deathwatch is one of the few forces capable of defeating warriors so imbued, and perhaps the only group in the Jericho Reach capable of taking the offensive in such an engagement without catastrophic losses.

PRIMARY OBJECTIVE

Destroy the Shine: Merely slaying the imbued warriors only strengthens the Blood God's grip on a world, as the bloodshed acts as a sacrament to Khorne. A Kill-team seeking to deny Khorne's might to the Stigmartus must scatter the skull mound and break the bonds of the profane rituals empowering it. A skilled Librarian could disrupt the energies of the shrine, or cleansing fire could bring its ruin. The armouries of Watch Fortress Erioch may contain devices capable of ending such corruption as well, if the Watch Captains can be convinced to issue them.

SECONDARY OBJECTIVE

Destroy the Nearby Warrior Lodges: Even without the unnatural vitality granted by their shrine, the bloody-handed initiates of the Stigmartus warrior lodges are more than the equal of the Imperial Guard. Sending them to meet their master weakens the Stigmartus' military might, and denies the Stigmartus the ritual teaching necessary to recreate the destroyed sanctum. A canny Kill-team will avoid rousing them all at once, for the lodge-brothers are as numerous as they are bloodthirsty.

TERTIARY OBJECTIVE

Raze the Defiled Ground: While the Deathwatch cannot afford to let its Kill-teams get bogged down in extended engagements, there are some dangers that can only be removed by the most diligent extended purges. Kill-teams with sufficient ordnance may wish to scour the landscape where the shrine once stood, pitting blessed promethium against the lingering taint of the warp. Doing so risks being engaged by Stigmartus reinforcements, but righting some affronts is worth any risk.

COMPLICATIONS

The Bones of Martyrs: The followers of Khorne are not discriminating in their choice of opponents, seeking only to shed as much blood as possible. This is as likely to lead them into clashing with mighty heroes as slaughtering the weak, and the skulls of both are taken with equal relish. It is possible that a Kill-team could find the defiled bones of a Battle-Brother amidst the grisly sacraments of Khorne. To return these bones to the halls of the fallen warrior's Chapter would reverse a great dishonour. But even the bones of a Space Marine can only take so much abuse, and if they are damaged while in the Kill-team's care, the defiling of the remains may be on the heads of the would-be rescuers.

TURNING POINT: LABYRINTH

Rogue psykers, daemon-calling sorcerers, and other strange adepts are counted in the ranks of the Stigmartus, but they are mercifully rare. However, on some battlefields, a great coven of such heretics will gather, called by some unknowable voice or purpose. While the malefic arts and sorcerous might gathered in some conclaves is enough to utterly scour away the opposing forces, direct action is never the way of these groups. They are said to be guided by Tzeentch, the inscrutable Weaver of Fates, and they act according to his will alone.

As soon as these adepts arrive, all the spoils and prisoners of the Stigmartus armies are offered to them for use in their rites. Sometimes the warriors of the Stigmartus are picked themselves, and hauled screaming to the sacrificial altar. When the energies harnessed in the coven's ritual are sufficient, the sorcerers call a fragment of Tzeentch's own realm into the material world. Crystal spires erupt from the ground, wreathed in baleful warpfires and glittering with the reflection of otherworldly light. They gather in no sane pattern of formation, instead creating a devilish labyrinth that cannot be navigated by any sane man. This restriction matters not to the Stigmartus, crazed as they are in their degenerate worship.

These bizarre mazes are not simply monuments to the power of Chaos, however suitably they fill that function. The realm of Tzeentch weaves throughout all of space and time, and paths through it can take the walker to impossible vistas that never were—or guide his path unseen past entire garrisons of guards. Even the infinitesimal fragments capable of manifesting in the material realm are sufficient to send whole platoons of heretic warriors across the face of a world.

MISSION OVERVIEW

The forces of the Imperium view the establishment of these crystal mazes as barely less profane than the twisted hellscapes of a daemon world. Even without the tremendous strategic advantage granted by the pathways of the labyrinth, such a manifestation of the Ruinous Powers would be a top priority for destruction. However, the Achilus Crusade has learned at great cost that brute force cannot undo the machinations of the Changer of Ways. If a labyrinth is undone while still infused with the power at its heart, the energies contained within it flow out unchecked, delivering with them the rawest possibilities of change concealed at the heart of the warp.

The surest way to unmake the maze is to assault the eldritch powers guiding it from within, but to call that path "sure" is madness for most warriors. Only the most pure of heart and dedicated in spirit can hope to find his way through the twisting paths against the malign will of Chaos, and to triumph against the horrors that guard it.

PRIMARY OBJECTIVES

Navigate the Maze: Reaching the power source at the heart of the maze requires keen senses, a strong will, and unshakeable faith. The guidance of a psyker can also lead the Kill-team through the maze, but this is not without its own risks. This should be treated as an Extended Test requiring three or more successful checks, at the GM's discretion. Unlike a typical Extended Test, each check can be made with any of several skills: a **Difficult (–10) Psyniscience Test**, a **Hard (–20) Scrutiny Test**, or a **Very Hard (–30) Willpower** Test. Failing any of these tests means the Kill-team has been temporarily lost in the maze, and must deal with phantasms, warp taint, or the minions of Chaos. The members of the Kill-team should make **Difficult (–10) Willpower Tests** or gain 1d5 Insanity Points or one Corruption Point, at the GM's discretion. Alternately, the Kill-team may have to fight daemons or the forces of the Stigmartus.

Disrupt the Power Source—Once the Kill-team reaches the centre of the maze, they must undo the sorcerous workings that sustain its presence in real space. This is usually a small group of bound daemons of Tzeentch, such as Pink Horrors (see page 111 in **Mark of the Xenos**). Chaos Space Marine Sorcerers (see page 112 in **Mark of the Xenos**, or give the Chaos Space Marine on page 363 of the **Deathwatch** Rulebook a Psy Rating of 4 or more and a selection of Psychic Powers) also have the arcane prowess to sustain the portal. In rare instances, the Stigmartus will dedicate the energies of a powerful artefact of Chaos to anchor the maze.

Regardless of the nature of the power source at the labyrinth's heart, once it is slain or destroyed, the spires of otherworldly crystal will be unable to maintain their presence in real space. Each maze undone in the Jericho Reach to date has fallen in a different manner—one fading like mist, another detonating in a shower of crystal shards. It is a dire warning that even as his power is unmade, the Changer of Ways can still demonstrate his mad influence.

SECONDARY OBJECTIVES

Rescue the Explorator: The twisted halls of the Great Schemer have claimed many of the loyal servants of the Imperium, doomed to wander the winding network until insanity claims them. The Kill-team stumbles on an Explorator of the Adeptus Mechanicus who has been wandering the maze for an untold amount of time. Through some miracle of the Omnissiah, the Explorator has stayed alive and maintained his sanity. The Kill-team must escort the unfortunate Explorator out of the maze, keeping safe from the dangers that assail them at every turn.

TERTIARY OBJECTIVE

Avoid All Corruption: When a Kill-team's task takes it to the very threshold of the daemonic realms, even the most vigilant Watch Captains understand if their warriors return somewhat tarnished in spirit. To maintain complete purity in such a mission is a worthy goal, however, and merits the rewards of a successful Objective.

TURNING POINT: PLAGUE CAULDRONS

Those of the Stigmartus who revere the Lord of Flies are eager to spread their lord's "gifts" to the unbelievers. They brew noxious plagues in great rusting cauldrons, releasing a foul mist over nearby battlefields, leaving even the toughest soldiers coughing out blood and pus. The toxic miasma can reach for many kilometres, so that any army attempting to approach its source will drown in their own blood before arriving. As if this were not deadly enough, the acolytes attending the cauldron concentrate the plague into a serum that can used to coat the blades of the heretic host. Warriors mighty enough to slay a dozen Stigmartus fighters collapse in a delirious fever after only the slightest nick from such a blade.

MISSION OVERVIEW

Strength in arms cannot conquer a plague, and even the wrath of a Space Marine cannot cure the air of the fumes floating through it once the plague cauldrons are filled with their fell brew. Any Kill-team assigned to neutralise the plague cauldrons of Nurgle should be assigned a countermeasure on setting out for their mission—a sacred censer to purify the air, blessed oils that can counteract the plague brew's unholy potency, or rare archaeotech med-serums that can cure any disease. Loss of this countermeasure constitutes failure of the Mission, and will be viewed most unfavourably by the Kill-team's superiors back on the Watch Fortress.

PRIMARY OBJECTIVES

Deliver the Neutralizing Agent: Once the Kill-team reaches the plague cauldrons and deals with their fanatical guardians, they must use the countermeasure they were given at the beginning of the Mission. This may require a Medicae, Logic, or Tech-Use test, at the GM's discretion.

Destroy the Inert Cauldrons: The vessels that held the plague are steeped in its essence, and leaving them intact risks another batch of the virulent sludge being brewed. Destroying them thoroughly may require heavy weapons fire or explosives.

SECONDARY OBJECTIVE

Destroy the Concentrated Plague Serum: The foul elixirs stewing within the cauldrons are not the only source of the virulent plague toxin. The pustulent heretics who tend the brew also skim off particularly foul batches of scum from the cauldron's broth and concentrate it into a serum for smearing on blades or suitable for delivery to important targets with Needle Rifles. Though the serum is sufficiently altered that it could not reconstitute the actual plague brew, leaving these deadly supplies for retrieval by the Stigmartus is inadvisable.

TERTIARY OBJECTIVE

Destroy the Weapon Caches: The plague cauldrons are not only deadly instruments of war, nor are they simply sites

of profane worship and dedication for the followers of the Lord of Decay. They are a nexus of activity for all Stigmartus operations done in service of Nurgle. As such, they are often well supplied with stockpiles of the deadliest weapons in the Stigmartus arsenal, as well as shipments of weapons due to be treated with the toxic serum derived from the cauldrons. Depriving the Stigmartus of this armoury would severely hinder their fighting strength.

COMPLICATIONS

Effects of the Plague: The plague cannot breach the environmental seals of Astartes power armour, but if a member of the Kill-team is foolish enough to take off his helmet, or if his armour takes sufficient damage to breach the environmental seal (see Damaging Power Armour on page 163 of the DEATHWATCH rulebook), then the plague will begin to affect him. After being exposed to the plague for one Round, the exposed Space Marine must make a **Very Hard (-30) Toughness Test** or become infected. The test must be repeated for every minute spent exposed. Infection inflicts a level of Fatigue every hour, and 1d5 Wounds per hour (ignoring Armour and Toughness Bonus) once unconscious. Non-Space Marines must pass an **Arduous (-40) Toughness Test** to resist infection instead, and are slain after one hour of infection. Curing the infection is not possible while within the plague fumes, and requires an Arduous (-40) Medicae Test.

TURNING POINT: THE SIREN TOWER

Of all the dire threats of Chaos, from the fearsome weapons of Chaos Space Marines to the dire corruption of mutation, there is one threat reviled above all others. No man is so hated in the Imperium as a traitor who has willingly cast aside his allegiance to the God-Emperor and forsaken his vows of service. Even alone, such wretches are a blight on Mankind. Gathered in the hosts of the Stigmartus, they are an unholy scourge. Worst of all, they are adept at producing more of their ilk.

The Stigmartus turn to Slaanesh to further the spread of their lies, for the wiles of the Dark Prince can penetrate the stoutest of hearts. The focal point of these efforts lies in sorcerous obelisks empowered by unspeakable rites. Designated "Siren Towers" by the Achilus Crusade's officers, these cyclopean edifices emit a seductive call capable of propagating itself over even the most secure and heavily-encrypted vox channels. Imperial forces attempting to coordinate over established vox networks find their messages replaces by a haunting song that calls the listeners to treason and blasphemy. While a Siren Tower stands, the forces of the Imperium must operate deaf and dumb, lest they provide the Stigmartus with reinforcements from their own ranks.

MISSION OVERVIEW

A Space Marine is hardier of spirit than an ordinary man, being chosen from the most worthy, tempered by trials and battles, empowered by the gene-seed, and instructed in faith by hypno-indoctrination. But not even the will of a Space Marine can utterly deny the power of Slaanesh. A Kill-team entering a Siren Tower's area of influence must operate with silent vox-links, communicating only by voice and signal, or risk being beguiled by the song of the Tower. In game terms, this means Support Range for maintaining Squad Mode may be limited—to short vocal range, or visual range if other noise impedes hearing spoken commands (see page 213 of the **DEATHWATCH** rulebook for more details). If the Kill-team is exposed to the Siren Tower's call, through reckless use of their own vox-links or by overhearing an open channel, they suffer a 10 penalty to all Willpower tests while they listen. Listening to the song for an extended period of time may incur Corruption Points, at the GM's discretion.

PRIMARY OBJECTIVE

Destroy the Siren Tower: The song of a Siren Tower will only cease at its utter destruction. To do any less only drives the song into frenzied crescendo, as if it possessed a will of its own to defy its attackers and flaunt its power. The Kill-team would be well advised to requisition heavy ordnance for this purpose, though the stones of a Siren Tower are not so sturdy that sufficient application of basic weaponry cannot wear them down.

SECONDARY OBJECTIVE

Slay the Traitors the Tower has Seduced: Despite the best efforts of the Commissariat and similar agencies, discipline within most Imperial forces is not sufficient to order a complete vox silence across all fronts once a Siren Tower begins its call. Throughout the vast ranks of the Imperium's war machine, some inevitably slip through the cracks and are left exposed to the lure of Chaos. These newly seduced traitors make their way to the source of the song that now grips their hearts to dedicate their lives to the Prince of Excess. They will oppose any attempt to interrupt the song with whatever firepower they were able to steal from their one-time comrades.

TERTIARY OBJECTIVES AND COMPLICATIONS

The following Objectives are not core parts of a Mission to destroy a Siren Tower, but can be included at the discretion of the GM. Though they function similarly to Complications, these goals should be treated as Objectives wherever relevant, such as assigning Requisition or awarding Renown.

Traitor Officer: A high ranking officer within one of the Imperial forces present has been exposed to the call of the Tower and is on his way to rendezvous with the Stigmartus. He must be apprehended and terminated, to prevent any important secrets he knows from being divulged. At the GM's discretion, he may be protected by a personal guard, or have other assets with which to defend himself against the Kill-team.

Stigmartus Commander: A powerful leader of the Stigmartus is present at the Siren Tower. This warrior is high in the favour of the Dark Gods, and comes to commune with them at a site dedicated to their profane powers. He may be a Chaos Space Marine or a foe of similar prowess, and will be protected by a group of his best warriors. He may even have brought a dedicated contingent of his own troops to pay homage at the Tower. Slaying such a powerful and influential war-leader would throw the Stigmartus into disarray, and might result in strife within their ranks as others seek to replace him.

HADEX COMPLICATIONS

The Deathwatch presence at Watch Fortress Erioch has faced and bested many foes, from Ork Warbosses and warbands of Chaos Space Marines, to the worst monstrosities vomited forth from the Tyranid Hive Fleets. Yet the malign will of the Hadex Anomaly cannot be brought to battle, much less slain. Like a festering sore on the galaxy itself, the Anomaly's red glow blights the orderly workings of space and time with unnatural foulness. The orders of the Watch-Commander say that the conditions imposed by the Hadex Anomaly are a hazard to be circumvented, like the native conditions of a Death World, but this belies the number of Deathwatch operations gone awry under its baleful gaze.

In 659.M40, a scant handful of years after the Anomaly's opening, an Enslaver Plague swept unopposed through the hives of Gemre, because the Kill-team sent to purge the initial outbreak arrived in the wrong system, their Navigator driven mad by the crimson glare he saw even in the warp. The punitive measures resorted to in the aftermath of the infestation mean that Gemre is no longer present in the charts or records of the Imperium, but the Deathwatch has not forgotten this first failure. It was not to be the last.

USING HADEX COMPLICATIONS

The following Complications can be used in addition to or instead of the standard Complications found on page 231 of the DEATHWATCH rulebook. Roll on Table 1-3: Hadex Complications to determine Complications randomly, or simply select a result from one of the following lists.

TABLE 1-3: HADEX COMPLICATIONS

1d10	Complication Type
1-3	Roll again on Table 1–4: Temporal Complications
4-6	Roll again on Table 1–5: Spatial Complications
7-10	Roll again on Table 1–6: Daemonic Complications

TABLE 1-4: TEMPORAL COMPLICATIONS

d5	Complication
1	Altered Passing
2	Early Arrival
3	Flow Rifts
4	Time Bubble
5	Too Late!

Altered Passing: The flow of time is erratic within the area where the Kill-team must work. In some areas, time speeds by, but in others, it slows to a crawl. The boundaries of the time-flows may not stay constant, making mapping them difficult at best. The Kill-team may have landed in a slow-time zone, delaying action, or their target may be operating in an area where the relative temporal flow allows him to respond to external operations with lightning speed.

Early Arrival: The Kill-team arrives at their destination to find their target has not yet materialised, and the summons for their arrival was never sent. There may be a chance now to neutralise the threat before it becomes a major issue, but then again, their meddling in the past may change things enough that a new enemy is wrought of their actions.

Flow Rifts: Time is not normally thought of as a danger or hazard, but small pockets of erratic time float through the area, tearing apart whatever is unfortunate enough to pass through them. Even the enhanced constitution of a Space Marine may suffer when blood is flowing through his arm fifty times faster than the rest of his body! Spotting and avoiding these rifts is only possible by observing what passes through them—they are invisible by default.

Time Bubble: An effect eerily similar to a stasis field has erupted around the Kill-team's area of operations. Nothing can enter or leave, and as far as can be told, time is only passing on one side of the barrier. The barrier may be blocking the path to an objective or resource, or even trapping the Kill-team from returning once their task is done. The Kill-team must discover a way to bypass or undo the field in order to complete their Mission. Alternately, the barrier could provide protection against interference, only to disappear when the strange circumstances that spawned it go out of alignment.

Too Late!: Upon arriving at their destination, the Kill-team discovers that their journey took far more time than should have been possible, and the threat they were to excise has triumphed. They must salvage the situation as best they can, and attempt a reversal of the situation if possible. It may be beyond their strength to alter what has already been done, but the Watch Captains will not tolerate surrender to circumstance.

TABLE 1-5: SPATIAL COMPLICATIONS

d5	Complication
1	Blinking Targets
2	Interference
3	Twisting Paths
4	Unexpected Aid
5	Variable Locations

Blinking Targets: The location of one or more of the Kill-team's Objectives has developed a nasty habit of blinking in and out of reality at odd intervals. This means there is only a narrow and unreliable window to deal with it before it disappears. It also means the Kill-team must move out the moment they are finished, or be prepared to discover just where exactly the area goes when it disappears…

Interference: Enemy interference arrives suddenly, perhaps thrown directly into the midst of the Kill-team. These foes are likely as bewildered as the Battle-Brothers themselves, but they will fight to the death against their hated enemies. The occurrence may repeat itself, each time as unpredictable and inexplicable as the last. But surely these foes must be being taken from somewhere…

Twisting Paths: Space itself has gone awry under the warping light of the Hadex Anomaly. Straight paths become circuitous routes covering far more ground than is actually present, and walking between two points in plain sight of each other is like traversing a maze. The Kill-team may also have to deal with their errant travels taking them into unexpected hotspots or hazards.

Unexpected Aid: A boon arrives in the form of friendly forces brought to the Kill-team's location unexpectedly. They may be willing to assist in the Mission, or at least to strike against the foes of the Imperium in their own ways. However, convincing them that the Kill-team is not a trick of the Chaos Powers to deceive them may take some work. In fact, it would be very strange for the machinations of Chaos to work in Deathwatch's favour, even once—are these allies all that they appear to be?

Variable Locations: The Kill-team's Objectives are not present at their usual locations, and have started moving about on their own. Even fortified, entrenched targets may end up moving hundreds of kilometres in the blink of an eye. The Kill-team must chase down these newly mobile targets, or perhaps identify a pattern that they can use to strike at them as they arrive.

TABLE 1-6: DAEMONIC COMPLICATIONS

d5	Complication
1	Aethyric Manifestation
2	Assault from the Warp
3	Corrupt Vision
4	Daemonic Spying
5	Will of the Anomaly

Aethyric Manifestation: Warp energies erupt around the Kill-team manifesting as rains of blood, soporific fogs, flashes of eldritch lightning, or sprays of foul slime. The Kill-team must battle their way through the unnatural storm and escape before the warp's touch corrodes their sanity and corrupts their flesh. The strange manifestation may also foul the trail they follow, or hide a threat just beyond its borders.

Assault from the Warp: The air is rent apart as the warp vomits forth a host of daemons. They are likely to assault the Kill-team, but might be more interested in other targets. The Kill-team must then decide whether to pursue and eradicate this new threat, or to focus on the mission. The daemons might even attack the same target as the Kill-team, as the most unwelcome of allies. Devout Battle-Brothers could be unwilling to tolerate the aid of daemons, however.

Corrupt Vision: A phantom or mirage appears to tempt the Kill-team astray. It may be a false vox-transmission or distress signal, or the apparition of an ally in need. The vision could even be an apparition mimicking a hated foe of one the Battle-Brothers. Pursuing this vision will waste valuable time, and possibly lead the Kill-team into a dangerous trap or hazard. It may have a bit of truth to it, however, or serve as an omen of the future. Can the Kill-team trust any vision of the warp?

Daemonic Spying: The bulwark of reality against the Immaterium is thin here, and daemons can easily peer across it. Innumerable entities watch the Kill-team's efforts and track their every step—entities known to work with the enemies of Man. The information they gather may end up in the hands of the Kill-teams immediate foes, or may serve to further a distant threat in the future.

Will of the Anomaly: There are those who believe the Hadex Anomaly is a sentient, living thing, given to its own alien desires and whims. The Kill-team should have little reason to doubt this as they feel a malign presence invading their thoughts, crushing their wills, and eroding their identities. The longer the Kill-team stays in the influence of the Anomaly, the harder it becomes to think, speak, or remember times before the current Mission. They may forget tactics or facts learned before they set out, perhaps even the briefing of this very Mission.

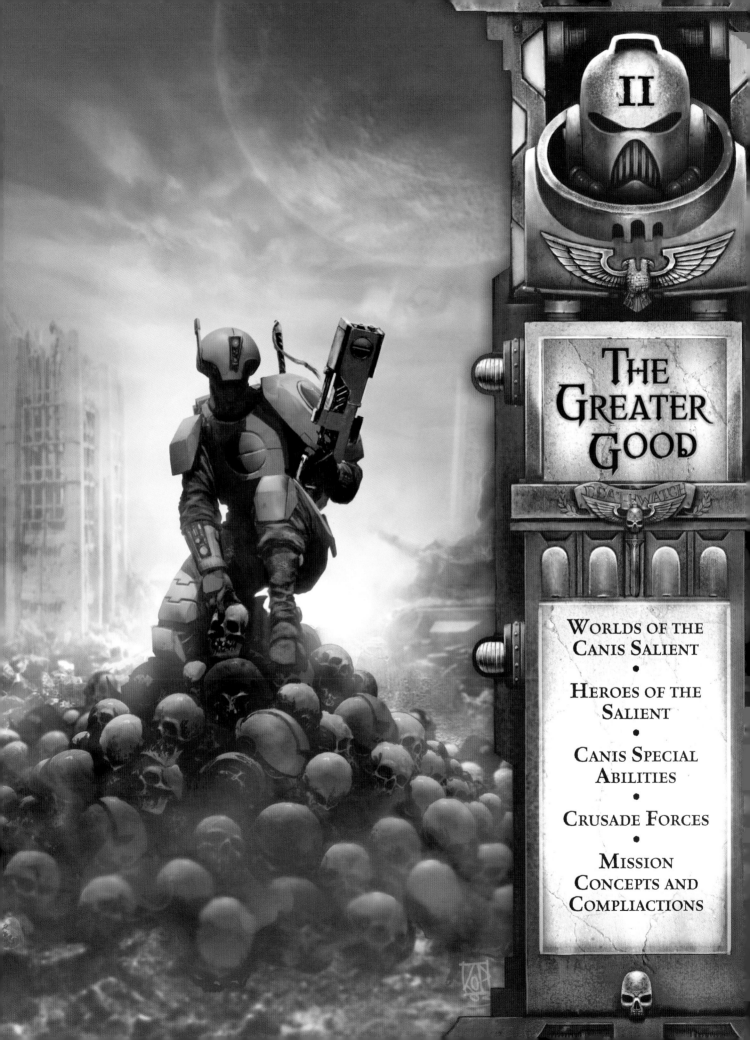

THE GREATER GOOD

DEATHWATCH

CHAPTER 2: THE GREATER GOOD

"Your people are plagued by the terrors we call the Mont'au, as we once were. Too easily, your kind falls to savagery and barbarism, and too readily you embrace such things as good and necessary. We offer another path—a path free of the discordant brutality that haunts you. Our way is unity, peace, reason, and progress, and we offer it to all who crave it, whether they know it or not."

–Por'O Tsua'Malor Ta'cha Shi'nesh Kunas'ro

Covering territories that are amongst the oldest of those claimed by the Achilus Crusade, the Canis Salient has seen little progress since its foundation, as the tenacious and insidious Tau continue to hold out against the forces of the Imperium. Amidst this ongoing war, the pervasive diplomacy and promises of unity offered by the Tau undermine worlds the crusaders have already claimed, and the ravening menace of Hive Fleet Dagon has managed to cross the heart of the Jericho Reach and crash into the flank of the Canis Salient's advance.

The Canis Salient is home to a very different kind of war from the Orpheus and Acheros Salients. Instead of a screaming tide of monstrous, fearless, and relentless foes, the Tau Empire is a cunning and careful enemy, reliant on advanced technology and intelligent strategy to triumph in battle. Just as significant is their propensity for peaceful cooperation, which means that the Tau are potential allies against more savage foes such as the Tyranids who now threaten both sides warring over the Canis Salient. Where war in the Acheros and Orpheus Salients is to the death, with neither side willing or able to show mercy, the Tau are a foe who fight according to rules, are capable of mercy, honour their dead, and know well the benefits of mutual cooperation to overcome a greater enemy.

This potential for mutual cooperation is continually threatened, however, by those whose loathing cannot permit them to see that some foes are deadlier than others. While the Tau are a threat well known to the men and women of the Canis Salient, they are regarded by many within the Achilus Crusade's command structure and within the Inquisition as being the lesser of two evils when compared to the newly arrived Tyranid menace, and it is strongly believed that there are those amongst the Tau who regard the Tyranids with similar dread. For all their efforts to engineer some form of temporary alliance, others within the Canis Salient, foremost amongst them Lord Commander Ebongrave, will not tolerate such actions and work to undermine what they see as the pervasive and deceptive nature of the Tau weakening the resolve of other servants of the Imperium.

This chapter provides detailed account of the Canis Salient, including a number of the worlds and personalities present within the warzone. It also providing adventure hooks and backdrops for campaigns set within the Salient, whether the mission involves warfare or diplomacy.

OVERVIEW OF THE CANIS SALIENT

"…Bastian Tramisch, Nils Gravier; you all are found guilty of consorting with xenos, conspiracy to consort with xenos, laxity in the first degree, failure to perform Throne-given duties, and failure to show proper deference to a senior Adept. For these crimes, you are sentenced to death. Proctor, you may fire when ready. In the name of the Emperor and His holy law."

–Judge-Senioris Magritte Venken, concluding the sentencing of convicted xenos-sympathisers on Wrath

The territory covered by the Canis Salient includes dozens of worlds stretching from the edge of the Iron Collar to the Black Reef, with most of those worlds having been claimed in the earliest years of the Achilus Crusade. These territories, long established under Imperial rule in all but a few cases, are still far from stable and prosperous parts of the Emperor's domain due to the sedition and unrest spread by the Achilus Crusade's oldest enemy, the Tau Empire.

Before the Canis Salient bore that name, countless worlds thought compliant by the Crusade's hierarchy rose up and struck back against the Imperial authorities that claimed to rule over them, casting the Crusade into turmoil even as its founding father was lost to the Immaterium. It required the swift and brutal response of the Adeptus Astartes, in particular the secretive forces of the Deathwatch, to quell these rebellions with terror and bloodshed, giving those worlds new reason to dread the Emperor's wrath.

Yet now, as stability is returned to these rebellious worlds and the war against the Tau pushes ahead into the war-torn systems of the Greyhell Front, a new threat manifests in the Canis Salient. The Tyranid menace, which has so swiftly undone decades of triumphant conquest within the Orpheus Salient, now presses upon worlds at the edge of the Canis Salient, threatening Imperial and Tau forces alike. While some will give no quarter and show no mercy to the Tau even in the face of the Great Devourer, others have begun to feel that standing side-by-side with the Tau against the Tyranid menace may be the only way for the Achilus Crusade to survive.

BEFORE THE CRUSADE

The coreward extent of the Jericho Reach had always been something of a frontier region, with relatively few settled worlds and fewer that provided a major contribution to the Sector's wealth and stability. Because of this comparatively sparse settlement, little in the way of coherent records of the region remained from that time, requiring that most of the intelligence about those worlds be gathered anew by Explorators and Rogue Traders braving the Jericho-Maw Warp Gate, or extrapolated from the scattered accounts of those who had pushed through the warp storms surrounding the Jericho Reach.

However, it was news from this frontier zone that provided much of the impetus necessary for Tiber Achilus' Crusade to be founded. Word that the Tau, who had swiftly reclaimed all they had lost during the Damocles Crusade and were now pushing out to claim yet more Imperial worlds, had somehow entered the Jericho Reach left many ill at ease. The prospect of facing extensive Tau expansion across the Eastern Fringe was not one that many wished to countenance, especially so soon after the Tyrannic War had ravaged the region.

As the Achilus Crusade mustered, scouting expeditions were undertaken, identifying worlds viable for conquest and colonisation and locating regions where the enemies of Man were particularly numerous. By the time the Crusade began, extensive maps and charts of the Jericho Reach had been drawn up and were being used by Achilus and his command staff to plan their war in exacting detail.

EARLY CONQUESTS

The first years of the Achilus Crusade were spent conquering a carefully selected ring of worlds around the Well of Night, worlds that would collectively be known as the Iron Collar in years to come. Of these, Spite was the closest to the territories claimed by the Tau, and was planned from the outset to be a staging post from which the second phase of

THE HISTORY OF THE ACHILUS CRUSADE

This section provides an overview of the Achilus Crusade, specifically as it relates to the Canis Salient. A broader look at the history of the Crusade can be found in THE ACHILUS ASSAULT.

the Crusade could be launched, pushing towards the Black Reef to overwhelm the Tau held territories clustered around the impassable anomaly.

Spite was conquered quickly, with the Tau unable to mount a proper defence so far from an allied world, and those few xenos who were found during the conquest were swiftly put to death as an example to others. The world's industry was swiftly and efficiently turned to the support of the Crusade, while fortifications were built to house the world's new garrison and serve as a command centre for the impending advance.

As the Iron Collar was forming, seventy percent of the Crusade's available forces were being mustered on and above Spite, a strike force that was intended to smash asunder the Tau presence between the Iron Collar and the Black Reef, conquering with a speed and brutal efficiency that could only have been inspired by legends of the Great Crusade.

The push began in earnest with Operation Hammerfall, a brutal multi-world offensive that sought to conquer Rheelas, Argoth, Kaggeran and Wrath, overwhelming the expected Tau defences. Rheelas fell within hours, followed swiftly by Kaggeran and Argoth, and these worlds were quickly garrisoned and declared compliant, with the Crusaders having found only minimal signs of contact with the Tau, against all expectations. As these worlds fell, the Imperium descended upon Wrath to find that the Tau were waiting for them, resulting in almost three weeks of brutal conflict before the Tau withdrew their forces and departed the system entirely.

The Crusade's strategists and eager generals urged Achilus to press the advantage, but the Lord Militant's cautious nature won out, and over a year passed while supply lines were reinforced and defences bolstered in preparation for the seemingly inevitable Tau counter-offensive. While this occurred, Adeptus Astartes forces, spearheaded by several companies of the Storm Wardens Chapter, began to push further ahead, raiding and striking against Tau-held worlds closer to the Black Reef to test their defences and prepare them for a full assault by the forces that were mustering on Wrath.

When the advance resumed, the actions of these Adeptus Astartes Task Forces had wrought a map of worlds defended by the Tau, worlds that could be made compliant, and worlds which could provide little benefit in the short-term, giving Achilus' generals and admirals a clear route towards the systems of the Velk'Han Sept, in particular the Tau capital of Tsua'Malor. World after world was conquered, creating a snaking path of compliant systems leading to Ravacene, where a Tau counterattack stalled the Astartes-led assault.

While Achilus had always planned for a long war, the Chapter Master of the Storm Wardens, Lorgath Maclir, who led the forces on Ravacene, could see victory within months, but that victory was swiftly slipping from his grasp even as he demanded every available soldier to support a crushing offensive. Maclir planned to overwhelm Ravacene with the massive numbers of men and ships available to the Crusade, breaking the Tau defence and opening a path to Tsua'Malor and the other worlds of the Velk'Han Sept.

The reinforcements never arrived. As the fighting on Ravacene raged on, the unthinkable happened—worlds previously thought compliant rose up and struck against the Imperium, sowing discord and destruction along the Imperial supply lines. To compound matters, as the Salient's forces withdrew from Ravacene to put down these rebellions, Lord Militant Achilus was lost, and the entire Crusade ground to a halt in abject shock. What had seemed like a swift and decisive string of victories had succumbed to catastrophe.

REBELLION AND MOURNING

With the Crusade's progress halted by the twin disasters of organised rebellion and the death of the Lord Militant, the overwhelming majority of Imperial operations in the Jericho Reach fell into disarray. With no organised movement of reinforcements or distribution of intelligence, Imperial Guard regiments and Imperial Navy battlegroups found themselves either embroiled in intense conflict or isolated from the war, and supply lines all but collapsed under the pressure of the situation.

It was the intervention of the Deathwatch that saw the Crusade begin to recover. Largely aloof from the operations of the Achilus Crusade until that point, Deathwatch Kill-teams and larger Task Forces appeared almost out of nowhere to aid the beleaguered crusaders, using their own long-established infrastructure to coordinate the defence where it was most needed and serving as a stabilising influence on countless worlds. It is arguable that the actions of an unknown number of Deathwatch Kill-teams and the oversight of Watch Commander Mordigael saved the Achilus Crusade during what was seen at the time to be its darkest hour.

In particular, the swift and expertly coordinated efforts of several Kill-teams were utterly instrumental in putting down the seditionist group known as the Unity on Argoth, Rheelas and Kaggeran, their actions serving to destabilise and demoralise Tau forces to the point that the Imperial Guard garrisons could easily round up and execute the leaderless and scattered rebels.

As rebels and traitors burned for their betrayal, the Crusade began to move once more. Under the collective designation of Operation Tridentis, the newly ascended Lord Militant Tetrarchus set about dividing the Crusade's efforts and pushing forward on three fronts: the Orpheus, Acheros and Canis Salients. The Canis Salient formed around the worlds from Spite to the Black Reef, and was charged with reinforcing the worlds already claimed by the Achilus Crusade and renewing the war against the Tau that had been Tiber Achilus' primary goal.

The Greyhell Front

With the formation of the Canis Salient and the placement of Lord Commander Sebiascor Ebongrave—formerly a member of Achilus' command staff and one of the minds behind the successes of Operation Hammerfall—as its commander, the work of purging worlds of xenophile rebels became the first priority. Within days of his promotion to command of the Salient, Ebongrave gave his first general order—the quarantine of Argoth, Rheelas and Kaggeran, the three worlds that had suffered the worst of the rebellions.

The quarantine was made public knowledge almost immediately, with scores of propagandists composing material to emphasise the regrettable necessity of such grim punishment on so colossal a scale. With this act, Ebongrave hoped to use the Quarantined Worlds as an example to the other worlds in the Canis Salient, demonstrating to them that the Imperium would not suffer rebellion and that any who rebelled would find themselves condemned to a cruel and unenviable fate.

With the quarantine, and the establishment of several Adeptus Arbites precincts across other worlds within the Salient to ruthlessly purge any lingering rebellious groups, the matter of pacifying the Canis Salient was well under way, and Ebongrave turned his attention to the war against the Tau. Ebongrave is unwilling to make the same mistakes that had cost the Crusade in the past; his forces are meticulous, ruthless and entirely focussed on the elimination of every trace of Tau presence and ideology on every world conquered. Progress has been slow, for few worlds touched by Tau philosophies are willing to surrender to the iron rule of the Imperium.

At present, the bulk of the fighting is within the Greyhell Front, a collection of worlds heavily contested by Tau forces. The war within the Greyhell Front is brutal and relentless, and complicated by the politics and espionage both sides are engaged in alongside their military actions. Infiltrators working on both sides to undermine the efforts of their enemies have bred an atmosphere of distrust amongst Imperial Guard and Tau-aligned Gue'vesa forces both, while Ebongrave's paranoia has resulted in frequent purges of units suspected of having been subverted by the Tau. Between the purges and the casualty rates suffered by front-line units, the attrition rate for the Imperial Guard on the Greyhell Front is high.

The greatest setback of recent years saw deeply entrenched Tau sympathisers attack Spite, causing massive amounts of damage to several cities and the fortifications around Ebongrave's own command centre. This assault, devastating and unexpected, only heightened Ebongrave's paranoia, and extensive purges of personnel at every level of his command were undertaken, with over a year passing before the upheaval caused had calmed down.

Stalemate and a New Enemy

The war in the Canis Salient has ground to a brutal stalemate, with the Imperium unable to gain significant footholds within the Greyhell Front, and the Tau forced to employ every trick and stratagem they know to fend off the Crusade's forces. The endless conflict has seen hundreds of billions of Imperial Guardsmen dead to the guns of the Tau and the paranoia of their commanders, and morale has been slipping for years.

To make matters worse, the Canis Salient is confronted with a new peril. On a handful of worlds along the Salient's rimward edge, the Tyranids have begun their inexorable invasion, and neither the Tau nor the Imperium is in a fit state to meet such a threat. Ebongrave is unwilling to contemplate the notion of relenting against the Tau to confront the Tyranids with the Salient's full strength, and is so far content to try holding them at bay with expendable penal legions filled with men and women marked as traitors during his intermittent purges. To their credit, these legions of condemned souls are giving everything to hold back the Tyranid onslaught, but they are not sufficient to withstand the numberless swarms.

At first, many amongst Ebongrave's staff spoke up of the possibility of dealing with the Tau, arranging a truce or ceasefire to deal with this terrible threat to both civilisations. These suggestions were met with charges of blasphemy and treason, and those who had spoken up quickly found themselves on the front lines facing the Tyranids. Such suggestions are now no longer made within earshot of the Lord Commander, instead going above Ebongrave's head to agents of the Inquisition or to Lord Militant Tetrarchus' staff. Efforts have been made to establish peaceful contact with the Tau, but Ebongrave's paranoia has repeatedly proven to be a hindrance in that regard, sabotaging the efforts of the Imperium's diplomats.

Between the Tyranids and the Tau, the Canis Salient is under extraordinary pressure, and there seems to be no sign of that pressure being relieved at any point in the near future.

WORLDS OF THE CANIS SALIENT

"Every one of these worlds belongs to Him-on-Terra already; they merely require His servants to enforce that dominion over them. Any soul who claims otherwise is a coward and a traitor, worthless to the Imperium except as an example to others whose belief may falter."

–Excerpt from Volume IV of Lord Militant Achilus' memoirs

Though the war against the Tau is mostly contained to the Greyhell front, the planets of the Canis Salient still face threats from all sides. Tau spies and sympathisers have infiltrated systems all across the Salient, and Lord Commander Ebongrave's paranoid hunt for these enemy agents has torn apart the stability of Imperial rule on many worlds.

WRATH

"Unidentified vessel, you are trespassing within the territories of a fortified world; transmit clearance ciphers immediately or you will be fired upon."

–Final transmission received by the Vash'ya Skether'qan Ol'eldi

While the fortress-world of Spite drives the Canis Salient's forces onwards, Wrath guards the worlds already claimed and watches for treachery, sedition and the scourge of xenophilia. Wrath oversees matters of security and defence across the Salient, its gaze spread across dozens of worlds thanks to the arcane sophistication of the Eyes of Wrath, a surveillance network linked by the minds of dedicated Astropaths whose every thought is triple-encrypted by the most complex ciphers the Adeptus Astra Telepathica are willing to divulge.

A world of unrest, its primitive populace still not entirely pacified, Wrath is not universally fortified like Hethgard or united in defence like Karlack. Instead, it is covered in countless smaller fortified structures, each housing some distinct facet of Imperial rule, defended not only from alien aggression, but also from the actions of recidivist groups. This scattering of fortresses has produced an isolationist mind-set amongst Wrath's adepts, with each group working apart from others who serve Terra, separated by thick, blast-proof walls. Lord Commander Ebongrave encourages this sense of mistrust and paranoia, for he believes it to be a vital state of mind when combating the insidious Tau.

Beyond the fortress walls, on the shores of the numerous islands that form Wrath's only land masses and roaming the vast seas in primitive ships, is the native population of Wrath, their world subjugated to the will of some distant Emperor. Still retaining a fierce sense of independence, these people continue to struggle against Imperial rule where they can, and while many refuse the aid of outsiders who may simply replace the rule of the Imperium, some have chosen to seek assistance. A few groups return to the old gods who ruled long ago and whose realm can be seen as the glowering crimson star that rules the night, while others find allies in the servants of the grey-skinned outworlders who speak of unity.

HISTORY

Never regarded as a particularly significant world during the time of the Jericho Sector, Wrath had been largely ignored for most of the Age of Shadow before the arrival of the first emissaries of the Tau. These visitors offered the people of Wrath an opportunity to join with others of their kind, to sail the sea of stars and a return to the glory and might their ancestors once possessed. This much can be gleaned from testimonials and interrogations performed shortly after the Imperial conquest of the world, though there is little more information on the event.

Operation Hammerfall saw the initial conquest of many of the worlds in what is now the Canis Salient, including Wrath. With several companies of the Space Marines at their head, Crusade forces smashed into Argoth, Rheelas and Kaggeran simultaneously, subduing the populations and governments within hours of making planetfall. Finding no evidence of a Tau presence on any of those worlds, Lord Commander Ebongrave ordered the next stage of the advance: Wrath. Located a short distance from a major warp route that led towards worlds known to have fallen to the Tau, Wrath had been earmarked by Lord Militant Achilus as a prospective fortress-world early in the Crusade's planning phase, and was an obvious target for the Imperium.

The Tau, apparently, had come to a similar conclusion, and had placed elements of their fleet and ground forces within the system, concealing their presence with advanced technology so that they could ambush the crusaders. As the battlegroup's transports reached Wrath's orbit, the Tau struck, crippling half a dozen vessels before the Imperial Navy could respond. Only the swift retaliation of the 2nd and 3rd Companies of the Dark Sons Chapter, accompanying the battlegroup, prevented the total destruction of the Imperial forces above Wrath, allowing Imperial Guard and Adeptus Astartes forces to make planetfall and clash with the Tau Fire Caste forces on the surface. The ground war was brutal and swift, with Tau forces continually in motion from island to island to elude the rapidly advancing Space Marine forces, and the Imperial Guard who followed behind them. After eighteen days of almost continuous conflict, the Tau withdrew completely, retreating back towards more securely held worlds.

While arguments raged about the next course of action for the Crusade's forces, architects and engineers descended upon Wrath to begin its fortification, while the Imperial Guard turned its attentions to pacifying an aggressive and resistant native population, and the Dark Sons departed for newer warzones. Within a decade, a veritable city of structures had sprung up along Wrath's equatorial archipelago and an army of Adepts had arrived to take their places within the Jericho Reach's newest fortress-world.

Since then, little has changed on Wrath. Intermittent insurgent actions against the Imperium have caused disruption in some places, and probing attacks by the Tau and an assortment of itinerant raiders over the years have tested Wrath's defences, but no enemy of any strength has set foot upon Wrath as they did when the Imperium first claimed it.

Planetary Datafax: Wrath

Population: Estimated 108 Million

Tithe Grade: Solutio Prima

Special Notation: Secondary Command Centre for the Canis Salient, Primary Internal Security Centre for the Canis Salient

Geography/Demography: 85% of surface is covered in water, with an extensive chain of equatorial islands currently occupied by the Imperium. Wrath's water has an extremely high mineral content and is not regarded as fit for human consumption without purification and filtration.

Government Type: Departmento Munitorum-appointed Commander/standard military hierarchy

Imperial Commander: Regent-Castellan Hallin Tarnassus III

Adept Presence: High; the Departmento Munitorum employ Wrath as a major command centre and supply depot for Canis Salient operations, while extensive Adeptus Arbites and Adeptus Administratum presences monitor Imperial activity within the Salient.

Military: Extensive. 65% of Wrath's population is engaged in actions of a military nature or in support of military operations. Actual armed forces (as opposed to support personnel) comprise 29% of the population, consisting primarily of Imperial Guard and Adeptus Arbites.

Trade/Economy/Addendum: Wrath has no exports of any kind, and has high supply requirements in terms of munitions and food. Wrath is at the heart of the "Eyes of Wrath", a multi-planetary surveillance system on a colossal scale covering many of the Imperial-held worlds in the Canis Salient.

The Eyes of Wrath

To date, the surveillance network dubbed the "Eyes of Wrath" extends across a multitude of worlds within the Canis Salient, stretching back to Spite, and as far into the front lines as Bekrin and Veren in the Greyhell Front. At the direction of Lord Commander Ebongrave and Regent Castellan Tarnassus, any Imperial force on almost any world in the Canis Salient can be subjected to intensive purity testing and be monitored for heretical or treasonous activities from afar, their deeds recorded in secret and transmitted by the encrypted thoughts of Astropaths to Wrath, and from there to any other world within the network. The Eyes of Wrath are the single greatest tool Lord Commander Ebongrave possesses for rooting out and eradicating the insidious taint of the Tau. Enough information exists here to allow the Eyes of Wrath to be an asset in any Deathwatch campaign set within the Canis Salient. However, more information on the subject can be found on pages 104 and 106 of **The Achilus Assault**.

Native Populace

Wrath's native population are a technologically regressed branch of humanity, made aggressive by long millennia of confinement to a single resource-poor world. Records indicate that Wrath has never been particularly well favoured by the Imperium even during the days of the Jericho Reach, and the ruins of an orbital way-station are the only significant and enduring Imperial structure remaining in the system from before the Age of Shadows.

The people of Wrath are tall, swarthy and heavily built, within prescribed human norms, and well adapted to the planetary conditions, having a high tolerance for the mineral content in the world's waters, which otherwise causes illness and allergic reactions in non-native humans. The general lack of resources, and the scarcity of arable land, has resulted in a belligerent nomadic lifestyle focussed around ocean-going ships capable of supporting an entire clan.

Imperial settlement has changed little; the natives regard outsiders as thieves for taking what little valuable land exists, and act against Imperial authorities when they can. Contact with the Tau Empire before the arrival of the Achilus Crusade has led to small xenos sympathiser groups springing up, though most natives regard the Tau as undesirable outsiders, much as they view the Imperium. However, what is worrisome is the increasing tendency of the natives to return to an old religion, focussed upon the gods of a distant realm of Aithess, rather than accept the Imperial Creed. Order Dialogous analysis suggests that this may be a mutation of the term "Hadex", in reference to the anomaly that blights the heart of the Jericho Reach, leading to some unpleasant conclusions about the indigenous religion of Wrath that cannot be repeated here.

KEY LOCATIONS

The following are a number of significant locations on Wrath, ranging from overt manifestations of the monolithic rule of the Imperium, to locales intended for more clandestine purposes.

Bastion Ocularis

A spire standing almost a kilometre tall, the Bastion Ocularis is one of the tallest structures on Wrath, and one of the most significant. The Bastion serves two distinct, but interlinked, purposes. The first is as the administrative and military capital of Wrath, home to its Imperial Commander and command centre for the world's garrison. The second purpose, which dominates the majority of the spire's internal volume, is as the heart of the Eyes of Wrath.

Colossal chambers filled with cogitators and infolooms, attended by thousands of lexmechanics and tens of thousands of purity-screened scribes and ordinates, fill much of the upper levels of the Bastion Ocularis, linked to vox networks, pict-thieves, spoor-trackers and every other conceivable form of surveillance device, and supplied with thousands of personal testimonies, mission reports and interrogation logs gathered every day from Arbitrator patrols and purity testing. Above that is chamber after chamber filled with sanctioned psykers and astropaths in auto-séance trances or gathered in choirs to perform the vital task of sending and receiving this colossal amount of gathered and compiled data to and from every other world under the gaze of the Eyes of Wrath.

Access to the Bastion Ocularis is heavily restricted—visitors are subject to intensive purity testing and interrogation before they can access more than the spire's ground level, and permanent staff are subject to continual scrutiny and routine tests even more intensive than those imposed on the rest of Wrath's population, in order to ensure the absolute loyalty and purity of those who labour over this most vital and sensitive of facilities.

The Bastion Ocularis, as a sign of Imperial authority on Wrath, is an obvious target for terrorist attacks and seditious protests, and there have been numerous attempts each year to damage, interfere with or otherwise disrupt the Bastion or its operations in the three decades it has stood. Retaliation against these crimes is swift and universally merciless, with those responsible surviving only long enough to be thoroughly interrogated by the Adeptus Arbites, the Inquisition, or sometimes both.

Officio Redigire

Based within a small, unassuming building within the long shadow of the Bastion Ocularis, the Officio Redigire is ostensibly a minor office of the Administratum on Wrath. It is officially responsible for certain matters of doctrinal oversight within the Salient regarded as being too obscure and overly complex for anyone not of the Administratum to care about, but which grants it access to a startling quantity of information.

In truth, the Officio Redigire is a front for the Inquisition, and while some in the higher echelons of the Canis Salient's chain of command have their suspicions, actual evidence is impossible to find beneath the mountains of official bureaucracy and legislation that surround the Officio and its function. Rumours within the Inquisition itself suggest that the Officio is so thoroughly infiltrated by the Inquisition that even the lowest scribe has ties to the Holy Ordos. Whatever the case, this minor but remarkably influential office is a façade for Inquisitorial activities, as are many like it across the Jericho Reach and Calixis Sector.

Headed by Praefect Primus Hannis Durander, the Officio Redigire building on Wrath serves as a safe house, prison and listening post for passing Inquisitors. The interior of the building appears to be nothing more than what it claims to be, yet hidden passages and subterranean vaults lead to interrogation chambers, stasis vaults and even a substantial weapons cache, which has been expanded to contain small quantities of Deathwatch equipment at the request of the Master of the Vigil. Access to the building is through the public entrance, guarded by Inquisitorial Agents disguised as Wrath planetary defence force, or via the subterranean Teleportarium, constructed decades ago by Inquisition-affiliated tech-priests to allow unseen entry to the facility from anywhere on the planet or any suitably equipped starship in orbit. The Teleportarium, for obvious reasons, is the main method of entry for Battle-Brothers of the Deathwatch, as entering an Administratum facility on foot would draw unwanted attention to both the Officio Redigire and the Deathwatch.

The Float

Rather than being a single location, the Float is the common name given to the ghetto-like settlements that exist on the shores of the islands upon which the Imperium has built its fortresses. Consisting of rough floating platforms and lashed-together boats, these shanty-towns are home to most of the native population of Wrath, and are ill-regarded by the local planetary defence force, the Adeptus Arbites, the Inquisition and most of the Adepts present on Wrath.

With no discernably planned layout, and connected together by rope and chain from large floating sections, the Float is a maze at the best of times, and even harder to navigate when the population disconnect the platforms and rearrange their "district". The populace of the Float has little love for the Imperium, and discontent within one of the thousands of ad-hoc "districts" frequently flares up into mob violence or seditious activity. This in turn spurs the local planetary defence force or the Adeptus Arbites into action in order to quell these rebellious acts, though such purges are typically stymied by the irregular and unpredictable arrangement of each district.

It is common knowledge that the Float is a breeding ground for cults, rebels and heretical sentiment. While action to cleanse the area has been planned in excruciating detail, the overwhelming majority of Wrath's unskilled workforce comes from the native population, and to eliminate it entirely would leave the world lacking a vital resource, forcing those plans to be placed on hold indefinitely.

ARGOTH

"On this day, as punishment for their sins against the almighty God-Emperor of Mankind, the benighted worlds of Argoth, Kaggeran and Rheelas shall be isolated from His most glorious domain. No ship may approach those worlds, no servant of Him-on-Terra shall set foot upon them, and no mercy shall spare them from the just consequences of their misdeeds. So shall it be until the ages have expunged the taint of their peoples."

–Lord Commander Sebiascor Ebongrave, issuing General Order 169

The hive world of Argoth has, like many populous worlds in the Jericho Reach, suffered greatly through the ages, but few worlds reclaimed by the Imperium suffer as Argoth does. Once a teeming hive world many thousands of years old, which had endured the long nightmare of the Age of Shadows largely intact, Argoth now faces a slow and cruel demise at the hands of the Imperium.

Quarantined and isolated from the desperately needed supplies of food, water and mineral resources supplied by nearby Rheelas and Kaggeran, Argoth starves. In a few short years, the world's population has been reduced to roaming bands of scavengers and raiders, with the most desperate driven to madness, cannibalism and blasphemy as supplies dwindle to nothing. In a matter of generations, Argoth will be a wasteland, a savage realm of steel caves and haunted old

manufactories, populated by the barely-human degenerate descendants of those hardy enough to endure their world's isolation. Not long after that, the world will be dead and filled with the bones of those the Imperium condemned.

Lord Commander Ebongrave seems unconcerned by the brutality of the fate to which he has condemned the Quarantined Worlds, seeing so cruel a punishment as fitting for the crime of consorting with xenos. He would sooner leave worlds to die in this fashion than risk the spread of their perceived taint, content in the knowledge that the worlds can be repopulated by true, loyal citizens of the Imperium in due course. In spite of this, however, it is rumoured that he has sanctioned a handful of missions to the Quarantined Worlds, perhaps in search of some method of more swiftly ridding them of the taint of the insidious Tau.

HISTORY

Argoth, like the nearby worlds of Rheelas and Kaggeran, was colonised by the Imperium in early M32 under the expansionist mandate of a succession of Lords Sector. Little in the fragmentary records of that era remains, but there is no evidence to suggest that any of the worlds in what was then known as the Arkalas Cluster were anything more than a collection of backwater colonies adjacent to a well travelled warp route.

The uncertain history of the Age of Shadows does not mark Argoth with any particular significance beyond the mere fact that it survived that benighted era, leaving the world as little more than a footnote. Raids by pirates, traitors and heretics—commonplace across the Jericho Reach during the Age of Shadows—plagued the worlds of the Arkalas Cluster, by that point joined together as a single political entity referred to as The Unity, but history seems largely to have passed Argoth and its sister worlds by.

This changed in the latter years of the 8th Century of the 41st Millennium, less than a decade after the conflict known as the Damocles Crusade. Expanding outwards from their home world, and having reached the coreward edge of the Jericho Sector, the alien Tau began to establish a strong presence within the region, variously conquering, treating with or simply colonising the worlds they came across. Argoth was a distant goal at the time, many months travel for even their fastest ships, but it was more populous than any other world encountered by the nascent Velk'Han Sept, and allied with other resource-bearing worlds, and thus a prize to be coveted. Swift messenger ships carrying Water Caste dignitaries followed the intelligence-gathering drone-scouts, conveying greetings on behalf of the Tau Empire and expressing a desire for peaceful cooperation, endeavouring to appeal to The Unity as like-minded individuals in a hostile galaxy.

The Tau could attempt little more than this opening preamble before the Imperium arrived to reclaim their worlds. Unwilling and unable to fully muster a defence against the crusaders, the Tau fell back from Argoth, Rheelas and Kaggeran, while gathering a force to contest the Imperium on Wrath, closer to the worlds the Tau had already claimed. However, the brief time the Tau had been in contact with The Unity would be sufficient to shape the fate of Argoth and its sister worlds for years to come.

PLANETARY DATAFAX: ARGOTH

+++ ALL PLANETARY DATAFAX ACCURATE AS OF ISSUING OF GENERAL ORDER 169+++

Population: Estimated 61 Billion

Tithe Grade: Aptus Non (post quarantine)

Special Notation: Quarantined under General Order 169. Travel to Argoth is strictly prohibited under all circumstances.

Geography/Demography: Temperate/dry climate. No indigenous life, atmosphere is incapable of sustaining human life and has not been conducive to the development of any other life forms. Populace dwells within three atmosphere-sealed hives, constructed during the early millennia of the Imperium.

Government Type: None—Argoth's pre-existing organised government was replaced by the Adeptus Terra, which has subsequently been removed under General Order 169.

Imperial Commander: None

Adept Presence: None. All Imperial personnel were evacuated from Argoth upon issue of the quarantine order.

Military: Non-existent—societal collapse on Argoth is 98.114% likely within the first two years of isolation, removing all capability for an organised military.

Trade/Economy/Addendum: Argoth is under strict quarantine, preventing all interplanetary trade or distribution of resources, under General Order 169. Local economy is believed to be nonexistent, due to a lack of natural, usable resources. Projections indicate that a subsistence-level hunter-gatherer society is inevitable within two decades, and that this is incapable of sustaining a hive world's population for any length of time.

THE ARKALAS CLUSTER

The worlds of Argoth, Rheelas and Kaggeran were, during the time of the Jericho Sector, collectively known as the Arkalas Cluster, and existed close together within a pocket of relatively stable warp space. During the Age of Shadows, their proximity and relative safety of interstellar voyages between these systems allowed the worlds to remain in contact with, and in support of, each other using only relatively crude warp-going vessels.

It should come as little surprise, then, that the worlds themselves grew together politically, as their fates were inexorably linked together. According to the limited observations released by the Deathwatch during the planning of Operation Hammerfall, the worlds of the Pelegiath Cluster collectively existed under the rule of a political body known as The Unity from approximately M36 onwards, forming a tiny pocket-empire not dissimilar to those encountered by the Imperium during the Great Crusade.

However, unlike a few other enduring worlds within the Jericho Reach (such as Karlack and Castobel), those governed by The Unity did not maintain a properly Imperial government, nor did they retain their faith in the God-Emperor, forcing considerable corrective action on the part of Administratum and Adeptus Ministorum elements of the Achilus Crusade to re-establish Imperial rule. This matter was complicated by actions taken by The Unity to ally with the Tau Empire, a matter that would surely have resulted in even greater expansion of the territory claimed by the Tau had the Achilus Crusade not swiftly annexed these worlds.

GENERAL ORDER 169

In 786.M41, Lord Commander Ebongrave issued the orders for the quarantine and blockade of the worlds of the Arkalas Cluster. General Order 169 applies to any and all forces aligned with the Crusade, and prohibits all travel to and from Argoth, Rheelas and Kaggeran under penalty of death. The quarantine is enforced by vessels drawn from Battlegroup Atlas, which patrols the three systems and is under orders to interrogate any Imperial vessels that enter the systems, giving one opportunity to trespassers to state their identities before opening fire, while firing without hesitation against non-Imperial vessels. In addition to this basic duty, the patrol ships also monitor the state of the worlds behind their cordon, reporting back to Lord Commander Ebongrave regularly.

Only at the express order of the Lord Commander, or by Inquisitorial mandate, can a vessel break the quarantine and venture to these forbidden worlds, though such permission is seldom given.

With the Space Marines of the Storm Wardens Chapter at their forefront, the crusaders assigned to Operation Hammerfall descended swiftly and decisively upon the Arkalas Cluster. On Argoth itself, Chapter Master Maclir of the Storm Wardens led the charge personally, descending from orbit by Thunderhawk to assault the palace of the most senior leaders of The Unity. Within hours, compliance was achieved on all three worlds, and spurred on by their successes, the Achilus Crusade moved on swiftly, leaving behind basic garrison forces.

Within months of the supposed conquest of Argoth, The Unity and countless other secessionist groups on worlds regarded as compliant struck against the Imperium, each of them supported or encouraged by the Tau. Operation Hammerfall ground to a halt, denied the reinforcements Maclir needed to press his attack and overrun the Tau-held world of Ravacene. The advance of the Achilus Crusade was stalled in a storm of betrayals so swift and sudden that their timing could only have been carefully orchestrated.

Even as Imperial Guard and Adeptus Arbites forces put down these rebellions, disaster struck. Lord Militant Achilus was lost to his Crusade, and its advance was halted on every front by the sudden loss of its leader and founder. As the Crusade mourned, secessionists on Argoth struck back against the Imperium, and hostilities between Imperial and Unity forces became increasingly vicious. The arrival of two Deathwatch Kill-teams, directed by Inquisitor Lor Tremayle and scores of Acolytes, swiftly and brutally put down the rebellious elements wherever they were found and provided the Adeptus Arbites and Imperial Guard forces the opportunity to regroup and renew their efforts.

With the ascension of Lord Militant Tetrarchus to the command of the Crusade, General Ebongrave was given authority over the newly formed Canis Salient. His pride injured by the loss of worlds that had been conquered by his armies, and his hatred for the alien stronger than ever, Ebongrave gave his first order after his promotion—the quarantine of Argoth, Rheelas and Kaggeran. As the worlds upon which the uprisings had been most vicious, they were to serve as an example to others that betrayal and sedition would be punished mercilessly.

Since the quarantine began, Argoth has suffered more greatly than its neighbours, being far more dependent upon off-world supplies than the other two worlds. In the decades following, more than 90% of Argoth's population is estimated to have died in the desperate violence that now characterises its hives, the state of the world observed by orbital augury from Imperial Navy vessels blockading the planet.

Key Locations

The following section contains details of a number of significant locations on the surface of Argoth.

Hive Korianthus

During the long years of the Age of Shadows, Hive Korianthus was the home of the ruling council of The Unity. From the fortress known as the Pinnacle, at the very top of Hive Korianthus, The Unity ruled across the worlds of the Arkalas Cluster.

In the millennia before the Age of Shadows began, Hive Korianthus was the planetary capital of Argoth, an honour and responsibility gained simply by being the oldest and largest of the world's three hives. As the Jericho Sector collapsed, it seemed as if Argoth would fall as many populous worlds had, unable to sustain themselves and lacking the infrastructure of the Imperium to maintain them. Unwilling to see their world starve, the planet's ruling nobility set about trying to strengthen ties with the other worlds of the Arkalas Cluster, restoring simple starships to defend the systems and carry goods between them and thankful that the distances were small enough to be traversed by calculated warp jump.

As Argoth's situation stabilised, and then began to improve, the needs of the populace grew, and the world's Adeptus Mechanicus congregation found themselves needing to test the limits and tolerances of every machine they could produce and maintain, pushing them further than their doctrine would permit and succeeding in spite of it. As their successes accumulated, so too did their certainty, and over the millennia, the congregation ceased giving worship to the Omnissiah and the Machine God, viewing themselves as masters of the machine.

When the Imperium returned to Argoth, it was a Techmarine of the Storm Wardens Chapter who discovered the forge-citadel of these presumptuous hereteks, and the Adeptus Mechanicus wasted no time in laying waste to the defiled temple and its impure mechanisms, as Skitarii phalanxes butchered the apostate mechanics who commanded Argoth's technology.

At present, Hive Korianthus is a ruin. Much of the city was damaged during the initial assaults of Operation Hammerfall, and little opportunity existed to repair and remake the city before Unity forces began their uprising. The upper tiers are entirely inhospitable without well maintained rebreather equipment, while the lower levels and underhive depths are a crumbling wasteland, prone to hive-quakes and collapse, with ancient atmosphere processors failing due to lack of maintenance. Isolated pockets of survivors exist, but they are few in number and growing fewer by the day as the air becomes increasingly toxic and food supplies become ever more scarce.

Hive Tiestomadan

During the time of the Jericho Sector, Hive Tiestomadan was a centre for mass industry within the region, containing the highest concentration of manufactories anywhere within the Subsector. However, while it could produce vast quantities of equipment, little of what it produced was regarded anywhere within the Sector as anything other than cheap bulk goods.

The situation changed with the fall of the Jericho Sector. As The Unity came into being, the manufactories of Hive Tiestomadan were the only places capable of manufacturing a variety of items in sufficient quantities to supply three worlds, and the city's prestige grew. The number of engineers and technicians within the city grew with every passing year, as necessity forced the manufactories to produce ever-more-complex items.

Unlike Hive Korianthus, Tiestomadan emerged from the return of the Imperium relatively unscathed, its status as a manufacturing hub important to the burgeoning Achilus Crusade, and its relative lack of political status making it a far lower priority than Korianthus. As a result, when the engineers of Korianthus were forced to flee the purges of the Adeptus Mechanicus, they fled to Tiestomadan, going into hiding amongst the manufactories and biding their time. Similarly, when The Unity rose up against the Imperium, it was from Tiestomadan that the rebels gained their arms and armour, some using designs gifted by the Tau in good faith, and from Tiestomadan that they drew the bulk of their numbers.

The city fell after eighteen weeks of conflict in a war that saw millions die for meagre gains, and was left a ruin in the aftermath of the rebellions. However, the hive's nature has allowed it to endure longer than the others, taking advantage of technology to aid the hunt for food and the maintenance of life-sustaining machinery, and while its populace are much-depleted after decades of isolation, they remain far closer to the civilisation they once were than the populations of Korianthus or Akirrorhineus.

Hive Akirrorhineus

Almost too small to be worthy of being termed a Hive, Akirrorhineus was still a massive city at its peak, originally formed as a conglomeration of scattered mining settlements before the world's worthwhile natural resources became scarce. It was not until the establishment of The Unity that Akirrorhineus gained notoriety as a source of supplementary labour for the other two cities.

Isolated from the Imperium, the worlds under The Unity lacked contact with the Black Ships of the Adeptus Astra Telepathica, and thus had no way of dealing with the new generations of psykers being born. With no means of sending the psykers away as they had always done, an alternative solution was required. The few remaining astropaths and other sanctioned psykers on Argoth, Rheelas and Kaggeran were put into service passing on their knowledge to those who shared their gift and given the responsibility of monitoring the populace for emergent psykers, eliminating those too dangerous to live and training those who could be of use to The Unity.

The Collegium Psykana sprang up in the relatively small and isolated city of Akirrorhineus, to act as a hub for this solemn duty, and for millennia, its staff oversaw the training of generations of witches and seers, far from the light of the Astronomicon and the gaze of the Emperor. By the time the Imperium returned to Argoth, Akirrorhineus was a haunted and heavily depopulated shell of a hive, with much of its populace having relocated to the other cities to escape the psychic fallout from the Collegium Psykana. While it had produced numerous skilled and stable psykers to serve The Unity, the techniques of the Collegium masters were a far cry from the age-honed and meticulous methods of the Adeptus Astra Telepathica. The city was obliterated without mercy upon discovery of this fact, though none who are there will speak of the method used to bring that nest of witches to the Emperor's Judgement. Rumours amongst the loose lipped and foolish tell of silver-clad warriors who could wield the Emperor's holy fire and wrathful lightning as easily as a man wields a lasgun, who turned the city into a pyre in a single week. Rumour mongers who tell such tales swiftly vanish, but the rumours persist nonetheless.

PELEGIUS

"Imperious Fortis actual to Tau flagship: Cease fire. I say again, cease fire… we… we surrender."

–Captain Tylian Kynassis, 145th Scintillan Battlegroup.

Located only a short distance behind the Greyhell Front, Pelegius has been contested by Tau expeditions and Imperial crusaders alike for decades. The planet's wealth of natural resources means that both sides regard it as extremely valuable, yet that same worth has resulted in a world which is inimical to human or Tau life.

However, it is not merely mineral resources that draw the gaze of man and Tau alike to Pelegius, and it is not merely the toxin-saturated, irradiated environment that poses a threat to those who seek to claim this bounteous world. Whatever occurred in Pelegius' past, it has left remnants behind to be discovered by the curious and the avaricious. Lurking beneath the desert sands are monstrous invertebrates, mutated by countless generations of rad-exposure and grown to colossal proportions with no greater predators to challenge them. Clutches of dormant macroscorpion eggs and nests of hibernating tyrannopedes are amongst the perils awaiting those who find themselves on Pelegius, awakening at the slightest disturbance of their otherwise-barren habitat.

Deep beneath the surface, remnants of a different sort can be found, by those willing to search for them. Ancient ruins of a long-dead civilisation exist kilometres beneath the shifting sands, and both human and Tau excavations into these ruins have only provoked greater curiosity. The Tau wonder at the technological marvels that could have built these glittering cities and wonder at the cataclysm that saw them abandoned and buried, while the Adeptus Mechanicus vocalise binaric litanies of warding and sanctity as they delve into ruins that are as likely to be a fragment of mankind's Dark Age of Technology as a broken shard of an alien civilisation, in search of the long-lost secrets that they know must reside deeper within.

Upon the surface, a bitter conflict rages between armies of fast-moving skirmishers and heavy vehicles, with both sides relying on the protection of advanced rad-warded armour, rebreather systems and the sturdy hulls of battle tanks to stave off the hostile environment as they engage in a long and vicious series of raids and feints. Tens of thousands of Skitarii troopers, their augmetic forms largely immune to the poisons and radiation that would slay normal men, supported by elite Imperial Guard forces clad in hostile environment suits clash against environment-hardened battlesuit teams of ever-more-sophisticated design.

HISTORY

Little is known about the early history of Pelegius. Few accounts of it remain from the time of the Jericho Sector, and it seems that there may have been little to begin with, the world having been a blasted wasteland since long before the Great Crusade. If any during that time discovered the mineral wealth of Pelegius, or the ancient ruins beneath its surface, no evidence remains of their discoveries.

Regardless, whether the world was known to the authorities within the Jericho Sector or not, it was identified by forward scouts for the Achilus Crusade while the Iron Collar was being initially fortified, and marked as a world requiring investigation rather than military intervention. Six months later, an Imperial Navy Battlegroup led by Captain Tylian Kynassis moved into the system to conduct a preliminary survey, only to discover that the Tau had arrived there first. Faced with a newly deployed waystation and a significant Tau force surveying Pelegius itself, the Scintillan 145th Battlegroup was heavily outgunned and caught by surprise in a battle that left most of the group as drifting hulks, and ended with the group's Captain and the flagship *Imperious Fortis* surrendering to the Tau.

When word of this reached Crusade High Command, retaliatory actions began almost immediately, directed not only at the Tau, but at the traitorous Captain Kynassis. The magnitude of this reprisal was, however, limited by the needs of Operation Hammerfall, and while the Tau fleet was driven from Pelegius' orbit, it was not without cost to the Imperial Navy. With the world now freed from xenos dominance, the Adeptus Mechanicus began to move in, the survey ship *Meticulous Scrutiny* arriving two days after the retaliation force had given the "all-clear". After an eight week survey that saw hundreds of servitors, menials and lay-technicians succumb to the hostile environment and indigenous macrofauna, Magos Thaniel Axiom declared the world to be rich in valuable natural resources and sent a series of astropathic messages urging that Lord Militant Achilus begin the exploitation of those resources as soon as possible.

Before that could occur, the Tau returned in strength, employing vox ciphers secured from the *Imperious Fortis*' cogitators to deceive and confuse the Imperial forces. However, in spite of their trickery, the Tau could not completely drive the Imperial fleet from the system, and both sides withdrew to the clustered asteroid fields and gas clouds at system's edge to regroup and prepare for a renewed assault. In the decades that have followed, this state of affairs has changed little. Neither force can easily gain the upper hand against their enemy due to a slow trickle of reinforcements, sufficient to replenish losses but insufficient to give a significant advantage,

THE POISONED WORLD OF PELEGIUS

Pelegius is a world inimical to human life, toxic and radioactive to a point that an unprotected human will sicken and die within days. These conditions are not only lethal to humans; there is little that can withstand such horrific conditions, and all but the hardiest of creatures will struggle to exist on Pelegius for long without sophisticated protective equipment or equally potent natural advantages. The macrofauna native to Pelegius is immune to the effects of their world's environment, having evolved to withstand it over countless generations.

The toxins in the atmosphere force an unprotected creature to attempt a **Difficult (–10) Toughness Test** or suffer 1d5 Toughness Damage, plus an additional +1 per Degree of Failure. This Test is required after every hour of exposure. Equipment that provides a bonus against inhaled poisons grants its normal benefits, and this Test is considered to be a resistance against poison for all purposes.

RADIATION

Radiation is a common hazard across the galaxy, found erupting from crude fission reactors and the blasted craters caused by atomics, as well as occurring naturally in the cold void of space and upon countless worlds for countless different reasons. Pelegius is one such world, with lethal amounts of ambient radiation. For every hour a creature is exposed to the irradiated environment of Pelegius, it suffers 1d10 Toughness Damage, which is reduced by an amount equal to the lowest armour value on the creature (even small amounts of protection are of some use, but leaving part of the body exposed renders the entire suit essentially worthless). For creatures with Unnatural Toughness, this amount (after deductions for armour) is divided by a value equal to the Unnatural Toughness multiplier, rounding up—so for a Space Marine with Unnatural Toughness (x2), the amount of Toughness Damage suffered from radiation is halved, while a creature with Unnatural Toughness (x3) takes only a third of the Toughness Damage.

Any creature that suffers more Toughness Damage at one time than its Toughness Bonus (determined before taking the damage) suffers a level of Fatigue as well. Toughness Damage and Fatigue caused by radiation cannot be recovered from while still exposed to radiation. Creatures with the Daemonic, Machine, Stuff of Nightmares or Tyranids Traits are immune to the effects of radiation.

Different sources of radiation will cause differing amounts of Toughness Damage—the decades-old crater caused by an atomic warhead may only cause 1d5-1 Toughness Damage from lingering radiation, while the heart of a plasma reactor may cause 2d10 or more.

PLANETARY DATAFAX: PELEGIUS

Population: Estimated 300,000

Tithe Grade: Aptus Non; world currently under Administratum evaluation to determine Tithe Grade.

Geography/Demography: Hot desert, with ambient surface temperatures ranging from 28°C at the poles to 64°C in equatorial regions. Pelegius has a significantly higher baseline level of ionising radiation than the Terran standard, and the climate is generally inhospitable to humans. Population centres are shielded, self-contained temporary dome-habs, with external activities performed in sealed protective suits.

Government Type: Joint Administratum/Adeptus Mechanicus expeditionary governing body, pending long-term establishment of a colony.

Imperial Commander: Praefect-Majore Aniran Revisch of the Divisio Praebenda, Magos Thaniel Axiom, delegation 343-Sigma.

Adept Presence: High; Pelegius is an exceptionally valuable resource world, and consequently subject to considerable attention from the Adeptus Terra. Further, military action by the Tau has required a large garrison force to be deployed.

Military: High; Pelegius is a world currently contested by the Tau, and consequently a large Imperial Guard presence exists on Pelegius.

Trade/Economy/Addendum: Pelegius has considerable worth as a mining colony, with new sources of rare or valuable materials discovered regularly by the extensive survey expedition. The hostile conditions are regarded as an obstacle worth overcoming to benefit from a world so rich in minerals vital to the ongoing war effort. The presence of the Tau demonstrates that they crave such valuable resources as well. Continual supplies of food, potable water, and medicae consumables (primarily counterseptics, antitoxin and antiradiation drugs) are an absolute necessity.

MINERAL WORTH

Pelegius is a world of extensive naturally occurring mineral resources, the overwhelming majority of which (of those so far catalogued) are valuable to the ceaseless industry necessary to keep the Imperium functioning. This abundance of natural wealth makes Pelegius extremely important to the ongoing Achilus Crusade. With sufficient labour and after the development of an appropriate infrastructure, Pelegius is believed to be able to support potentially as much as a tenth of the projected raw material requirements of the Crusade, and the expeditionary government on the surface have advised a Tithe Grade of Exactis Extremis.

Pelegius' abundance of resources is believed to be a major contributor towards its inhospitable nature. Many of the raw materials discovered on Pelegius are extremely toxic, radioactive or both, and combined with the world's comparatively close proximity to its powerful white star, has resulted in a level of ambient surface radiation that builds to lethal levels in a human body after mere hours of exposure.

---

due to the more desperate needs of other war zones. A long war of intermittent skirmishes have characterised the void around Pelegius for a very long time. Amidst this, a similar ground war has sprung up, with both Tau and Imperial forces clashing across vast expanses of irradiated desert while engineers, archaeologists and administrators seek to uncover the secrets of Pelegius.

KEY LOCATIONS

The following section contains details of a number of significant locations on the surface of Pelegius.

Outpost Aleph

The oldest and largest of the Imperial settlements on Pelegius, Outpost Aleph is a colossal latticework of shielded, self-contained hab-domes connected by environment-sealed tunnels that span an area more than eight kilometres across. Equipped with powerful vox and augury systems to pierce the interference caused by Pelegius' background radiation, Aleph serves as the central command centre for all Imperial scientific and military operations across the planet, and its outermost domes are heavily fortified to serve as bunkers and barracks for the Imperial Guard and Skitarii garrisons.

What few know about, however, is the true extent of Outpost Aleph. At the heart of the complex, unseen by all but the tech-priests who work there, is the Aleph dig site, the true reason for the complex's location. Extending more than sixteen kilometres below the surface, the dig site took the efforts of thousands of servitors, menials and lay-technicians to excavate, and dozens of Archaeosavants and other tech-priests to study and catalogue the artefacts and ruins found within.

Their findings have been woefully inconclusive as of yet. While the inhabitants are likely to have been humanoid, almost nothing remains that suggests whether the ruins are of human origin or xenos construction. Worse, a string of serious industrial accidents have claimed the lives of hundreds of menials and destroyed thousands of servitors over the past year, while several tech-priests have simply gone missing during forays into the deeper zones. Thanks to the presence of infiltrators in service to the Inquisition, investigation of these incidents is underway, with many suspecting that whoever created the ruins may not be entirely gone.

Tirmorodan Mountains

A ring-shaped mountain range enclosing a dune sea some eleven hundred kilometres across, the Tirmorodan region has been the site of more clashes between Imperial and Tau forces than almost any other region on the planet, with neither side able to gain a foothold in the dune sea for more than a matter of weeks. The Tirmorodan Mountains themselves have been identified as a particularly abundant source of metals valuable for the production of starship armour, while the territory within the ring is believed to be home to one of the largest archaeological sites on Pelegius, though neither side has been able to accurately confirm this due to the almost ceaseless hostilities.

The passes leading through the mountain range are heavily guarded and key positions have been extensively fortified, serving as strongpoints from which both Tau and Imperial forces can launch raids and expeditions into the dune sea. As each side pushes deeper into the contested territory, temporary encampments are established to allow scientists and engineers an opportunity to delve beneath the shifting surface and learn of what exists under the sands. Ambushes and raids swiftly condemn these opportunistic digs to failure, leaving the bodies and equipment to be buried beneath the ever-changing dunes. These attacks are met with swift retaliation, with the Imperium and the Tau denying one another the opportunity to study the region in more detail.

Yet some doubt exists. While those of a military inclination are swift to blame their foes for each failure, a small but mounting collection of evidence suggests that a proportion of those lost encampments are just that—lost, having been suddenly and inexplicably depopulated and destroyed by something other than Imperial or Tau weaponry. Confronted with this evidence, most are quick to blame the deadly and voracious indigenous creatures or some attempt at deception from their foes… for the prospect of another force on Pelegius that opposes both human and Tau alike is a disquieting one.

Azkharraeon Flats

Believed to be the location of the primary Tau compound, the Azkharraeon Flats are stable, rocky wastelands in contrast to the shifting sands that cover most of Pelegius, and they are found few hundred kilometres north of the equator. Imperial expeditions have thus far avoided the equatorial regions of Pelegius, mainly due to the extremely high temperatures common there, but Tau physiology is believed to be far more capable of enduring high temperature/low humidity environments, explaining a greater willingness to establish themselves in places where humans cannot thrive.

Scouting missions, performed by specially augmented Skitarii, have determined that much of the Tau compound is maintained and operated by drones, directed by a few hundred Tau engineers and scientists. Limited pict evidence of the heart of the compound shows a device that appears to be an extremely potent fusion cutter, believed to be employed to drill into the dense rock of the Azkharraeon Flats, though what the Tau have found beneath the surface there remains unknown.

The Tau garrison on Pelegius appears to consist almost entirely of battlesuit-equipped infantry, as conventional Tau combat armour cannot provide adequate protection against the hostile environment. Lighter battlesuits are favoured, and armoured environment suits of a similar design (though unarmed) are used by the Earth Caste personnel on Pelegius as well.

D'SHAS'KA

"Cadres 211, 261 and 272; hostile incursion in sector 74; an immediate response has been mandated by Shas'O Tsua'Malor Aloh'shas Elan'nan and ratified by Aun'ui Tau'n Len'ra. Form up as a contingent under Shas'el Tash'var D'ka Cha'ro. Air support is being allocated to you now, Shas'el. Tau'va!"

–Fire Caste Strategic Command, D'Shas'Ka

Located spinward of the Greyhell Front, D'Shas'Ka 4 is several weeks travel from any other world in the Velk'Han Sept, and represents the furthest extent of Tau dominated territory from the Black Reef and Tsua'Malor. However, in spite of such claims, D'Shas'Ka 4 is not a world entirely under the peaceful rule of the Greater Good. While largely unperturbed by the Imperium, D'Shas'Ka 4 is a world pressured by invasion from another front—the Chaos-tainted legions of the Stigmartus.

While clashes between the Tau and Stigmartus forces are not unheard of, they are rare, with the Stigmartus typically content to turn their fury upon other humans, particularly the Imperium. The Stigmartus do not regard the Tau as particularly significant when compared to their loathing for the Imperium, and tend only to attack Tau worlds when provoked or when some ulterior motive drives their cruelty. The binary system of D'Shas'Ka, referred to by Imperial astrographers as Seraph 131, seems to be of some significance to a faction within the Stigmartus, driving their urge to stain its worlds and stars with the blood of the Tau. The eventual goal of the Stigmartus on D'Shas'Ka's primary world remains unknown, in spite of careful scrutiny by the Inquisition.

The system consists of six worlds, one of which is presently habitable, orbiting a mid-sized yellow star akin to Terra's sun,

PLANETARY DATAFAX:
SERAPH 131

Population: Unknown—xenos-occupied world.

Tithe Grade: None Applicable.

Special Notation: World currently claimed by xenos aggressor (cf: Tau Empire).

Geography/Demography: Temperate/wet. Seraph 131 is an extremely verdant world, covered in an extensive variety of indigenous flora and fauna but no native sentient life. No prior human colonisation attempts have been made, for reasons unknown, though it is speculated that Seraph 131 should be classified as a death world.

Government Type: Xenos hierarchy.

Imperial Commander: None.

Adept Presence: None.

Military: Xenos military garrison, numbers unknown.

Trade/Economy/Addendum: A full survey and classification expedition to Seraph 131 has not yet been performed, due to the presence of hostile xenos forces. As a result, what little information exists is derived from ancient archive material, orbital augury and intelligence gained from covert military/Inquisitorial operations.

XENOS OCCUPATION

The world designated Seraph 131 in Imperial records is officially regarded as a xenos-occupied world, the system having been claimed by the Tau and designated "D'Shas'ka" (Tau for "Twin Suns", referring to the system's two stars) at some point before the formation of the Achilus Crusade. The world is ruled as a minor colony of the subordinate political entity referred to as the Velk'Han Sept. Inquisitorial intelligence-gathering has determined that the world's government is referred to as the D'Shas'ka Shan'al, or "Twin Suns Coalition", which is ruled over by the highest-ranking Tau of the Fire, Water, Air and Earth Castes, presided over and advised on the true course of the "Greater Good" by a senior Ethereal. The specific identities of these individuals are unknown, but it is believed that they are not actually on Seraph 131 at all, but rather upon an orbital station above it.

Tau facilities on Seraph 131 are thinly scattered fortified compounds, defended by Tau warriors, supported by Kroot auxiliaries and drone-controlled auto-defences. The fortifications are somewhat uncharacteristic of Tau settlement, as the Tau are known to dislike defensive warfare, and are believed to exist primarily to fend off the intrusion of aggressive native flora and fauna.

THE ARGENT REVELATIONS

Prognosticator Gallius, a Silver Skulls Librarian serving within the Deathwatch centuries ago, penned a massive tome of prophetic visions witnessed over his decades of service, which to this day resides within the Librarium of Watch Fortress Erioch, studied by Librarians and Inquisitors alike. Over the centuries, it has given a remarkable amount of insight into threats faced by the Deathwatch in the Jericho Reach, to those with the wit and will to decipher the cryptic words and sigils.

One of these transcribed visions speaks of "An angel under twin suns, and the branded legions who strive to defile her", which seems to refer to Seraph 131 and the Stigmartus forces assailing it, in a remarkably clear and lucid fragment of prophecy amidst thousands of pages that have taken countless savants to decipher.

while a small white dwarf companion star orbits the edge of the system from a considerable distance, making entry into the system from the warp dangerous to the unwary due to shifting gravity wells. The habitable world, orbiting fourth from the primary star, has an irregular day-night cycle due to almost constantly bombardment with either direct or reflected light from one or both stars, with eclipses providing the few occasions of true darkness. This abundance of light and warmth, and the world's ideal distance from both stars, has resulted in a fecund and verdant world regarded by the Tau as being ideal for habitation, though somewhat cooler and wetter than their physiology may be used to.

Following usual Tau tactics, there are few static defences throughout the system; instead, the Tau rely upon scattered drone-controlled sentry stations and a fast-responding defence fleet operating from the orbital station above the fourth planet (which also serves as the primary Air Caste habitat for the Tau colony in the system, the Air Caste being unsuited for life on a planetary surface). The colonial efforts on D'Shas'Ka 4 are somewhat different from conventional Tau strategy, however. So vital and aggressive is the indigenous life that the Tau have been forced to establish fortified compounds to maintain an effective presence on the surface, using these scattered strongpoints as the primary settlements from which to engage in forays into the dense forests.

A significant Kroot presence has been established on D'Shas'Ka 4, primarily because of the sheer density and aggression of the indigenous creatures. These Kroot have thrived on the verdant world, and continue to do so, with a fourth generation of D'Shas'Ka Kroot beginning to appear in the last year. The Tau colonists, however, have not been as successful. Earth Caste xenobiologists struggle to catalogue the sheer quantity of species to be found on D'Shas'Ka 4, and rigorously drilled Cadres of Fire Warriors are on constant alert to repel attacks from particularly tenacious wildlife or from Stigmartus forces making planetfall, seldom staying in one place for more than a few weeks at a time.

Particularly troubling to the leaders of the D'Shas'Ka Coalition is that the diversity and viciousness of both the local flora and fauna and the frequency of Stigmartus attacks has been increasing steadily for the last decade, and while the Shapers of the Kroot gladly embrace the fury of the wild as a challenge to be overcome, the Tau are less pleased with this development. Their anxiety has only increased with the first forays of the Imperium to D'Shas'Ka. In place of a warfleet aimed at xenocide and conquest, swift and stealthy courier vessels have represented the overwhelming majority of the Imperial intrusion into the system, with each and every one of them bearing servants of the Inquisition.

Each visitation has heralded a series of high-level negotiations, with the adepts of the Inquisition conferring with Tau diplomats for weeks at a time before departing silently. Unknown to the Tau, these missions are the operations of a Coven of Ordo Malleus Inquisitors who have been observing and working to counter the actions of the Stigmartus, following a string of omens and prophecies that revolve around the heretical organisation. Seeing a pattern in the Stigmartus attacks on D'Shas'Ka 4, members of this Coven have acted to bolster the Tau defence against Chaos-aligned forces and guide their hand to combat such foes without overtly showing their involvement.

KEY LOCATIONS

The following section details of a number of significant locations on the surface of D'Shas'ka.

Shas'ar'tol D'Shas'Ka

The command centre for all Fire Caste operations within the D'Shas'Ka system, the Shas'ar'tol D'Shas'Ka is a sprawling complex of scanning arrays, vox-relays and buildings filled with drone-assisted substrate stacks, collating immense amounts of strategic and tactical information from every Fire Warrior Team, battlesuit and vehicle on the planet in order to provide accurate minute-by-minute insight into the state of every skirmish and firefight currently ongoing.

The Tau use of these technologies is commonplace in many warzones, allowing them to respond efficiently and coherently to enemy actions and take best advantage of the experience of veteran commanders. The Shas'ar'tol D'Shas'Ka is staffed by several hundred Earth Caste technicians, Water Caste adjutants, and a select staff of experienced Fire Caste officers (typically those who have suffered debilitating injuries in the field and who cannot currently serve on the front lines), led by Shas'O Tsua'Malor Aloh'shas Elan'nan, a young and promising Commander born upon the Velk'Han Sept's capital world.

Insertion Point Alpha

Unbeknownst to the Tau, the Inquisitorial missions to Seraph 131 have not purely served a diplomatic purpose. Viewing a Tau world under attack by a mutual foe as an unrivalled opportunity to reach orbit undetected, an operation was undertaken during an early diplomatic mission to insert a mixed detachment of Inquisitorial agents, ranging from seconded Deathworld Veterans, to infiltration specialists, xenolinguists, tech-priests and a trio of astropaths, to observe Tau movements and report back to their masters.

Under strict orders to not engage the enemy, the observation detachment has established a central base of operations within a region largely unexplored by the Tau, while discrete teams move about the planetary forests and jungles for weeks at a time, working to intercept and decipher Tau vox transmissions, and awaiting covert supply drops from subsequent Inquisitorial missions. To date, no extraction plan has been formulated that will not result in the cessation of diplomatic operations with the Tau, but the placement of the insertion group has resulted in Inquisitorial savants devising a number of distinct hypothetical infiltration scenarios, should conflict be required. Many of these scenarios have been discussed at length with the Chamber of Vigilance, as one or more Deathwatch Kill-teams would be ideal for precision operations—such as sabotage or assassination missions—deep into enemy territory, or for spearheading a potential invasion.

None outside of the Inquisition and the Deathwatch so far know about Insertion Point Alpha, and only a few within those organisations are aware of its existence. For the time being, an invasion of Seraph 131 is purely hypothetical, as are any further armed missions into the system.

Fio'mont'yr

Literally translated as "the blooded earth", this region has been identified as a common place of conflict between Tau and Stigmartus forces, and much blood has been spilt there as a result. The frequent fighting is not why the place grows in infamy amongst the Tau, however. Fire Caste forces who have fought in the area are known to have a particular dread and loathing for the region, for a variety of unsettling reasons.

The most worrying of these is an increased tendency for the Tau to be aggressive and short-tempered, even with bonded teammates, which has forced more than one Cadre to be redeployed elsewhere on the planet, or even off-world, to gather their composure and reaffirm their loyalty to the Tau'va. However, it was not until agents of the Inquisition were made aware of the region's influence that an arguably greater threat became known. The indigenous flora and fauna within the region resemble in many ways those of surrounding regions, yet they have diverged physiologically and behaviourally in a quite drastic manner, becoming increasingly savage and predatory in ways that do not conform to evolutionary patterns known in the xenobiological lore of the Imperium. The fact that these divergent species seem most concentrated in regions that are frequently used by the Stigmartus as landing and encampment sites suggest that they may be the result of an insidious and startlingly swift-acting warp-taint brought to D'Shas'Ka by the servants of Chaos.

WATCH STATION ANDRONICUS

"The auguries of the outpost in the Andronicus system are conclusive—elements of Hive Fleet Dagon are moving at some speed towards worlds conquered or contested by the Tau Empire. This Chamber urges you, Lord Militant, to act quickly and decisively as we have advised."

–Excerpt from encrypted Inquisitorial Astropathic transmission sent from Watch Fortress Erioch to Achilus Crusade High Command on Karlack

Situated upon a barren and distant rocky world, orbiting a cold and feeble star, Watch Station Andronicus is an oddity in that some knowledge of it exists beyond the warriors and vassals of the Deathwatch. The Watch Station exists upon a world already used by others in the Imperium, chosen because of its isolation and lack of any other worth.

Upon this airless, worthless world, two structures exist that watch the void for threats to the Imperium. The first and most ancient is an outpost of the Adeptus Mechanicus, claimed long ago by the wiles of the Inquisition to spy upon the many enemies of Man. The second is a Watch Station of the Deathwatch, its armouries containing powerful weapons and its archives holding a wealth of lore on the many xenos threats to Humanity.

HISTORY

In the earliest days of the Imperium, the Adeptus Mechanicus extended their reach across the nascent Jericho Sector, claiming worlds beyond the gaze or interest of the newly ascended lords who ruled it. They were destined to serve as hidden research cloisters and other facilities too valuable for outsiders to know of, concealed from the attentions of those not devoted to the Machine God and Omnissiah. The eighth world of the Andronicus system was one such world, a worthless ball of rock located in a system difficult to reach for any but the most skilled Navigator. The rare phenomena that surround the system within the warp made it ideal for long-range observation, and the Priesthood of Mars constructed upon it an observatory, referred to as the Mirador, to seek paths through the warp to further the Quest for Knowledge.

In 813.M36, as the Jericho Sector fell into anarchy and was consumed by warp storms, the Adeptus Mechanicus congregation on Andronicus Octus made contact with agents of the Inquisition, seeking to broker a pact to ensure the Mirador's safety even amidst the anarchy of a collapsing sector. Dubbed the Carthenis Dictum after the ruling Magos of the facility, this agreement passed the control and protection of Andronicus Octus to the Inquisition, who in turn placed it under the stewardship of Watch Fortress Erioch's Master of the Vigil.

In the decades that followed, the Deathwatch set about constructing a facility of their own on Andronicus Octus, while Techmarines delved deep into the arcane lore of the Adeptus Mechanicus to learn the secrets of the Mirador. In time, Watch Station Andronicus was completed and deemed fit for purpose, and a Keeper stationed there to guard over it and the secrets secured deep within stasis vaults and librarium archives.

Since its completion, the Watch Station has seen a great many Kill-teams operate from it, employing the Mirador to seek out targets and respond to them swiftly and decisively. A staff of several hundred tech-priests and lay-mechanics serve the operational and maintenance requirements of the Mirador, aided by a dozen Astropaths who communicate the observatory's findings and project their divinatory powers over great distances. With the coming of the Achilus Crusade, servants of the Inquisition once more returned to the Mirador, adding teams of Acolytes and Throne Agents to the personnel stationed on Andronicus Octus, while scores of serfs loyal to the Deathwatch serve the Watch Station's Keeper.

At present, the gaze of the Mirador is turned upon the distant Orpheus Salient, attempting to pierce the shrouding effects of the Shadow in the Warp, but so far to no avail. However, this focus upon the Great Devourer gave the Deathwatch unprecedented forewarning of the Tyranid incursions into the Canis Salient, allowing the Imperium to act against the encroaching menace.

USING WATCH STATION ANDRONICUS

Technically two linked facilities, Watch Station Andronicus can serve as both a well stocked base of operations for a Kill-team, and a readily available source of missions. The Mirador serves as a vital intelligence asset for the Inquisition and the Deathwatch alike, providing both organisations with the means to perceive distant worlds and disturbances in the warp and find pathways through it that are unknown to others.

GAZING FROM THE MIRADOR

Characters stationed at Watch Station Andronicus may wish to call upon the aid of the Mirador to give them additional intelligence on a forthcoming mission, or to seek out a known threat. While operating the ancient and arcane machinery of the Mirador is no simple task, a Battle-Brother of sufficient renown can be given the opportunity to direct the piercing attentions of the Mirador's spirits.

Any Battle-Brother of Distinguished or higher Renown may request the aid of the Mirador during the Preparation Phase of any mission he begins at Watch Station Andronicus, costing him 20 Requisition. To give proper direction and to analyse the information received requires a **Challenging (+0) Scrutiny Test** or a **Challenging (+0) Psyniscience Test**. The information revealed should be determined by the GM and be generally vague, and typically more akin to prophecy rather than concrete facts, with more information revealed with more Degrees of Success. It is recommended that the GM make this Test in secret, as it is possible that misleading or misinterpreted information could send a Kill-team astray.

WITHIN THE ARMOURIES OF ANDRONICUS

Watch Station Andronicus has an extremely large and well maintained armoury, supported by dozens of artisan-serfs and arming servitors to ensure that the Kill-teams operating from Andronicus are well equipped in wargear maintained with the utmost reverence.

Andronicus' armoury contains an ample supply of all items requiring a Renown Rank of Famed or lower, and a handful of extremely valuable and revered items sealed behind stasis fields and retrieved only upon permission from the Watch Station's Keeper. Each of these items is a precious relic of the Deathwatch or another Chapter of the Adeptus Astartes, and each is utterly unique. A sampling of these items is provided below:

Throneforged: Perhaps the most ancient and spiritually significant of relics to be found within the Jericho Reach, Throneforged is a Bolter of the venerable Phobos pattern, constructed within the forge-cities of Mars and issued to Battle-Brother Temoth Ulrecht of the Imperial Fists Legion in the earliest days of the Great Crusade, before the Primarchs had been found. This much and more is known to Deathwatch artificers, for the weapon is micro-engraved with the saga of its history, preserved in ceramite and meticulously restored from archived transcripts each time the weapon has seen damage. Throneforged is a Master-Crafted Bolter with the Devastating (1), Proven (3) and Sanctified Qualities, which automatically confirms any Righteous Fury results against Chaos Space Marines. In addition, such is the weapon's revered nature that the wearer gains a +10 bonus to all Fellowship-based Tests made when dealing with other Space Marines. Throneforged has a Requisition Value of 50, and requires a Renown Level of Hero to obtain.

Serpent's Bite: Notable more for number of lives it has taken than for the warriors who have carried it, this ancient needle rifle has been a favoured tool for assassination missions performed by Kill-teams in the Jericho Reach for thousands of years. Designed to fire mono-edged adamantium darts loaded with the most deadly death-world toxins, the Serpent's Bite is a far more powerful weapon than a conventional needle rifle, capable of slaying more resilient or more heavily armoured foes. Serpent's Bite is an Astartes Sniper Rifle which deals 2d10+2 Rending Damage with a Pen of 4 and the Razor-Sharp and Reliable Qualities. In addition, its Toxic Quality deals 2d10 Damage to an enemy failing a Toughness Test. Serpent's Bite has a Requisition Value of 60 and requires a Renown Rank of Hero to obtain.

Andronican Cowl: Constructed from similar technology to the Mirador, the Andronican Cowl is a powerful tool for a sufficiently skilled Librarian. The cowl's technology is fundamentally the same as that of a Psychic Hood, but capable of far more accurately detecting changes to the flows and tides of the Immaterium. A perceptive Librarian can turn that precision to his advantage, discerning the actions of enemy psykers and moving to halt them. The Andronican Cowl is a Psychic Hood, which grants a +20 bonus to all Focus Power Tests made to nullify enemy psychic powers. In addition, the Andronican Cowl grants the wearer a +10 bonus to all Psyniscience Tests. The Andronican Cowl has a Requisition Value of 50 and requires a Renown Rank of Hero to obtain.

The most common mission involving Watch Station Andronicus is information-gathering. The Mirador is an exceptionally powerful asset, one of the best tools for this purpose the Deathwatch has, and arguably one of the reasons for their ability to respond swiftly, often pre-emptively, to threats across the Jericho Reach. The amount of information that reaches the augurs of the Mirador is colossal, and little of it can be properly interpreted and verified, requiring the intervention of Kill-teams and Acolyte cells to investigate many of the leads the facility produces. Some of these missions are fruitless, while others have been monumentally successful, allowing the Imperium to intervene and halt potentially catastrophic events.

Often, merely learning of an impending threat isn't sufficient, and these information-gathering missions merely serve as reconnaissance for more decisive actions. Such informed assaults have proven invaluable over the centuries, halting dozens of xenos incursions before they could truly begin. On rare occasions, information gathered by the Mirador unlocks sections of the Omega Vault, spurring the Deathwatch into action to discover the meaning of each new revelation, and often drawing them into unexpected conflicts across the Jericho Reach.

Watch Station Andronicus is a large and well supplied outpost, containing a vast range of armaments and resources useful to a Kill-team, and able to support several Kill-teams simultaneously if the situation demands it. A limited supply of Astartes vehicle assets are stored and reverently maintained within the depths of the Watch Station, as are a collection of relics and powerful archaeotech devices stored within stasis vaults accessible only by the express consent of Andronicus' Keeper, presently an Imperial Fists Techmarine by the name of Vandar Illych. By the standards of the Jericho Reach's Watch Stations, Andronicus is frequently visited by a wide range of personnel, many of whom linger for a protracted period of time, often to gather intelligence from the Mirador, or to study in the archives of Andronicus' librarium.

HEROES OF THE CANIS SALIENT

"It is by the efforts of the innumerable masses, directed by the singular will of a few, that Mankind triumphs. When humanity is divided in intent, we are vulnerable, and to be so divided is an affront to the unity that the Emperor sought to create for us. It is why the Tau Empire is so capable of ensnaring the weak of will—all of humanity craves a unified purpose, and when we are divided, the grey-skinned menace leads the foolish astray with their own form of unity. If we cannot provide the purpose that the masses crave, then we shall dishonour everything the Emperor created."

—Excerpt from Cardinal Malbethe's treatise "Musings Upon the Necessity of Purpose," unpublished under Inquisitorial mandate

While there are countless billions of the Emperor's servants contributing to the ongoing conflict within the Jericho Reach, only a few have the power or will to shape the fates of worlds. A few of the most notable of these powerful individuals within the Canis Salient are described below.

LORD COMMANDER SEBIASCOR EBONGRAVE

"It is by the machinations of the enemy that we are brought low, that we find defeat when victory was assured. It is by the works of the xenos that our honest and Throne-given right to rule the stars is challenged… but not by any xenos. It is not the savage beast clawing at our walls that threatens us so, but those xenos who can speak with our words and whose lies infiltrate our dreams and subvert our goals. Only through absolute vigilance and the perfect purity of hate, can our dreams and intentions be made incorruptible, immune to the malediction of xenos promises, and only through their extinction can we find freedom from their taint."

—Sebiascor Ebongrave, Lord Commander of the Canis Salient, addressing the Salient general staff

The burden of command weighs heavy upon some, though few would deign to admit such weakness. Sebiascor Ebongrave is a telling example of this, with his increasing paranoia and the brutal purges he has initiated proving to be just as detrimental to the Canis Salient's progress as secessionist and xenophile terrorism have been. In his unwillingness to compromise his war against the Tau in order to properly confront the Tyranid encroachment into the Canis Salient, he has ordered the executions of dozens, perhaps even hundreds, of senior Adepts and high-ranking Imperial Guard and Imperial Navy officers, made a score of political enemies, and unknowingly hindered operations sanctioned by Lord Militant Tetrarchus.

Ebongrave's steadfast—and some claim, insane—refusal to so much as relent in his onslaught against the Tau has more than once proven detrimental to the Achilus Crusade, and his paranoid loathing has caused him to perceive the insidious hand of the Tau at work in every setback, every challenge

USING LORD COMMANDER EBONGRAVE

Sebiascor Ebongrave is something of an uncertain element in regards to Deathwatch operations. A xenos-hating and Emperor-fearing man to an extreme degree, he is in some ways a model servant of the Imperium, yet his actions and paranoia are detrimental to the ongoing efforts of the Canis Salient and a hindrance to the operations of the Inquisition and the Deathwatch within the Salient.

Ebongrave's relentless gaze upon all aspects of Canis Salient operations—for fear that should he not apply such scrutiny, the Tau would capitalise on his failing—makes covert operations, particularly diplomatic missions, far more difficult than they should be, and it is currently standard procedure within the Canis Salient to operate away from other Imperial forces, avoiding contact with any persons or locations that could reveal their operations to Lord Commander Ebongrave. This serves as an additional complication for a given mission, preventing a Kill-team from drawing upon any Imperial Assets save those made available to them by the Inquisition, and means that none outside the Deathwatch or Inquisition may know about the mission under any circumstances. The secret must be maintained at any cost and by any means necessary, including but not limited to the elimination of witnesses.

However, that is not to say that Ebongrave cannot be an ally to the Deathwatch. His loathing of the Tau means that he will willingly support any operations that see the forces of the Velk'Han Sept bloodied. As a result, any mission within the Canis Salient where the primary objective includes the elimination of Tau forces, may be performed openly with Ebongrave's support (normally under the auspices of Watch Captain Scarion, described later in this chapter), which grants the Kill-team far easier access to the support of Imperial Guard and Imperial Navy forces, adding a bonus 3d10 Requisition to the Kill-team's Reserve Requisition for the duration of the mission, as Guard and Navy forces receive orders to give aid to Deathwatch working with Ebongrave's favour.

to his command and every operation undertaken without his authority. In particular, the Inquisition and the Deathwatch are a source of unending frustration for Ebongrave, for they are utterly beyond his control and seem to operate with a complete disregard for his war. All that said, while he distrusts them immensely, he can be supportive of Deathwatch operations from time to time, if they involve the extermination of Tau forces or Tau sympathisers. As a result he has cultivated an effective working relationship with Watch Captain Scarion, who Ebongrave views as an honourable warrior who knows how things should be done, much to the amusement of the politically savvy Scarion.

LORD CAPTAIN GRAVIS TERROZANT

"A man's loyalty is purest in times of peace—his masters reign supreme and naught can be gained by turning from them. In war, however, a man is presented with choice: his master, or his master's foes. No matter how meaningless a choice—seldom is the alternative to loyalty worth the cost even when the choice exists—it is a choice nonetheless, and nothing tempts a man like the illusion of free will."

—Attributed to Arch-Heretic Lanzethar Muraddin

Few men have been as valuable to Imperial operations within the Canis Salient as Gravis Terrozant, whose extensive smuggling operations throughout the region have allowed a steady stream of technology, intelligence and slave labour to flow back to the Imperium, while plying the worlds of the Velk'Han Sept to spy upon and destabilise the Tau-claimed worlds. In particular, the Inquisition has gained an immense amount from Terrozant's actions, granting its leaders the insights and opportunities they need to effectively combat Tau expansion into the Jericho Reach, all the while supplying the young, ambitious Rogue Trader with the wealth and political might he craves.

It is because of this well rewarded value to the Imperium that Terrozant has remained so decisively loyal to the Emperor, in spite of the opportunities the Tau could offer and the political pressure that Lord Commander Ebongrave places upon him. Ebongrave's paranoia has perceived the free-roaming Rogue Trader as a threat to the ongoing war against the Tau, and the resultant enmity has forced Terrozant's operations to move further afield to escape Ebongrave's notice. Still invaluable to the Inquisition and to Lord Militant Tetrarchus' operations, the Rogue Trader's need to bypass Ebongrave's interference is proving to be a costly and time-consuming hindrance, and one that has more than once made him reconsider his place within the Achilus Crusade.

Ebongrave's fears, while justifiable to some, are a fiction. Terrozant's loyalty to the Imperium has been tested by Ebongrave's paranoid interference, but he has seen enough of the Tau to know that they offer little alternative for him. More likely, perhaps, is the possibility that he could abandon the Crusade and return through the warp gate to venture into the Koronus Expanse. Armed with technology stolen from the Tau, he could easily set about making his name through conquest and exploration. While not as damaging to the Achilus Crusade as his theoretical defection would be, the disillusionment of so valuable a servant of the Imperium would still be a notable setback.

For the time being however, the support of the Inquisition and of Lord Militant Tetrarchus' general staff is sufficient to hold Terrozant within the Jericho Reach, where his mercenary army, espionage, slaving and smuggling operations continue to benefit the Canis Salient. His frequent ventures beyond the Greyhell Front have seen him become a valuable asset to Deathwatch missions pushing towards the otherwise hard-to-reach Velk'Han Sept.

PLENIPOTENTIARY-DESIGNATE URWIN SIRE

"It is said that a single word in the right place at the right time can halt armies and change worlds. This isn't quite true: it normally takes more than one word."

—Plenipotentiary-Designate Urwin Sire

As a diplomat, Urwin Sire is a member of a group within the Imperium seldom acknowledged and rarely lauded—for reasons historical and sociological, the emphasis of the Imperium tends far more towards exhorting warriors rather than scholars, scribes and others for whom knowledge and language are their weapons. Nonetheless, Sire is a diplomat, and an extremely effective one at that, a fact that has earned him no small amount of importance.

Nevertheless, his placement within the Jericho Reach has found even the keen-witted Urwin Sire a little out of his depth. Where most of the diplomatic missions organised by the Adeptus Terra exist to secure the compliance of newly claimed worlds, or to ensure that an Imperial Commander performs his Throne-given duty, it is rare for the Imperium to enter into diplomatic contact with xenos. Indeed, the great majority of such contact is performed by the Inquisition or by a Rogue Trader, rather than by the Adepts of the Divisio Legatus.

Urwin Sire is, at present, the senior member of the Achilus Crusade's diplomatic staff, and a member of Lord Militant Tetrarchus' inner circle of advisors. Much of the day-to-day management of his subordinates is handled by an assortment of aides and assistants who oversee the relatively mundane

---

USING LORD-CAPTAIN TERROZANT

Gravis Terrozant is an infrequent but useful ally for the Deathwatch, his ventures past the Greyhell Front serving to provide the Inquisition and the Deathwatch with priceless intelligence on Tau movements, and providing access to the worlds of the Velk'Han Sept where few others can.

Intelligence about Tau operations and resources is a crucial asset to Deathwatch operations, providing insights into the capabilities of Tau technology, dispositions of their armies and fleets, layouts of Tau facilities and other knowledge valuable when planning missions against the Tau. Beyond that, knowledge of human dissidents and resistance movements on Tau-controlled worlds can provide much-needed support for Deathwatch operations deep behind enemy lines, and similarly the presence of the Deathwatch can bolster the morale of such groups and encourage them to redouble their efforts.

However, access to the Velk'Han Sept is an asset like no other. Almost unprecedented, the ability to push deep behind the front lines and strike against Tau forces on their own worlds is too useful an ability to ignore. Such missions are extremely dangerous and almost entirely lacking in support, but they are nonetheless often necessary when attempting to assassinate highly placed Tau personnel or secure the most valuable of intelligence.

USING PLENIPOTENTIARY-DESIGNATE SIRE

Urwin Sire is both an unusual choice for an ally in Deathwatch, and a fitting one. The nature of his missions are far from typical for a Kill-team, requiring a degree of individual restraint and social skills seldom possessed by even the most gregarious of Battle-Brothers. However, for this very reason Sire is an invaluable asset in such situations, his undeniable talent for negotiation allowing him to thrive in circumstances in which few Space Marines find themselves comfortable.

In most diplomatic missions involving Sire, he can be expected to perform a significant portion of the work, but he is eager to take advantage of the tactical and strategic acumen of the Deathwatch and other armed forces within his negotiations, employing them as advisors when debating military matters or discussing the Tyranid threat with Tau diplomats (who, it should be noted, often employ senior Fire Caste officers in much the same way). In such situations, Sire's presence allows a Kill-team to make peaceful contact with enemies, which can either prove to be a valuable intelligence-gathering opportunity, or a situation that challenges preconceptions.

Alternatively, Sire can also serve as a behind-the-lines advisor, providing insights by vox to a Kill-team dealing with impromptu alliances made in the field to face a common foe. In such situations, Sire's aid grants assistance—a +10 bonus and an additional degree of success—on Charm, Deceive, Inquiry and Scrutiny Tests when dealing with temporary allies.

matter of ensuring that newly conquered human worlds are integrated into the Imperium as swiftly as possible, allowing Sire to concentrate his attentions upon an issue far more unusual and far more pressing. With the encroachment of Hive Fleet Dagon, Sire has been tasked with ensuring that the Imperium can concentrate as much of its might as possible on repelling the Tyranid threat, by whatever means are necessary. For the most part, this has revolved around securing support from otherwise reluctant worlds, but on a few occasions it has required entering into negotiations with the envoys and ambassadors of the Tau Water Caste.

These missions have always been fraught with peril; few in the Imperium will honestly place their trust in the good will of a xenos species and it is unlikely that the Tau regard the Imperium any more favourably. Yet, mutual antipathy between two warring species has rarely been the largest problem—instead, the paranoia and unending xenophobia of Lord Commander Ebongrave have done more to sabotage non-hostile interactions with the Tau than any actions performed by Sire or the Tau during negotiations. As a result, tensions run high between the Imperium and the Tau, though it is known that there are several highly placed individuals on both sides of the war who believe that the Tyranids are threat that must be met by both civilisations without distraction from an ongoing conflict. Time and again, the Deathwatch

have been called upon to oversee matters of security for these missions, or to establish first contact with an enemy officer who favours cooperation in the face of Hive Fleet Dagon, operating secretly at the behest of the Inquisition with Sire's keen diplomatic mind providing advice.

WATCH CAPTAIN ANDAR SCARION

"Lord Commander, I can assure you that the Deathwatch presence on Veren was purely a mission of extermination against Tau sympathisers on that world. Indeed, I discussed it with you several weeks ago."

–Watch Captain Andar Scarion

A member of the Astral Claws Chapter, Scarion's arrival at Watch Fortress Erioch in 782.M41 was met with controversy. His Chapter's actions in recent decades had caused a significant amount of unrest amongst some in the Imperium. Nonetheless, after much deliberation Scarion was permitted to commence his Vigil, and for forty-five years he has served the Deathwatch with honour, achieving the rank of Watch Captain more than fifteen years ago.

A proud and ruthless warrior with a keen grasp of strategy and military politics, Scarion has proven to be a valuable asset in liaising with the Achilus Crusade's officers, capable of navigating the invariably complex political landscape of the Crusade. This has not prevented him from taking to the field, however, and on many occasions Scarion has had cause to clad himself in his warplate and take up bolter and lightning claw against the enemies of mankind.

In recent years, Scarion has moved frequently between the fortress worlds of Spite and Wrath, working tirelessly to manage the growing madness of Lord Commander Ebongrave and trying to keep it from influencing the Deathwatch's missions within the Canis Salient. In spite of his responsibilities, he has managed to keep a careful watch over a half-dozen Kill-teams

USING WATCH CAPTAIN SCARION

Andar Scarion's focus is primarily upon the Canis Salient, and consequently Kill-teams assigned to him will be operating almost exclusively within that region. Scarion's efforts to limit Ebongrave's interference in Deathwatch operations typically allow for a wide variety of missions to be undertaken—overt cooperation with Canis Salient forces is made possible through Scarion's careful management, while covert missions benefit from his actions to prevent news reaching the Lord Commander.

A Kill-team under Scarion's authority is expected to perform in an exemplary manner—nothing short of perfection is sufficient, and failure to match his expectations can result in the loss of renown. For every two Objectives a Kill-team fails to complete during a mission while under Scarion's command, every member of the Kill-team loses 1 point of Renown.

operating within the Salient, often taking up his customary arms and joining them in the field where opportunity permits or necessity dictates.

Scarion is a harsh commander at the best of times, the difficulties of the Achilus Crusade's political landscape causing him continual stress, and while his pride does not allow him to voice discontent about his circumstances, he expects the Kill-teams under his command to perform to the most exacting of standards and does not tolerate laxity, weakness or failure.

As is common to many of his Chapter, Scarion regards non-Astartes with a mixture of scorn and pity, holding that the Astartes ideal is fundamentally superior to the frailty of humanity. He masks this well in times of politics, but discards the façade when amongst other Astartes, seeing little issue with collateral damage amongst human allies and regarding them as expendable. This has caused considerable ill-will between him and Battle-Brothers more inclined towards benevolence, such as those of the Blood Angels, Salamanders and Space Wolves Chapters.

Watch Captain Andar Scarion

WS	BS	S	T	Ag	Int	Per	WP	Fel
63	51	71 (12)	59 (10)	52	59	46	50	57

Movement: 6/12/18/36   **Wounds:** 24

Skills: Awareness (Per), Charm (Fel) +20, Ciphers (Chapter Runes) (Int) +10, Ciphers (Deathwatch) (Int) +10, Climb (S), Command (Fel) +20, Common Lore (Adeptus Astartes) (Int) +10, Common Lore (Deathwatch) (Int), Common Lore (Jericho Reach) (Int) +10, Common Lore (Imperium) (Int) +10, Common Lore (War) (Int) +20, Concealment (Ag), Deceive (Fel) +20, Demolition (Int), Dodge (Ag) +10, Drive (Ground Vehicle) (Ag), Drive (Skimmer) (Ag), Evaluate (Int), Forbidden Lore (Adeptus Astartes) (Int) +10, Forbidden Lore (Xenos) (Int) +10, Forbidden Lore (Deathwatch) (Int), Intimidate (S) +10, Literacy (Int) +20, Navigation (Surface) (Int), Pilot (Personal) (Ag), Scrutiny (Per) +20, Scholastic Lore (Codex Astartes) (Int) +20, Search (Int), Silent Move (Ag), Speak Language (High Gothic) (Int), Speak Language (Low Gothic) (Int), Tactics (Assault Doctrine) (Int), Tactics (Defensive Doctrine) (Int), Tactics (Void Combat) (Int) +20, Tracking (Int).

Talents: Air of Authority, Ambidextrous, Astartes Weapon Training, Bolter Drill, Bulging Biceps, Call to Vengeance, Combat Formation, Crushing Blow, Fearless, Heightened Senses (Hearing, Sight), Hip Shooting, Hunter of Aliens, Iron Discipline, Iron Jaw, Killing Strike, Master Orator, Mighty Shot, Nerves of Steel, Quick Draw, Rapid Reaction, Resistance (Cold, Heat, Psychic), Sprint, True Grit, Two Weapon Wielder (Ballistic, Melee), Unarmed Master, Unarmed Warrior.

Traits: Bolter Mastery, Size: Hulking, Space Marine Implants, Touched by the Fates (3), Unnatural Strength (x2), Unnatural Toughness (x2).

Armour: Astartes Power Armour (Head 8, Body 10, Arms 8, Legs 8) and Iron Halo (Protection 50; Overload 01).

Weapons: Exceptional Astartes Bolter-Meltagun Combi-Weapon (100m; S/3/5; 2d10+9 X; Pen 5; Clip 28; Rld Full; Reliable, Tearing; [Meltagun] 20m; S/–/–; 2d10+12 E; Pen 13; Clip 1), Astartes Bolt Pistol (30m; S/4/–; 2d10+7 X; Pen 5; Clip 14; Rld Full; Tearing), *Tiger's Claw* Relic Lightning Claw (1d10+25 E; Pen 8; Power Field, Razor-Sharp, Special, Tearing), Astartes Combat Blade (1d10+16 R; Pen 2), 3x Frag Grenades, 3x Krak Grenades.

Gear: 4 Bolter magazines, 2 Bolt Pistol magazines, assorted encrypted data-slates containing intelligence about Deathwatch missions, staff of Deathwatch Serfs and Adjutants, Bionic Eye.

BROTHER VIGILANT, DEATHWATCH CHAPLAIN

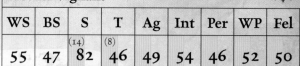

"Masters of the Watch, I come before you with nothing but the plate I wear and this most sacred of weapons. All else I have lost. I require only a purpose, that I might direct my righteous fury and earn absolution for the sins I am about to divulge."

—Brother Vigilant, before the Chamber of Vigilance after his arrival on Watch Fortress Erioch

Of the events that have occurred within Watch Fortress Erioch in the last decade, few have been met with such scrutiny as the arrival of an individual known as Brother Vigilant. In the final hours of 812.M41, a badly damaged Inquisitorial courier vessel arrived at the edge of the Erioch system, broadcasting the ident-ciphers of Inquisitor Arryn Cerano, a member of the Ordo Xenos who had departed only a month before on some urgent, unknown mission. Cerano was nowhere to be found, and most of the crew of the courier died from void exposure or radiation sickness within the following week, leaving only a single clue as to what had brought the vessel to Erioch.

Within the courier's hold was a stasis-crypt, active and containing a single Space Marine in a sus-an membrane coma, clad in battle-scarred black warplate and clutching a Crozius Arcanum that had seen much use. Without delay, he was rushed to Erioch's Apothecarion to be awoken from his comatose state, while his armour and weapon were taken before the Forge Masters so that their machine spirits could be properly attended to and interrogated.

Upon the nameless Battle-Brother's awakening, Watch Commander Mordigael gathered the Chamber of Vigilance at the newcomer's urgent request, to hear his case. Three days passed, as he explained himself and put his fate at the mercy of the Master of the Vigil. Whatever was said is sealed by agreement of the Master of the Vigil and the Inquisitor of the Chamber, never to be spoken of again, and the bearer of this news was granted leave to swear the Apocryphon Oath and begin a Vigil without end, taking the name Brother Vigilant in place of his own.

However, instead of taking to the field immediately, Brother Vigilant spent three years in intense study, learning the many rites and rituals of the Deathwatch, before he emerged to do battle with the Emperor's enemies, bearing once again the scarred and war-worn Crozius Arcanum he arrived with, having taken up the mantle of Deathwatch Chaplain.

At present, Brother Vigilant operates from Watch Station Andronicus, departing frequently with itinerant Kill-teams venturing deeper into space contested by the Tau. It is believed that his desire is to see Watch Station Skapula reclaimed, and is ever watchful for some means of accomplishing that feat, or some other piece to a puzzle he alone is privy to.

Brother Vigilant								
WS	BS	S	T	Ag	Int	Per	WP	Fel
55	47	(14) 82	(8) 46	49	54	46	52	50

Movement: 5/10/15/30   **Wounds:** 23

Skills: Awareness (Per), Charm (Fel), Ciphers (Xenos Markings) (Int) +20, Ciphers (Chapter Runes) (Int) +10, Ciphers (Deathwatch) (Int), Climb (S), Common Lore (Adeptus Astartes) (Int), Common Lore (Deathwatch) (Int), Common Lore (Imperium) (Int), Common Lore (War) (Int), Concealment (Ag), Dodge (Ag), Drive (Ground Vehicle) (Ag), Forbidden Lore (Deathwatch) (Int), Forbidden Lore (Xenos) (Int), Interrogation (WP) +20, Intimidate (S) +20, Literacy (Int), Navigation (Surface) (Int), Pilot (Personal) (Ag), Scholastic Lore (Codex Astartes) (Int), Search (Per), Silent Move (Ag), Speak Language (High

Titus Valdius — Ultramarines
Personal Reflections ++ 817.M41

I have defended my home from the ravening hordes of xenos, purged heretics and daemons that threaten the very Imperium itself, but this secondment to the Deathwatch in the far flung edge of the galaxy is the hardest challenge I have ever had to face. These Battle-Brothers of my Kill-team take the teachings of the Codex Astartes so lightly, it is a wonder they have seen success at all.

As I found myself listing from my resolve, I sought to straighten my mind with our Chaplain, but even that would test me. This Chaplain calls himself "Brother Vigilant" and hides not just his Chapter, but his very name. However, despite my initial reaction to this Battle-Brother, he holds great wisdom. His guidance has allowed me to not only integrate with my Kill-team, but cooperate with them as well. . .

Gothic) (Int), Speak Language (Low Gothic) (Int), Tactics (Assault Doctrine) (Int), Tracking (Int).
Talents: Ambidextrous, Astartes Weapon Training, Bulging Biceps, Crushing Blow, Duty Unto Death, Fearless, Hatred (Chaos Space Marines, Mutants, Eldar, Tau), Heightened Senses (Hearing, Sight), Icon of Duty, Iron Jaw, Killing Strike, Litany of Hate, Nerves of Steel, Quick Draw, Resistance (Psychic Powers), True Grit, Two Weapon Wielder (Ballistic, Melee), Unarmed Master, Unarmed Warrior.
Traits: Size: Hulking, Space Marine Implants, Touched by the Fates (2), Unnatural Strength (x2), Unnatural Toughness (x2).
Armour: Astartes Power Armour with Skull Helm (Head 8, Body 10, Arms 8, Legs 8; +10 to Intimidate Tests) and Rosarius (Protection 50; Overload 01).
Weapons: Astartes Bolter (100m; S/2/4; 2d10+5 X; Pen 5; Clip 28; Rld Full; Tearing), Astartes Bolt Pistol (30m; S/3/–; 2d10+5 X; Pen 5; Clip 14; Rld Full; Tearing), Combat Blade (1d10+18 R; Pen 2), Crozius Arcanum (1d10+23 E; Pen 7; Balanced, Power Field).
Gear: Black Hooded Robes, 4 Bolter magazines, 2 Bolt Pistol magazines.

USING BROTHER VIGILANT

Brother Vigilant is one of the many mysteries of the Deathwatch, his origins and purpose continually obfuscated by the necessary caution and secrecy that surrounds the organisation. His zeal and fury make him a potent asset for a Kill-team, though Brother Vigilant's personal objectives may hinder or interfere with the Kill-team's own mission.

In any instance where Brother Vigilant accompanies a Kill-team, his counsel and spiritual guidance grant the Kill-team a +1 bonus to their Cohesion, and he counts as a member of the squad for the purposes of Squad Mode abilities. However, the mission gains an additional Secondary Objective—Brother Vigilant's own personal goals, typically the retrieval of information or an object of some sort. These do not have to be known to the Battle-Brothers; they're merely required to aid the Chaplain in whatever manner he requests, and ensure his survival.

Brother Vigilant's Icon of Faith Talent can be found on Page 108 of **RITES OF BATTLE**.

CANIS SALIENT SPECIAL ABILITIES

"Charge the cannons! Move! Move! Move!"

—Watch Captain Scipio

Within the Canis Salient, Deathwatch Space Marines have had to develop techniques to combat the technological capabilities of the Tau forces along with the savagery of their allies. In addition to the direct physical threats posed by the xenos, Battle-Brothers must also contend with the charisma and religious heresy of the Tau Empire. At times, the Tau attempts at open discourse may pose an even greater threat than their efforts to physically overcome Crusade forces.

On several occasions, worlds thought cleared of the Tau later proved to still be subject to their influence as hidden resources emerged. These instances have resulted in disruption of Imperial supply convoys and loss of the lives of many loyal soldiers of the Imperium. This combination of deadly combat capability and treacherous heresy is every bit as dangerous as the threat posed by the Chaos forces within the Acheros Salient. When combined with the false front of courtesy and friendship that the Tau often pose, it can begin to fracture the psyche of anyone who is not properly prepared to face it.

CANIS DEMEANOURS

The battles within the Canis Salient have seen an ongoing struggle between wars of words and active battle. The corruption instilled by the Tau and their allies is an insidious force. Humans subjected to it are often beyond saving. The Deathwatch must face the constant challenge of identifying those humans contaminated by this exposure and determining if they can be saved or if they must be eliminated along with their xenos comrades. The great danger is that the depravity of the Tau can be hard to detect and near impossible to cleanse. For some humans, once contaminated, no amount of penance can ever purify their souls of this xenos taint.

The war with these forces can change the outlook of some Battle-Brothers that confront it. This section offers a series of new Personal Demeanours for those Battle-Brothers who fully experience the Crusade within the Canis Salient. For players considering these Demeanours, it is worth remembering that these shifts should be gradual. Space Marines live extended lives and are often slow to adapt their minds to changes in their environment. Any change in Personal Demeanour should be due to a series of events rather than one sudden dramatic conflict. Though, as these are personality traits, there certainly may be individual Space Marines who change more often. There is no XP cost required for a shift in Demeanour. Refer to DEATHWATCH page 32 for more information on Personal Demeanours.

FLEXIBLE

As the Crusade forces continue to battle within the Canis Salient, they are constantly exposed to new Tau tactics and additional Tau allies. Different commanders exploit different strategies as they press the battle. Different auxiliary races have different capabilities and combat styles. Some of these auxiliary races may even have resources that are previously unidentified or all but unrecognisable. All of this variation requires that a Space Marine be well versed in different aspects of the Codex so as to be capable of identifying and utilising the most appropriate response for each new threat.

For some Battle-Brothers, this challenge is a tremendous opportunity. These Space Marines are thrilled by the prospect of each battle turning into a surprise. They see each new foe as a chance to learn and to test their tactical acumen as they swiftly adapt their approach. They embrace this idea enthusiastically.

When preparing for a mission, Space Marines who espouse this philosophy seldom choose armaments based solely upon the task at hand. Rather, they select materials that could resolve the current conflict and also have the broadest range of possible applications. They believe that preparedness is the heart of success. In this way, they can best adapt and overcome any unexpected threat to the Imperium. It is never enough for them to have the right tool for the right job. Instead, they must have the right tool for any task that they might reasonably face.

IMPATIENT

All too often, Tau forces attempt to embroil the Crusade with extended negotiating tactics. Of course, as these discussions wear on, the Tau have ample time to manufacture new equipment, reinforce their outposts, and deliver additional support to their forces. Further, any exposure to the Tau— even over a negotiating table—brings with it the risk of contamination. At the same time, Imperial forces may even be recalled from the conflict so that they can be assigned to more volatile fronts. In this way, the delays offer a tremendous benefit to the Tau but seldom work out in the favour of the Imperium.

For many Space Marines, particularly those of the Deathwatch, this tolerance of xenos requests has been permitted to continue for far too long. The negotiators prattle on incessantly much to their dismay. The Battle-Brothers demand a forceful and immediate resolution to the issues at hand. Rather than waiting for permission from their Crusade allies, these Deathwatch members choose to take matters directly into their hands. When they have mission assignments, they conduct them directly, forcefully, and without delay. There can be no discussion with the xenos, for the only mercy they deserve is that of a swift death. Anything else can only damage the Imperium. The Achilus Crusade can ill-afford to offer any concessions at this stage.

MANIPULATIVE

The Tau Empire constantly strives to contaminate Imperial forces with their philosophical beliefs. They readily offer various forms of aid, though any assistance always bears the taint of the xenos and the constant risk of heresy. It was through this heresy that the worlds of the Canis Salient originally fell to the Tau. Some believe that in order to recover these human worlds for the Imperium, there must be more than the application of military might. Of course, the forces of the Ecclesiarchy are ready and able to preach the divine word of the God-Emperor, but the most devout are seldom willing or able to enter any sort of dialog with these xenos.

A rare few members of Deathwatch Kill-teams have developed the knack to stifle their fury sufficiently that they might interact with the xenos. Through endless rituals of meditation and purification, they have inured their minds and souls to the taint of heresy. With these preparations in place, they willingly engage in social discourse with Tau envoys, acknowledging that at times a discussion might provide Imperial forces with more time to martial their resources. These Battle-Brothers believe that some degree of understanding is necessary to eliminate this xenos threat and to eventually cleanse humanity of its taint. They believe that only once they can effectively manipulate their foes through social and mental trickery can they ultimately overcome them on the battlefield.

PATIENT

There are many active battlefronts within the Canis Salient, but there are others where the war has gone cold. In these locations, physical conflict waits upon verbal interactions confined to a meeting room. Because of this, military units are forced to maintain a state of constant preparedness. These negotiations might break down at any time. In such an event, forces are deployed with all haste, as part of an effort to catch the opposition unprepared for an attack. Maintaining a state of vigilance for hours can be challenging. Maintaining that same state for months or even years can be exhausting.

In the face of such a continuous stress that has no physical outlet, troops can have a wide variety of responses. Some Space Marines choose to embrace the act of waiting as an opportunity to develop a greater degree of self-discipline. These Battle-Brothers focus their time into training, study, and hyper-vigilance. They realise that an attack might come at any moment but accept that their duty at this time lies in the simple act of waiting. This ability to wait out the enemy can pay dividends in more active conflicts as well. Knowing the opportune time to strike, and having the patience to wait for that time to come can save precious lives and resources. While rushing in headlong may satisfy a visceral craving for violence, it is seldom the best tactic to overcome an opponent.

STUDIOUS

Dealing with the worlds in alliance with the Tau forces can expose the Achilus Crusade to a broad range of different types of xenos. While the influence they spread is undoubtedly hazardous to their very souls, the presence of these varied life forms and their divergent technologies present a new range of challenges. In the frantic pace of a violent battlefield, not even a Space Marine can immediately identify every weapon when fired nor recognise the weak point in every defence. This becomes even more important when these technologies are encountered for the very first time.

Some Space Marines believe that knowledge of the enemy is necessary in order to effectively vanquish the foe. These Battle-Brothers choose to closely observe their defeated opponents and maintain exceptionally detailed notes regarding their biology and technology. With each additional encounter, they strive to broaden their knowledge so that it may be shared with their Battle-Brothers and with the agents of the Inquisition. Between conflicts they may choose to more closely examine their notes as they delve in to the anatomy and structure of trophies or samples acquired through combat. In many instances, this may complement the specialties of an Apothecary or Techmarine, but this approach is not necessarily limited to Space Marines who follow those paths.

SUSPICIOUS

When forced to interact with xenos, there are cultural and psychological differences that may be insurmountable. Actions that are well within the boundaries of normal human actions may constitute a heinous offense or even a betrayal to a xenos. Similarly, a xenos might have little regard for the standards of the Imperium. Its actions could easily violate respected codes of conduct. As truly learning the ways of such a vile foe reeks of heresy, only those who would willingly imperil their souls take the measures necessary to discover and prepare for these difficulties and properly address them.

Instead of accepting such a risk, the Battle-Brother has chosen to follow the more direct path. In any dealing with a xenos—or a human who might have been contaminated by such a foe—he always expects a betrayal. Battle-Brothers who embrace this creed are always prepared for the inevitable. They realise that at any time, a xenos might produce a seemingly innocuous device that turns out to be a bomb of untold power. Alternatively, these blasphemous creatures could wield unimaginable psychic talents or have unknown technology capable of concealing a waiting ambush. These Space Marines often choose to resolve situations with direct military action, as this always eliminates the risk of a confrontation under less favourable conditions.

CANIS SOLO MODES

Battles within the Canis Salient require Battle-Brothers to deal with a broad variety of unusual opponents. The auxiliaries of the Tau Empire have substantial resources to draw upon and a range of technological innovations. In order to combat this, Space Marines must adapt their fighting styles based upon the opponent at hand. Because of this diversity, it is not uncommon for individual members of a Kill-team to face opponents with substantially different gear and combat techniques. This has led to situations in which the use of Solo Mode is particularly appropriate as distinct squad members face vastly different opponents.

To address this diversity, Deathwatch Space Marines active in the Canis Salient have pioneered several distinctive Solo Modes. These are particularly appropriate for those fighting within this region but may also be useful in other places. In order to master any of these techniques, a Space Marine must first work alongside someone who has become skilled in their use. The primary concentration of these individuals remains within that Salient of the Achilus Crusade.

AERIAL WARRIOR

Cost: 250 XP
Type: Passive
Required Rank: 2
Effects: Tau forces employ an unusual number of troops that are fully capable of flight. The most common of these are the Vespid Stingwings, but their drones and even their heavily armoured battlesuits are capable of firing down upon Imperial targets while aloft. This can pose a substantial problem for Imperial units that lack either the inherent ability for flight or the necessary adaptations and training to engage in combat while aloft. Even a Space Marine equipped with a jump

pack lacks the ability to stay aloft long enough to effectively engage certain opponents in flight. Though ranged weapons remain an effective option, many of these opponents are far more vulnerable to a well executed melee attack.

To overcome this difficulty, some Space Marines have chosen to drill extensively in the use of their jump packs for just such combat situations. When faced with a flier, these Battle-Brothers activate their jump packs and use them to reach their targets so that they may engage them directly. This counts as a Charge action, leading to a Grapple taken with a +20 bonus. Once successful, the Space Marine uses his jump pack sparingly, partially using the opponent's natural lift to slow their fall. For as long as the Battle-Brother maintains control of the grapple and the foe lives, both remain aloft.

Improvement: At Rank 4, the Space Marine has become so adept with this technique that after the initial Grapple is established, his opponent suffers a −20 penalty to any attempts to break the Grapple. At Rank 6, this penalty is increased to −40.

CLOSE QUICKLY

Cost: 250 XP
Type: Active
Required Rank: 2
Effects: Tau units possess exceptionally deadly ranged attacks, but are often substantially less proficient in melee combat than their Imperial counterparts. As a direct consequence, standard Imperial tactics for these situations dictate that Space Marines should avoid protracted ranged combats. While this is tactically sound, it often results in situations in which the charging Imperial forces are left moving towards an armed enemy with little opportunity to take cover from enemy fire.

A few Space Marines active within the Canis Salient have honed their abilities to execute an attack at the completion of an all out sprint. Their daily practice regimens focus on short runs, making countless sprints without armour while holding a running chainsword in each hand. In several facilities, the practice drill areas have been expanded, specifically so that a melee practice ritual, with a well equipped servitor, may include an extended charge. Some of these servitors are even equipped with ranged weapons, so that the Battle-Brothers may practice dodging incoming fire as they execute their charge.

Those Marines who practice this mode may increase the distance moved prior to executing a Charge Action. They may move up to their Run distance and still receive the Weapon Skill bonus on a Charge. However, due to the additional time spent in motion, the movement uses up their Reaction until their next turn.

Improvement: At Rank 4 or higher, the Space Marine has become so proficient at this using this movement that his Weapon Skill bonus on any Charge Action is increased to +20. At Rank 6 or higher, he does not lose his Reaction when executing such a Charge.

DENY THE HERESY

Cost: 250 XP
Type: Passive
Required Rank: 2

Effects: Any Imperial forces active within the Canis Salient are invariably forced to deal with adherents of Tau dogma. Under many circumstances this may mean interacting with them in a setting where physical conflict is unlikely to be a solution. However, even a discussion with such adherents runs the risk of contamination. An Imperial agent in this sort of situation could be damned to lose sight of the Emperor's glory under the influence of such blasphemous heresies.

Some Space Marines have adapted Ecclesiarchy techniques to purify their minds and souls so that they might more effectively resist these influences. Through careful focus, they close their minds so that the corruption has no opportunity to take root, even while they remain within its presence for hours or days. This technique has proven exceptionally vital to Deathwatch Kill-teams forced to operate deep behind enemy lines or Battle-Brothers that must interrogate prisoners.

Once a Space Marine has learned to "Deny the Heresy" he receives a +20 bonus to resist any Interaction Skill Tests.

Improvement: Space Marines that learn this technique increase the bonus to +30 when they reach Rank 4. At Rank 6, the Battle-Brother has mastered the ability to the point that he may overcome other's resistance, gaining a +20 bonus to any Intimidate Skill Tests.

LEGACY OF HATE

Cost: 100 XP
Type: Active
Required Rank: 3

Effects: After millennia of separation, many human cultures within the Jericho Reach forgot their connection to the Imperium of Man. As they lost their government, they also lost their understanding of the Imperial Cult. When the Tau Empire established contact with these systems, the humans were easy to subvert. Without the guidance of the Ecclesiarchy and the resistance that comes from faith in the God-Emperor, these souls knew not the dangers of xenos contagion. Soon, their culture was overrun with xenos beliefs, and their souls damned to eternal darkness.

With the arrival of the Achilus Crusade, all that has changed. As Imperial forces establish contact with worlds, the inhabitants of those systems garner a fresh opportunity for redemption. However, before they can embrace their salvation, their beings must be purified of the xenos taint. The strength of the xenos brainwashing is such that this stain does not easily come clean.

Some Deathwatch members have intently studied Inquisition and Ecclesiarchy texts that detail the approved methodology for purifying a subject. Through this research, they have identified key factors common to xenos influence and adapted the systems for their own use. As a consequence, whenever they deal with a being under xenos influence they receive a +30 bonus to all Interaction skill tests. In this way, they can better extract information from these fallen humans and sometimes even recruit them to the Imperial cause.

Improvement: At Rank 5, this bonus increases to +40.

PRIMARCH'S GUARD

Cost: 200 XP
Type: Passive
Required Rank: 2

Effects: Because of the array of ranged armaments in use by the Tau forces within the Canis Salient, Space Marines are ever dependent upon the efficiency of their power armour. Constant rains of devastating fire have resulted in many battlefields having only the most limited amount of cover. On many occasions, Space Marines are forced to advance towards the enemy in the face of withering fire with only their faith and their power armour for defence.

Many Space Marines within the Canis Salient have discovered that this faith is adequate protection. In point of fact, at those times when their actions are most true to their chapter's teachings, they seldom come to harm. While it is unclear if this is a direct consequence of their belief or a simple statistical anomaly, the evidence is overwhelming. Under specific conditions, which seem to vary between different Space Marine chapters, power armour is more protective than normal.

Those Battle-Brothers who learn this technique gain a bonus of +2 Armour Points on all locations for any protective gear while committing an action that is consistent with their Chapter Demeanour. This bonus applies during any turn in which such an action is undertaken. As soon as they cease to exemplify the essence of their chapter, the effect fades.

Improvement: At Rank 5, this bonus increases to +3 Armour Points. At Rank 8, it increases to +4.

REND THE XENOS

Cost: 100 XP

Type: Active

Required Rank: 1

Effects: Forces of the Tau race are invariably equipped with advanced technology that is particularly well suited for long ranged engagements. In stark contrast, many of their auxiliary forces, particularly the Kroot, utilise far more primitive gear, which is often better suited for melee engagements. In many cases, these disparate forces may be used in the same engagement, such that the Tau can effectively engage their opponents in both ranged and melee combat. These auxiliaries can be utilised so that Tau forces have an opportunity to disengage from close-combat and resume their ranged attacks. In this way, these comparatively primitive forces can provide a disproportionate advantage within the context of the larger battle.

Within the Canis Salient, some Space Marines have identified this problem and taken measures to resolve it. These Battle-Brothers have closely studied the primitive armour and equipment used by these auxiliary races. By combining a basic knowledge of this gear with an understanding of the xenos physiology, they have identified key physical vulnerabilities. In combat situations, they work to carefully exploit these vulnerabilities, taking full advantage of their physiological enhancements and Imperial technology. When facing foes equipped only with Primitive Armour, their attacks completely ignore the armour's AP.

Improvement: At Rank 5, Battle-Brothers with this ability do an extra 1d5 damage for each successful melee attack against foes in Primitive Armour. At Rank 7, this increases to 1d10.

SNIPER'S TRAINING

Cost: 250 XP

Type: Active

Required Rank: 3

Effects: In any combat situation, an attacker who can freely target the enemy without fear of return fire holds a substantial advantage. When battling the Tau Empire—as in the Canis Salient—Imperial forces seldom enjoy this sort of superiority. Their xenos technology includes weapons with substantial range and a variety of equipment designed to offer the advantage of concealment.

As Deathwatch Kill-teams have continued to face opposition with these talents, several have worked to improve their accuracy at the most extreme combat ranges. This is a part of an ongoing effort to identify and exploit any technological advantages that can be identified in the ongoing conflict with the Tau forces. With extensive practice and minor enhancements to their targeting systems, lethality within an extended range may be substantially increased.

For Battle-Brothers that choose to focus on this technique, extend the range of all bolt weapons when firing a single shot. Long Range increases to three times Range, Short Range increases to Range, and normal Range increases to twice the listed Range.

Improvement: At Rank 6, the increased Ranged categories apply to all Astartes Weapons.

CANIS SQUAD MODES

The Tau Empire fields a well equipped army that is unified by embracing a central dogma. These foes excel at the use of combined arms tactics and at the subjugation of their opponents through psychological as well as physical manipulation. In order for the Achilus Crusade to effectively counter these abilities, they must also learn the use of psychology and the art of cooperation between different types of units. Only by developing and enacting these comparable techniques can they hope to remain effective against the xenos in a consistent manner.

Deathwatch Kill-teams are innately well suited to engage and overcome such foes as the Tau. Their Inquisitorial training ensures that the Battle-Brothers know the foe's weaknesses and the best ways to exploit them. However, even these established techniques can be refined through continued exposure. As Space Marines continuously engage Tau forces within the Canis Salient, Squad Mode Abilities have been refined that specifically counter the most common Tau tactics. During the time between missions, many Battle-Brothers work with their peers to spread word of these alternative approaches.

See the **Using Salient Squad Modes** sidebar below for more information on how these Modes may be integrated with Oaths.

USING SALIENT SQUAD MODES

The Squad Mode abilities presented within this book are intended to benefit an entire Deathwatch Kill-team when they are activated. However, they are not necessarily immediately available to a squad. Learning one of these new abilities requires mission experience within the appropriate Salient of the Achilus Crusade as well as the expenditure of XP to gain the new ability. In addition to those requirements, just as with all Squad Mode abilities, these specific abilities must be made available for a specific mission.

These Squad Modes may be made available for the mission by taking the applicable Salient specific Oath prior to the mission. To take the Salient specific Oath, only the current Squad Leader needs to have purchased the Oath. However, only Battle-Brothers who have individually purchased the Salient specific Squad Modes will be able to gain their advantages when they are activated. This restriction follows all the same rules as Chapter Specific Squad Modes, giving the benefit only to those with access to it. In this way, the Salient Specific Squad modes are also treated as Chapter Squad modes for abilities such as Tactical Expertise (DEATHWATCH Rulebook page 85), granting Battle-Brothers who have not purchased the ability access to it under special circumstances.

Note that under either of these conditions, the Deathwatch Kill-team need not be active in the Salient where the ability was learned. Once the Squad Mode Ability—and if necessary the Oath—is mastered, it may be freely employed on any appropriate Mission.

ATTACK PATTERNS

These techniques are specifically designed to counter the Tau's technological advantages and to work to preserve humans from the xenos influence.

Close the Gap

Cost: 250 XP
Action: Full Action
Activation Cost: 2
Sustained: No
Effects: Because of their weapon technologies, Tau units tend to favour long-ranged combat engagements. While Space Marines are generally capable of matching the Tau in such battles, the forces of the Imperium garner a substantial advantage when they can close with Tau forces to employ their superior close-combat techniques. In these situations, the Tau are unable to fully utilise their ranged weapons, and often succumb to the superior capabilities of the Achilus Crusade.

Deathwatch members active within the Canis Salient have worked extensively to develop new techniques that work towards eliminating the Tau ranged advantage. One such technique involves squad mates working together to move towards the Tau swiftly and then knocking the xenos out of position. In addition to increasing the opportunity for melee combat, this often has the additional function of preventing an alien from effectively targeting a valuable Imperial resource.

When a Space Marine activates this ability, he and all squad members within Support Range may use a Full Move Action to run towards an opponent and immediately execute a Manoeuvre Action. Characters with the Sprint Talent may also utilise this ability during the Full Move.

Improvement: If the Battle-Brother is Rank 4 or higher, all characters receive a +10 bonus to their Manoeuvre Action. If he is Rank 6 or higher, all characters may add an additional 4 metres to the distance they move.

Identify and Eliminate

Cost: 250 XP
Action: Full Action
Activation Cost: 1
Sustained: Yes
Effects: The Tau are particularly adept at designing technological devices that are capable of blending in effectively with their environment. The best known of these are the various iterations of their Stealth Suits that are used both for scouting and to launch unexpected attacks upon their enemies. These suits are far more effective concealment than any comparable man-portable Imperial gear. Typically, Imperial forces are only able to identify the presence of these Stealth Suits when their systems begin to interfere with the normal function of standard sensor systems.

A few Deathwatch Kill-teams have developed strategies that take advantage of the sensor interference caused by the Stealth Suits. While limited in its efficacy, if several Space Marines work together to identify the source of the interference, they can begin to triangulate and narrow down the location of the hidden opponents. This substantially reduces the region that must be searched to locate a Stealth Suit, but it is by no means a sure method for successful elimination of the xenos intruders.

When a Space Marine activates this ability, he may immediately make an Awareness Test to try to identify the location of any concealed enemies, including Tau Stealth Suits; see **DEATHWATCH** page 367. For each squad member within Support Range, he receives a +5 bonus to the attempt. If he succeeds by two or more degrees of success, he confirms the presence and reduces the Weapon Skill and Ballistic Skill penalty caused by the Stealth Field's Active Mode for all squad members to −20.

Improvement: If the Battle-Brother is Rank 5 or more, then the Weapon Skill and Ballistics Skill penalty is reduced by 10 for each degree of success on the Awareness Test.

Terminate the Machine

Cost: 100 XP
Action: Half Action
Activation Cost: 1
Sustained: Yes
Effects: Among their many heresies, the Tau also embrace the blasphemous notion of synthetic intelligence. Throughout their culture and even on the battlefield, the Tau employ countless drones as servants. These devices bear no living components. Instead, they are controlled by purely synthetic intelligences, designed to obey their xenos masters in all things. Similarly, their vehicles and buildings utilise sapient systems, some of which are far more sophisticated than the animalistic drones.

Such devices are anathema to the ways of the Imperial Cult and the Adeptus Mechanicus. They provide yet another justification for the Achilus Crusade to cleanse the Canis Salient of this hideous taint. Extended exposure to these entities might breed acceptance. That attitude could only lead to future damnation.

Some Space Marines have studied samples of Tau Drones under the tutelage of Techmarines and Magos of the Adeptus Mechanicus. Their study has focussed closely upon the most vulnerable portions of these devices, particularly those components which store ammunition and fuel. When a Battle-Brother trained in this technique activates this ability, he and all squad members in range become far more adept at targeting these components. All of the Space Marines' weapons count as inflicting Explosive Damage against Hordes of Drones. If the weapons already inflict Explosive Damage, add +2 magnitude damage to the attack instead.

Improvement: If the Battle-Brother is Rank 4 or higher, the Penetration value of all weapons fired against Drones is increased by 2.

DEFENSIVE STANCES

The Tau are particularly fond of delaying combat actions by entering into additional negotiations. Within the Canis Salient, some Space Marines have identified techniques well suited to resisting as well as exploiting this facet of combat with these xenos.

Brace for Charge

Cost: 250 XP
Action: Reaction
Activation Cost: 1
Sustained: No
Effects: Some of the auxiliary units that work with the Tau forces are particularly focussed upon melee combat. This provides a potent addition to the ranged weaponry that the main Tau forces favour. In this way, the different xenos breeds effectively complement one another, representing a grave threat to Imperial Forces. When defenders are engaged by these combined forces, if they choose to enter close combat with the auxiliaries, the long-ranged Tau units are able to freely move and target more vulnerable Imperial assets.

To overcome this issue, some Deathwatch Kill-teams have developed methods for laying down a substantial volley of fire against incoming hordes at the last possible instant. This often succeeds in either blunting or eliminating the charge attack. Consequently, the Battle-Brothers and any supporting Imperial forces are able to avoid melee combat and maintain their rate of fire.

When a Space Marine activates this ability, he and any squad members within Support Range may immediately execute a Suppressing Fire action. If the acting unit is pinned by this action, it is unable to complete its attack actions.

Improvement: If the Battle-Brother is Rank 4 or higher, all acting characters gain the +20 Full Auto Burst attack bonus on the Suppressing Fire Action. If the Battle-Brother is Rank 6 or higher, the targets of the attack suffer a –5 penalty to their Pinning Test for each point of Magnitude eliminated by Suppressing Fire.

Parlay Terms

Cost: 300 XP
Action: Full Action
Activation Cost: 3
Sustained: Yes
Effects: Tau philosophical beliefs are, in many ways, opposed to unnecessary conflict. While the xenos remain anathema to the Imperium as a whole, the raging conflicts within the Jericho Reach have led to a number of situations in which these normally opposed forces have entered into ceasefires and even temporary alliances. This has led to a tremendous degree of uncertainty within some battlefronts, as Tau and Imperial Forces alternate between violent conflict and peaceful negotiations.

Members of the Deathwatch who are active within the Canis Salient have identified this issue and developed techniques to exploit it. Key among these are methods to build a false sense of trust with the xenos, so that they lower their defences and may be easily slaughtered. Understanding of these methods is dependent upon a basic grasp of the Tau psychology, so that it may be fully manipulated.

When a Space Marine activates this ability, he may immediately make a **Challenging (+0) Command Test** against the leader of the opposing force. Each additional squad member within support range adds a +5 bonus to the Test. If successful, the opposing forces immediately cease attacking to attempt to negotiate with the Kill-team. If the Space Marines resume combat after a successful test, the xenos count as Surprised. This ability may be used no more than once per encounter.

Improvement: If the Battle-Brother is Rank 5 or more, the bonus for additional squad members is increased to +10. If the Rank 7 or more, the xenos suffer a –10 penalty to resist the interaction test.

Virtue of Ignorance

Cost: 250 XP
Action: Reaction
Activation Cost: 1
Sustained: Yes
Effects: The Tau always favour a strategy that preserves lives, often with the intention that survivors may be brainwashed into an alliance with the xenos forces. This attitude actually forms a substantial portion of the race's combat tactics. Whenever possible, these aliens use whatever means necessary to persuade their foes to enter into peaceable discussions so that loss of life on both sides might be prevented. Their grasp of human psychology is such that, even amongst Space Marines, these xenos still manage to enjoy the occasional success.

Overcoming such treachery requires extensive mental fortitude. By interacting as a squad, Deathwatch Kill-team members can remind one another of the treachery of the xenos and the purity of their cause. In this way, they become far less susceptible to the seductive lies of the alien.

When a Space Marine activates this ability, he and all squad members within Support Range receive a +20 bonus to all attempts to resist interaction skills initiated by xenos.

Improvement: If the Battle-Brother is Rank 5 or higher, he may immediately issue a counter argument that attempts to persuade the xenos of the fallacy of their arguments. This counts as an Intimidate test, which receives a bonus of +5 for each squad member within Support Range. At Rank 7 or higher, the resistance bonus increases to +10 per squad member within Support Range.

CANIS OATHS

As Space Marines engage the xenos of the Canis Salient, they must focus on the purity of the Imperial word and the damnation that the xenos present with their blasphemous beliefs. While the Tau weapons endanger the body, their alien understandings may corrupt the mind and the soul. These Oaths present various combat techniques that Kill-teams within this region have developed to overcome this unique range of threats.

OATH OF DENIAL

The Tau forces within the Canis Salient are both well established and well equipped. As their forces maintain a presence on worlds that rightfully belong to the Imperium, they continue to exploit the natural wealth of these planets. In so doing, they steal materials needed by the Achilus Crusade and take valuable resources away from every citizen of the Imperium. This injustice must be stopped, so that the xenos might be forced to stretch their supply lines to a place beyond the Jericho Reach.

Cost: 250 XP
Prerequisite: Techmarine, Devastator Marine, or Tactical Marine.
Effect: Kill-teams that choose to swear this oath begin by reciting the sacred mantras of detonation under the direction of a Deathwatch Techmarine. This is followed by intense memorisation of the architecture, vulnerabilities, and defensive capabilities for all known structures and combat vehicles located within the expected combat zone. Finally, explosive ordnance is prepared and issued to each Battle-Brother in preparation for the mission, in accordance with the ancient rites. All Kill-team members receive a +10 bonus for Demolitions Tests and a +10 bonus to Ballistics skill when using grenades.

Squad Mode Abilities: Identify and Eliminate, Tank Buster, Terminate the Machine.

TABLE 2-1: CANIS OATHS

Oath	Prerequisite	Benefit	Squad Mode Abilities
Oath of Denial	Techmarine, Devastator Marine, or Tactical Marine	+10 Bonus for Demolitions, Grenades, and Heavy Weapons	Identify and Eliminate, Tank Buster, Terminate the Machine
Oath of Adherence	Librarian or Tactical Marine	Reduce all Cohesion Costs by 1	Virtue of Ignorance, Soak Fire, Fire Support
Oath of Resolution	Tactical Marine, Apothecary, or Librarian	+10 Bonus to all Scrutiny Tests	Parlay Terms, Virtue of Ignorance, Tactical Spacing
Oath of Xenocide	Apothecary, Assault Marine, or Devastator Marine	All bolt weapons gain Devastating (1)	Close the Gap, Brace for Charge, Bolter Assault

OATH OF ADHERENCE

The Tau forces are driven by their ritualistic beliefs to spread their philosophy—just as they spread their presence—like an infection across the galaxy. Only through dedication to the Imperium and adherence to its doctrine can the human citizens of the Imperium hope to resist the xenos influence. Understanding and loyalty provide a path to salvation for those who might otherwise come under the sway of these heretical beliefs. The Imperium depends upon assistance from the Deathwatch and Inquisition forces to stamp out threats, so that the Imperium might continue to safely shepherd their Imperial flock.

Cost: 300 XP

Prerequisite: Librarian or Tactical Marine.

Effect: As the Battle-Brothers prepare for a mission using this Oath, they focus their purification efforts upon renewing their vows of adherence and loyalty to the Imperium. As each piece of armour is donned and each weapon cleansed, the inscriptions and blessings are renewed. With their devotion renewed, the squad's sense of camaraderie and loyalty to one another is also refreshed. For the duration of any mission that invokes this Oath, the squad may reduce all Cohesion Costs by 1 point to a minimum of 1 point.

Squad Mode Abilities: Virtue of Ignorance, Soak Fire, Fire Support.

OATH OF RESOLUTION

The Imperium is dedicated to the annihilation of all xenos, but the resources are not always at hand to undertake such a weighty task. Because of this, even those with the most zealous hatred of the alien must sometimes acknowledge the tactical necessity of parlay. Many can even accept the necessity of an extended treaty given sufficient extenuating circumstances. As the Achilus Crusade continues to face fierce resistance in both the Orpheus and Acheros Salients, such exceptions have been made more and more often with Tau forces. The conditions of these pacts are always consistent with Ecclesiarchy standards, but they always leave a feeling of contagion in the minds and souls of those involved.

Cost: 250 XP

Prerequisite: Tactical Marine, Apothecary, or Librarian.

Effect: When a Kill-team undertakes a mission against Tau forces, the Inquisition must initially research and analyse any treaty agreements that are in place within the contested region. As part of their preparations, the Battle-Brothers must review the terms, so that they realise what actions are permissible without compromising the treaties. Within the confines of the Jericho Reach, the Deathwatch must concede negotiation rights to the authorities of the Achilus Crusade, so they seldom have the authority to delineate or alter these terms. In spite of this fact, the Tau are often interested in attempting to refine their agreements through negotiations with these Space Marines. When a Kill-team undertakes this oath, they receive a +10 Bonus to all Scrutiny Tests.

Squad Mode Abilities: Parlay Terms, Virtue of Ignorance, Tactical Spacing.

OATH OF XENOCIDE

Within the Canis Salient, the various worlds under Tau influence maintain a broad range of relations with the forces of the Achilus Crusade. In some of these systems, the two powers have reached a level of understanding so that they tolerate one another's presence. In others, the forces are engaged in all out war. It is these latter systems that are most often relevant to Deathwatch Kill-teams. While units affiliated with the Crusade are best suited for negotiations with the xenos, there are no other forces so capable of eliminating the alien threat as the Battle-Brothers.

Cost: 250 XP

Prerequisite: Apothecary, Assault Marine, or Devastator Marine.

Effect: Kill-teams that swear this Oath begin their preparation with a thorough review of xenos atrocities. Images of systems wiped out by the xenos taint, individual acts of barbarism, and humans forced into servitude are ingrained in their memories through hypno-conditioning. Often, emotional content focussed on hatred and anger is implanted at the same time. This combination unleashes each Battle-Brother's fury, so that it overpowers all other emotions. With this oath in place, the Space Marines are prepared to annihilate their foe, attacking with such fervour it leaves their opponent reeling.

As the Battle-Brothers focus their anger into their weapons, each shot becomes even more deadly. For the duration of the mission, all of their bolt weapons gain the Felling (1) weapon quality.

Squad Mode Abilities: Close the Gap, Brace for Charge, Bolter Assault.

CRUSADE ASSETS

"He might be as mad as a cut Grox but I'll give old Ebongrave credit for keeping the Crusade armouries full; I swear half the equipment used in the Crusade must end up here. Though I guess you can never have too many tanks, as my old sergeant use to say…"

–Guardsman Phen Taga, 51st Wrath Regiment (MIA)

The Deathwatch can call upon a wide variety of support within the Canis Salient to aid them on their missions. Many of these units and assets are specially developed to deal with the Tau and the way they wage war, such as the Canis Delegations of Imperial envoys and diplomats trained in xeno relations (such as they are to the Imperium) or specially trained tech-priests with a knowledge of the blasphemous technology of the Tau and how best to combat it. Others are the result of Lord Commander Ebongrave and his paranoia over the sedition upon his worlds and the treacherous shadow he perceives over his staff. Such support includes the Eyes of Wrath which seek out rebellion on dozens of worlds or the skilled jailers and interrogators which know just how to wring the truth from a captured Tau warrior.

At the GM's discretion he can allow players to acquire assets for their missions from **Table 2-2: Canis Salient Assets**. These assets represent Salient allies, specialised equipment and even obscure information that the Kill-team can acquire using Requisition in the same way that they would select weapons and armour from the Deathwatch. Each asset has its own description and game effect as detailed below and has a set Requisition cost and Renown requirement. For more details on Requisition and Renown see page 138-139 of the **DEATHWATCH** rulebook.

TABLE 2-2: CANIS SALIENT ASSETS

Asset	Requisition Cost	Renown
Agents of Wrath	15	Respected
Captured Tech	20	Respected
Imperial Envoy	20	Respected
Mechanicus Tech-Adept	15	—
Tau Prisoners	20	Distinguished
Xeno-Archaeologist	15	—

AGENTS OF WRATH

In addition to tapping into Lord Commander Ebongrave's vast network of spies, certain privileged individuals (or cunning ones) can use the system more aggressively and actually deploy agents to worlds on which he has an interest. The Eyes of Wrath is a data gathering network spread across the worlds under Imperial control within the Canis Salient and comprises billions of pic feeds, vox traps and modified servitors and servo-skulls. Its control and extension is largely governed from Wrath and only expands at the behest of those most trusted to the Lord Commander. This asset allows the Kill-team to use Agents of Wrath to spy on a certain individual or location, even outside of the planets directly under the control of the Imperium. This does take time though and the further flung the world, the longer it will take to establish, as determined by the GM. Once in place, the spy will allow the PCs up to date information on the subject, or, if left to his devices, can gather background data on the target. The exact nature of this information is up to the GM, but should at the very least provide some useful data for the PCs.

CAPTURED TECH

In very rare circumstances, desperation among the armies of the Imperium forces them to turn a foe's own weapons back upon their creators. Such tech is almost impossible to reliably control or repair, so it usually only good for a single use and usually restricted to equipment such as atmospheric craft or power generators rather than weapons which are difficult to use with any degree of safety. This asset represents a captured piece of Tau tech that the Kill-team can employ in their mission, such as an Orca Dropship or pulse-generator. The primary use of such a piece of tech will either be subterfuge to infiltrate a Tau defensive zone or as a one shot weapon to power an alien device or set of a large explosion. The exact device the Kill-team has acquired is up to the GM, and how they use it is up to the PCs, but in addition to any other effects it will provide an additional 3d10 Kill Markers to a single objective when used against the Tau.

IMPERIAL ENVOY

Many Imperial commanders believe that diplomacy is the last resort of a weak and the defeated foe, and has no place when fighting the alien. But even such men would agree that diplomacy does have it uses, and against foes like the Tau can be of benefit to the Crusade. This asset places a skilled Imperial Envoy at the disposal of the Kill-team, with access to a support team of negotiators and orators. It is up to the PCs how and when they choose to employ the Envoy, and it is up to the GM to determine how effective they are and how receptive are those they deal with. However, using the diplomatic core should at least improve a target's Disposition (see **DEATHWATCH** page 276) by one or two levels. An Envoy is not restricted to dealing with the Tau, and can represent the Kill-team in any setting (provided those they want to deal with are not completely hostile), such as on human worlds or even within the structure of the Imperium's military.

MECHANICUS TECH-ADEPT

Alien technology is anathema to the Adeptus Mechanicus and a blight upon the holy name of the Machine God. Despite this, there are those among the orders of Mars whose task it is to understand the function of such cursed objects, so that the Imperium's armies might better know how to combat their foes and overcome diabolical xenos weaponry. In the Canis Salient, members of these orders work to defeat Tau technology and help to counter its effects on the Imperial War effort. A Tech-Adept specialised in Tau technology provides the Kill-team with the Forbidden Knowledge Skill (Xenos Tech) +20, which may be used at any time during the mission. In addition, whenever the Battle-Brothers must interact with a piece of Tau technology, they may add +20 to the test. Whether this help comes from the actual presence of a Tech-Adept or a specially crafted servitor in the care of the PCs, is up to the GM.

TAU PRISONERS

In the years of fighting between the Crusade and the Tau, numerous prisoners have been taken by both sides. While in the Imperium's case, many of these aliens spend their final days in Lord Commander Ebongrave's interrogation chambers or those of the Inquisition, some are held as hostages, either because they are important or skilled. This asset grants the Kill-team control over on or more Tau prisoners of some worth (the exact nature of the prisoner is up to the GM), who may be exchanged or used as a bargaining chip when dealing with the Tau. Generally the Tau value the lives of their soldiers, especially those of rank or from the higher castes, and will trade for them if the terms are fair. The exact worth of such prisoners and how the Kill-team employ them to complete their mission is up to the GM and the PCs, but it should at the very least give them additional leverage (equal to a +20 on a test) in a diplomatic situation.

XENO-ARCHAEOLOGIST

The Jericho Reach is an ancient sector of space settled by alien races long before the arrival of man. Among its secrets are numerous tomb worlds and scatterings of alien artefacts as well as anomalies like the Black Reef; legacies of ancient wars and terrible catastrophes. Within the Canis Salient there are numerous worlds that still bear the mark of these long forgotten empires, many of which are of keen interest to both the Inquisition and the Deathwatch, for what knowledge they might be able to provide the Imperium. This asset gives the Kill-team access to a xeno-archaeologist team to help in the exploration or recovery of alien artefacts. The exact makeup of the team is up to the GM and could include explorator tech-priests, servitors, guardsmen or simple adepts and scholars. Whoever is in the team, it will give the PCs access to all Common, Scholastic and Forbidden Lore skills with the word Xenos in their title. In addition, the team might, at the GM's discretion, have specialised equipment which will be of aid to the Kill-team.

Canis Salient Campaigns

"Never trust diplomatic solutions and amiable truces. They are just different words for war, and another way of cheating us of victory. Many are the brave men which have lost far more to a treacherous peace than an honest conflict."

–Rear Admiral Redglave Holast, Wrath System Fleet

The war against the Tau has brought new challenges and new perils for the Imperium since the young race's emergence on the eastern fringe. Unlike the naked aggression and mindless rage of so many of the God-Emperor's foes, the Tau often meet force with reason, subtlety and manipulation. Regions like the Canis Salient in the Jericho Reach are a prime example of this kind of unconventional warfare and duplicitous dealing, as the rolling juggernaut of the Achilus Crusade continues its bitter struggle to destroy the Velk'han Sept and those worlds that have fallen prey to their false alliance and lies of hope. Against the careful hand and advanced technology of the Tau, the Imperial forces under the paranoid leadership of Lord Ebongrave have found themselves divided and fractured by a foe bent not on their annihilation but rather their assimilation. On the battlefield, the Tau are often more than a match for the Imperial Guard, though they lack the latter's numbers, but it is in the council chambers of planetary lords and the back alleyways of far flung Imperial worlds that their true malevolence can be felt. It is in these places that agents of the Tau Empire spread sedition and undermine Imperial morale with promises of a place in their glorious collective and the chance at a future free from the yoke of the God-Emperor's tyranny.

For the Battle-Brothers of the Deathwatch, the nature of the Tau presents unique dangers when fighting in the Canis Salient. As often as not, they will be tasked with diplomatic missions or other politically motivated undertakings rather than simple assassinations or open conflicts. This can be uncertain ground for Space Marines, bred to fight and devoted to the teaching of the Emperor and the destruction of all xenos, and they may face instances during which their enemies cannot easily be identified by their allegiance or opposition to the Imperium or the race to which they belong. In these cases, the Battle-Brothers must use their wits as much as their boltguns and choose their friends, and their foes, with care, lest their actions or acts of violence provoke unforeseen consequences.

Running Canis Salient Campaigns

The Canis Salient offers both players and GMs a diverse and unique setting for their adventures and a chance to experience a different kind of war not to be found in either of the other two major warzones of the Reach. What offers this varied kind of play is the nature of Tau themselves and the unique way in which the grey-skinned aliens wage war. While it is entirely possible to face cadres of Tau warriors on the battlefield in one of the dozens of Salient battlefields, the real danger they present comes from the ideals they hold dear and the insidious ideas they spread to human worlds, dividing populations and eroding the Imperium's grip on the Sector. The Tau are an empire of reason as much as might, and just as the vanguard of a great host will ride before it, so too do the diplomats and envoys of the Tau Water Caste try to maintain open communications with the Imperium, and its worlds, even as the Tau armies march to war. Thus PCs may find themselves actually dealing face-to-face with the Tau without it descending into bloodshed and war.

To capture the unique nature of the Canis Salient, and get an idea of how conducting missions against the Tau can influence or change his campaign, the GM can use some of the themes presented below. These themes represent some of the core ideals and aspects of the Salient and why it differs from either of the other two. When creating adventures set within the Salient, the GM can use these themes as a guide to give him an idea of what kinds of challenges a Kill-team operating against the Tau might face, as well as drawing inspiration from them for his own campaigns.

Diplomatic Solutions

Unlike the ancient Imperium, clinging violently onto its vast and fractious domain, the Tau are a young race, new to the galaxy and full of both hope and optimism for the future of their kind. While they often employ their fleets and cadres of battlesuited warriors to hold their domains and expand their systems, sections of their empire have been secured by the expert skills of their Water Caste (the Tau teachers, envoys and diplomats), weaving together a complex web of treaties and pacts with other alien races and worlds. This has created a vast cosmopolitan alliance within the Tau empire, and though the Tau remain firmly at the top of the hierarchy, those who have sworn to join with them to support the Greater Good (the Tau philosophy of unity under a common cause and solidarity of all races) are placated by their belief in equality and unity, sold to them as part of the diplomacy used to win their trust. This is a key difference between the Tau and the Imperium, and while mankind uses the Imperial Creed and devotion to the God-Emperor to demand obedience in its citizens, the Tau offer a chance to stand at their sides and share their vision of the future as a partner race rather than mere cogs in a vast machine.

It is little wonder then that when the Imperium and Tau first met, their differing ideologies caused just as much violent conflict as the fact that the Tau were foul xenos. The Tau considered mankind a prime candidate for induction into the empire, and in fact before they became aware of the scope and size of the Imperium, numerous human worlds were given that honour. Even now, many years later, the Tau continue to use diplomacy as a primary tool when dealing with the Imperium, often ready to listen to human leaders or make alliances even in the midst of full blown conflicts. Mankind's fractious nature has always been a boon to the Tau in this respect, and for every dozen warlords, Imperial officers or planetary governors that refuse to deal with the aliens (usually for fear of reprisals and the attention of the Ordo Xenos) there will be one dissatisfied with the yoke of the Imperium or the excessive tithes of the Administratum and who sees an opportunity for his own freedom in the promises of the grey-skinned aliens. These "traitors" to the God-Emperor, and the opportunities they present the Tau, have been enough for the aliens to aggressively pursue diplomatic missions across the eastern fringe and all along the borders of their empire. They aim to slowly erode the Imperium's control over its far flung sectors and worlds distant from the direct intervention of its armies.

Among these regions are the Jericho Reach and the holdings of the Velk'han Sept. Though isolated from the rest of the empire, Velk'han is nevertheless of interest to the Tau ruling castes and its survival considered important. For this reason, among others, the Tau Water Caste is heavily active in the Sept, using its influence and skill to both cement the Tau borders as well as expand to other sympathetic worlds within the Sector.

A War of Words

The Imperium has no shortage of rhetoric when it comes to aliens like the Tau, and every honest Imperial citizen knows the dangers such xenos represent. For those far behind the lines or isolated from the blazing edge of the Crusade's advances into the Salient, the Tau are considered, if they are considered at all, as equally vile as the Tyranid or the Ork in the threat they pose to humanity's survival. Those who live in the shadow of the Tau Sept or face them on the battlefield may think differently, especially if they have previously faced the mindless bloodshed of the Stigmartus or the alien hunger of Hive Fleet Dagon. This is the major concern of Lord Commander Ebongrave—that lies spread by the Tau and their offers of unity and treaty with mankind will lead to sedition and desertion within the ranks of his men. It is a fear so grave that it has led him to excessive acts such as the quarantining of whole worlds. Whether or not such a threat of mass desertion really exists, Ebongrave maintains a constant and brutal propaganda war against the Tau, reminding his soldiers and citizens at every turn of the evils of this treacherous alien race and the false peace they offer. It is a buffer that the gentle pressure of the Tau philosophy seems to be constantly eroding, prompting Ebongrave and his propaganda ministries and information brokers to push back even harder with stronger campaigns demonizing the Tau and reminding every citizen of his duty to the God-Emperor.

The GM can use this ever present and pervasive Imperial propaganda on worlds across the Canis Salient, reminding the PCs of Lord Ebongrave's constant fear of the diplomatic advances of the Tau, and to a lesser extent the dangers of real sedition among marginal Imperial worlds or those recently brought back into the Imperium by the Achilus Crusade. Posters will show menacing Tau warriors, covered in the blood of innocent citizens, their alien features exaggerated with an all too human sneer on their features, usually accompanied by words like "It Could Happen Here," or "Beware the Insidious Xenos!" In addition to posters and slogans scrawled across walls, vox-criers are often employed to wander town streets, preaching warnings against the Tau. These augmented messengers of Ebongrave paint a dark picture of life under the Tau from their vox-mouths. In their words, the Tau are brutal slavers, subjugating worlds into their cruel empire, an empire where they are the masters supreme and all other races mere cattle to build their cities or die in their endless bloody wars. The illusion of freedom that they offer is nothing more than an invisible collar of servitude, which once donned cannot be taken off. Worst of all, to serve the Tau is to turn your back on the God-Emperor and damn yourself in not just this life but for all eternity.

Keep Your Enemies Close

Despite the propaganda of Lord Ebongrave, or his fears for the loyalty of his men (real and imagined) the Imperium does resort to diplomacy itself when brute force either cannot or will not get them what they want. Like the Tau, the Imperium maintains a diplomatic core of Imperial envoys and military liaisons that will deal with elements of the Water Caste when needed, even during open engagements between humanity and the Tau. For the most part Ebongrave is unaware of these dealings (while he does not know of the extent to which some of his officers deal with the Tau, he does benefit from the intelligence they garner, and believes it to come from more conventional techniques) and it is his sub-commanders, or those in the field, who utilise these channels of communication as a means of spying on the Tau or in the hopes of feeding them false information. Legions of adepts work constantly for the Imperial forces, going over the transcripts of any diplomatic meeting with the Tau, sifting through the (often poorly) translated words looking for clues as to the aliens true intent. The same adepts work with the envoys, crafting questions for them to ask or topics for them to deal with, so they might glean a little more information. This wealth of data is then checked against Tau communication intercepts and information gained from the interrogation of Tau prisoners to create a more informed picture of the Tau's military intentions or the disposition of their forces. Sometimes the Ordo Xenos many even work with the Imperial diplomats and their agents and share their own information on Tau activities, though usually only when it suits their purposes.

This air of paranoia and distrust in any diplomatic dealings the Imperium has with the Tau can be used to colour non-combat encounters the players have with the empire. The GM can have NPCs, especially those loyal to Ebongrave's sub-commanders or working for the Eyes of Wrath (Ebongrave's spy network), try to use the PCs to get information from the Tau they meet, or offer them additional mission objectives beyond those set down by the Deathwatch. While Imperial Guard and Naval commanders have no direct control over the Ordo Xenos or the Kill-teams of the Deathwatch, it will not stop them or their underlings from trying to exploit a Kill-team's presence in this way. This can put the PCs in a tough situation if they are following a directive to aid or support the Tau in some way (usually for the secretive objectives of the Inquisition), for even the slightest hint of treachery (such as agents stealing data or documents from the Tau) could lead to violence.

A Reasonable Foe

Unlike so many of the foes the Battle-Brothers will face during their secondment to the Deathwatch, the Tau have a value for the lives of their warriors and are willing to seek other ways of resolving conflicts if it would mean avoiding an unacceptable level of casualties. Whereas the Tyranids or the Orks will throw their warriors into the fray with little regard for appalling loss of life, and the minions of the Dark Gods are more than willing to spill their own blood for their masters, the Tau see no great glory in such costly victories. Even the callousness with which the Imperium throws away the lives of its soldiers has given more than one Tau commander pause, and made him question the sanity of a race that is so ready to die for a leader practically dead Himself. Neither are the Tau as obsessed with holding ground or making defiant last stands as their Imperial counterparts—their ideology does not exalt duty unto death in the same way as the followers of the God-Emperor. A Tau commander will be more than willing to retreat, saving the strength of his men and machines, only to return later when the conditions are more favourable to victory.

All of this is because at their heart, the Tau value reason and embrace a military and diplomatic flexibility largely unknown within the Imperium and practically non-existent among the other races and adversaries of the Jericho Reach. For the Imperium, this means the Tau often act or react in ways that can seem strange or unexpected, such as sudden withdrawals or even offering truces when an Imperial commander would press an attack despite the costs. Mistakenly, sometimes the actions of the Tau are seen by Imperial soldiers as cowardice and an unwillingness to lay down their lives for their empire in the way every warrior of the Imperium is ready (in theory) to die for the God-Emperor. Seasoned officers and elite organisations like the Deathwatch know better and have long since stopped underestimating the Tau or doubting their resolve when it comes to matters concerning their empire and the ideal of the Greater Good.

Truces and Treaties

Much of the border with the Tau within the Jericho Reach is shored up with truces and treaties as much as it is with the ships of the Imperial Navy and the legions of the Imperial Guard. While there exists no official diplomatic stance between the Imperium and the Tau Empire (the official line is that the Tau, as xenos, have no right to exist within the Imperium of Man), in many of the system bordering Tau held worlds across the Canis Salient, planetary governors will maintain truces with the aliens. In most cases there is no official record of such treaties or pacts and the fact that a world or region allows

the Tau to co-exist is an unspoken agreement. These areas of cease-fire usually only endure until the Achilus Crusade takes a renewed interest in a region, and then men that were once happy to leave the xenos alone as long as they themselves were left alone will "rediscover" their fervour and hatred of the enemies of mankind and once again take up arms against their neighbours. The more isolated worlds will sometimes formalise such treaties. These treaties are not an open alliance with the Tau, but rather an understanding that both races would adopt a stance of non-aggression, leaving the other to its own worlds and regions. As the Crusade wages its war across the the region, little distinction is seen between such treaties and open sedition against the God-Emperor, and though many planetary governments try hard to hide evidence of their accord with the Tau, the Inquisition fills many cells with such traitors.

The GM can use the concept of truces and treaties with the Tau to play on the PCs' sense of honour, or to complicate dealing with outlying Imperium worlds and their governments. This will be especially true when dealing with people that lived in the Reach before the arrival of the Crusade. For many worlds, the presence of the Tau was seen as a buffer against the more aggressive and dangerous aliens of the Sector, and while they harboured no love for the empire, they were content to "live and let live" (usually because there was little they could do to match the Tau even if they wanted to, rather than for any deep moral reasons). As the PCs travel farther from the core Crusade worlds of the Salient, they may encounter more and more of these kinds of peoples and cultures. This can lead to conflict with locals and Tau alike if they choose to attack the Tau on such a world or if they discover a world's past dealings with the Tau, causing them to question the loyalties of the local humans.

Strange Alliances

On more than one occasion, the Imperium has made temporary alliances with the Tau in the face of a greater threat. Rarely is such an alliance the result of careful planning by either side or do they represent any true joint military operation. Rather they are usually desperate coalitions against aggressive and numerically superior foes or simply both forces engaging a common foe at the same time in the same place. These alliances are also fragile creations at the best of times and prone to collapse as soon as the danger is past or conflict averted, and in some cases less honourable commanders may even take the opportunity for a few opening salvos before the other side is aware the truce has ended. Despite this, the Tau remain one of the few alien races the Imperium can trust even this far, and one whose presence can be stomached long enough to face a common threat. In the Jericho Reach, the Tau have more than once been ignored in favour of more dire enemies, and in recent years, with the arrival of Hive Fleet Dagon and the pressure it has placed on the Crusade's resources and manpower, local Imperial commanders have more than once accepted aid from or alliance with the aliens to deal with a tendril of the Tyranid menace.

The concept of Tau as allies can provide the GM with lots of interesting avenues and plots to pursue in his campaigns. Especially given that the player characters are

members of the Deathwatch, an organisation that exists for the purpose of hunting down and eradicating xenos threats, the possibility of teaming up with the Tau, even temporarily, can force them to question their devotion or even what they think they know about the foes they are fighting. It can also give the enemy a more human face, and characters might even find themselves respecting and admiring their allies or becoming intrigued by their tech and strange philosophies. The GM can use these kinds of relationships to have recurring Tau NPCs appearing in adventures, sometimes as allies and sometimes as adversaries, becoming all the more rich and meaningful to the players because they are not simple mindless killers or unreasoning alien horrors. These kinds of encounters can also be an excuse for the Inquisition to put pressure on the Battle-Brothers, or even question their loyalties (probably only by insinuation) for fear they have somehow become infected by the alien's perverse ideals and their adherence to the "Greater Good."

REIGN OF MADNESS

All those that spend any time in the Canis Salient are inevitably touched by the paranoia and madness of Lord Commander Ebongrave. It is a miasma that pervades the Sector and a shadow that hangs over the heads of all who serve in the Imperial forces of the Salient. Even by the bloodthirsty and callous standards of some Imperial commanders, Ebongrave is dangerously unstable and prone to actions that can be as horrific for his own men as for his foes. Those close to Ebongrave, and those in the higher echelons of the Imperial Guard and Imperial Navy that serve under him, have learnt to tread carefully around the man, lest they provoke his anger and suffer the consequences. This can often be as swift as it is brutal and more than one commander has "disappeared" for speaking out against the Lord Commander, or when even the barest hint of sedition is cast upon their names. Those who remain know well enough not to ask too many questions about those who vanish suddenly from their posts in this way, though rumours persist of remote prison colonies and hidden gaols where these dissidents live out their lives cut off from the Crusade and the Imperium. It is a state of affairs that has fostered immense distrust among Ebongrave's generals and those beneath them in the chain of command, and has doubtless cost the lives of Imperial solders because an officer was more concerned with appearing loyal than acting on his own initiative even when he knew full well an action or tactic would meet with failure, destruction and death.

Ebongrave's madness is not restricted to the military arms of the Crusade alone and every world within the Salient has been touched in some way by his actions. For many this means a constant fear of the Lord Commander's enforcers, who scour Imperial worlds for signs of taint or sedition against the God-Emperor, though in practice hunt down and deal with anyone and anything Ebongrave feels is a threat to his power. Ebongrave also imposes his own laws on many worlds within the Salient, playing with the lives of their populations like a child might play with his toys. This can mean that in places he feels are becoming breeding pits for rebellion, there will be harsh laws against public gatherings, movement after dark or outside urban zones and a heightened enforcer presence (usually formed from conscripted local gangers or ex-guardsmen who revel in bullying and intimidating in the name of the Lord Commander). In other places, though, a rumour or whim might cause Ebongrave to issue a mandate to its people. For example, on the feral world of Sybalos, when a pair of brothers killed an Imperial envoy, it was decreed that no brothers of the blood could be raised together, forcing male children to be displaced and taken from their mothers, all because of the imagined threat they might pose once they came of age.

For organisations like the Inquisition and the Deathwatch, Ebongrave's erratic behaviour can be both a boon and a burden, and has at times afforded them more freedom to act within the Salient (the Lord Commander encouraging them to hunt down his foes), though at others has placed them within the crosshairs of the mad lord. Largely though, the greatest danger to those from outside the region is the unpredictable nature of the aid and support they will receive from the forces of the Crusade. Local commanders are usually more concerned with how their own leaders will view their actions, and while an Inquisitor or a Kill-team will only be around for a short time, the shadow of Lord Commander Ebongrave will remain.

Imaginary Threats

Many of the threats Lord Commander Ebongrave responds to seem to exist only in his own mind. Even in a reactionary and xenophobic organisation like the Achilus Crusade, his actions have drawn the attention of Lord Militant Tetrarchus and the Crusade's highest commanders. Only his continued military successes and his illustrious history have kept him from being removed from command by Tetrarchus, that and the simple fact that the Warmaster has precious few commanders of Ebongrave's calibre and a war on three fronts against three very determined and capable foes. Thus Ebongrave is given largely free reign within his Salient to command as he sees fit, even if that might mean dispatching battlegroups to put down rebellions "before they begin" or arresting prominent members of his own military and the Salient planetary governments on suspicions about their activities. It seems Ebongrave's greatest fear is that somehow there is a grand conspiracy against him. Be it an alien plot or the work of his own generals, he sees usurpers at every turn and traitors hiding in every shadow. The result of these largely imaginary threats is that when anyone could be a traitor, everyone is a traitor until proven otherwise (and even then many do not survive the process that proves their innocence).

The GM can have a lot of fun with Ebongrave's paranoia and the imagined enemies he sees at every turn, leaving the PCs wondering if they are about to be dropped onto a world crawling with hostile forces or merely surprised agri-workers. The best threats of course are those that come with a grain of truth, and hint at something larger just below the surface, possibly even something unknown to the Lord Commander himself. This could be a suspicion of rebellion on a remote world or rumours of a human alliance with the Tau that turns out to be something else entirely, such as the first flowering of a Chaos cult or the stirring of an altogether more ancient evil. Imaginary threats can be used to keep the

PCs guessing and create a universal sense of unease when operating within the Canis Salient, which in turn could lead to the Battle-Brothers becoming infected by Ebongrave's paranoia, seeing foes in every outlying world and the spark of sedition in the eyes of every Imperial commander and planetary governor they meet.

Excessive Force

Another of Lord Commander Ebongrave's trademarks is that he can be heavy handed when it comes to dishing out punishment or reacting to signs of sedition. A prime example of this are the so called "Quarantined Worlds" of Rheelas, Argoth and Kaggeran, blockaded and cut off from the Imperium on suspicion of rebellion. This is the kind of man Ebongrave is, a man who would sacrifice whole worlds with a wave of his hand if he even thought they were a threat to his control or the success of the Crusade. More than once Ebongrave has disbanded Imperial Guard regiments or sent them to penal worlds after confrontations with the Tau, for fear the aliens' ideology had somehow infected them. Worlds near the edge of the Greyhell Front are also a prime target for the Lord Commander and he has undertaken purges of high ranking officials for fear that even one in a hundred is somehow in league with alien or heretic forces. These brutal tactics have earned him the ire of many of the Imperium's most powerful organisations as he removes or sidelines powerful figures in the Adeptus Mechanicus, Ministorum or Administratum who would not otherwise be under his direct command. Even the Inquisition has suffered from Ebongrave's purges, agents without official sanction swept away or disappearing, creating an even more tangled web of the already complicated relationship the Lord Commander has with the Ordos.

Ebongrave's use of excessive force and extreme measures within the Canis Salient can cause the player characters lots of problems. While the Imperium is no stranger to overkill, the GM can use the Lord Commander's actions to complicate the Kill-team's mission objectives. This could be the arrival of Imperial forces in the midst of delicate negations with a marginal Imperial world, sparking an open conflict or a purge of a city's populace, and forcing the xenos cult or heretics the Battle-Brothers are hunting even further underground. Excessive force can also be used as an opportunity by the GM to provide the PCs with timely support. This can be especially suitable if Lord Ebongrave believes the actions of the Kill-team are somehow dealing with a threat to his control. In this case, the Kill-team might find themselves given all manner of assets to complete their task, while more desperate frontline commanders go wanting. Finally, during his time as commander of the Canis Salient, Ebongrave has left deep scars on many worlds as a result of his actions, and many important and powerful individuals have been taken by his agents (to who knows where). All of these ghosts can make for adventures in their own right as the PCs may find themselves digging up the past or hunting down these vanished "traitors" to complete their own missions or fulfil the will of the Inquisition.

DEATHWATCH ACTIVITY

"I'd sooner face a Hive Tyrant than the Tau Water Caste's honeyed words. At least when the Hive Tyrant opens its mouth you know it's trying to bite your damn head off!"

–Brother Ulnar, Space Wolves 7th Great Company, Seconded to the Deathwatch

The Deathwatch maintain constant missions within the Canis Salient, either aiding the forces of the Crusade directly or, more often, working for the Ordo Xenos in the shadows between warzones. The Canis Salient is starkly different to the other two arms of the Crusade and the Deathwatch has had to develop different tactics and different priorities when operating within its boundaries. This is the result of the Tau and their approach to warfare and the seditious influence they have had over worlds within the Sector. Whereas Kill-teams deployed against the Tyranids or against the Chaos Legions must usually only contend with the mindless belligerence of their enemies, those sent to the Canis Salient face a less certain confrontation and a far more cunning foe.

ENVOYS AND BODYGUARDS

There are few warriors more capable than the Battle-Brothers of the Deathwatch, and when an Inquisitor must undertake a vital mission for the Ordos or travel deep into the wilds of the Canis Salient, he will likely wish their support. Given the diverse and eclectic nature of an Inquisitor's work, this can take a Kill-team anywhere from the warzones of the Greyhell Front or the decaying cities of the Quarantined Worlds to the depths of the Black Reef or even the grand alien streets of Tsua'Malor. Depending on the Inquisitor and his mission, this could range from simple protection to more "active" roles such as striking at the Inquisitor's foes or going into regions or places where only the superior physiology of a Space Marine could endure. Whatever the task such a mission demands, the overriding priority will be to keep the Inquisitor alive at all costs.

ASSASSINATIONS AND SABOTAGE

Kill-teams excel at taking out specific targets and small surgical strikes, away from the random carnage of open war. Against the Tau, the Deathwatch have no shortage of targets for such assassination or sabotage missions and when a job absolutely needs to get done, a Kill-team will be deployed to take care of it. Largely these kinds of missions are concentrated around the worlds of the Greyhell Front, where they will have the greatest impact, and on worlds like Veren, Dakinor and Baraban, Deathwatch Kill-teams will fulfil these roles when available. Beyond the Greyhell Front, Ebongrave will use the Deathwatch (when his influence can extend to pitting them against his foes) to destroy the "infrastructure of rebellion" as he calls it, within the Imperial worlds of the Salient. This will usually mean killing humans rather than aliens, but this is not something the Deathwatch or certainly Inquisition has ever shied away from.

DIPLOMATIC MISSIONS

The Tau Water Caste maintains envoys on many worlds along the Greyhell Front, even as fighting rages between the Imperium and the Tau Empire. Though there is little hope such a gesture will ever bring any kind of peace to the Sector, they do serve a purpose, and diplomatic missions to meet with these alien envoys occur regularly. The nature of such meetings (kept out of official records) is to hammer out some accord between individual forces or create some concession for a short time, always so that one side or the other might gain some temporary advantage. In this way, diplomatic missions are as much about war as actual fighting and Deathwatch Kill-teams may attend as a show of force to intimidate the other side.

TAU LEADERSHIP

An area of great interest to the Ordo Xenos, and therefore by extension the Deathwatch, is the Tau leadership. Little is understood by the Imperium about the Tau's higher command structures, and the exact role certain individuals such as the so called "Ethereals" play in the governance of the aliens. Many Ordo Xenos Inquisitors have made it their ambition to understand exactly how the Tau chain of command works and several operate within the Canis Salient, either capturing Tau subjects for interrogation or infiltrating far behind enemy lines to observe the Tau on their home worlds. Where these Inquisitors go, the Deathwatch will often follow, Kill-teams tasked with protecting Inquisitors and fighting a path back to Imperial space should things go wrong.

SEDITIOUS WORLDS

Lord Ebongrave's madness has already claimed several worlds suspected of sedition against the Imperium, though many more are under his careful observation. While the Deathwatch does not normally concern itself with the pacification of populations, they will sometimes get caught up in events while hunting down alien spies or interlopers. These supposedly seditious worlds (guilty in the eyes of Lord Commander Ebongrave) can quickly become flashpoints between the Imperium and rebel forces, drawing Kill-teams into engagements they might not have originally anticipated. Given that many of these worlds are also remote or situated in the grey area between Tau and human controlled space, when fighting does commence, the Kill-team alone must represent the Imperium's interests and may be all that stands between order and complete anarchy.

WARFARE OF THE VELK'HAN SEPT

"Such mindless hatred these humans hold that they must call a "Crusade" to protect themselves from imagined enemies. I did not choose to war with them, but if they so wish it, I shall deliver them to the emperor-god they so adore."

–Shas'Ui Han'to Tamino, Veren Fire Warrior

The Tau Empire does not seek out war in same way as the Imperium of Man, nor does it possess the mindless aggression of so many of the other xenos races encountered by the Achilus Crusade. For the Tau, war is always a measured response to a situation, an exact application of force designed to yield the most advantageous outcome. If the Tau can complete their objectives without the need for conflict, then they will often choose this path, preserving the lives of their warriors and their resources. When war is unavoidable, or is the most expedient way to expand or protect the empire, then the Tau will not shy away from it. Even though they did not seek it in the first place, like all their undertakings, Tau warfare is carefully considered and meticulously planned. Unlike the blunt force that the Imperium applies to military engagements, or even the reckless hate and attrition tactics of such races as the Tyranids or Orks, the Tau will only fight where and when they need to, either to break a foe or destroy his command and logistic support. As every Fire Caste general knows, wars are not won by simply dying for what you believe in.

Within the confines of the Jericho Reach, the Velk'han Sept Tau are similar to the rest of their kin in their approach to war. The Mal'caor Shi, the commanding military of the Velk'han, takes the precepts of careful planning and tactical warfare very seriously, perhaps even more so given their distance from the First Phase Worlds of the empire and consequently their reduced access to significant resupply or reinforcement. Outnumbered many times over by the seemingly endless regiments of the Imperium Guard and the supporting Crusade forces, the Mal'caor Shi fights a constant battle of attack and manoeuvre to preserve its forces in the field and across the Greyhell Front. The arrival of elements of Hive Fleet Dagon has further complicated matters causing "spot fires" to spring up around the Tau Sept and forcing them to divert cadres originally destined to oppose the humans. The only small consolation is that the Tyranids seem to be tying up Imperial forces as well in their indiscriminate attacks. Among the greater conflicts taking place between the Tau and the Imperium, the Mal'caor Shi is also aware of the Deathwatch's involvement in the Sector. At first little distinction was made between the heavy human shock troops known as the Adeptus Astartes and their black armoured assassination squad variants. Recently though, Tau strategists of the Sept have begun tracking their movements and observing their tactics as a separate entity, with the goal of developing tactics unique to dealing with them.

FLUID WARFARE

The Tau see no wisdom in holding ground simply for the sake of protecting a stretch of dirt or the battered ruins of a city or town. Instead Tau warfare is based around the concept of attack and manoeuvre, and often a Tau Hunter Cadre will completely retreat from an area if it means preserving their strength for a decisive counterattack later. More than one Imperial commander has said that trying to bring a Tau to battle when he doesn't want to is like trying to grasp at smoke or chase shadows. This is largely due to the fact that the Tau always set up their defences, or plan their attacks, with solid tactical retreat plans in place. Experienced Shas'O will often have multiple rally points, escape routes and contingency plans in place for their force. Thus if they find themselves in an untenable situation, they can order a calm and ordered withdrawal with quick moving units like Crisis Suits or infiltrated ones like Stealth Suits harassing the enemy and covering the retreat. Tau armies are often completely mechanised, with ample Devilfish transports for the warriors, allowing them to outpace most enemies.

A TECHNOLOGICAL SUPERIORITY

While the Imperium boasts a practically limitless supply of men to hurl into battle, the Tau's resources are far more modest. This, combined with the value they place on their own troops (even their alien auxiliaries), means that the Tau will try to ensure their soldiers have the best armour, weapons and vehicles they can produce. In addition, any given task will be performed by a machine (such as a gun drone) if possible, rather than place a Tau life at undue risk. To this end, the Tau have developed an abundance of technology, many examples of which are among the most advanced forms encountered by the Imperium. Compared to the relatively poor equipment of the average guardsman, each Tau has at his disposal advanced armour, potent infantry weapons and mechanised support. Tau Fire Warriors are rarely encountered alone and on foot, and usually have their own dedicated armoured transport to protect them, as well as support from vehicles like Hammerhead or Sky Ray Gunships and swarms of drones with a variety of weapon systems. A greater ratio of technology to men also means that even the lowliest Fire Warrior La'Rua can call in close air support or the aid of Crisis Battlesuit Teams.

ALIEN AUXILIARIES

The Tau make extensive use of alien auxiliaries such as Kroot and Vespid mercenaries, numerous minor xenos races and even humans. These auxiliary troops are vital to the Velk'han Sept's war effort in the Jericho Reach, as the Tau alone could not hope to hold the borders of its empire against the Imperial advance. As often as not, Deathwatch Kill-teams deployed against the Tau will be facing their allies, and may never come into contact with the grey-skinned aliens at all. This becomes more prevalent for operations on the Imperial edges of the Greyhell Front, where the Tau employ large numbers of their auxiliaries as a buffer between their Sept and the humans. While most of the auxiliaries a Kill-team will encounter will be thoroughly indoctrinated into the philosophies of the Greater Good, some may not be so committed to the Tau cause. This can be especially true among the human regiments under Tau command or among some of the aliens indigenous to the Jericho Reach, which are simply fighting for their home worlds and have little love of either the Tau Empire or the Imperium.

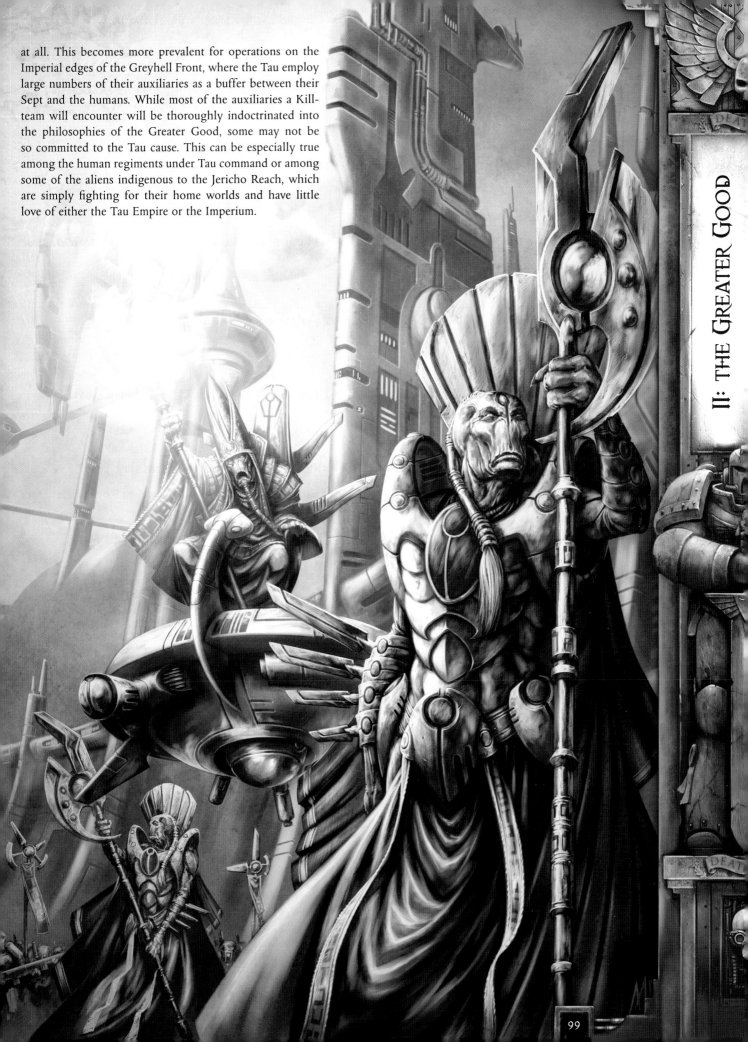

CANIS MISSION CONCEPTS

"Tau don't think like us, it's those beady little brains of theirs. They attack when they ought to be retreating and retreat when they ought to attack. Don't trust to your fancy tactical training or strategizing—just do what I do—shoot the little devils as soon as you see them, and then shoot them again for good measure!"

—Subaltern Gryn Hess, 74th Scintillan Regiment

Within the Canis Salient, Lord Commander Ebongrave's forces clash with the Tau around the edges of the Black Reef and in the chaos of the Greyhell Front. At the same time, Ebongrave's agents hunt down traitors and seditionists among the Imperial-held worlds, keeping the Crusade's forces and its holdings in his iron grip. Amid the madness and carnage of this conflict, the Deathwatch fight their own war against the Tau, a war as much about destroying the alien menace as it is understanding them and bending their leaders to the will of the Imperium through any means available. Canis is as dangerous for a Kill-team as any other Salient, and though it does not suffer from the mindless aggression of the Tyranids or the vile taint of the Dark Gods, it presents its own challenges, perhaps the greatest of which is dealing with such a canny and technologically advanced species as the Tau. The Inquisition, and the Ordo Xenos especially, have a great interest in the war against the Tau, and where the interest of the Ordos falls, the Kill-teams of the Deathwatch are never far behind.

There are a variety of missions and adventures that GMs can base within the Canis Salient, both against the Tau forces and concerning those problems created by Ebongrave's madness. Common types of missions include envoy and diplomatic forays to learn more about the threats the Tau present, or suppression missions at the Lord Commander's request to hunt down traitors or put down rebellions. Equally Kill-teams may be called upon to aid other Imperial forces or Adeptus Astartes Chapters in open conflict with the Tau, or act as special forces working behind the enemy lines to disrupt and destroy. Below are some examples of these kinds of missions, demonstrating how the war against the Tau is unlike fighting any other kind of foe. The GM can use these mission overviews either as the jumping off point for a more detailed adventure or adapt the ideas and themes presented within them for his own unique adventures.

HELL AT HIGH ANCHOR

"These aliens have no wit, no skill at lying like us humans. Dealing with them is like dealing with children, and like children they can be led and manipulated with relative ease. No, I don't consider the Tau much of a threat, merely another minor footnote in the glorious history of our Imperium."

—Ambassador Dianus of the Canis Delegation

OVERVIEW

The fighting on the feral world of Veren has dragged on for years without apparent advantage to either side, or any clear strategic impact on the greater war within the Greyhell Front. Despite the cautionary advice of his generals and the counsel of his tacticians, Lord Commander Ebongrave continues to divert men and resources to the world in the hopes of wiping out all Tau presence. Unknown to Ebongrave, some of the local commanders have been working secretly with Imperial diplomats to ease the tensions on Veren and create some kind of truce or ceasefire. The commanders consider their actions far from treacherous, and certainly have no love of the Tau, but embittered by years of pointless fighting, they believe their men and material would be better used on more important worlds. This is also the culmination of years of Tau Water Caste envoys creating lines of communication with the Imperials, offering an alternative to struggling to take an apparently worthless world. In recent times, a delegation has arrived to deal more directly with the Tau, sent, some say, by Lord Militant Tetrarchus himself, to try and secretly stem Ebongrave's excesses within the Salient (of which the battle for Veren is considered a part). This delegation of Imperial diplomats are known as the Canis Delegation and are led by ambassador Dianus, an aged man with experience dealing with the Tau.

The site of this meeting and the location where talks have taken place in the past is an orbital installation known as High Anchor. Created from the remains of the prow of the Imperial battleship *Divine Hand*, it was dragged into orbit shortly after the hostilities began, for use as a forward base (the location of the rest of the *Hand* and the fate of the battleship are unknown—the prow was discovered when Crusade scouts first entered the Veren system). High Anchor is both massive and heavy fortified (many of its old guns still functioning) and also acts as a mustering ground for Imperial regiments, so is usually teaming with Imperial Guardsmen. The station has been restructured so that the tip of the prow is now its peak, thus many of the decks are at odd angles and the crew must walk on walls or climb ladders across the floor to reach their destination. The old torpedo bays have been retrofitted into the diplomatic suites and are restricted to any but the highest ranking officials and officers. It is here that the Canis Delegation has been meeting with the Water Caste envoys and where inroads are being made to ease the pointless bloodshed on Veren's surface.

The player characters will first learn about Veren and the talks at High Anchor when they are tasked with protecting Inquisitor Vharys during his visit to the station. Vharys of the Ordo Xenos has "invited" himself to the proceedings under the pretence of representing the Inquisition's interests and offering insight into the Tau. Vharys's real reason for attending is more sinister and far more simple: revenge. Years ago Vharys lost his mentor, Inquisitor Goran, during negotiations with the Tau on Bekrin, when fighting broke out. Vharys has learnt that Nai'Ioth, one of the Water Caste diplomats present at the death of his old master, will be there, and plans to kill him. Vharys is also sympathetic to Lord Commander Ebongrave and his Eyes of Wrath, and though he has not informed the Lord Commander of all the dealings on Veren (knowing the likely heavy-handed response), he hopes to derail the talks and keep the war raging. He has requested the support of a Deathwatch Kill-team (the PCs) believing that when the fighting starts, they will side with

him and keep him alive, as he knows the Tau are no fools and their delegation will be well protected.

As the proceedings begin to get underway, the Kill-team is contacted by Inquisitor Patrina, another—more radical—Ordo Xenos Inquisitor operating in the Canis Salient. She informs the Kill-team of Vharys's plan to kill Nau'Ioth, and warns that this development could lead to further destabilisation in the region. She requests that the Kill-team do everything in their power to prevent Vharys from killing Nai'Ioth.

PRIMARY OBJECTIVES

Protect Inquisitor Vharys: Vharys wants to kill Nai'Ioth, and will choose to do so in the middle of the talks as publicly as possible (probably using his master-crafted bolt pistol). This will happen after a day or two, giving the PCs a chance to get the feel for High Anchor (and a chance for Vharys to properly identify his target). Even if the Kill-team has managed to speak to Vharys about his plan, he will still attempt to go through with it. Whether or not he succeeds in killing Nai'Ioth, drawing and firing a gun in the meeting will cause all hell to break loose, and the Water Caste's own Fire Warrior cadre will be quick to respond.

Prevent an Assault on High Anchor: Once Vharys makes his play, things will go from bad to worse and unless the Kill-team somehow intervene, the Tau will launch an attack on High Anchor to recover their diplomats (while the diplomats and their bodyguards will try to fight their way to the hull), and the Imperium will respond. There are two main courses this development can take. The first is that if the Kill-team can wipe out the Water Caste diplomats then they may be able to dissuade an attack on the station (though the Tau will still be incensed and likely launch some other kind of attack). The second is to aid Inquisitor Patrina. She believes that now that Vharys has gone through with his plan, the only way to calm the Tau back down is to either kill Vharys or hand him over to the Tau agents. This may seem like a radical proposition to the Kill-team, however Patrina will continue to remind them that the Canis Salient is already stretched thin, and if the situation escalates, the Tau threat may intensify too much for the Deathwatch to handle.

SECONDARY OBJECTIVES

Find the Tau Spy: During the days leading up to Vharys's attack, the Kill-team will be contacted by an Imperial Guard commander about the presence of a Tau spy somewhere in the depths of the station. It seems his vox officers have detected odd signals coming from the cold chambers near the ragged base of the station. He sent some men but they did not return and fears there might be some kind of alien presence down there. The reality is a number of Tau drones have been seeded into the station's base and are intercepting Imperial vox traffic. To kill them all is no easy task and means going into the hard vacuum of space and climbing through the torn and twisted decks where the prow once connected with the rest of the battleship, hunting small agile (and armed) drone discs.

TERTIARY OBJECTIVES

Recover the Imperial Intercepts: If the Kill-team take care of the drones lurking on the base of the ship, they will also discover records within their data cores of recent downloads to a point within the station itself. This has been done by Nai-Ioth (as much an agent for the Tau military commanders as the Water Caste) and in his chambers are stored hours of Imperial vox transmissions which he plans to take back with him when he leaves. Getting the recordings should be no easy task, as his chambers are always guarded and any open conflict with the Tau will bring the talks to an end. There may be other ways to get rid of the recordings, depending on how creative the Kill-team wishes to be, such as initiating a radiation burst in the chamber which would wipe them or crafting a tiny servo-construct to sneak in through the vents to get the data-store.

COMPLICATIONS

The Grip Tightens: During the Kill-team's time on High Anchor, the GM can complicate matters by having agents of Lord Ebongrave, probably aware of Vharys's plan, working to heighten tensions with the Tau. This can be anything from rabble rousing in the lower decks with the Guardsmen to targeting lone Tau as they travel to and from their chambers. If the Kill-team try to keep the peace in these instances, or save one of the aliens from an attack, it will go a long way later to prevent open conflict.

A Matter of Honour: Despite Imperial propaganda, the Tau are far from cowards and for much of their delegation this will be the first time they have ever laid eyes on a Space Marine. The GM could have some of the bolder members of the Fire Warrior cadre challenge the Kill-team to contests of arms to see what they can do. While the Tau would be no match for the Space Marines physically (and would not be so foolish as to try to best them in hand-to-hand or feats of strength) they could test their marksmanship and small squad tactics, perhaps even using some of the Imperial Guard training arenas in the decks below. If the Kill-team acts with honour (even if they best the Tau) then the aliens will remember and might be more willing to hear them out when the fighting starts.

OUTCOMES

The Kill-team must make a hard choice between backing up Inquisitor Vharys or helping Inquisitor Patrina capture or kill him. If they blindly follow Vharys then they will be hard pressed to keep him alive, and even if they protect him from the Water Caste bodyguard, the Tau will try their best to kill him and his actions will spark a naval engagement in low orbit as the Tau try to take out High Anchor. If they side with Inquisitor Patrina, or even manage to stop Vharys, then they will earn the respect of not only the Imperial officers and Canis Delegation but also the Tau. More likely is that the outcome falls between these two, and when fighting starts, the Kill-team must choose how to stop it before it destroys the station.

ACROSS THE STYGIAN BREAK

"That celestial briar patch is the key to the whole Greyhell Front. If the Tau somehow find a safe route through the Black Reef before us, then they can flank our front lines and threaten Wrath directly. Needless to say, we cannot let that happen…"

–Lord Captain Hyram Selt, *Sword of Vigilance*

OVERVIEW

The Black Reef slashes across the centre of the Canis Salient like a festering wound, a tangled web of celestial anomalies and spatial fluctuations that make it a stretch of void almost impossible to cross. For the Tau, this solar hazard shores up their left flank and protects many of their worlds from direct assault by the Imperium, forcing the Crusade to instead take the much longer route through the Greyhell Front and the narrow warp passages between its worlds. Surrounding the vast span of the reef (many light years across) is an area of space known as the Stygian Break. The break is the point at which the relatively stable and normal stretches of void give way to the punishing gravity storms and warp tides of the reef, and marks the point at which a vessel becomes at risk to being torn apart or lost among its shoals.

Ever since the Crusade first encountered the Tau and conflict began, the Imperium has sought to find a route through the Black Reef and flank the xenos worlds beyond. In recent years, fears that the Tau might do the same have prompted Lord Commander Ebongrave to dispatch scouts into the reef to discover the aliens' plans, though few ever return. Among the handful of men to cross the Stygian Break and come back to tell the tale is the Rogue Trader Telas Kai aboard his ship the *Ancient Fable*. Kai returned with stories of worlds within the reef and some manner of ancient machine at its heart, possibly the cause of the vast gravity storm and break down in the physical laws which pervades the region; he called this machine the Black Heart and upon his return to Wrath promised Ebongrave that if given the chance he could find it once again. Kai believes that if the Black Heart can be reached, then perhaps it can be controlled allowing safe passage across the reef for Imperial vessels or even used as a weapon against the Tau. Unsurprisingly, Ebongrave has leapt at the chance to master the Black Reef and the significant advantage it would give his forces in their struggle against the Velk'han Sept, and so has given his support to Kai, along with the aid of the Mars Class Cruiser *Sword of Vigilance* under Captain Hyram Selt, a staunch and loyal servant of the Lord Commander.

While the Imperium has been studying and exploring the Black Reef, the Tau have not been idle. In fact, having maintained worlds bordering the anomaly for years before the arrival of the Crusade, they know a great deal about it. The Tau scholar Aun'El Basel'kyth in particular has devoted much of his life to the study of the reef and had heard stories about the Black Heart and the Syrshin, a race of reptilian aliens said to dwell there, long before Kai claimed to have been there. Basel'kyth believes that the Black Heart is some kind of singularity engine with the ability to alter the properties of matter and gravity in localised space, and was created by the Syrshin's ancestors to ward against some ancient evil. He understands well the dangers it would mean for his people if humanity found such a device and turned it against the empire and so has been forming his own expeditions into the reef to find the Heart. So far these have not meet with success, but he has learnt much about the nature of the region and discovered that Tau ships, due to their unique method of warp travel, can penetrate deeper into the reef than their Imperial counterparts before suffering the worst effects of the gravity storms. Basel'kyth remains determined to reach the Black Heart first, or at very least prevent the humans from doing so.

The PCs have become embroiled in this race to the Black Heart because the Ordo Xenos has long had a keen interest in the Black Reef and rumours of the alien empire which once dwelt, or perhaps still dwells, within its borders. The Deathwatch also believes that there might be clues to other more dangerous threats than the Tau hidden within the remains of this empire, left undisturbed since long before the first humans arrived in the Jericho Reach. For both these reasons and the importance of preventing the Tau from securing a safe passage through the Black Reef, the Inquisition has deployed a Kill-team aboard the *Sword of Vigilance* with orders to ensure the success of the mission and recover alien artefacts and intelligence from within the reef.

PRIMARY OBJECTIVES

Reach the Black Heart First: The journey to the Black Heart is not going to be easy for the Imperial expedition, even without the danger posed by the Tau. Following Kai's half remembered route, the *Ancient Fable* and *Sword of Vigilance* (with the PCs on board) will have to navigate the debris and violent celestial phenomena which plague the void beyond the Stygian Break. The GM can throw literally anything in their path from Chaos tainted space hulks to rogue Tyranid hive ships, swept off course by the malign nature of the Black Reef. Equally time and space do not function normally within the reef and they may find themselves going around in circles, crossing paths with the same worlds and wrecks at wildly varying times in their own existence, which are themselves adrift in time and space. This could lead to some interesting situations in which their vessel lands on a world that remembers them from years before and has statues dedicated to their honour for deeds they have not yet done. Whatever transpires during the voyage to the Black Heart, it should be no simple feat, and the GM should give the players the sense that they have truly stepped off the map once they cross the Stygian Break.

Capture or Destroy the Syrshin Singularity Engine: At the centre of the Black Reef is the aptly named Black Heart, a macro-system of dozens of worlds all erratically orbiting a single black star (the Syrshin Singularity Engine). Such are the brutal gravitational and warp energies close to the Singularity Engine that it is impossible for a vessel to approach beyond several billion kilometres. The only way to reach it is to make planetfall on one of the outlying worlds and ride the gravity plumes inward (one of the thousand kilometre-long funnels of air and water that spring up between worlds when they pass close to each other) using atmospheric craft hopping from one world to the next, like using stepping stones to cross a river. The GM can have anything he wants on the worlds of the Black Heart as countless ships and numerous species have washed up here over the millennia. Most numerous is the Syrshin (or at least their primitive descendants) that wander the worlds, worshipping the black star as a god.

SECONDARY OBJECTIVES

Destroy the Tau Vessel: Aun'El Basel'kyth has deployed the Tau Explorer Class vessel *Dai'Sun* to follow the Imperial expedition into the Black Reef and keep watch on their progress. A full Hunter Cadre consisting of several hundred Fire Warriors, various specialised battlesuits and Tau armour are aboard the *Dai'Sun*, with orders to stop the humans reaching the singularity device, should they find its location. The GM can use the *Dai'Sun* and its military forces to dog the expedition's steps as they travel to the Black Heart and then openly oppose them when they try to planet-walk to the Singularity Engine. The Tau are wise and careful planners and will not throw away their strength foolishly, choosing when and where best to strike. In the midst of the Black Reef, their vessel will also have a speed advantage over the Imperial vessels and should be able to slip away if need be.

Find Basel'kyth's Research: If the Kill-team manage to corner the Tau or board their vessel, there is a chance they might be able to secure Basel'kyth research on the Black Reef (a copy of which was given to the captain of the *Dai'Sun*) and learn some of what the Tau know of the anomaly. Kai knows the Tau have been researching the reef and can suggest this objective to the PCs if they find themselves in a position to attempt it. The Tau will try to destroy the information rather than let it fall into enemy hands, so the Kill-team might find themselves in a race against time if they board the *Dai'Sun* should its captain try to trigger a self-destruct.

TERTIARY OBJECTIVES

Recover the Syrshin Artefacts: Many of the planets now orbiting the Black Heart were once worlds of the Syrshin and are still home to the remains of their ancestors' cities. The Inquisition and Deathwatch will both have an interest in such artefacts as they might hold clues to why the reptilian xenos chose to use the Singularity Engine to destroy their empire rather than let it fall to an unknown enemy, an enemy which is faintly depicted in some of their carvings and statues, looming with skeletal hands out of the dark.

COMPLICATIONS

Gravity Flux: The Black Reef is a dangerous place for ships and there is the constant danger of collision with rogue debris and other void flotsam and jetsam. The GM can use these perils to slow the expedition down at any point by having it sustain damage from such debris, possibly forcing it to make anchor at some remote world or giving their foes a chance to close in.

An Ancient Evil: Something very bad happened to the Syrshin empire, something that created the Black Reef and destroyed dozens of worlds. This should be especially evident on the worlds of the Black Heart, giving the ruins and remains a pervading sense of dread and the feeling of something lurking unseen nearby. The GM should play up this legacy of evil to give the reef a haunted feel—something is not quite right…

OUTCOMES

If the Kill-team defeats the Tau and reaches the Black Heart, they will have succeeded in their mission but will discover that its secrets remain locked away—it will become apparent by exploring the ruins of the Black Heart and observing it close up that the black star is the result of a weapon having been triggered rather than a weapon in itself. What they can potentially bring back with them is the Tau's research on the reef, which will be a great boon to the Imperium, and artefacts of the Syrshin which will gain them favour with their Watch Captain. It is possible, though, that if too many men are lost or even one of the ships destroyed that they may have to turn around and return empty handed, as Kai will only risk his own life to a point, and as a Rogue Trader is not compelled to stay.

A TWO FACED COIN

"I don't know who's worse, those bloody grey-skinned aliens or the scum who deal with them. I mean some of these "criminals" would trade with the damn Tyranids if they could get one to stop chewing his face off long enough to make a deal."

–Chief Arbitrator Arban Cobolt

OVERVIEW

Even during the most brutal of conflicts, there are those who will try to trade with both sides to turn a profit. Wars against the Tau are especially prone to these problems given that the aliens have a reputation for reasonable dealings and an openness to negotiations, as opposed to the fierce hatred fostered against all outsiders by the Imperium. Sometimes, members of the Imperial forces will even stoop to selling and buying from the Tau, offering up everything from tactical information to battle tanks in exchange for wealth or rare alien devices. From the Tau perspective, such trade opens up a chink in the Imperium's armour and allows them gather vital information or spread sedition on human worlds, and support rebellions often for the price of just a few technological trinkets or the relatively rare materials humans seem to crave. The Inquisition works tirelessly to stamp out this kind of trading with xenos, but the Canis Salient is a vast place and there are dozens of potential worlds were humanity and the Tau come into contact and such deals can be made. Even after employing the aid of the Adeptus Arbites to regulate stellar trade within the Salient, the Inquisition has failed to catch some of the more notorious offenders and the problems only seem to be getting worse.

The cause of the sudden increase in illicit trade with the Tau has much to do with the arrival of Vladorf Kyro, a boss in the infamous Kasballica crime syndicate. Kyro hales from the marginal Imperial outpost of Footfall in the Koronus Expanse (a noted den of thieves and pirates) and has, like many others, a keen interest in the movement of traffic through the nearby warp gate (a secret not as secret as the Imperium would like to believe). When he learned of the Tau and the trading opportunities the aliens presented, he sought permission from his bosses to travel to the Jericho Reach and expand the organisation's interests. Since then, Kyro has created a solid base of operations within the Canis Salient and brought over several other crime bosses to help him funnel profits back through the warp gate to the Kasballica. Kyro has no love for the Tau, but covets the wealth they have to offer and sees nothing wrong with passing on information and materials to them—after all, it's not like his small contributions will turn the tide of the war. Recently though, Kyro has been getting greedy and gathering more information and "liberating" much larger stocks of Imperial weaponry to sell to the Tau. Even some of Kyro's underlings are getting nervous and fear that their boss might be looking to break out on his own and keep the wealth meant for the Kasballica for himself. If this is true, the crime syndicate will likely send some people through the warp gate to have a word with Kyro, and things could get messy indeed.

While Kyro has been building his criminal empire within the Canis Salient, the Inquisition has discovered its first solid lead into the xenos trade. A minor rebellion on Yeynar Prime (a tiny Agri World on the far edges of the Greyhell Front) has recently flared into open war. Always a marginal world, the people of Yeynar were resistant to control by the returning Imperium; though they had no love for the Tau either, they simply wished to be left alone. With no real defence forces, the world was quickly occupied and the Crusade's attention focussed elsewhere. For years, minor rebel activity on the world persisted and its crystal jungles were home to roving bands of guerrilla fighters, though they posed no real threat to the Imperial garrison. In the last few months, things have escalated and the rebels have come into possession of heavy weapons, explosives and even armoured vehicles, some of which bear the markings of Imperial regiments stationed light years away. Rumours have also been heard of stealthed alien vessels making secret landings in the wilds of Yeynar and Tau scout drones spotted at the edge of the system. The Ordo Xenos has dispatched a Kill-team to deal with this matter before it becomes worse and hopefully find the source of the alien trade and the rebel weapons, while, in the process, putting down the rebellion once and for all.

PRIMARY OBJECTIVES

Destroy the Rebel Base: Deep within the crystal jungles of Yeynar is an extensive rebel base, built with thrones from Kyro and some support from the Tau. The unique resonating nature of the crystalline jungle trees (which emit radio waves when hit by strong solar winds) has prevented the local planetary defence force from finding the base using conventional orbital sensor devices. The base is also mostly underground, a warren of tunnels and pits dug into the soft earth of the jungle floor and shored up with crystal planking. To find the base, the Kill-team must try to track a rebel force back to the base or capture a rebel and extract the location through interrogation. The base is largely immune to aerial or orbital attack given the thickness of the jungle overhead and a shield generator provided by the Tau to cover its most important structures. This means the Kill-team must go in on foot, pushing their way through the razor-sharp foliage and avoiding any ambushes the rebels might devise. In support they will be able to call upon elements of the 74th Scintillan Regiment, diverted from the Greyhell Front lines to help put down the rebellion.

SECONDARY OBJECTIVES

Uncover the Greyhell Cold Trade/Capture Kyro: Apart from smashing their way into the rebel base and destroying its leaders and weapons (no easy task given their numbers and the additional Imperial Guard equipment they have received), to halt the rebellion springing up again, or a similar rebellion springing up elsewhere, the Kill-team must uncover evidence of the Greyhell Cold Trade and Kyro's involvement in supplying stolen arms to rebel worlds. The GM can provide clues to Kyro's involvement both at the rebel base and also in Yeynar's capital (Yeynar City) if the Kill-team can peel back the world's seedy underbelly and hunt out those sympathetic to the rebels. Once the Kill-team arrive, Kyro will try to destroy any evidence and make a run for it, throwing rebels in the Kill-team's path while making his escape. This could lead to a running battle through the rebel base (or the under-streets of Yeynar City) to capture Kyro before he can get off world. If the Kill-team can get even a single piece of evidence (such as transit records or a willing underling of Kyro) then the Inquisition will be very interested in exposing the entire operation and hunting down all its members.

Stop the Rebel Counter-Offensive: When the Kill-team attacks the rebel base (or once the rebels learn of the impending attack) they will launch an offensive on Yeynar City. This is something they have been preparing for a while (though they wanted to gather more armoured fighting vehicles before committing), but the arrival of the Kill-team has forced their hand. With at least as many main battle tanks as the 74th Scintillan Regiment and PDF combined and several artillery batteries, it will be a brutal and close fought battle. The Kill-team (provided they are not at the rebel base) can swing the battle with their presence if they work to take out the elite rebel units and their commanders, but likely Yeynar City will suffer significant damage.

TERTIARY OBJECTIVES

Capture of Kill the Water Caste Envoy: There is a Tau envoy dealing with both Kyro and the rebels at their base. Though the Tau have only limited involvement in the rebellion, they are mindful of the opportunities it might present should Imperial control of the world falter. The envoy also has a good knowledge of Kyro's operations and could be useful in taking apart the Greyhell Cold Trade. He is well protected with numerous Fire Warrior bodyguards and an elite Stealth Suit team. Killing the Tau envoy could also have other ramifications for Yeynar and draw greater attention from the aliens as they seek retribution for the act.

Kill the Kasballica Hit Squad: The Kill-team are not Kyro's only problem, the Kasballica have sent a hit squad of death cultists and assassin servitors to take care of Kyro. Led by a ruthless bounty hunter named Cayn, they will likely try to shadow the Kill-team and use them to find Kyro. Then if Kyro escapes, they will try to intercept him before he gets off world, and if the Kill-team gets him first, they will set an ambush to take out both the crime boss and the PCs. Of course Cayn is a reasonable man and if the Kill-team hand Kyro over, he might even go so far as to offer his help against the rebels.

COMPLICATIONS

Tau Warrior Cadre: The GM can make things more challenging for the PCs by adding a Tau Hunter Cadre to the rebel forces. This force can contain anything the GM chooses from the Tau arsenal, and will probably be making camp near the rebel base to protect the Water Caste envoy and even train the human troops in the use of Tau weaponry.

Fist of the Lord Commander: If the PCs call for more Imperial aid (or things turn against the Imperial forces on Yeynar), Ebongrave himself might hear of it and send orders to cleanse the world. This would mean the 74th Scintillan Regiment's own transport group and its supporting escorts (along with whatever vessel brought the Kill-team to the world) firing at ground targets from orbit. This could make the battle for Yeynar City even more chaotic as rebels and Imperials clash amid whole city blocks vanishing to lance strikes.

OUTCOMES

The real danger on Yeynar is not the rebels, and not even the Tau, but rather Kyro and his illicit criminal empire. Whatever else happens, Yeynar will take a mauling, though even if the Imperial forces are defeated by the rebels, it will be a localised defeat, and with control of the planet's low orbit and reinforcement at hand, the world can always be retaken. If Kyro escapes, he will need to be hunted down (perhaps running as far as the warp gate, or even deeper into Tau space if he realises that the Kasballica are after him), and only when he is caught and his agents (scattered throughout the Salient) are found, will the cold trade be defeated.

COMPLICATIONS

Complications are a way for the GM to alter the nature of a mission, potentially change its objectives and add further challenges for the PCs. They offer a chance for the GM to represent the fog of war and the general maxim that no plan survives contact with the enemy, and they also force the PCs to think on their feet as the nature of their mission changes around them and they must adapt and survive if they are to be successful. More details on Complications and their uses can be found on page 231 of the DEATHWATCH rulebook.

Presented here are a selection of complications specific to the Canis Salient, which might befall the player characters when operating within the region and opposing the Tau and their alien allies. GMs should feel free to use them as he sees fit, either adding them to his own missions, any of the missions in this chapter or simply taking elements from them to further develop his adventures.

TABLE 2-3: CANIS SALIENT COMPLICATIONS

1d10	Complication
1	Alliance of Necessity
2	Alien Experiments
3	Cadre of Hunters
4	Ceasefire
5	Defectors
6	Flashpoint
7	Hand of Madness
8	Outgunned
9	Uncertain Allies
10	Xenos Mercenaries

ALLIANCE OF NECESSITY

With the arrival of Hive Fleet Dagon in the Canis Salient, both the Imperium and the Tau have found themselves targets of the Great Devourer. This has at times forced an alliance of necessity upon both empires as they join forces to repel the advance of the swarm or cleanse a world of Tyranid infestation. Such alliances are short lived in most cases and once the back of the beast has been broken, the Imperium will once again remember its hatred of the alien and the Tau will respond in kind. This complication can be used to turn a mission on its head, forcing the Kill-team to reassess its mission objectives, as while fighting the Tau, the shadow of the Hive Fleet descends on their location. The Tau might even come to the Kill-team's rescue if they are far from Imperium support, making them choose which threat to pursue and how to respond to such unexpected help.

ALIEN EXPERIMENTS

Unlike the Imperium, which follows the rigid doctrines of the tech-priests of Mars, the Tau are always improving the performance of their weapons and technology. Even in the short time the Imperium has faced the young xenos empire,

the Tau have created new and potent versions of their tanks, battlesuits and infantry weapons. This rapid advancement demands rigorous field testing, and the Tau within the Canis Salient are no exception when it comes to trying out new wargear. The GM can use this complication to enhance the stats of a Tau weapon, armour or piece of equipment. Regardless of the type of item enhanced, it should only increase Damage or Armour Points by 2-4 and only increase tests by +20 at most. Such items usually have drawbacks though (they are in the test stage after all), and should gain a negative Weapon Quality like Overheats or Inaccurate.

CADRE OF HUNTERS

Many Imperial commanders mistakenly believe that the Tau are bereft of any real martial culture, though any who have ever had a chance to see the Fire Caste train its Fire Warriors knows differently. Among the greatest of the Fire Caste's soldiers are Tau who relish warfare and the chance to test themselves against the foe. Many of these follow the battle philosophy of Mont'ka, or killing blow, and form small Hunter Cadres (often using stealth suits) to go deep behind Imperial lines looking for worthy prey. This complication represents the Kill-team attracting the attention of such a Hunter Cadre of skilled Fire Warriors and can take place almost anywhere within the Canis Salient. The Cadre will dog the Kill-team's steps, striking and then retreating to test their strength before setting an ambush to take them down.

CEASEFIRE

Not all encounters with the Tau will meet with violence and there are recorded instances in the Canis Salient of truces and talks being called by both sides (though usually without the knowledge of Lord Commander Ebongrave). This is often only so that both sides can catch their collective breath and rally their forces for more fighting and only very rarely leads to any kind of lasting ceasefire. However, the mere fact that the Imperium and the Tau empire have a history of dealing with each other in this way has led to more commanders exploring these options. The GM can use this complication to force the Kill-team to complete their mission without resorting to excessive bloodshed. Far from making things easier, in such times of détente the Kill-team might find themselves without support should they launch a lone war against the Tau or, worse, suffer the wrath of their commanders for breaking an oath of truce.

DEFECTORS

Rare though it may be, the danger of desertion and defection among the Imperial Guard and Imperial Navy is an ever-present danger. Unlike many of the Imperium's foes, soldiers fighting the Tau know that should they lay down their arms and surrender, the enemy will not immediately tear them to pieces or sacrifice them to the Dark Gods. This option for escape from the horrors of war has kept the Imperial Guard's Commissars busy in the Greyhell Front and is always at the forefront of Lord Commander Ebongrave's mind when he raises a new regiment and sends it off to fight. The GM can use this complication to have a unit allied to the Kill-team either surrender (especially appropriate if they already had low morale and/or weak commanders) or even turn traitor and attack them. Space Marines and other such elite and devoted formations would never stoop to this, but among the teaming masses of conscripts there always those willing to sell their loyalty for respite from their hardships.

FLASHPOINT

For long years, the Tau were ensconced in the coreward edge of the Reach before the arrival of the Achilus Crusade and the return of the Imperium. During that time they surveyed dozens of worlds and set up scores of colonies. They also made alliances with many of the Jericho Reach's inhabitants as well as numerous human worlds. It is only now as the Crusade pushes deep into Tau space that the true extent of this web is being revealed and the Tau are responding to protect their empire. The GM can use this complication to draw additional Tau interest to the Kill-team's locale. It could be that the world the PCs are operating on or the races they are dealing with have ties to the Tau, and the xenos are roused to action to defend their interests by sending a Hunter Cadre into the fray. Clever PCs may even be able to discover where the Tau's true interests lie and use them against the aliens.

HAND OF MADNESS

Lord Commander Ebongrave is as much a hindrance as a help to the crusading forces at times—his contradictory orders and micro-management of his generals has led to more than one catastrophic loss of life or defeat. His reputation and unassailable position as Lord Commander, however, makes him practically untouchable, and those under his control follow his order as much out of fear as respect. The GM can use this complication to have Imperium forces within the Kill-team's area of operations behave erratically or become untrustworthy, as they are given direct orders from Ebongrave. This could be to move a division to a remote location to protect against some imagined attack, bombarding a city from orbit (while the PCs are in it) to "quell" sedition or even relieving the entire command staff of their posts and paralysing the war effort until their replacements can arrive.

OUTGUNNED

The Tau are skilled weapon-smiths and excel at creating devastating infantry and support weapons for their Fire Warriors. Few armies can boast the amount of firepower to soldier ratio that the Tau have and each is equipped with a far more deadly weapon and more sophisticated armour than the average Imperial Guardsman, demonstrating the value they place on their troops. The GM can use this complication to up the firepower of the Kill-team's Tau adversaries by giving them additional equipment and weapons to defend their objectives. This will mean more support weapons like Devilfish troop carriers and Hammerhead grav-tanks, as well as newer weapons like man-portable railguns and more drone support. It will not mean more Fire Warriors on the ground, but the ones the Kill-team does encounter will be more heavily equipped than normal.

UNCERTAIN ALLIES

Sedition and secession have always been problems for the Imperium, given the length and breadth of the God-Emperor's domain, and the Canis Salient is no exception. Adding to the usual discontent and rebellion found within more stable sectors is the fact that many worlds, especially those on the fringes of the Tau Sept, have only just been reintegrated into the Imperium having spent centuries fending for themselves and growing dangerously independent. The GM can use this complication to have the Kill-team team's allies be less than trustworthy, especially when facing the Tau in battle. This could range all the way from seditious planetary governors who will sell them out, to treacherous Imperial Guard regiments raised from the new worlds which will withdraw from battle when the Kill-team could use their support the most.

XENOS MERCENARIES

The alien philosophy that drives the Tau is difficult for many Imperial commanders to understand and goes against millennia of teaching that only humanity has a right to exist and all other forms of life or alien cultures are poison to mankind's dominion over the stars. The reality is that the Tau empire is not just one race but a collective of races (albeit with the Tau in control) and, because of the openness they have shown other xenos, they can call upon a variety of alien mercenaries and allies when they go to war. The GM can use this complication to introduce unexpected or unusual forces fighting under the banner of the Tau. Whether these are the more common alien mercenaries like the Kroot and Vespid or something completely new (possibility native to the Jericho Reach) these alien allies can be anything the GM wishes, and may well be armed with Tau gear and weapons.

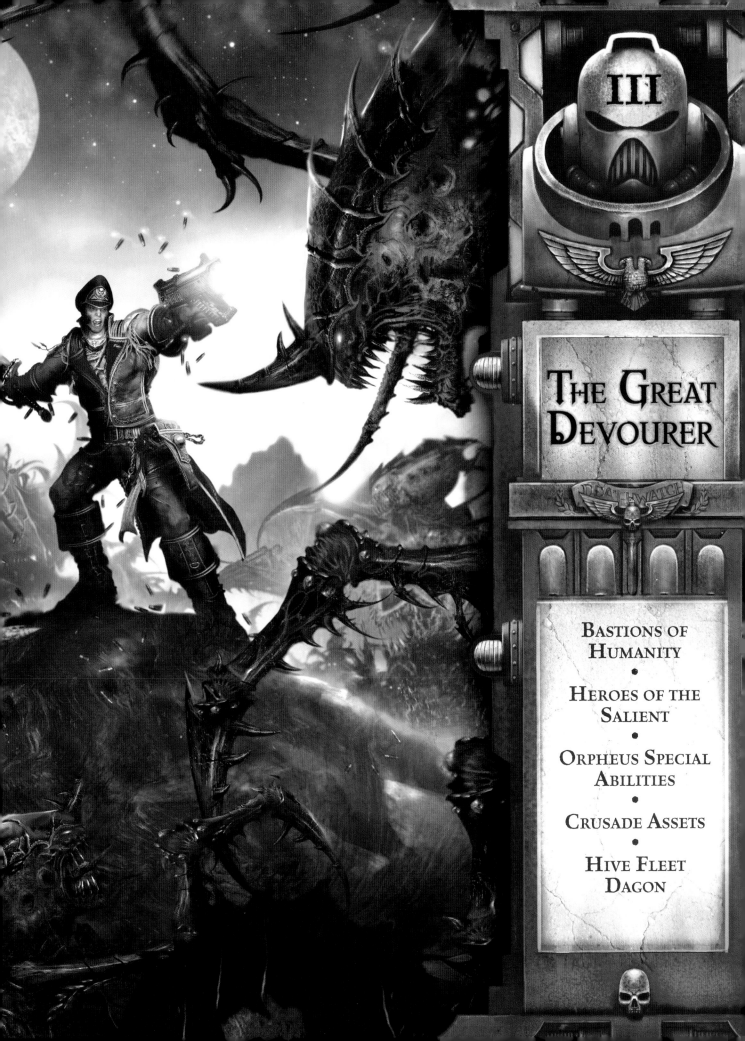

THE GREAT DEVOURER

CHAPTER 3: THE GREAT DEVOURER

"There is no peace to be had amongst the stars. The sum total of human endeavour must be bent towards the singular goal of survival, and to falter in this task for even a moment is to court the extinction of mankind. We cannot permit laxity or negligence of any kind, for it is the duty of every man and woman in the Imperium to lend their every effort to the matter of survival."

—Confessor Corvinus, at the outset of the ill-fated Margin Crusade, addressing the Crusade's command staff

The Orpheus Salient was once the largest and most successful of the three routes of advance established by Lord Militant Tetrarchus, gaining more ground than either the Canis or Acheros Salients, and rivalling the combined accomplishments of both those fronts. Its worlds are numerous, and many of them have begun to contribute to the continued might of the Achilus Crusade.

However, in recent years, this once successful front suffered perhaps the greatest setback imaginable, with world after world assailed by the ravenous forces of Hive Fleet Dagon. The Tyranid threat has seen the once strong Salient divided and its forces scattered. At present, only the decisive will of a few of the Orpheus Salient's commanders, and the might of the Adeptus Astartes—including, but not limited to, the intervention of the Deathwatch—maintains the Salient's remaining worlds in the face of an inexorable foe.

This chapter describes some of the many worlds of the Orpheus Salient. Some are battling against the terrible hunger of the Tyranids, while others gather their strength in preparation of such an assault, and others still remain oblivious to the peril that stalks the void. It also details a few of the leaders of men whose will and prowess help the Crusade's armies stand firm against the encroaching menace.

THE HISTORY OF THE ACHILUS CRUSADE

This section provides an overview of the Achilus Crusade, specifically as it relates to the Orpheus Salient. A broader look at the history of the Crusade can be found in THE ACHILUS ASSAULT.

OVERVIEW OF THE ORPHEUS SALIENT

"Victory needs no explanation; defeat allows none."

—Imperial maxim

The territory of the Orpheus Salient covers dozens of worlds, some of which are many weeks' travel through the warp from the Well of Night. This vast expanse of void is a challenge to conquer and a challenge to defend with the ever advancing forces of a Crusade, but until recently, the Orpheus Salient was the most stable and secure of the three Salients in spite of these difficulties.

In the thirty years since the Orpheus Salient was established, countless millions of men and women have fought, bled and died to claim and defend the worlds in the Salient, and as a result, more than sixty star systems were returned to the rule of the Imperium. But the history of the Orpheus Salient is not merely a tale of the triumph of the righteous, but also a warning to those who become complacent.

BEFORE THE CRUSADE

While little of the history of the Jericho Sector remains within the archives and libraria of the Imperium, fragments still exist. During the planning stages of the Achilus Crusade, the Administratum tasked ten thousand Curators-Historical with uncovering what little information could be found to guide the Crusade's forces.

The territories claimed by the Orpheus Salient once fell within two Subsectors, running along the rimward edge of the Jericho Sector. Of the two, the one closest to the Well of Night was the Schwartzmark Subsector, likely named for that dark and starless region, while the other was Zacchaeus' Expanse, believed to have been named for one of the explorers or heroes who claimed the region for mankind in the first place.

The Schwartzmark Subsector was ruled from either Castobel or Vanir—records are somewhat confusing on the matter—and contained dozens of agri-worlds, mining colonies, and other valuable resource-bearing worlds, the twin hive worlds producing a vast quantity of the manufactured goods required by the Jericho Sector. Lord Militant Achilus and his advisors felt that the worlds in this region, due to their proximity to the warp gate, could be swiftly reclaimed and turned to the support of the Crusade.

Zacchaeus' Expanse was a far less significant part of the Jericho Sector, being largely composed of feral and frontier worlds, never fully brought under Imperial rule. It is unknown why these worlds were left so untouched for so long, but some suspect that their presence on the very edge of the Imperium may have led to a belief that they were cursed, so far from Holy Terra and the source of the Emperor's Light. Lord Militant Achilus regarded this region poorly, seeing it as a matter for later concern, unworthy of attention compared to more immediate matters.

The Early Years of the Crusade

On 7252777.M41, Lord Militant Tiber Achilus began the Achilus Crusade, emerging from the Jericho-Maw Warp Gate and immediately pushing towards Spite, Calisi, Alphos, Hethgard, Pyrathas, and Karlack, six worlds identified by Achilus and his strategists before the Crusade's outset as ideal footholds within the Jericho Reach.

By 782.M41, the Crusade had established itself upon Hethgard and begun the long and arduous task of fortifying it against enemy assault, serving as the rimward flank of the Iron Collar. Over the next four years, forces based on Hethgard, under the command of Lord General Antevan Creaigne, pressed forwards in fitful expeditions along the Reach's rimward edge.

First to become compliant was Avalos, a verdant agri-world that readily accepted the rule of the Imperium and was swiftly charged with the solemn task of providing food to the Crusade. However, for reasons unknown, the world's tithes did not come as readily as had been planned or anticipated, a problem that has continued to plague Avalos.

Shortly after Avalos was claimed came Viyan-sen, believed to be a former penal mining colony, now inhabited by an extremely violent and predatory abhuman breed, which was the subject of a thorough campaign of extermination by the White Consuls after the missionaries who landed there were hunted down and eaten by the natives.

In quick succession after the purging of Viyan-sen came the conquest of three worlds. First was the wind-ravaged death world of Scirae, where hurricanes and flesh-stripping dust storms constantly scour the surface of the world, weathering it down to strangely smooth plains of sand and rock, allowing only burrowing and avian creatures to exist. After Scirae, came Sentinel 434, an abandoned Adeptus Mechanicus warp observatory, reclaimed swiftly by explorators to aid in future advancement through the Reach. last came Freya, a mining world teeming with indentured labourers, who would swiftly be put to work for the Imperium, supplying the Crusade with vast quantities of unprocessed ores and crude promethium.

Without warning, nine years after the start of the Crusade, Lord Militant Achilus was declared dead, his flagship lost in the Immaterium while on a routine voyage returning to Karlack after inspecting the defences on Alphos. With the death of Tiber Achilus, the Crusade's advance ground to a halt as its remaining commanders turned their attention to the matter of succession.

The Formation of the Salient

In the aftermath of Achilus' death, General Solomon Tetrarchus was elevated to Lord Militant and supreme commander of the Achilus Crusade. His first act was to gather the Crusade's command staff, several Astartes commanders, and other senior Imperial officials, to an assembly now known as the Council of Ashes. In a bold move, Tetrarchus sidelined many of Achilus' favoured generals, tacticians and key staff, replacing them with those he preferred and who would support his ambitious new strategy.

This strategy involved dividing the strength of the Crusade, which had thus far been directed against the Tau-held worlds in and around the Black Reef, into three distinct fronts, or Salients. The first of these, the Canis Salient, consolidated Imperial forces fighting to claim Tau-held worlds, while the second, the Acheros Salient, was intended to push through the heart of the Jericho Reach and claim the core worlds. The third, established almost a year after the Council of Ashes concluded, was the Orpheus Salient, which was to conquer the rimward flank of the Reach.

At the head of the Orpheus Salient was Lord General Mikal Curas, one of Tetrarchus' protégés and a promising officer who many regarded as being too untried as a General to command the entire Salient. Curas swiftly proved his detractors wrong, advancing further and faster into the Jericho Reach than any other Salient, claiming dozens of worlds within the space of two and a half decades.

Early Victories

With the other Crusade supported by the Calixis Sector—the Margin Crusade into the Halo Stars—failing, the Orpheus Salient took full advantage of the influx of new troops being siphoned off from those who would have otherwise perished serving Confessor Corvinus' faltering endeavour. Hundreds, even thousands of regiments were committed to the Orpheus Salient's advance, and their deployment was not to be in vain.

Deciding that lightning-fast assaults upon disloyal worlds, beheading their corrupt leadership, was the best strategy, General Curas selected his first target carefully.

Six months after the Salient's formation, the many moons orbiting the resource-rich gas giant Shoinmunt came under the rule of the Imperium. Ruled by a coalition of pirates and raiders who plagued the surrounding systems, Shoinmunt took four full months to claim in the Emperor's name. At roughly the same time, Imperial Guard forces made landing on Treyen, finding a primitive world easily converted to the worship of the Emperor. The Imperial Guard left behind a token garrison as the Adeptus Ministorum deployed their missionaries to begin making the world compliant. Soon after, contact was made with a world designated Aurum, and an Adeptus Ministorum Mission was deployed to commence conversion of the native populace.

In early 789.M41, at the advice of advance scouts who had already delved deep into the Reach, Battlegroup Santos arrived in orbit above Castobel, to fanfare and celebration, with Battlegroups Icarus and Daedalus arriving shortly after. Castobel had, like a few other worlds in the Reach, remained loyal to the Imperium in spite of the Age of Shadow, and welcomed the Crusaders with open arms. A hundred days of celebration followed, and the scribes, surveyors and logisticians of the Departmento Munitorum descended upon Castobel to calculate the wealth it could give to the Imperium, while millions of preachers and hundreds of confessors spread amongst the populace to ascertain the strength of their faith.

A month into the celebrations, Battlegroup Icarus departed the orbit of Castobel, moving to Freya to reclaim it, the mining world having succumbed to a recidivist group during the years since Achilus' demise.

The Salient's battlegroups pushed deep into the Jericho Reach, establishing an outpost on the promethium-rich world of Herisor, rediscovering the toxic frontier world of Atonement, and locating the desert world of Cocijo, which was arid when all prior Imperial records claimed it to be a verdant and populous agri-world, with no sign as to the cause for such a change. Eight other worlds were drawn back into Imperial rule, with only two requiring bloody conquest. On the jungle-choked Iskarrion, three years of brutal guerrilla warfare between Astartes of the Dark Sons Chapter and the world's native Chaos worshippers saw much of the world's surface burned to ash as the Space Marines ruthlessly scoured the land for the enemy and removed their taint. Meanwhile, on the grave world of Haarcharoden, seven years of fierce trench warfare against savage abhuman slave legions and their sorcerer-tyrant masters saw thirty-five million Guardsmen dead, along with eleven Space Marines of the Relictors detachment deployed to assassinate the sorcerers' leader.

Having encountered little strong opposition during the Orpheus Salient's advance over the previous eleven years, it was decided in 798.M41 by Lord Militant Tetrarchus to withdraw almost a third of the Salient's ships and soldiers and almost all their allied Adeptus Astartes forces, redeploying them to the Acheros and Canis Salients where their might could be more effectively used. Depleted in strength, but with morale still strong from so many swift victories, the Orpheus Salient's remaining Battlegroups continued to press on, locating and claiming the ocean world of Manuxet, the foetid penal colony of Xyan, and the feral world of Jove's Descent by late 804.M41.

The Salient's next major turning point was in 805.M41, when warp storms that had plagued part of the region cleared, revealing new worlds to claim. Almost immediately, Battlefleet Argo withdrew from the front lines to explore and conquer these newly unveiled worlds, locating the former shrine world of Eleusis, long corrupted by forces loyal to the Ruinous Powers, calling themselves the Charnel Oracles. Aided by General Derian Arkelius, Lord Admiral Anastasia Arkelius, and Lord Commissar Vance Theren, three of the greatest military minds in the Crusade, Curas turned his attentions to how best purge Eleusis of its tainted overlords.

Eleusis fell within a month of Battlegroup Argo arriving within the system. The initial conquest—dubbed Operation Onslaught—took a week to plan and mere days to execute, with three weeks of subsequent skirmishes and pacification efforts before General Curas was content to declare the world compliant. For his triumph, Curas was awarded the Achilus Halo with Full Aquila by Lord Militant Tetrarchus.

While Imperial rule was being established on Eleusis, dozens of other worlds fell, most newly revealed by the dispersal of the warp storms. The Orpheus Salient grew from strength to strength, pushing as far as Sedu and the Slinnar Drift, breaking the hold of the Kingdom of Vanir, and establishing contact with the proto-hive world of Beseritor. In all, by 812.M41, the Orpheus Salient had made compliant 63 worlds and begun providing vast quantities of food, raw materials and manufactured goods for the rest of the Achilus Crusade.

That state of affairs would not remain for long.

THE SHADOW IN THE WARP

On 8999812.M41, astropaths across the Jericho Reach began reporting increasing difficulties in sending and receiving messages, particularly within and around the worlds claimed by the Orpheus Salient. Shortly thereafter, Navigators began experiencing difficulties locating the Astronomican and other, closer navigation beacons, while astropaths and other sanctioned psykers across the length of the Orpheus Salient began suffering from horrific nightmares, driving many mad with visions of an endless, hungry darkness and other portents of doom.

The tiniest fragments of information emerging over the months that followed seemed to indicate that elements of the Crusade force had been lost and worlds previously deemed secure had now come under siege by some unknown enemy. For over a year, the Salient's forces entrenched themselves, waiting for an unknown foe to arrive in orbit.

Throughout 814.M41, information began to arrive, starting with a barely coherent message from a patrol group above Herisor, which appeared to claim that the Tyranids had arrived. Soon thereafter, a Deathwatch vessel returning with great haste from newly silent Freya presented the same conclusion—that the Tyranids were in the Jericho Reach.

An uncommonly large Deathwatch task force was assembled to cleanse Herisor, while the Templars of Blood 3rd Company, who had been instrumental in the conquest of Eleusis, voyaged out to distant Zanatov's Harbour at the request of Lord Militant Tetrarchus to investigate the origin of these creatures. Of the Astartes who set foot upon Herisor and cleansed it of enemies, less than half returned, and when the Templars of Blood's Strike Cruiser *Blood Sword* returned from Zanatov's Harbour, they reported no signs of life whatsoever from a world that had once been a haven for illicit trade.

At the end of 814.M41, Lord Militant Tetrarchus sent out a declaration to all corners of the Jericho Reach that named this Tyranid menace as Hive Fleet Dagon. At that point, it was indisputable—the Tyranids were advancing through the Jericho Reach, and the Shadow in the Warp had enveloped the Orpheus Salient, where forces had been stretched thin and depleted by the needs of the Canis and Acheros Salients. Worlds that had been producing men and resources for the rest of the Crusade were now under dire threat from an enemy many had believed to be long gone, defeated decades ago at great cost to the Ultramarines.

DARK DAYS

A little over two years have passed since the threat was given a name, and almost half a decade since its effects were first felt upon the Orpheus Salient. With the acknowledgement of a Tyranid presence in the Jericho Reach, the Deathwatch began operating more openly within the Orpheus Salient, applying their hard-won skill to bolster the precarious defences of worlds thought safe.

At the same time, other Astartes forces allied to the Achilus Crusade began to withdraw from the Greyhell Front to face the Tyranids. Meanwhile, several Chapters despatched forces to join the Crusade purely to confront the creatures that struck such a grievous wound against the Ultramarines, and several more Battle-Brothers answered the call to take the Apocryphon Oath and serve a vigil within the Jericho Reach, bolstering the numbers of the Deathwatch.

With the fall of Herisor and Freya, the Tyranids had already penetrated deep into the Orpheus Salient's territories. Swiftly more and more worlds came under attack, until even Hethgard itself was caught in the Great Devourer's maw. Soon over a third of the Orpheus Salient's worlds were under immediate threat, and several more overrun entirely with no hope of reclamation.

Countless billions of lives and dozens of worlds hang in the balance already, yet their fate is only part of the problem. Should the Tyranids reach the Well of Night and venture successfully through the warp gate, their infestation will be able to spread to the distant Calixis Sector and beyond, striking at parts of the Imperium wholly unprepared for a threat like the Tyranids.

Bastions of Humanity

"To muse upon the number of men in the Imperium is to court madness and futility, for we far outnumber the stars in the sky and grow in number with every passing moment. Better then to muse upon the worlds upon which mankind treads, for they are a number far more easily regarded by the reckoning of men."

–Noted philosopher Dero Cavanne

The planets of the Orpheus Salient have fallen under the looming shadow of Hive Fleet Dagon. Countless worlds in the Salient have already been lost to the ever-hungering jaws of the Tyranids, but some still stand in defiance of the endless tides of beasts. These bastion of the Orpheus Salient stand as the last line of defense holding back Hive Fleet Dagon from pouring into the rest of the Jericho Reach.

HETHGARD

"A fortress unmanned is as a corpse—it bears the shape of what it is supposed to be, but lacks the vital heart and strength that comes from life, and is instead hollow and purposeless. A fortress manned by a number of soldiers is amongst the most wondrous and terrible things to behold, for few things stand firm against stone and steel with flesh and blood behind it."

– Attributed to Rogal Dorn

No servant of the Emperor has ever set foot upon Hethgard and felt anything but awe at the scale of what man has created there. The fortresses of Hethgard are a monument to warfare, a testament to the toil and labour of millions and the blood that millions more will shed in defence of the Imperium.

Hethgard exists for one purpose: to defend the rimward flank of the Crusade's advance, to prevent the enemies of man from reaching the Well of Night and the Jericho-Maw Warp Gate within it. To that end, it has been remade as a world fortified, with every square kilometre of its surface and many hundreds of metres below ground devoted to the protection of its defenders and the repulsion of an invading force.

Designed by a coterie of Divisio Tactica siege engineers and Adeptus Mechanicus artisans, Hethgard's fortifications have been carefully arranged to allow for the swift and effective detection and destruction of invaders, its structure devised by ancient strategic lore, arcane formulae, and the results of intensive prognostication.

Hethgard has held off several attacks over the decades of the Achilus Crusade, its defenders overcoming all those who have sought to oust them from the world's fortresses. However, now Hethgard's garrisons are confronted with a foe unlike any they have previously encountered—Hive Fleet Dagon is poised to overwhelm the world, and Hethgard's precision-designed defences are pitted against an enemy that seems to be without number and entirely uncaring of the horrific casualties that Hethgard's guns cause.

HISTORY

Originally a mining world serving the Schwartzmark Subsector of the Jericho Sector, Hethgard has been under human dominion for over seven thousand years. According to the limited records available, an Adeptus Mechanicus survey expedition set foot upon Hethgard in 312.M34, evaluating the world as having extensive mineral resources sufficient for several millennia of intensive tithing.

For centuries, Hethgard's wealth went to nearby Castobel, its abundant raw ores shipped in massive refinery-haulers to the bustling hive world. Even as the Jericho Sector collapsed into anarchy, Hethgard continued to supply the still-loyal Castobel for several centuries as the two worlds' respective infrastructures diminished in the absence of the Imperium.

Hethgard's population fractured into distinct nations and city-states over the generations that followed, with clans of miners struggling to survive on the limited quantities of food and potable water available on so barren a world. These factions changed frequently over the millennia, shifting due to wars and alliances and adapting in response to the intervention of off-worlders. Some of these outsiders were occasional supply ships from nearby Castobel, while others were raiders and the vassals of petty dictators who sought to exploit Hethgard's wealth for themselves.

By the time the Achilus Crusade reached Hethgard, seven weeks after the fleet passed through the warp gate, Hethgard's population was divided into eleven distinct nations, eight of which capitulated without hesitation to the Imperial forces that appeared suddenly and menacingly in the skies above them. The remaining three chose to defy the Imperium, digging in and fortifying the mines beneath their cities to stave off annihilation by orbital bombardment.

For four long years, the Imperium fought against the entrenched population, with millions of men delving deep into the mines from the already compliant cities to wage war with those who refused to accept the Emperor. The commander of the Imperial Guard on Hethgard, Lord General Antevan Creaigne, was an expert in more traditional forms of combined arms warfare, used to relying on the might of armour and artillery in conjunction with his infantry, and struggled to deal with the brutal tunnel fighting that denied him the use of much of his forces. Worse, it became quickly apparent that the forces arrayed against them were more than mere heathens and separatists, but were instead driven by servants of the Ruinous Powers, a group identified by the Inquisition as the Stigmartus, a known heretic faction encountered on many worlds across the Jericho Reach by scouting expeditions.

Warp spawned sorcery and blasphemous rites joined insane fanaticism and vicious close quarters-battle, and only the intervention of an Astartes Task Force—comprised of Battle-Brothers from the Storm Wardens, Relictors and Dark Sons Chapters and several battalions of Storm Troopers—was able to break through the bloody stalemate and cleanse the Stigmartus' taint from the world once and for all, after an eighteen-hour assault.

With Hethgard claimed, its fortification could begin. After millennia of exploitation, Hethgard's resources were all but depleted, as had been predicted so long ago, but mining was not the reason the Imperium had returned to Hethgard. The newly repatriated citizens of Hethgard were put to work almost immediately, charged with removing the last of their world's mineral wealth even as the landscape was remade around them. Hethgard's mountains and volcanoes were carved and shaped by the searing fire of orbital lances, clad in massive armour plates and fitted with batteries of macrocannon and surface-to-orbit missile silos.

By the time the Orpheus Salient was established, the mountain fortress of Bastion Primaris was complete, and nine hundred kilometres of tunnels had been excavated, extending out from the fortress to reach the three nearest cities and their mines, turning caverns into storage vaults, munitions dumps and barracks. In addition, work had begun on both stand-alone firebases across the planet, and the process of turning the cities into secondary fortresses, an undertaking that would take decades to complete.

Hethgard's defences were first tested a few months later, when a flotilla of raiders from deeper in the Reach arrived to extort resources from the miners, as they likely had been doing intermittently since before the Achilus Crusade began. Unprepared to face the full might of Hethgard's defences, the raiders were obliterated within minutes of arriving in orbit. Since that first assault, countless foes have attempted to strike at Hethgard and been found lacking, but only two instances in the decades-long history of the fortress world are particularly noteworthy.

The first came in 796.M41, when an Ork warfleet appeared in-system, broadcasting its identity in the self-aggrandising manner common to Orks. Xenolinguists swiftly translated the declaration of identity as being from a Freebooter band known as the Brass Eye, led by Kaptin Azrukk Ur Nazdakka. The Brass Eye fleet was massive—dozens of ships and millions of Orks, whose belligerent mentality saw the fortress as a challenge concealing valuable technology to plunder. The Orks had emerged from the warp mere hours out from Hethgard itself, dangerously close, but avoiding the picket ships and sentry stations and granting them a measure of surprise over the forces stationed below. Less than 20 hours after arrival in-system, the first Orks had

BASTIONS AND FIREBASES

The defensive benefits of a fortress are something that will appear frequently during missions on Hethgard, given the ubiquitous nature of fortifications across the planet. As a result, it's useful to know how strong those defences are. The following rules describe "creating a breach." In all cases, a breach is large enough for a Hulking creature or two Average creatures to pass through. Each size category larger requires twice as much damage to create an appropriate breach, while each size category smaller requires only half as much damage.

On the surface, the standard curtain walls found on each firebase and bastion are ceramite-clad ferrocrete, two metres thick. This provides 48 Armour Points as Cover, and requires 40 points of damage to create a breach.

The external gates are triple-layered plasteel composite, providing 42 Armour Points as Cover, requiring 35 points of damage to breach.

Enclosed bunkers are tougher still, comprised of three metres of plasteel-reinforced ferrocrete with armaplas internal cladding to minimise shrapnel from damage to the bunker. This provides 64 Armour Points as Cover, and requires 70 points of damage to create a breach.

Within the tunnels, the fortifications are less substantial, but still noteworthy. The majority of tunnels are simple bare rock, but those in secure regions of the planet are faced in machine-fitted slabs of rockcrete. This has an Armour Value of 16 and requires 25 points of damage to breach, though this is typically only a concern for creatures capable of burrowing. These secure sections are fitted with defensive alcoves sufficient to conceal an Imperial Guardsman and provide him with cover against an aggressor, and heavy armaplas bulkhead doors to seal off compromised sections, which provide 32 Armour Points as Cover and require 25 points of damage to breach.

made planetfall, employing crude drop pods to land swiftly and begin their assault.

The Ork assault was predictably long and gruelling, the greenskins' tenacity and bloodthirsty joy difficult to quell even with the heavy firepower and millions of men defending Hethgard. After eighteen months of non-stop conflict, the Orks were still deeply embroiled, having forced their way into the tunnels through several of the smaller firebases. Eventually, through brutal attrition, the Orks' will was broken, their forces on the ground reduced to scattered pockets of resistance and their fleet driven off. In order to contain any re-infestation, annual purges of the formerly Ork-occupied regions are mandatory.

The second major attack occurred years later, and was a far more successful assault. On 5212809.M41, the picket ship *Achilus' Eye* detected a localised warp anomaly approximately seven hundred thousand kilometres from Hethgard. A day later, four picket ships and two of the sentry stations were destroyed, and an unidentified spherical object had arrived in Hethgard's orbit. Astropaths given secret Inquisitorial ciphers immediately notified their masters of the strange and menacing presence as it disgorged vast numbers of smaller, spherical craft, which plummeted to the world below.

The spherical war engines, and their bizarre amorphous occupants, possessed a terrible power to unmake flesh and steel, projecting auras of incandescent fire that turned all it touched to black ash and noxious vapours.

For fifteen weeks, these creatures—who remain unidentified to this day in spite of the best efforts of the Ordo Xenos—tore across Hethgard for reasons unknown, but which Departmento Munitorum propagandists attributed to "the envious malice inherent in all xenos breeds." At the start of the sixteenth week, aid arrived, in the form of the Deathwatch Strike Cruiser *Wrathbringer*, bearing four veteran Kill-teams clad in priceless suits of Tactical Dreadnought Armour, who struck swiftly from orbit by Teleportarium, clashing with the greatest concentrations of the unknown xenos. Thirteen Astartes died in the savage combat, their blood spilt to locate some weakness or vulnerability in their foes. For their sacrifice, the Deathwatch overcame their foes—the unknown xenos withdrew in the face of heavy casualties, their ship retreating under fire from the *Wrathbringer* and Hethgard's defence fleet, and torn asunder before it could translate into the warp.

Hethgard was regarded as a fortress second only to Karlack in its might, but even a world that well defended could not adequately prepare for what was to come next—Hive Fleet Dagon. In 816.M41, the first vanguard ships arrived, followed soon after by larger kraken and eventually a colossal Hive Ship. None could have predicted that the Tyranids would have pushed so deep into the territories claimed by the Salient that quickly, and to have them assaulting one of the worlds of the Iron Collar was an eventuality that few had the courage to consider.

The world is now under continual assault by the Tyranids, and while the defenders have the advantage of massive fortifications and extensive stores of supplies, the Tyranid presence prevents those supplies from being moved to worlds elsewhere in the Salient as was their original purpose. In besieging Hethgard, the Tyranids may have inadvertently set in motion the slow and painful demise of the entire Salient, starving it of vital reinforcements and supplies.

KEY LOCATIONS

The following are a number of significant locations on Hethgard, still holding out against the continued onslaught of the Tyranids.

Bastion Primaris

The single largest and oldest of Hethgard's fortresses, Bastion Primaris is built within the hollowed out shells of three of Hethgard's tallest mountains, with the billions of tonnes of rock excavated from within turned into outlying firebases and picket-forts.

The very peak of the Bastion, 13 kilometres high, is capped with a colossal defence laser battery, greater in magnitude than the weaponry found aboard ancient battleships and powered by a geothermal power plant many kilometres below the planet's surface. The entire complex is wreathed in many layers of protective void shields and clad in sixty metre thick plasteel-ceramite composite armour plate, rendering the entire fortress nigh-impervious to assault by land or from orbit.

Within the Bastion's immense walls are thousands of barracks sufficient to house over a million men, armouries, manufactories and generatoria to keep them supplied with weapons, power and ammunition for generations, and immense storage depots and supply vaults containing potable water, preserved food and raw materials to supply not only Hethgard but the conquering armies of the Orpheus Salient as well.

Deeper within are archive crypts, shrines, the chambers of the astropathic choir, and the strategium-maximus, designed to serve as the command centre for both Hethgard and the entire Orpheus Salient beyond it. The strategium-maximus in particular is a monumental chamber, fitted with unending rows of cogitators arranged in precise accordance with ancient numerological and technomantic rites, and equipped with some of the most sophisticated hololithic projectors and vox-simulacra available. It grants a commander intricate and precise simulations of any conceivable strategic scenario, rendered in light and sound a hundred metres across.

Since its creation, the Bastion Primaris has never fallen, and only recently have its defences been truly tested, by the unrelenting tide of Tyranid monstrosities that now roam across Hethgard's surface and scuttle within its tunnels. In the last few years, the lower depths of the Bastion have been infiltrated by subtle and cunning beasts, and though they have been driven back each time, they press deeper with every new attack.

Hethgard Anchorage

Ringing the nearest of Hethgard's three moons, the Anchorage is a massive network of docks, hangars and cargo yards, originally constructed to ease export of unrefined ores and the import of necessary supplies. Shortly after the conquest of Hethgard, a massive effort was made to reconsecrate and expand upon the Anchorage to allow it to support the great battlegroups and flotillas of transport ships that would soon be a near-constant presence in the world's orbital space.

Since that time, the Anchorage has been a hive of activity, operating at all hours to keep hundreds of starships of all

PLANETARY DATAFAX: HETHGARD

Population: Estimated 338 Million

Tithe Grade: Solutio Particular

Special Notation: Primary Command Centre for the Orpheus Salient

Geography/Demography: Hot/Desert; primary planetary climate is arid with high temperatures and a dense legacy smog/smoke cloud layer caused by now-dormant volcanoes, which maintains the high surface temperatures (typically between 28 and 35 degrees Celsius). The planet has no surface water, though many subterranean reservoirs exist. Much of the landscape is dominated by artificial structures in the form of abandoned mines and quarries, and extensive fortifications. Beneath the surface exist tens of thousands of kilometres of tunnels and caverns, most of which are of Imperial origin, with a minority being the remnants of mines created during the Age of Shadow.

Government Type: Departmento Munitorum-appointed Commander/standard military hierarchy.

Imperial Commander: Steward Militant Lukas Vierling, on behalf of Lord General Mikal Curas.

Adept Presence: High; the Departmento Munitorum employs Hethgard as a primary command centre and supply depot for Orpheus Salient operations. Significant Adeptus Mechanicus and Adeptus Ministorum presences exist as well, for the same reason.

Military: As a fortress world, 85% of the Hethgard population is engaged in actions of a military nature or in support of military operations. Actual military forces (as opposed to support personnel) comprise 48% of the population, consisting primarily of Imperial Guard, with contingents of Adeptus Astartes and Adeptus Mechanicus Skitarii in support, both of which operate under their own, independent, chains of command.

Trade/Economy/Addendum: Hethgard has no remaining natural resources of worth; its sole worth to the Imperium is as a fortress against the enemies of mankind. Hethgard requires extensive quantities of materiel, due to its large garrison and lack of natural production. Internal economy is a Munitorum-regulated rationing and requisition system.

MINES AND RUINS

Hethgard was founded as a mining world during the 34nd Millennium, and had remained as such for the long millennia of the Age of Shadow, its populace becoming a scattered and disparate collection of cities and nation-states squabbling over natural resources and trading with the few remaining factions capable of interstellar travel, giving up the world's natural resources in exchange for food and equipment.

When the Achilus Crusade arrived in 778.M41, the majority of the population acquiesced to the Imperium immediately, with many of those who did not embrace the Crusaders unwilling to pit their meagre strength against the armies and ships arrayed against them. However, a minority resisted, retreating into the mines and caverns that had once been Hethgard's lifeblood and waging a brutal guerrilla war with the crusading forces, costing hundreds of thousands of lives in the process as savage tunnel fighting became a daily occurrence.

The resistance element on Hethgard appeared to be composed primarily of traitors and cultists, in an uprising fomented by agents of the heretic coalition known as the Stigmartus, whose insidious presence continues to plague the Achilus Crusade on countless other worlds across the Jericho Reach. These foul and deluded servants of the Dark Gods profaned many chambers, mines and caverns in the course of their defence, and saw surface settlements despoiled by their depravity, forcing the Imperium to obliterate all traces of their desecration in the four years of the conquest.

To this day, numerous parts of the now-extensive tunnel network beneath Hethgard's surface have been declared morally hazardous by the Inquisition and are forbidden to all troops who have not undergone thorough purity testing before assignment—and even they are subject to intense scrutiny afterwards. The danger of heretic taint upon these locations is not one to be dismissed lightly.

FORTRESSES AND TUNNELS

Since its conquest, Hethgard has been a world in a constant state of change. Billions of tonnes of rock have been excavated to form tunnels and caverns extending for kilometres beneath the surface, the rock shaped into massive interlocking blocks according to STC designs to create an extensive network of fortresses and firebases on the surface.

The fortification of Hethgard has been ongoing since it was conquered, part of a decades-long plan devised by the finest siege engineers and strategists in the Crusade, to create a world entirely covered in overlapping fields of observation and fire, where no foe could make a landing without being obliterated by defensive fire from at least three fortified positions.

As of late 811.M41 the fortresses of Hethgard were deemed 70% complete, though the world has repelled numerous assaults during the intervening years. The first and largest fortresses were established within vast mountain ranges, sheathed in interlocking plasteel plates a metre thick and a mile across and fitted with powerful surface-to-orbit weaponry and artillery batteries. Beneath these initial redoubts, the first tunnels and stasis-locked supply vaults were constructed, eventually forming a labyrinth that now spans almost the entire planet.

kinds active and well supplied. Since the Tyranid assault begin, the Anchorage has been a battleground, fending off Tyranid bio-ships while attempting to repair and rearm the system defence ships. Heavily armed and armoured armsmen and Adeptus Mechanicus Skitarii troopers patrol the docks and hangers, fending off the Tyranids as best they can with flamer, shot-cannon and melta-cutter.

Depth 1281

Sector 903/Cell 11/Depth 1281, to give its full designation, is so named because it exists 1,281 metres below Hethgard's surface. The deepest extent of the tunnel network, Depth 1281 exists as a demesne of the Adeptus Mechanicus, claimed while the world's fortifications were still being designed.

Officially, Depth 1281 is a temple-forge, established by the Achilus Crusade's Adeptus Mechanicus contingent to minister to the spiritual needs of the Martian Priesthood and their vassals. Unofficially, it serves as containment for archaeotech devices of unknown provenance, as well as technology of xenos and heretical origins requiring careful study. Heavily warded and sealed, not even air can pass into or out of Depth 1281 without being subject to intensive augury by cautious and meticulous machine spirits. Certain members of the Inquisition have suspicions about the temple-forge at Depths 1281, but their investigations are hindered both by the secretive nature of the Adeptus Mechanicus, and possibly elements within the Inquisition seeking to gain access to the temple's contents.

Artisan Thol Xannaster is regarded as Hethgard's senior-most member of the Cult Mechanicus, and master of the temple-forge within Depth 1281, maintaining its outward appearance by overseeing the manufacture of limited quantities of high-technology equipment for Crusade personnel. This consists of items too difficult to produce in conventional field manufactories, but within the means of a significant Mechanicus congregation, such as plasma weaponry, power weapons and similar. In truth, he is merely the public face of the temple, serving at the pleasure of Magos Zoloman Raetzel, a high-ranking member of the sect known as the Crucible Resolviate, with a reputation for gleaning even the most obscure secrets from technology that many regard to be irredeemable in the optics of the Machine God.

Since the start of the Tyranid invasion, little has been heard from Depth 1281, but from time to time Phalanxes of Skitarii have been observed moving from the region armed with powerful and startlingly effective weaponry, vanishing back from whence they came without a single word after obliterating a Tyranid infestation. Whatever secrets lay within Depth 1281, they are clearly ones which could help turn back the Tyranid menace from Hethgard, yet the Adeptus Mechanicus maintain their silence about the matter.

An'karrah, the Cursed City

The last stronghold of the resistant population on Hethgard, An'karrah has lain abandoned for decades, having been quarantined by order of the Inquisition following the successful elimination of its inhabitants in the early years of the Crusade.

Much of the surface city was obliterated by orbital bombardment during the campaign to claim Hethgard, leaving little more than ash, rubble and radioactive glass as a testament to the deadly wrath of the Imperial Navy. However, extending below the ruins for almost six hundred metres are the mines and catacombs that the heretic armies used to defy the Imperium for so long.

The disused tunnels and mines are still marked with the dried blood of sacrificial victims and the blasphemous runes of unholy rites performed by those who had fallen from the Emperor's light, in spite of the cleansing by melta and flamer that accompanied the final assaults upon this last benighted stronghold. Rumours persist, passed around mainly amongst the rank-and-file during quiet moments, that some force still lurks in the ruins of An'karrah, or that something still worships in the vile fanes and at the dark altars that the Inquisition found there. Such rumours are, of course, punishable by a variety of means, depending on the mood of the Commissar or Preacher who overhears such impiety.

Alas, there seems to be some nugget of truth to those rumours—cloaked figures have been witnessed passing the sentries and checkpoints leading to An'karrah, unhindered by the Stormtroopers and sanctified weapon-servitors who guard the few remaining passages into the cursed city. While rumours of such things cannot be tolerated amongst the lower ranks, those of higher station contemplate such things more carefully and more solemnly, speculating that some element within the Inquisition could be delving into forbidden matters.

As the Tyranid assault on Hethgard has intensified, the ruins of An'karrah have proven to be a weakness in the fortress world's defences, a gap in the network of fortresses and tunnels that the Tyranids have exploited in great numbers. In response, greater concentrations of troops have been stationed at the entrance passages, seeking to fend off the vile creatures. Thus far, these soldiers have been successful in their efforts, driving the Tyranids back deeper into An'karrah. However, few who have served as part of the An'karrah watch, as this section of the garrison is known, are willing to speak of their time there, and a minority of them return changed, harder and crueller than they were before. The Inquisition and the Commissariat alike seek these individuals, fearing that they have become tainted, but the Tyranid onslaught makes this difficult, and cruel, war-hardened men is exactly what Hethgard needs to defend against the beasts of Hive Fleet Dagon.

USING HETHGARD

Hethgard is a fortress besieged, assailed by an enemy that cannot comprehend fear or surrender. Very few worlds in the Orpheus Salient are as strategically significant as Hethgard, as the home of the Salient's command centre and its placement as the rimward flank of the Iron Collar. Consequently, it is not unusual for Deathwatch Kill-teams to be deployed to Hethgard, their expertise and skill proving invaluable across the planet.

As a world devoted to warfare, a siege mentality is hardly unusual to Hethgard, and Hethgard's defenders are no strangers to warfare. However, it is rare to encounter an enemy so mindlessly tenacious and as adaptable as the Tyranids, and their onslaught is the fiercest conflict that Hethgard has ever known. The might of the Astartes is engineered for such conflict, and the extensive fortifications allow the Emperor's Finest to more easily defend against such overwhelming numbers.

Campaigns set on Hethgard should emphasise the constant and unrelenting nature of the conflict—at any given moment, the Tyranids will be attempting to breach the defences of at least a dozen different locations across the planet. Soldiers are continually being deployed and redeployed to confront the greatest concentrations of Tyranid creature, field hospitals are perpetually overworked, and gangs of menials rush back and forth from supply depots carrying all manner of wargear to the front lines. The continual rush and bustle are characteristic of Hethgard at war, and the cramped conditions of the world's fortresses and tunnel networks serve only to exacerbate this. In spite of the fearsome presence of the Astartes, and the awe they're regarded with, moving through the crowds with any haste is an awkward affair, counting the Guardsman-filled tunnels as a treacherous environment (DEATHWATCH Rulebook, page 206), imposing a −10 penalty on all Agility Tests made to Run or Charge through the crowded confines.

A sense of claustrophobia is another important aspect of Hethgard campaigns. The crowded tunnels contribute towards this feeling, but more crucial should be the constant sense that escape is, if not impossible, exceptionally difficult. Landing platforms and airbases are in continual use to perform aerial scouting, bombing runs and to move supplies and personnel to and from the Anchorage and the ships there, with access for other purposes strictly limited by the Lord Commissar's instructions. The Tyranids are swift to capitalise on gaps in the defences, and burrowing creatures like Raveners and Trygons are common adversaries in the tunnels, followed by Termagants, Hormagaunts, and Genestealers that arrive in their wake to flood the depths with flesh and chitin.

Campaigns focussed on the defence of Hethgard are a brutal and arduous affair, an almost literal example of an irresistible force against an immovable object. With the defence of surface bastions handled by hundreds of thousands of Guardsmen and servitor-slaved weaponry, the skills of a handful of Deathwatch Battle-Brothers are wasted amongst the deafening fusillade that erupts from each fortress. Their efforts are far better suited to daring forays into the heart of the swarm, and savage tunnel fighting where the numbers of the Tyranids cannot so easily be brought to bear.

CASTOBEL

"For almost six thousand years, we have stood strong against sedition, heresy and xenos domination, holding true to the light of the God-Emperor. For almost six thousand years, we have been alone in the darkness, a single beacon of light amidst the shadows of discord and depravity. No longer must we suffer so, no longer must we endure in silence… for we are reunited with our distant brothers, who return to deliver us from the shadows that have encroached upon this Sector for millennia! Praise the Emperor, and praise His valiant Crusaders!"

–Lord Commander Ortana Lokk

Regarded as the jewel of the Orpheus Salient, Castobel remained loyal to the Imperium through the Age of Shadow and welcomed the crusaders with open arms, turning its resources to the support of the re-conquest of the Jericho Sector.

Castobel is a bustling, industrious hive world, with a production capacity that eclipses that of every other world so far conquered by the Achilus Crusade, and the sheer numbers of people within Castobel's hives provide an ample supply of recruits for the Imperial Guard and Imperial Navy. Castobel is a fine example of how Lord Militant Achilus envisioned the progression of his namesake Crusade—conquered worlds contributing to the conquest of others, forging a newly self-sufficient Jericho Sector with each victory.

In recent years, Castobel's fortunes have changed. With the arrival of Hive Fleet Dagon, Castobel has come under siege by the Great Devourer and a world once responsible for supplying a small but significant proportion of the Crusade's men and materiel has virtually shut down. The Tyranid blockade and the invasion force on the ground has all but caused Castobel to grind to a halt, and its populace now huddles in fear of the ravenous beasts outside their walls.

However, all is not yet lost. Of all the worlds in the Orpheus Salient under assault by the Tyranids, Castobel may yet be freed of their menace. Castobel is barren and lifeless but for the masses in the four remaining hive cities, with little in the way of resources for the Tyranids to consume. Thanks to the decisive action of Lord Castellan Lokk, an unsteady stalemate has arisen, with the Tyranids unable to gain ground and bio-mass enough to replenish expended forces quickly, stealing away their greatest advantage: seemingly limitless numbers.

With time and bloodshed, the Tyranid threat on Castobel could be ended, leaving a population hardened by war and eager to enact revenge upon the monsters that tried to destroy their home.

HISTORY

Castobel is ancient, with some historical evidence to suggest that it predates the Imperium, having been colonised by humanity at some point during the Dark Age of Technology. In the days of the Great Crusade, Castobel joined the Imperium after a brief and bloody war eliminated its original ruling caste, which was swiftly replaced by a governor installed by Crusade forces.

When the Imperium first claimed Castobel, it was already a prosperous hive world, with four colossal cities emerging from the lifeless ash wastelands of a world dedicated to industry. Under Imperial rule it grew further, with several of the smaller wasteland settlements developing together into two additional Hives by the middle of the 33rd Millennium, and gaining stewardship of Battlefleet Jericho's primary dockyard a few centuries later.

When the Jericho Sector collapsed into anarchy, Castobel endeavoured to remain aloof from the disarray, remaining staunchly loyal to the God-Emperor in spite of the Sector's collapse. Using what remained of the Sector's fleets, including loyal remnants of Battlefleet Jericho, Castobel's Imperial Commander worked tirelessly to maintain the Emperor's law on several nearby worlds. Still, the isolation took its toll on Castobel and its colonies, and the world could not remain as it once was. After centuries separated from the Imperium, the hive cities on Castobel had become virtually independent city-states, unified only by their common faith in the Emperor.

That faith was fought for more fiercely than almost any other facet of life on Castobel. Separated from the higher authorities of the Adeptus Ministorum, the ruling families of the six cities found common ground in the need to maintain the religious structure that had for so long defined Castobellan life. The result was an organisation known as the Aquilan Pluracy, which took the place of the old Castobel Diocese as the highest religious authority on the planet, maintaining the temples and ensuring the populace remained appropriately reverent towards the Emperor.

This state of affairs remained largely unchanged for severa millennia in spite of raids by aliens, renegades and heretics, until 789.M41, when Battlegroup Santos arrived at the edge of the system to be greeted by vessels that had once belonged to Battlefleet Jericho. Upon discovery of their kinship, a message was sent to Lord General Curas immediately, informing him that Castobel was loyal to the Imperium and wished to return to the fold.

A hundred days of celebration followed, and at the end of that time, the 1st Castobel Reborn were raised and sent forth to serve the Imperium, while Lord Commander Ortana Lokk of Hive Tyralos was selected to rule as Imperial Commander and Lord Castellan of Castobel. By the end of that year, a further hundred regiments had been raised, with more on the way in every passing year. In the years since, over two thousand regiments of Castobel Reborn have been mustered and distributed across the Jericho Reach, alongside vast quantities of materiel.

That all changed, as so much in the Orpheus Salient did, when the Shadow in the Warp descended upon the Jericho Reach. Castobel came under assault in the early months of 817.M41, after more than four years of mounting interference within the warp. Once again isolated from the Imperium, Castobel's forces—its planetary defence force and the three hundred Imperial Guard regiments mustered since 812.M41 but left stranded by increasingly difficult warp travel—immediately set about bolstering their home world's defences and preparing for the arrival of a monstrous aggressor.

The Tyranid onslaught was swift and terrible, and they managed to overrun Hive Trimalov within six weeks of the first creatures making planetfall. Billions died, torn apart and devoured by mindless, slavering beasts and towering,

PLANETARY DATAFAX: CASTOBEL

Population: Estimated 109 Billion

Tithe Grade: Exactis Extremis

Geography/Demography: Heavy Industrial hive world; surface terrain consists primarily of polluted ash wastes. Extreme pollution and macro-scale industry over the course of several millennia have destroyed natural landscape and climate, as is typical for millennia-old hive worlds. Six primary hive complexes, with thirty-one lesser/peripheral settlements.

Government Type: Council of Hereditary Nobility, sanctioned and approved by the Adeptus Terra.

Imperial Commander: Lord Castellan Ortana Lokk, Lord Commander Ascendant of Hive Trimalov.

Adept Presence: High; as one of the few developed worlds within the Orpheus Salient, Castobel has a strong Administratum presence in order to oversee the massive tithe that is required of the world to support the Crusade.

Military: Castobel Planetary Defence Force (Light Infantry, 44 Regiments equivalent) commanded by Lord Castellan Lokk, Imperial Guard Garrison (11 Regiments) commanded by Brigadier General Titus Korven.

Trade/Economy/Addendum: Primary exports/tithed goods are basic munitions (las weapons, solid projectile weapons, and ammunition), agricultural and mining equipment, and Imperial Guard Regiments. Primary imports are fuel, food, potable water and raw materials for manufacturing.

THE LAST HOLDOUT

Unlike countless other worlds, Castobel remained loyal to the Imperium during the Age of Shadow, staying faithful to the Imperial Creed and maintaining the society that the Imperium had required of it when the Jericho Sector still existed. Though more akin to independent city-states than cities on a united world, the hives of Castobel hold to the authority imposed by the Aquilan Pluracy, which rules in the name of the God-Emperor. Consequently, when the Achilus Crusade reached Castobel, it found a world that welcomed it with open arms and was able to provide vast quantities of men and materiel. The world's survival is remarkable given the high resource demands of a hive world, yet it had somehow managed to remain strong and loyal for thousands of years of isolation.

As the Jericho Sector fell to darkness and sedition, the loyal remnants of Battlefleet Jericho fell back to the orbital docks above Castobel, accompanying whatever merchant vessels they could gather. As a result, Castobel was, over the following months and years, able to dominate a cluster of mining colonies and agri-worlds nearby, re-establishing a limited form of Imperial rule and keeping Castobel itself supplied with food and raw materials. In conjunction with advanced and ancient food processing facilities within Castobel's hives—which, upon the world's reclamation by the Imperium, became a subject of great interest for the Adeptus Mechanicus—these facilities allowed Castobel to function in spite of its almost total isolation.

As the millennia passed, the six hives became increasingly divided from one another, feuding and even warring over the already limited resources, and soon, the number of starships at Castobel's call and the number of worlds supplying it began to dwindle. Still, by the time General Curas' forces reached Castobel, it was more than able to provide billions of tonnes of material and millions of soldiers to the ongoing war effort, and proved to be a turning point within the Crusade, as the burden of supplying so vast an endeavour was no longer borne solely by worlds on the other side of the Jericho-Maw Warp Gate.

THE CASTOBEL REBORN

Upon Castobel's compliance, Departmento Munitorum surveyor companies descended upon the world to determine its capability to aid the Achilus Crusade. After a preliminary survey, lasting six months, it was declared that Castobel would be assigned the highest Tithe Grade, reflecting its massive capacity for supplying materiel and warriors alike. A further declaration was issued that the world could produce as many as a hundred Regiments of Imperial Guardsmen a year, each numbering as many as ten thousand men, without unduly impeding its ability to produce munitions and machinery.

Having already produced the 1st Castobel Reborn as part of the world's celebration of renewed Imperial rule, Castobel produced its first tithe of a hundred regiments a year later. The first muster saw Lord Militant Tetrarchus in attendance, and he gave the first hundred Castobel regiments the name of "the Reborn" and the right to bear his own insignia on their banners, to honour the first regiments founded within the Jericho Sector for thousands of years.

malevolent monsters. As the Tyranids destroyed Hive Trimalov and began to spread outwards to the other hives, Lord Castellan Lokk withdrew with his advisors to contemplate how best to defend against this enemy. When he returned after three days, he was grim and humourless, but stated that he knew what must be done.

While this occurred, the Tyranids had begun to move for Hive Tyralos, the second most densely populated of Castobel's hive cities. Hundreds of thousands of men—both soldiers and civilians bearing simple weapons as ragtag militias—stood in defence of Hive Tyralos as the evacuation began, selling their lives dearly to allow as many people to flee as possible. Then the order came through: withdraw into the city, lure the Tyranids in. An hour later, the skies burned with crimson light as Hive Tyralos died in atomic fire, the incandescent fury of its ancient reactors and generators unleashed to obliterate the swarm.

Both sides now exist in an unsteady stalemate. Castobel's defensive forces are depleted, weary and demoralised, and epidemics of Tyranid-spawned maladies rage through the populace. The Tyranids are similarly depleted in number and having been denied the bio-mass of Hive Tyralos—both their own and that of its populace—they cannot swiftly replenish their numbers nor easily muster the power for another assault. The war has settled into a routine of probing raids and attempted infiltrations of the remaining cities, with the defenders fearful of the skulking, hissing monsters that lurk outside their walls.

Yet hope, of a sort, remains. With the Tyranids starved of bio-mass and the reinforcements it would provide, the swarm is at its most vulnerable. If Castobel's defenders can deny the Tyranids long enough, the Tyranids might be crushed utterly, leaving the ships in orbit starving. This hope is a distant one, but one that many are clinging to.

KEY LOCATIONS

Below are a number of significant locations across Castobel's surface.

Hive Tyralos

One of Castobel's oldest and most populous hives, Tyralos predated the Imperium by several millennia, and contained a wealth of ancient technology dating back to the era of its original construction. When the Jericho Sector still stood, Tyralos was home to a major Adeptus Mechanicus presence, containing a coven of archaeotechnologists eager to uncover the secrets of the technology hidden within the depths of the hive.

As the largest congregation of tech-priests on Castobel, Tyralos' coven became the highest Adeptus Mechanicus authority on Castobel when the Age of Shadow descended upon the Sector, granting the hive considerable power and leverage over the other cities. The Cult of the Machine prospered within Hive Tyralos during its isolation, growing to challenge the Aquilan Pluracy within the city's depths.

When Castobel was reunited with the Imperium, so too were the coven's members reunited with their brother tech-priests, and efforts to unlock the secrets of Castobel's ancient technology were renewed by the newly arrived explorators. Many secrets were passed back beyond the Well of Night to forge worlds far from the Jericho Reach, for detailed investigation by the Mechanicus.

With the Tyranid invasion and the fall of Hive Trimalov, Hive Tyralos became the next most obvious target for the Tyranids. At the height of the Tyranid attempt to overrun the Hive, the Lord Castellan gave the order to sacrifice Tyralos to deny it to the enemy, an order met with much hostility from the Adeptus Mechanicus, who regarded the hive's contents as sacred. After fierce debate that raged for days, the tech-priests relented, under the condition that they would have a week to salvage what they could from the hive's depths and perform the correct rites to overload the hive's generatoria.

Hive Tyralos today is an irradiated ruin, barely resembling the towering city-complex it once was. As a testament to the fury of the city's destruction, the land a hundred kilometres in every direction around the city's ruins is irradiated and vitrified ash, utterly inhospitable to even the massively adaptable Tyranids.

Hive Trimalov

Once the largest and most powerful of Castobel's hives, Trimalov is now utterly devoid of human life for the first time in thousands of years. Possessed of a populace of more than twenty billion souls and home to Castobel's grandest cathedral, Trimalov was, for millennia, the world's capital, ruling in the Emperor's name over the other five cities.

Trimalov was, as well as the political heart of Castobel, the centre of the world's religious life. The Castobellan Diocese was based within Trimalov's cathedral, an immense edifice of gleaming marble and stark obsidian capable of containing over a million worshipful servants of the Emperor and dominating the hive's central spire. This cathedral grew in magnificence and opulence with every passing century, the tithes of the devout furnishing generations of Cardinals with the finest of goods.

The cathedral's glory did not diminish during the Age of Shadow, thanks to the Aquilan Pluracy, which sprang from the long alliances between the church and Castobel's ruling families. The Aquilan Pluracy saw the temples maintained and the people kept faithful through the long ages of isolation, ensuring that the world remained true to the Emperor's rule.

When the Imperium returned to Castobel, it was Trimalov's Lord Commander Ascendant who was made Imperial Commander and Lord Castellan of the entire world, elevating Trimalov once more to dominance over Castobel. However, the return of the Imperium was not as simple as some had believed it would be. The Imperium had changed since the Jericho Reach fell, most notably in the form of the Ecclesiarchy. Castobel's priests found themselves proponents of a heretic religion, adhering to a creed cast out after a brutal war of faith millennia after the Age of Shadow began. The priests of the Adeptus Ministorum descended upon Castobel to find the Temple of the Saviour Emperor still holding sway over the people, and set about replacing it with a more modern creed, to the dismay of the Aquilan Pluracy.

Trimalov is no more. It was torn open and infested by the Tyranid menace, its people butchered and devoured to feed their eternal hunger. The structure remains, a hollow shell standing in mockery of the long isolation Castobel endured. Its form is corrupted by spore chimneys and spawning pits, and vile xenoflora writhes with a mindless malice for kilometres in every direction, bursting from the ash and entangling steel, basking in the atomic heat of the city's ancient generatoria.

Hive Kevor

One of the four remaining hive cities, Kevor was constructed after the Horus Heresy within the spine of a mountain range, burrowing deep into the crust and extending for almost two hundred kilometres across the peaks. Possibly the most securely located and heavily defended of the cities, Kevor's highest spire now serves to house the Lord Castellan and his command staff.

Hive Kevor grew out from a string of mining settlements running along the length of the Kevor Mountains, the hive taking the mountains' name as the settlements expanded into one another and spread further and further out from their humble origins. By the time the mines within the mountains had run dry, nearly twelve billion souls inhabited Kevor and the city had become an established part of the landscape.

While the mountains no longer contain the resources they once did, the self-sufficient and stoic attitude of Kevor's populace remained strong, and the city's primary trade soon turned from mining to warfare, with much of the population joining Kevor's militia or leaving the city to serve on Castobel's few remaining warships. When the Imperium returned to Castobel, Hive Kevor provided over a third of the men recruited into the Imperial Guard, eclipsing all but the colossal Hive Trimalov in the number of soldiers mustered.

At present, Kevor remains defiant of the Tyranids skulking through the ash-choked mountain passes and swarming through the skies above the city. Its populace accepted the realities of war more swiftly than any others on Castobel, and their fortified mountain-hive promises to be difficult for any foe to overcome, even the Tyranids.

Hive Hessax

A short, broad hive spread across a vast expanse of ash desert, Hessax is the youngest and smallest of Castobel's hives, though still several thousand years old and home to more than ten billion loyal servants to the Imperium.

Hessax's location, as distant from the other hives as possible, is tied inexplicably to its purpose. Intended to manufacture components with which to maintain the vessels of Battlefleet Jericho, Hessax's isolation was a deliberate security measure to limit access to starship parts of such rare quality.

With the coming of the Age of Shadow, Hessax's role became increasingly crucial, its forges serving to maintain the limited flotilla that supplied and protected Castobel and its colonies from outside aggression. Production increased dramatically, for the city was the only place capable of providing the needed components to Castobel's makeshift fleet.

Since the return of the Imperium, Hessax has been no less busy. With only limited repair and resupply stations within the Jericho Reach, Lord Admiral Arkelius proposed to take advantage of any supply routes that could be found. In short order, Hessax's forges were turned to serving the Achilus Crusade's battlegroups. However, with the arrival of the Tyranids, fewer and fewer ships have been able to reach Castobel's orbit to resupply, and thus Hive Hessax stands dormant, its comparatively small size and isolation proving to be their best protection from the swarms of Hive Fleet Dagon.

Hive Orolan and Hive Ibellus

The two remaining hives on Castobel have long been regarded as a pair, rather than singly. Had the world continued to grow as it had done when the Jericho Sector still stood, they would likely have expanded into one another, becoming a single, massive hive rather than two distinct cities.

Situated less than fifty kilometres apart, the "twin hives" of Orolan and Ibellus are similar in many ways, their histories and populace intertwined by industry and tradition. Orolan has traditionally been dedicated towards the refinement and processing of raw materials, while Ibellus contained many of Castobel's most prolific manufactories, turning those refined materials into machinery and munitions.

Largely untouched by the politics that defined life in Tyralos and Trimalov, few but the nobility in the twin hives saw much change when the Age of Shadow fell, save for variation in work schedules and shipment deadlines. Similarly, the return of the Imperium saw increased activity within Orolan and Ibellus, but little else of note until recently.

The situation changed in late 816.M41, mere months before the Tyranids arrived; slightly more than two companies of Blood Drinkers Space Marines arrived in Castobel orbit aboard the Battle Barge *Crimson Sacrament*, damaged in conflict with some monstrous enemy. Several squads immediately made for Hive Hessax, seeking repairs and resupply from the forges there, while two full companies arrived in Hive Ibellus. Within weeks, the forces in Hessax had returned to orbit, but the 3rd and 4th Battle Companies that had come to Ibellus had spent the time fortifying the hive's tallest spire against an impending attack. Whether the *Crimson Sacrament* departed Castobel entirely or if it fights against the Tyranid fleet is unknown, but no sign of the vessel has been seen since it left orbit.

The arrival of the Tyranids saw Orolan and Ibellus subject to brutal orbital bombardment from the orbiting bio-ships, followed by wave after wave of monstrous aggressors. While Ibellus stood firm thanks to the prowess and tenacity of the Blood Drinkers, Orolan suffered greatly. Though it did not fall, thousands of warriors and millions of civilians were slain before the Tyranids could be driven back. The Blood Drinkers have remained within Ibellus, and much of the population of Orolan has retreated to the safety of their sister city and the Astartes who stand guard over it.

PHONOS

"No mercy to the Omnissiah's enemies, no pity for those who deny the Emperor, no respite for those who defy the might of Terra and Mars. They shall die hearing only the glories of the Machine God, unable to bear the power of His thunderous voice."

—Excerpt of data fragment Phi-Omega-Nu-Omicron-Sigma

Far from the Well of Night, in what was once the Zacchaeus' Expanse Subsector, lays a small, jungle-covered world that might otherwise have come to support a human colony in its own right, but for the intervention of the Adeptus Mechanicus. The world's original name is long lost to history, and it is now only known by a designation applied to it by the explorers who rediscovered it, based on the few data fragments discovered about the world: Phonos.

The world's only known man-made structures are at a single, isolated Adeptus Mechanicus facility, locked within a stasis field for what might have been thousands of years. However, Phonos itself was set upon by the Tyranids, and when the Imperium sent forces to investigate, they faced the full force of the Tyranid menace and paid dearly for it, losing most of Battlegroup Argo, including Lord General Curas, in the process.

HISTORY

Little is known of the history of Phonos, not even its true name, but what little has been pieced together from data-fragments and the initial reports of the explorators is as follows. At some point after the Horus Heresy, the Adeptus Mechanicus established a facility on an unclaimed world within the border territories of the Jericho Sector. The facility remained operational, subject to the will of the Jericho Sector's highest-ranking Magos as all Mechanicus Fiefs within the sector once were, for several thousand years. During that time, it adhered to a mandate of secrecy and isolation, limiting contact with the rest of the galaxy. Such a mandate is, typically, only employed to protect the most advanced and arcane of technology, such as archaeotech, rare configurations of Titan, and other mighty war engines such as the unique and terrible Ordinati.

As the Age of Shadow descended upon the Jericho Sector, the isolated facility cut itself off further, with all communication with the rest of the sector ceasing by the end of the 35th Millennium. It is believed that, at this point, the facility activated a stasis field generator contained within its structure, sealing itself off entirely. The last communication anyone received from the facility on the world now known as Phonos was a stream of unintelligible machine code, which forced its way between the minds of hundreds of astropaths, eventually stopping upon worlds containing datacrypts and archive repositories, cleansing them of any reference to the facility.

In the latter half of 812.M41, a Crusade expedition accompanied by a contingent of Adeptus Mechanicus Explorators reached a world known to the Mechanicus only as Phonos. As soon as the first report of Phonos' discovery reached Watch Fortress Erioch, the Omega Vault opened another of its many doors. Contained within the ancient, long-sealed chamber was a device, unrecognisable to all but the learned eyes of Watch Fortress Erioch's Masters of the Forge. The device appeared to be some form of control wand, apparently designed to interact with stasis field technology and believed to be linked to the facility on Phonos. Whether this is the case is yet to be seen, for nobody has yet managed to reach Phonos to employ the device and test the theory.

Little more than speculation exists about the facility and its contents, but the extensive nature of the security measures involved have led many amongst the Adeptus Mechanicus and the Inquisition to believe that the facility contains some form of extremely advanced weapon or war engine. Given that other data-fragments tell of the "Omnissiah's voice" and "the killing noise," many who are privy to such secrets believe that the device may be some powerful form of sonic weapon, kin to Ordinatus. If this is the case, then so deadly an engine of war would be a valuable asset to the defence of the Orpheus Salient, and a terrible threat if it fell into the hands of a group such as the Magi of Samech or the Stigmartus.

All that is known about Phonos for certain is that it is a world in the maw of the Great Devourer. When contact was lost with the Orpheus Salient, General Curas transferred his command to Battlefleet Argo, and set out to Phonos to investigate. Three and a half weeks later, Battlegroup Argo arrived at the system's edge, to bear witness to a world being devoured.

The Tyranids responded swiftly to Battlegroup Argo's presence; a beast interrupted while feeding, it struck with inhuman savagery, pouncing upon Imperial Navy squadrons and tearing them asunder with bladelimbs, feeder tendrils, bio-plasma blasts and pyro-acid sprays. Commanded by General Curas, Battlegroup Argo fought back valiantly, defiantly cutting apart the attacking bio-ships with salvo after salvo of continual fire. For eleven straight hours of fighting Battlegroup Argo held off the Tyranid advance as best they could, but outnumbered fifteen-to-one, they could only survive for so long, slowly losing one ship after another. The turning point came when the Mars-class Battlecruiser *Cardinal Xian* was boarded, its Captain choosing to sacrifice the vessel by overloading her reactor rather than suffer the fate of death by Tyranid claws. With so powerful a vessel lost, the end was in sight for the battlegroup.

The first that was heard of the fate of Battlegroup Argo came six months later, when the first of the straggling picket ships arrived back in Imperial space, having borne witness to the destruction of the Orpheus Salient's most lauded battlegroup, and the death of its supreme commander.

KEY LOCATIONS

The following are a number of significant locations on Phonos, many of which may have been ravaged and changed beyond recognition by the onslaught of the Tyranids.

Facility Phi-Omega-Nu-Omicron-Sigma

Untouched by time for six thousand years, the facility is enclosed within a stasis field, the structures within having remained exactly as they were the moment the field was activated.

From the outside, the facility appears to be a standardised design from the Adeptus Mechanicus STC canon, a Voss-pattern modular structure. Based on that and the observable configuration, certain details about the facility's structure can be ascertained. The surface elements of the facility are a latticework

PLANETARY DATAFAX: PHONOS

Population: Archive sanctity compromised, data lost

Tithe Grade: Aptus Non

Special Notation: Archive sanctity compromised, data lost

Geography/Demography: [Fragment Lost] is a humid, verdant world with a tropical climate. No known sapient indigenous life. No known settlement or habitation. World sequestered by the Adeptus Mechanicus for [Fragment Lost]

Government Type: Archive sanctity compromised, data lost

Imperial Commander: Archive sanctity compromised, data lost

Adept Presence: Archive sanctity compromised, data lost

Military: Archive sanctity compromised, data lost

Trade/Economy/Addendum: Unknown

THE NEPENTHE IMPERATIVE

The lack of available information on Phonos—which is not the world's original given name, but rather an extrapolation from a single archive fragment amongst those discovered by Adeptus Mechanicus data-historians cataloguing ancient Martian Librarium Vaults—is problematic to explorers. Only a few other details could be found within those fragments, including the location of the world, and references to an ancient Adeptus Mechanicus protocol referred to as the Nepenthe Imperative. According to what little information could be recovered on the subject, the Nepenthe Imperative is a meme-virus designed to spread to archives containing the targeted data, in order to prevent something being discovered. Many Magi consider the Nepenthe Imperative to be a myth.

THE SECRET OF PHONOS

An Adeptus Mechanicus research facility was discovered on Phonos in 7628812.M41 by the explorator vessel *Mathemantic Insight*, and it is this facility which is believed to contain whatever the Nepenthe Imperative was initiated to conceal. The facility itself is locked within a powerful and remarkably stable Stasis field, which the explorator mission was incapable of deactivating, leaving the facility as yet unexplored.

Many Logis have devoted millions of man-hours of effort from their attendant Lexmechanics in an attempt to discern what could be within the heart of the facility. As yet, they have been unable to reach any clear consensus as to what may be hidden there, though one clue does stand out above all others: in the Adeptus Mechanicus' vast array of cipher-dialects and code-languages, the word Phonos takes one of two meanings, depending on context and emphasis: sound, or murder. The fact that the archive fragments that gave this world its current name provide no clue as to context or intended meaning, suggests that either or both meanings may tell of what lays within the Stasis field.

of chambers and corridors covering approximately a square kilometre, equipped with servitor-slaved defensive weaponry and landing facilities capable of supporting bulk cargo lifters.

Given the nature of this facility, it is likely that it extends deep underground, providing storage areas and more extensive shrines and laboratories than those found on the surface.

Due to the presence of the stasis field, a closer and more thorough examination of the facility and its layout cannot be performed. However, the field has also prevented the Tyranids from approaching the facility, in spite of frequent attempts.

Table Mountain

Soon after the initial landing in 7628812.M41, the expeditionary force began establishing outposts for a garrison force, intending to expand upon them when reinforcements arrived. Table Mountain, a kilometre-high plateau in the midst of the broad valley north of Facility Phi-Omega-Nu-Omicron-Sigma, was selected to be the primary firebase, given its height and location, to provide anti-aircraft and surface-to-orbit fire against enemies attempting to land near the facility.

In 8040813.M41, Phonos came under attack, having lost contact with the rest of the Orpheus Salient a little over two weeks before. Bastions and firebases established across Phonos were overrun swiftly by a living sea of insatiable monsters, and crushed beneath the claws and hooves of countless millions of soulless predators. Within a week, all that remained was the Table Mountain compound, surrounded on all sides.

The Imperial Guard garrison—composed primarily of Guardsmen from the Gang Magna 632nd Regiment—held their ground, forcing back the Tyranids with disciplined, well directed fire repeatedly over the four days that followed, relying on the high ground and reinforced fortifications of their position to hold off the land-bound creatures, while the anti-air guns and defence laser destroyed Gargoyles and other airborne creatures.

The defence ended with the arrival of burrowing creatures, tearing upwards through the flat-topped mountain and bypassing the defences, slaying the Guardsmen. The last reports of the Guardsmen on the ground were recorded and transmitted to Battlegroup Argo when it arrived at system's edge, the final words of Phonos' garrison carried back to the Imperium on a damaged picket ship.

It is extremely unlikely that any trace of the compound remains intact; indeed, if the world has not already been consumed by the Tyranids, then it is currently being devoured.

CREDOS

"To stand in their sight, to be in their presence and bask in their glory, even through so pale an imitation as this… it is something that few can bear. Those who can stand proud before the gaze of a god often find their faith renewed and invigorated."

—Attributed to Lorek Thalin, 33rd Lord Cardinal of the Jericho Sector Arch-Diocese, 6443521.M33

Credos stands as a monument to the might of the Imperium and to the grand heroes that strove to unite mankind so long ago. For as long as the Imperium has laid claim to the stars themselves, Credos has existed to denote the impossible distances mankind has crossed and the strength of human ambition.

The world has seen many changes in the long millennia of its existence. The structure known as the Theopticon is said to have existed upon Credos' only continental mass since before the Horus Heresy, the statues of the Emperor and the Primarchs dominating the skyline with their size and majesty.

In the wake of the Horus Heresy, Credos became a world of specific importance in the Sector. As belief in the God-Emperor spread across the Imperium, temples and shrines were constructed to celebrate that faith, and worlds came together to share it. When the Church of the Saviour Emperor became the official religion of the Imperium, the many priests and clerics of the Emperor within the Jericho Sector embarked upon a pilgrimage to Credos, to stand beneath the gaze of the Emperor and His sons and consider the faith that they all shared. Over the course of many years, these priests resolved many disputes and came to many conclusions, determining the Sector's first Saints, the core tenets of faith, and the structure of the Sector's dioceses and which worlds would fall within them—in short, the entire religious landscape of the Jericho Sector.

In the millennia that followed, the Sector's Cardinals embarked upon a pilgrimage back to Credos once a decade, to discuss matters of politics and theology, their grand conclave being the only opportunity these powerful individuals had to all appear in the same place at the same time. However, the tradition was ended with the appointment of Arch-Cardinal Udo Asterus, who saw no need to discuss his power with those he considered beneath him, and Credos lay abandoned by all save the last generation of monks who maintained the temple.

Centuries after Cardinal Asterus' demise, Credos had been all but forgotten, its existence remembered only in the worlds of scholars, or so it was believed by the rulers of the Jericho Sector. For reasons which even today are unclear, the Deathwatch keep a watchful eye on abandoned Credos, despite the temple there being empty but for the desiccated remains of the monks who once dwelt there as caretakers.

For some five thousand years, the Deathwatch has maintained a vigil over Credos, employing a select group of trusted serfs to maintain the temple and the arcane machinery that keeps the immense statues from collapsing. During that time, many Battle-Brothers of the Deathwatch have voyaged to Credos, some to bear witness to the visage of their ancient fathers, while others confine themselves to the temple complex instead, venturing deep into the catacombs for weeks at a time.

The first Tyranid creatures made planetfall on Credos in late 816.M41, when a cluster of Mycetic Spores bearing vanguard organisms plunged into the ocean several hundred kilometres from the world's only land mass. It is believed that Credos, being largely lifeless, is a low priority for the Tyranids compared to populous worlds like Castobel or verdant ones like Phonos. Even so, the group of Deathwatch Serfs given stewardship of Credos must now contend with the likes of Genestealers and Lictors attempting to gain access to the mountain temple, slaying all they encounter to prevent knowledge of their presence reaching the Hive Fleet and bringing a greater concentration of Tyranids down upon them.

KEY LOCATIONS

There are only two locations of note on Credos—the Theopticon, and the temple that looks upon it. These are described in more detail below.

The Theopticon

Standing some six kilometres high at its tallest point, and consisting of ten remaining statues—the other eleven having been destroyed at some point during or after the Horus Heresy—in the image of the Emperor and nine of His Primarchs. The statues are not believed to be accurate depictions—few beings even during the Great Crusade could claim to have laid eyes upon the Emperor or His sons, and thus stylised representations or ones based on picts and existing art would likely have been the source instead.

The statues are constructed from carefully machined blocks of the hard yellow-brown stone common to Credos' surface, designed to interlock seamlessly with one another. Each is laden with arcane technology intended to help the statues endure the ages without being diminished by weathering or brought low by gravity, cunningly concealed so as to be invisible to all but the most meticulous inspection.

What also becomes apparent from close inspection is that the statues themselves are partially hollow, with chambers and passageways woven within their immense structure. Whether these tunnels were part of the original design or added later is a mystery, but given the sheer mass and enduring nature of the statues, it seems likely that were anything to be stored within them, there is little that would be able to liberate such items by force.

The Temple of the Vigilant Emperor

Significantly younger than the statues that gaze upon it, the Temple of the Vigilant Emperor was originally little more than an observation balcony, a habitation area and a small landing platform. Over the millennia, it has steadily expanded, initially into a sizeable monastery sufficient to house several thousand monks long-term, and keep several high-ranking priests in their accustomed manner for months at a time. As the wealth of the Jericho Sector Arch-Diocese grew, so did the size and opulence of the Temple of the Vigilant Emperor,

PLANETARY DATAFAX: CREDOS

Population: Estimated 1,500

Tithe Grade: Aptus Non

Special Notation: World sequestered by the Deathwatch, mandated by the Inquisition, clearance Omega Vermillion

Geography/Demography: Primary terrain is covered in surface water, with the crust existing some 10-15 kilometres beneath sea level. The only land mass above sea level is a single, mountainous continent.

Government Type: External; the single settlement on Credos is a monastery maintained by Deathwatch serfs.

Imperial Commander: Temple-Master Haddon Vire, on behalf of Watch Commander Mordigael of the Deathwatch.

Adept Presence: Non-existent—all personnel on Credos are affiliated with the Deathwatch.

Military: Minimal—approximately 1,500 serfs in service to the Deathwatch, all of which are trained for defence.

Trade/Economy/Addendum: No exports. Limited materiel supplies imported.

THE THEOPTICON

The only structure of any significance upon Credos is a range of colossal statues depicting the likeness of the Emperor and the Primarchs, collectively known as the Theopticon. Believed to predate the Horus Heresy, the Theopticon appears to have once consisted of twenty-one statues, with eleven of them—clearly those depicting the lost and traitor Primarchs—having been reduced to nothing more than rubble, leaving only empty spaces and shattered rock as testament to their presence. Each statue is some six kilometres high, carved from the hard yellow-brown stone of their surroundings, maintained by ancient and cunning technologies to help them endure the ages and stand under their own immense weight.

The statues are arranged in a vast arc, all facing inwards with each statue gazing at the same point as all the others—the highest peak on the small, mountainous continent. Into this peak is built a temple to the might of the Emperor, now maintained by forces loyal to the Deathwatch. Deathwatch personnel frequently make pilgrimages to Credos as a way of reconnecting with their spiritual and genetic fathers, though there are some outside the Deathwatch—amongst those few who know of Credos—who suspect some motive for the Deathwatch beyond Astartes spiritualism in their continued maintenance of the Theopticon and its temple.

as it has become known, eventually reaching a point where it rivalled some of the Sector's smaller cathedrals in size.

After the reign and death of Arch-Cardinal Asterus, the Temple of the Vigilant Emperor was ignored, becoming a footnote in history and a mausoleum for the monks who had dwelt there. However, the Deathwatch was not content to let such a fate befall Credos, and their efforts saw the Temple renewed. This time, military practicality and the spartan beliefs of the Adeptus Astartes prevailed over the greed and indolence once endemic amongst the Adeptus Ministorum, and the Temple became a fortress, reinforced against external attack, with many of its lower chambers repurposed to serve the Temple's new masters.

The Temple today is a bastion designed to be held by a small number of warriors against many, fitted with batteries of emplaced sentry-guns and servitor-crewed anti-aircraft weaponry. That, however, is only the surface of the Temple of the Vigilant Emperor. Beneath the mountain, and connected to a series of winding passages that lead into the statues themselves, the Temple's purpose becomes clearer. Vast quantities of arcane cogitators and sophisticated logic engines, connected to a colossal array of augurs, auspex feeds and a choir of astropaths fill the deeper chambers of the Temple, gazing upon the void and sending information back to Watch

Fortress Erioch continuously. Deeper still, the secure vaults within the statues themselves are often employed to store the most valuable and most dangerous of artefacts, hidden away from all but a chosen few.

Every so often, a matter of importance detected by the Temple's equipment requires the presence of a member of the Deathwatch to confirm and report on, a voyage often referred to as a pilgrimage. Indeed, many amongst the Deathwatch take the opportunity to reaffirm their oaths of service under the gaze of the Emperor and His loyal sons, while waiting for a Battle-Brother to return from the Temple's depths.

While not a Watch Station in the traditional sense, the Temple of the Vigilant Emperor on Credos serves a similar purpose, ensuring that the Deathwatch are aware of threats in the region and giving them the opportunity to prepare. At present, Credos' isolation and relative lack of Tyranid presence allows it to continue functioning, barely, but it is an asset so significant and valuable to the Deathwatch that the prospect of losing it to alien invasion is one that few wish to contemplate.

JOVE'S DESCENT

"It was… a singular experience. Never before have I felt such peace, such serenity, and such nobility of purpose as I felt when I set foot upon that world, as if an echo of our father's triumph was easing the pain of his death."

–Battle-Brother Saraqael of the Blood Angels

Found deep within the Jericho Reach, beyond all but the furthest-flung elements of the Achilus Crusade's forces, Jove's Descent is something of an enigma. Touched by heroes in the earliest days of the Imperium, the world somehow never became anything more than an insignificant footnote in the histories of the Imperium. Instead, all that remains are failed colonies and alien ruins, and the echoes of the long-dead that linger far longer than they have any right to.

Jove's Descent is a haunted and benighted place, yet one that holds many secrets and the interest of those who seek to understand the perils of tomorrow in the tales of long ago. The veil between reality and the Immaterium is particularly thin around the world, and the warp's unnatural power presses heavily upon it.

HISTORY

Believed to be named for the Rogue Trader Hadrian Jove, in the days of the Great Crusade, this world was the explorer's final resting place. His dying command, legend has it, was to send a distress signal to alert one of the Expedition Fleets operating near the region, to summon the forces of Imperium and purge it of the xenos that infested it.

Whatever the truth of the matter, three expeditions are believed to have arrived within the region, headed by warriors of the Legionnes Astartes, specifically of the Ultramarines, Night Lords, and Blood Angels Legions, or so is claimed by the apocryphal records of the era. Over the course of several years, these expeditionary forces made compliant over a hundred and thirty worlds within what would become known as the Jericho Reach.

WHERE THE VEIL IS THIN

Jove's Descent is a world touched by the warp, its influence leaking through the fragile veil between realms. This results not only in the strange phenomena that haunt this isolated world, but also affects the way that psykers draw upon the Immaterium.

Any Psyniscience Test made while on the surface of Jove's Descent gains a +20 bonus, but the character attempting the Test gains a number of Insanity Points and Corruption Points equal to his Degrees of Failure if the Test is failed, as horrifying, warp-spawned visions plague his witch-sight.

In addition, any character attempting a Focus Power Test at the Push power level may gain an additional +2 bonus to his Psy Rating (over and above the normal bonus granted by the Push power level), but must add +10 to all rolls on the Psychic Phenomena and Perils of the Warp Tables that he makes.

Jove's Descent, like many worlds in the region, was in the clutches of the Ghanathaar, an advanced, ancient non-humanoid xenos breed who were believed to have suffered some cataclysm millennia before to rob them of much of their former power. Little now remains that refers to the Ghanathaar, save for a few scattered references in the archives of the Blood Angels and Ultramarines, and the myths of those who now dwell on Jove's Descent.

As part of a protracted campaign of extermination, the Blood Angels forces made landing on Jove's Descent, waging a deadly war with the xenos inhabitants that cost the lives of thousands of Battle-Brothers. The details of this conflict are, alas, unknown to the modern Imperium, and even the Blood Angels themselves have little in the way of lore that speaks of the battles there. What is certain is that the Sons of Sanguinius eventually triumphed, scouring the world of the xenos that infested it, and soon after departed the Jericho Reach for reasons unknown.

The centuries that followed saw the Jericho Reach transformed into a fully fledged and loyal sector of the Imperium, and by late M31, the first attempts to colonise Jove's Descent were made. In the four millennia between the Jericho Sector's founding and the Age of Shadow, eleven distinct attempts to establish colonies on Jove's Descent were made, none of which were successful. Each colony fell afoul of some disaster that left only desperate survivors, reverting to an atavistic state in the untamed wilds after as little as a generation.

When the Achilus Crusade was first proposed, intensive research was performed on the Jericho Sector as it had been, combined with what information could be ascertained from the Deathwatch and from Adeptus Mechanicus Explorators braving the storms over the millennia. Jove's Descent, and its history of misfortune, were identified swiftly as a potential peril to Imperial reconquest of the Jericho Reach, and upon the commencement of the Achilus Crusade, the Inquisition saw fit to declare Jove's Descent as being under quarantine until a thorough investigation could be carried out.

At present, Jove's Descent is believed to be subject to Tyranid infestation, but this is supposition based on the world's position within the Jericho Reach. None can be spared to voyage out to that accursed world and discover the truth of the matter.

KEY LOCATIONS

Though little of Jove's Descent is mapped, a few locations are regarded as significant by both the inhabitants and by those few servants of the Imperium who have walked upon its surface.

Angels' Landing

A large clearing in the jungles on the north-eastern continent, Angel's Landing appears little different to countless other locations across Jove's Descent but for the crudely wrought totems and signs that adorn the clearing's edge. Each of these adornments bears familiar imagery—angelic figures clad in gold and crimson, the double-headed eagle, and the mailed fist clutching a pair of lightning bolts—reminiscent of the Imperium in general and the Blood Angels in particular.

PLANETARY DATAFAX:
JOVE'S DESCENT

Population: Planetary Survey Incomplete

Tithe Grade: Aptus Non

Special Notation: World currently subject to sociological and technological survey; travel to Jove's Descent is permitted only by express mandate of Achilus Crusade High Command.

Geography/Demography: Warm/Tropical; much of the planetary surface is covered in dense jungle.

Government Type: No singular government exists—multiple tribal communities catalogued.

Imperial Commander: None

Adept Presence: None

Military: Native warrior element within each tribe; not yet categorised.

Trade/Economy/Addendum: Internal economy appears to be a combination of hunter-gatherer and barter.

XENOS DOMINION

It is believed that at some point in the distant past, before the coming of the Imperium, a xenos species referred to in some sources as the Ghanathaar inhabited Jove's Descent. They were either wiped out or driven away at some point during the Great Crusade. Records of the time are incomplete at best, and there is no information remaining that describes the conflict, but some traces of them still remain. Sanctioned psykers of various kinds have noted that many locations—known to be regarded variously as cursed places and holy sites by the native tribes—have an odd psychic presence within them; the faint echoes of a campaign fought more than ten millennia before. Some Astartes, particularly those descended from Sanguinius have reported feeling the presence of their Primarch on Jove's Descent. Some believe that this suggests the Blood Angels fought at the forefront of the campaign that originally liberated the world from the Ghanathaar, while others warn of warp-spawned lies and illusions, mimicking the presence of the Primarch for their own sinister goals.

The obelisks and scattered, vine-choked ruins in these locations seem to be all that remain of the Ghanathaar's domain, but evidence exists to suggest that the culture defeated on Jove's Descent was little more than a backwards remnant of a far more powerful civilisation, laid low by some unknown apocalypse in the distant past.

CULTURE

The prevalent civilisation on Jove's Descent cannot easily be defined as any single culture, but rather as a collection of different tribes scattered across the planet's surface. To date, the Adeptus Ministorum has catalogued only a fraction of the different tribal structures and belief systems to be found on Jove's Descent. However, amidst that, a number of common themes have been observed.

A noteworthy proportion of the tribes observed seem to fall within one of two main categories: those who worship a primary deity analogous to the God-Emperor, as some remnant of pre-Age of Shadow Imperial civilisation, and those who appear to have fallen to worship of beings believed to be either the Ruinous Powers or the Ghanathaar. Other belief systems exist outside of these groups, but cannot be so easily categorised.

USING JOVE'S DESCENT

As a world largely untouched by the Achilus Crusade, missions on Jove's Descent will invariably lack any aspect of support from Imperial forces. The warp's influence upon the world, and the legacy left upon it by the Great Crusade, makes it a place of significance to the Adeptus Astartes in general, and the Blood Angels in particular, and not one that they will abandon to the Great Devourer.

Below are a number of seeds and ideas for possible missions set on or connected to Jove's Descent:

A cell of Acolytes, sent to investigate the psychic phenomena on Jove's Descent by Inquisitor Andarion, was lost when the Shadow in the Warp stifled astropathic communications across the Orpheus Salient. A week ago, Watch Station Erioch received a distress signal that originated with the cell's astropath, still on the warp-touched world. The Kill-team must brave the savage, tainted world and whatever Tyranids have reached it, to locate the Acolytes and rescue them, uncovering how their astropath was able to send a message from so deep within the Shadow in the warp.

A Battle-Brother of the Blood Angels or one of their successors (preferably one of the Kill-team, or an NPC comrade otherwise) is falling deeper and deeper into the clutches of the Black Rage, but a rumour within the psychic echoes of long-dead Blood Angels reaches the Battle-Brother and his allies, with the promise of some relief from the Curse.

Inquisitorial xenologists have studied what little evidence exists of the Ghanathaar, and fear that they may not be gone, merely hiding, and that the unknown xenos that attacked Hethgard may be related to this ancient xenos civilisation. The Kill-team are asked to venture to Jove's Descent, to unearth whatever they can from the ruins there.

Local tribes regard the clearing as a site of religious veneration, their priests—understood by Imperial scholars to be psykers almost without exception—visiting it to commune with "the Angels" who they claim once walked upon the world. Angels' Landing, they believe, is the place where these Angels first set foot upon Jove's Reach.

Given the strong psychic presence possessed by many Astartes, and the psychic phenomena so common to Jove's Descent, it seems likely that the Angels' Landing was actually a landing site for the Blood Angels strike force that fought there during the Great Crusade, their presence imprinted upon the world. The psychic shamans that guide the disparate tribes seem to possess the ability to discern these psychic echoes, gaining insight into a war that happened more than ten thousand years before, of which little record remains.

Needless to say, the prospect of such lore and insight is an attractive prospect to Imperial historians and to the Blood Angels themselves, who believe that it was not only their ancestors who walked upon Jove's Descent, but the Primarch Sanguinius. No Astartes could ignore evidence of his spiritual and genetic father's legacy, least of all the Sons of Sanguinius, and as a result, Jove's Descent remains of particular interest to the Blood Angels.

The Hollow Lands

The ancient and war-shattered ruins of a xenos city-fortress, these broken structures litter an area more than seventy kilometres across. The region is a twisted and corrupted place, covered in dry, ashen earth and black, thorny, twisted foliage, grown over the ruins of black glass structures that are said to have once dominated the horizon.

The local tribes refer to this place as the Hollow Lands, and regard it with great fear and superstition, with only the shamanic priesthood setting foot within its boundaries willingly, as a rite of passage and a test of prowess against the shades and revenants that haunt it.

The ruins that litter the Hollow Lands are thought to have come from one of the fortresses of the Ghanathaar, torn asunder by the Blood Angels during their war so long ago. Whatever dark science or foul sorcery the Ghanathaar employed during the height of their civilisation corrupted the land around the tower when the structure was destroyed, leaving a soulless and unnatural place, haunted by psychic echoes of the warriors who fought to destroy it, and the creatures that opposed them.

Hollow Land Revenants (Elite)

Those who brave the Hollow Lands are often set upon by things appearing to be shades or spirits, entities more likely to be psychic phenomena than true ghosts. For all their ephemeral nature, however, they can be quite deadly to the unwary or weak of will.

Hollow Land Revenant								
WS	BS	S	T	Ag	Int	Per	WP	Fel
43	—	58	11	40	05	51	60	—

Movement: 2/4/6/12   **Wounds:** 15
Skills: Concealment (Ag), Intimidate (S), Psyniscience (Per) +20.
Talents: Improved Warp Sense, Warp Sense.
Traits: Amorphous, Fear (1), Hoverer (5), Incorporeal, Natural Weapons (Revenant's Touch), Possession, Strange Physiology, Warp Instability, Warp Weapon.
Revenant's Touch: The warp energy that comprises these spectral entities is harmful to mortal life, burning at flesh and soul. In spite of being Incorporeal, the melee attacks of a Hollow Land Revenant can still harm physical creatures.
Weapons: Revenant's Touch (1d10+5 E, Warp Weapon).

WATCH STATION ARKHAS

"This is attempt 407 to pierce the Shadow in the Warp; 149 days have passed since the Shadow descended upon the Orpheus Salient. If this message is received, I urge you to respond as soon as possible. I will make another attempt during the next chronosegment."

–Loquator-Majore Emil Varras

The Arkhas system is located deep into the frontier territories claimed by the Orpheus Salient, within a region dubbed the "Tuam Transitional Nexus," a point where three distinct stable routes within the warp intersect, named for the Navigator who discovered it. The system itself contains many worlds, none of which are inhabited, though two—Arkhas III and Arkhas IV—both possess the capacity to support colonisation.

As a result, the Imperial Navy regards the Arkhas system as being a vital strategic location for the movement of troops, fleets and resources. However, unbeknownst to even the most senior officers within the Achilus Crusade, the Arkhas system was claimed long ago for exactly that reason.

Hidden within the gas clouds that wreathe Arkhas VII, the system's outermost planet, Watch Station Arkhas sits in constant vigil over the worlds now claimed by the Orpheus Salient, crewed only by a handful of tech-priests, a pair of Deathwatch serfs, and a single astropath. Set in place thousands of years before the Achilus Crusade began, tens of thousands of personnel have manned Watch Station Arkhas since its founding, each and every one adhering to the duty given them by their Astartes masters—be ever vigilant.

Appearing roughly like a pinwheel of black iron, Arkhas is concealed by cunning design and arcane technology, which have allowed it to remain unnoticed for its long watch over the Rimward edge of the Jericho Reach. The station is equipped with some of the most accurate and sensitive augur arrays the Adeptus Mechanicus can provide, under ancient compacts dating back to the Apocryphon Conclave, and is said to have been constructed above Mars itself.

Since its founding, Arkhas has been a rally point for numerous Kill-teams, but few have stayed within the station for more than a few hours before departing, either headed towards a vital mission, or returning from one before heading back to Erioch. Each time, they have departed bearing a precious crystalline data-coil, containing the Watch Station's augury logs and transcripts of the astropath's auto-séances, to be analysed at length by the Lexmechanics and Librarians stationed at Erioch.

In recent years, Watch Station Arkhas has been overseen by Emil Varras, a skilled and experienced astropath, oath-bound to Deathwatch service for more than two decades. Strong-willed enough to endure the burn-out that plagues many of his kind, Varras is nonetheless entirely blind and deaf and his flesh numb from the mind-searing effects of the Soul-binding, his senses deteriorating over the years as his powers have increased. A quiet, proud man, Varras has a particular talent for prophecy, his psychic senses keen even if his mortal ones are almost entirely gone. He turned this talent to gaze upon the furthest edge of the Jericho Reach, unsettled by the portents and omens that dominated his visions.

Varras' visions were lamentably accurate, foretelling a great and hungry darkness beyond the rimward edge of the Reach, which descended to cloud his sight at the end of 812.M41. Defiant of the Shadow in the Warp, Varras has persisted in attempting to cast his psychic gaze upon the void and attempts to send a new message out to any who can hear it. What little can be discerned from his attempts, he records as he has done for many years, upon a crystalline data-coil to be passed into the care of any Kill-team that sets foot aboard Watch Station Arkhas.

Amidst this, however, has come a new complication. The last few months have brought increasing numbers of vessels to the Arkhas system, as Navy patrols have withdrawn from the ferocity of the Tyranid advance and regrouped in the otherwise lifeless system. Composed primarily of elements from Battlefleet Daedalus under General Javier Casterlix and Commodore Ektor Cavanno, the forces gathered in the Arkhas system are oblivious to the Deathwatch, and muster for a renewed offensive against the Tyranids as soon as contact can be made with Hethgard to direct their assault.

PLANETARY DATAFAX: ARKHAS III

Population: None

Tithe Grade: Aptus Non

Special Notation: World is uninhabitable.

Geography/Demography: Temperate rocky desert; no indigenous life.

Government Type: None

Adept Presence: None

Military: None

Trade/Economy/Addendum: Arkhas system is well placed at an intersection between three primary transitional pathways within the Immaterium, and is thus of considerable strategic importance as a waypoint between key worlds along the Orpheus Salient and beyond; Divisio Tactica recommendation is that a resupply station be established within the system.

RALLY POINT EPSILON-FOUR

Due to its strategic location at a conjunction between stable pathways through the warp, the Arkhas system has been designated a rally point for Imperial Navy forces. A sentry ship will be placed in-system to rendezvous with regrouping Navy squadrons until such a time as a permanent station can be established.

WITHIN ARKHAS' VAULTS

Watch Station Arkhas has served the Deathwatch within the Jericho Reach for a long time, and in that time, many heroes have passed within its doors, and more than a few have left some sign of their passage within the station's armoury. A few of these items are described below, and are considered Relics in every way. They can only be requisitioned from within Watch Station Arkhas.

Forgeheart: Borne into battle by Re'kem of the Salamanders, a Battle-Brother who served his vigil within the Jericho Reach a century ago, this Meltagun was crafted by his own hands within Erioch's central armoury, and is renowned for the swiftness with which it sears through flesh, bone and steel. Forgeheart is a Master-Crafted Meltagun with a Pen of 15 and the Felling (1) Quality, requiring a Renown Rank of Hero and costing 60 Requisition.

Hallowed Razor: The personal weapon of Champion Heydrich, who served six vigils with the Deathwatch, two of them within the Jericho Reach. When he fell in battle, his blade was born to Arkhas' vaults by his Battle-Brothers, where it has lain ever since. The Hallowed Razor is a Master-Crafted Power Axe with the Razor-Sharp and Sanctified qualities, requiring a Renown Rank of Famed and costing 50 Requisition.

Omnissiah's Gaze: The work of Forgemaster Gharran, the Omnissiah's gaze is an Auspex of unmatched awareness, its spirit able to perceive more clearly than any other device of its kind. The Omnissiah's Gaze is an Auspex that grants its user an additional +20 bonus on all Tests made with the device. In addition, it can detect objects and phenomena up to 100m away, instead of the usual 50m, and can penetrate walls up to a metre thick. It requires a Renown Rank of Famed and costs 45 Requisition.

USING WATCH STATION ARKHAS

Located upon several swift and stable routes through the warp, Watch Station Arkhas has been a hub for Deathwatch movements along the rimward edge of the Jericho Reach for thousands of years, and even amidst the onslaught of the Tyranids and the Shadow in the Warp, the Tuam Transitional Nexus provides comparatively swift and reliable travel. As a result, many missions within the Orpheus Salient will begin at Watch Station Arkhas.

Arkhas' armoury is surprisingly large and well stocked, considering the Watch Station's small size, and while a number of the rarest items (any item requiring a Famed or Heroic Renown Rank) are absent from its stores, everything else is in plentiful supply.

In addition to logistical matters, Watch Station Arkhas can be a source of adventures in its own right. The powerful augur arrays allow a considerable amount of information to flow through and from the Watch Station, and the Loquator-Majore Varras' skill at prophecy can provide information leading to other worlds and other threats. His continued efforts to pierce the Shadow in the Warp may prove invaluable to the operations of the Deathwatch, the Achilus Crusade and the Imperium as a whole, if they bear fruit.

WATCH STATION PHAEDAS

"It is a marvel, a testament to the power of the Machine God… but nothing has ever caused me to question my faith in the Omnissiah so much as that place."

–Brother Aurelian Talach, Techmarine

Not a true Watch Station in the conventional sense, Phaedas is a relic of ages past, an archaeotech craft that bears no resemblance to any form of starship or void-station within Imperial records. If the Adeptus Mechanicus know of Phaedas' provenance, they are not forthcoming about it.

Phaedas is largely automated, its myriad machine spirits demonstrating sophistication that rivals those of the most ancient and revered of Titans. The vessel—if it can be defined as such—seems to operate based on incredibly complex logic paths, turning augury data into plotted courses, even able to travel short distances through the warp without a Navigator. Phaedas is comparatively small for an object capable of self-sustained travel through the warp—massing far less than the smallest warp-going craft in service to the Imperial Navy or Adeptus Astartes.

The station has space only to support ten Astartes, but contains a modest armoury and a supply vault sufficient for years of travel without requiring replenishment. It is also equipped with a launch bay loaded with a single Stormraven Gunship and a Drop Pod Bay equipped with a single Drop Pod, either of which is enough to deploy the Kill-team occupying it from orbit swiftly and with precision. Its small size and cunning design allow it to avoid all but the most careful of observers, making it extremely effective at conveying its Kill-team while remaining unnoticed.

History

The true origin of Watch Station Phaedas has been lost to the millennia, however, many Techmarines amongst the Deathwatch, Harl Greyweaver included, believe it has ties to Watch Fortress Erioch and the Omega Vault. There have been multiple recorded instances of the Watch Station dramatically changing course at almost the exact same time Techmarines aboard Watch Fortress Erioch recorded an Omega Vault event. This seeming link between the two mysterious stations has led to not only a full acceptance of Phaedas within the Deathwatch, but an almost permanent garrison in its cramped halls.

Throughout recorded history, the Watch Station has travelled to all corners of the Reach. It has been present at the some of the most of the major xenos events, and mysteriously it usually arrives prior to any signs that an incident is going to occur. Kill-teams operating on board are practised in reading the movements of the Station, and deducing when it has reached is destination. However, it is impossible to truly figure out the intentions of the arcane banks of cogitators driving the station, and Battle-Brothers act with extreme caution when using it for operations.

In 805.M41, Phaedas made a strange move that puzzled even Battle-Brothers who had served aboard it for decades. After astropathic messages regarding the conquest of Eleusis reached Watch Fortress Erioch the Watch Station radically changed course. Almost leaving behind the Kill-team that was operating out of it, Phaedas left the coreward edge of the Reach where it had been operating for months and began travelling at great speeds until it reached Jove's Decent near the rimward edge. There it stopped, much to the bewilderment of the Kill-team station onboard, and waited for almost a decade. Most assumed its archaeotech cogitators had finally given out, its machine spirit faded from millennia of tireless travel. But as the Shadow in the Warp descended upon the systems of the Orpheus Salient, Watch Station Phaedas sprung back to life. It is now a tool of utmost importance to the Deathwatch in the Reach, as it continues to move around the Salient in spite of the Shadow blocking all astropathic communication. It is currently the only way for Kill-teams to get a jump on the Tyranid swarm as it devours the Salient.

Structure

Despite moving around the Sector as readily as a starship, Watch Station Phaedas more closely resembles an ancient void-station, built into a small asteroid. Clearly of human origin, this archaeotech structure has no evidence of engines, or any normal void-ship structures. How it manages to move through the void has remained a mystery to all who have used it over the millennia.

The majority of Phaedas' internal structure is devoted to its essential systems, all of which run with an efficiency that disturbs the servants of the Machine God greatly, requiring little in the way of maintenance rites or mortal intervention. The only parts of the Watch Station that are readily accessible to its crew are at the fore—the Kill-team's cells, the armoury, the launch and drop pod bays, and the strategium.

This strategium, a tiny chamber compared to its like aboard the starships of the Astartes, serves much the same purpose as a starships bridge or a void-station's command centre, allowing the crew to interact with Phaedas' systems and direct it.

USING WATCH STATION PHAEDAS

As a mobile, stealthy base of operations, Watch Station Phaedas can provide a Kill-team with a potent asset to support their operations across the Orpheus Salient. Its small size can prove a limitation in some regards—larger Watch Stations may contain larger or more extensive armouries, or even vehicles, and may provide other resources, such as an astropath or room to support several Kill-teams—but in many cases this is more than compensated for by the station's ability to deliver a Kill-team to their target undetected, providing intelligence to them from its augurs as it hangs in orbit.

Being extensively automated, Phaedas can also serve as an adventure hook in its own right, its tendency to respond to signals from the Omega Vault can push a campaign down a different direction as the Kill-team finds themselves taken somewhere unexpected.

The sophistication of Watch Station Phaedas is a considerable advantage, but not without its difficulties. A character with Tech-Use +10 is required to operate Phaedas' systems, though no tests are required except in specific or unusual circumstances. When in orbit above a target location, a member of the Kill-Team may attempt an **Ordinary (+10) Tech-Use Test** in order to use the Station's augurs to gain information about that target. It is up to the GM to decide just what information the Station can gather. Generally, each degree of success should offer the Kill-Team additional intelligence.

The Watch Station's small size limits the capacity of its armoury, and while it is well stocked with most common items employed by the Deathwatch, rarer and more specialised equipment is in far more limited supply. As a consequence, no item with a Renown Requirement of Famed or higher is available if drawing from the Watch Station Phaedas armoury, and only one of each item with a Renown Requirement of Distinguished is available. In addition, no vehicles are available from, nor can they be stored within, Watch Station Phaedas, with the exception of a single Drop Pod and a single Stormraven Gunship (the latter of which can be used to retrieve the former from a planet's surface).

HEROES OF THE SALIENT

"I have seen many grand sights during this Crusade, but few grander than the spires of Castobel when a million souls mustered for war. It represents the triumphs we have achieved, the many worlds we have claimed, and the promise of scores of victories yet to be realised."

–Lord Militant Solomon Tetrarchus

Amidst the loss and horrors that have befallen the Orpheus Salient, a few individuals still stand strong and proud against the devastation wrought by Hive Fleet Dagon. Each of these heroes of the Imperium is vital to the continued war effort, for their will sees countless millions of soldiers and hundreds of starships mobilised to deny the Tyranids' advance.

GENERAL MIKAL CURAS

"No mercy; I want every false preacher on that benighted world put to the sword by the month's end!"

– General Curas at the beginning of the conquest of Eleusis

Lord General Mikal Curas was a man of great piety and formidable charisma, who earned the love and respect of the countless millions of men under his command. His career had seen him elevated to heights of power the likes of which defy the imaginings of most men, and he had risen to the challenge each and every time.

Born to a minor noble household on Luggnum, Curas served in the Imperial Guard for thirty years before the start of the Achilus Crusade, having reached the rank of Colonel. After serving as General Tetrarchus' second-in-command during the conquest of Hethgard, his skill was rewarded further by being asked to join the General Staff—the youngest officer within that select group. In the years that followed, Curas went from being Tetrarchus' advisor to a General in his own right.

When Lord Militant Achilus died and Tetrarchus was named his successor, he took the opportunity to further elevate the young officer to the rank of Lord General and Supreme Commander of the Orpheus Salient. Many felt that this appointment was foolhardy, for Curas was largely untried, and the remnants of Achilus' old guard were uncertain of such a young and ambitious officer. However, Tetrarchus' decision was proven to be a wise one when, within a few years, the Orpheus Salient had outstripped the Acheros and Canis Salients in victories and territory gained.

Curas' death and the loss of Battlegroup Argo was costly to the Salient's forces, which were already depleted and demoralised by the demands of the other Salients and the early predations of the Tyranids. Two dozen warships and more than a million crewmen died, and the man who had led the Salient's forces for twenty-five years was lost. The decision was made quickly to keep the fact from all but the highest levels of Crusade command—most are still unaware of Curas' disappearance, thanks to the communications blackouts caused by the Tyranids' advance.

This deception, perpetuated by Curas' closest advisors, has maintained the illusion of the General's presence, with orders being signed in his name and passed to those commanders who can still receive orders amidst the Shadow in the Warp. If any do suspect Curas' absence, the need for reassuring stability to keep morale from slipping further has ensured their silence.

Lingering echoes of his command still remain. While most communication across the Orpheus Salient is stifled and hindered by the Shadow in the Warp, astropaths on dozens of worlds still report receiving fragments of orders, communiqués and instructions from the General, bearing the ident-memes of Battlegroup Argo's senior astropath in spite of its destruction five years ago. Most dismiss these echoes as being scattered remnants of old orders given before his death, but some are not so certain, claiming that they have received messages sent after the General's death, and that they match no orders actually given by the Salient's leadership.

USING GENERAL CURAS

Being dead, General Curas is unlikely to have any direct influence over the Orpheus Salient in a typical, present-day campaign. However, he left a lasting impression upon the Jericho Reach with the worlds claimed under his command, and he was a well loved and highly respected commander of men, who earned the respect of the Space Marines he dealt with. A few who fought in campaigns Curas oversaw had their valour and prowess recognised by the General, often in the form of an official commendation, for Curas knew both the value that Space Marines place upon honour, and the worth of a closer bond between the Space Marines and the other forces of the Imperium.

NEW DEED: COMMENDED BY GENERAL CURAS

A Deed is a special benefit that a character may select at character creation. For more information on Deeds (and many more options), see RITES OF BATTLE.

Cost: 100xp

You fought upon many worlds in the Orpheus Salient, earning the personal regard of General Mikal Curas and being honoured by your superiors for it.

Effects: You gain the Skull and Motto honour (see page 211 of RITES OF BATTLE) bearing the name "Curas," which confers upon you a +10 bonus to all Fellowship-based Tests when dealing with Imperial Guard forces in the Orpheus Salient.

GENERAL DERIAN ARKELIUS

"To win a skirmish requires deadly warriors, the likes of which the oldest legends exalt. To win a battle requires dashing leaders of men, the stuff of grand tales and legend. To win a war requires forethought, planning and grand insight… things that lesser men seldom have a head for."

–General Derian Arkelius

One-third of the Triumvirate commanding the Orpheus Salient, Derian Arkelius is the eldest son of the Arkelius noble house of Scintilla—a masterful strategist and an ambitious young officer with dreams of succeeding General Curas. Unfortunately for Arkelius, his capabilities as a leader are sorely lacking for a man of his station, though he appears unaware of his deficiency in this regard.

As one of General Curas' advisors, his talent for strategic matters came to the fore, and he thrived as a member of the Salient's General Staff, devising the strategies that Curas implemented so successfully on Eleusis and many other worlds. However, his distance from the front lines has, quite at odds with General Curas, made Arkelius callous and uncaring of the men under his command, who he regards more as statistics to be calculated and variables to be accounted for.

Almost as soon as news of Curas' death reached him, Arkelius began lobbying to replace the late General, sending a barrage of astropathic messages, though none of them appear to have arrived given the lack of response and the smothering presence of the Shadow in the Warp. Arkelius' ambition, and the callousness with which he regards the men under his command, are a dangerous combination in the face of the Tyranids, and more than once he has clashed with Lord Commissar Theren over so reckless use of the increasingly limited forces available.

In the five years since the Triumvirate was formed, Derian Arkelius has become a shadow of his former self. His rivalry with his sister—always fierce—has grown in intensity, as control of the Salient's forces is now at stake, and the increasing pressure of commanding forces in the face of the Tyranid advance has taken a toll. Arkelius now seems far older than his years alone would suggest, and his mind is fraying, leaving little more than cynical ambition unrestrained by wisdom or caution, and an increasing sense of enmity towards any who he feels is a challenge or rival to his authority.

The worst of this hostility has not yet started to take a toll on the Salient's forces. He is continually protected by an honour guard drawn from his personal regiment, the 84th Scintillan Grenadiers, and his orders are vetted by Lord Commissar Theren and filtered through many layers of subordinate commanders. As yet, only the higher levels of the Salient's command have heard more than rumours about the General's worsening mental state, and few beyond Lord Admiral Arkelius and Lord Commissar Theren know how bad things are.

However, Arkelius has begun to make enemies, his decisions coloured by greed and ambition. Lord Castellan Lokk of Castobel is a particular source of consternation, being well loved by his men and a decisive and successful commander, while Steward Militant Vierling of Hethgard is regarded as a rival far closer to home, an officer extremely similar to Arkelius in talent and ambition. Worse still, Arkelius has managed to alienate the Astartes as well, regarding them as a dangerous and unpredictable element, a variable he cannot control or account for, and this distrust and resentment has hindered collaboration between the Imperial Guard and the Astartes on many worlds.

This is most evident on Hethgard, where he has repeatedly clashed with Captain Abroghan Callister, the commander of the Storm Wardens presence on the world, whose pride and temper do not allow him to tolerate "throne-room strategists," as he calls those who command armies without braving the front lines. He has also found enemies amongst the Deathwatch, who he regards as even more unpredictable than most Astartes, unbound as they are to the Achilus Crusade, and there is no love lost between General Arkelius and the few Kill-teams who have had the misfortune of dealing with him.

Now that the war has reached his command post on Hethgard, he has no choice but to deal directly with the men under his command, rather than to orchestrate their movement from afar as is his preference. A poor leader, incapable of relating to his men, and ill-suited to command in the heat of battle, Arkelius cannot easily bring to bear the strategic mind that won him such renown, and the world's defence can ill-afford to be in the hands of a commander so poorly suited to the situation.

USING GENERAL ARKELIUS

General Derian Arkelius is an individual with no love for the Space Marines, and whom the Space Marines are ill-disposed towards. His inclination towards analytical strategy, where the men at his command are numbers to be calculated and variables to be accounted for, is poorly regarded by Space Marine leaders everywhere, while he regards the Adeptus Astartes as glory-seeking and unpredictable elements that should rightfully be under the command of what he feels are proper Imperial authorities.

Needless to say, it is seldom advantageous for a Kill-team to be operating openly in a warzone overseen by General Arkelius, as the General's prejudices against the Emperor's Finest make cooperation with Imperial Guard forces difficult at best. Being in a warzone directly overseen by General Arkelius imposes a –10 Penalty on all Command Tests made to exert authority upon Imperial Guard forces subordinate to the General, due to standing orders not to cooperate with the Adeptus Astartes. This is, at present, most likely to occur on Hethgard, as Arkelius' command post is currently there.

In addition, missions performed openly within such warzones are far more likely to become complicated by Arkelius' distrust of the Astartes, often resulting in bad intelligence, friendly fire, or foes alerted to the Kill-team's presence as Imperial Guard forces act without regard for their erstwhile allies.

LORD ADMIRAL ANASTASIA ARKELIUS

"It is insufficient to cleanse world after world of the malefic taint of creatures such as these Tyranids. The dark void itself must be stained with the blood of this menace. It is not by the guns of the Imperial Guard or even the might of the Astartes that this will be done, but rather by the proud ships of the Imperial Navy."

–Lord Admiral Anastasia Arkelius

The younger of the Arkelius siblings in military service, Anastasia Arkelius has enjoyed a more successful career than her older brother, Derian, having reached the higher ranks of the Admiralty while still only in her first century. At the beginning of the Achilus Crusade, she served as a Rear Admiral, newly promoted, overseeing the movement of vessels through the Jericho-Maw Warp Gate and liaising with the Battlefleet Calixis Admiralty to maintain supply lines.

After Lord Militant Achilus' death, Arkelius found herself elevated to Admiral, as Lord Militant Tetrarchus began to rearrange the Crusade's command staff. Placed in command of the six Navy battlegroups of the Orpheus Salient—Icarus, Argo, Cerberus, Daedalus, Vishnu and Santos—she was shortly thereafter elevated to Lord Admiral and commander of all Imperial Navy forces within the Salient.

Being a fine tactician and a responsible commander, Arkelius understands the weight of command well, and the burdens of the Admiralty are great indeed, with the lives of hundreds of millions of souls on thousands of ancient, venerated and often irreplaceable starships, within her hands. She has earned the utmost respect from the crew of her flagship, the *Emperor's Nobility*, and by the Admirals, Commodores and Captains of her fleet.

Arkelius' flag can be found within Battlegroup Cerberus at present, as it has been since just before General Curas died. It operates close to the Iron Collar, and part of the group was anchored above Hethgard until the Tyranids reached the fortress world. From the battlegroup, Arkelius commands the other four remaining battlegroups (Battlegroup Argo having been lost with General Curas) as best she can, given the difficulties of communicating through the Shadow in the Warp and the scattered nature of those battlegroups due to withdrawals and defeats.

When General Curas was lost, and Lord Commissar Theren wrought his deception, Lord Admiral Arkelius was the first to be informed and brought into what would become the Triumvirate. To this day, she uses that, and the swiftness of her ascendance to one of the highest ranks in the Imperial Navy, to taunt and bait her elder brother into some rash course of action, maintaining a rivalry that has existed between them since they were children. That she is still willing to antagonise her brother, who is the most powerful Imperial Guard commander in the Salient and extremely valuable to the continued conflict there, demonstrates perhaps her greatest flaw in judgement, placing a long-standing family feud and her own pride above the defence of the Salient's remaining worlds. Without Lord Commissar Theren to mediate disputes between the two, the Orpheus Salient might have collapsed entirely years ago.

As is common amongst the officers of the Imperial Navy, Arkelius regards the Space Marines with a mixture of caution and respect. Few officers in the Navy feel comfortable with the Space Marines maintaining their own fleets, and an uncertain peace exists between the Navy and many Space Marine Chapters over the matter of war-fleets. However, Arkelius respects the Space Marines' prowess and effectiveness, though she is cautious of their ulterior motives. With the Deathwatch, the same is true, though to a greater extent, and she is far from appreciative when her vessels are commandeered for clandestine missions.

USING LORD ADMIRAL ARKELIUS

As a senior flag officer of the Imperial Navy, Anastasia Arkelius holds a cautious respect for the Space Marines, wary of their ambition and their secrets, grateful for their might and inspirational presence. As the highest ranking Imperial Navy officer in the Orpheus Salient, Arkelius is more aware of the comings and goings of interstellar forces across the Salient than almost any other person, with command of thousands of starships both military and civilian (due to the Orpheus Salient being a warzone, military authorities have oversight over civilian and merchant vessels). Consequently, she and her subordinates are frequently asked to provide support to the Deathwatch, for transport to, insertion into and extraction from a mission location when a Deathwatch vessel is not available or suitable for the task.

Lord Admiral Arkelius responds best to Kill-teams who have proven themselves on many occasions, and particularly those who have made an effort to cultivate a strong relationship with the Imperial Navy. On any Interaction Test against an Imperial Navy officer subordinate to Lord Admiral Arkelius, a Battle-Brother gains a bonus equal to the first digit of the character's Renown score, rounding down, and an additional +5 if they already have the Peer (Imperial Navy) Talent.

ADVENTURE HOOKS

Below are a number of possible adventure hooks relating to Lord Admiral Arkelius and the Imperial Navy forces under her command:

Portents of Attack: A patrol group despatched to Beseritor has not been heard from in several months, leading many to wonder if the hive world has come under attack. Lord Admiral Arkelius has petitioned the Deathwatch to investigate, and recover whatever intelligence the patrol may have obtained.

Message from the Lost: A derelict vessel appears above Aurum, its machine spirit broadcasting a distress signal identifying the acid scarred wreckage as part of the lost Battlegroup Argo, and a fragment of the captain's final logs, requesting the urgent attention of Lord Admiral Arkelius. The Kill-team has been requested to brave the potentially infested depths of the derelict, to locate and secure the vessel's datacrypt.

LORD COMMISSAR VANCE THEREN

"By the authority I bear in the God-Emperor's Name, you are charged with cowardice in the face of the enemy, of gross and treasonous negligence in the employment of His warriors and His resources, and of base incompetence of command. For such crimes, only the Emperor may pass judgement, and thus I condemn you to death that you may face His scrutiny."

–Lord Commissar Vance Theren, before the execution of Colonel Alastayr Vone

The most senior Commissar in the Orpheus Salient, Theren has presided over matters of military discipline since the first day of the Salient's foundation. A veteran of many conflicts, Theren has served both on the ground alongside the Imperial Guard, and as a Fleet Commissar with the Imperial Navy, giving him valuable experience in a variety of theatres of war, and making him an ideal choice for such high authority. His oversight onto all Imperial Guard and Imperial Navy activities within the Salient is carried out through the means of thousands of lesser Commissars stationed aboard starships and deployed within Imperial Guard regiments.

A dutiful and honourable man, Theren does not suffer the wasteful use of the Emperor's armed forces, regarding the lives of the Emperor's servants as something not to be expended frivolously or rashly. Indeed, quite at odds with the archetypal image of the Commissar, Theren cares about the men under his authority. This has caused him to clash with the Generals under his jurisdiction on several occasions, even going so far as to veto the battle plans of General Arkelius more than once, and having executed several senior Imperial Guard officers for negligence over the years of the Achilus Crusade. Further, he has reprimanded several of his subordinate Commissars for being overzealous in their punishments. The lives of the Emperor's servants are valuable and it is the responsibility of their leaders to ensure that the dutiful efforts of even the least of men are employed wisely, as Theren is swift to point out to his subordinates.

In spite of this atypical outlook, Theren is a stern disciplinarian, having established a collection of penal companies in order to deal with those who step out of line, and commandeering a special battalion of veteran troops to serve as military police, as he has found that squads of exceptionally disciplined men, unbound by regimental loyalty, make effective enforcers.

A devout servant of the Imperium, Theren cannot help but regard the Space Marines with due reverence, and long years of service within the Jericho Reach, interacting with Space Marine commanders, has given him a deep respect for their abilities, and the morale-bolstering effect their presence can have. Given the current state of the Orpheus Salient, he is ever willing to stand in support of the Space Marines and to accept their aid in fighting back against the Tyranids.

Part of the Achilus Crusade from the very start, Theren served closely with General Curas, and he held the General in high regard almost from the outset. Curas' death was a blow to Theren, though his stern demeanour will not allow his

sense of loss to show. He has begun to doubt the teachings that have defined his life in the face of an enemy unlike any he has ever faced. In spite of this, Theren is one of the few individuals holding the Orpheus Salient together, his discipline and sense of duty maintaining order in the most terrible of circumstances.

The deception maintaining the illusion of General Curas' continued service was Theren's idea, and he maintains control over it, mediating between the Arkelius siblings who form the rest of the Triumvirate, and providing overall command in spite of their familial rivalry. Amidst all this, he liaises with Space Marine forces within the Salient, cooperates with the Deathwatch, and handles much of the inter-organisational politics that so frequently blights Imperial operations, wrangling with the demands of the Administratum, Adeptus

USING LORD COMMISSAR THEREN

In the years since General Curas' death, Lord Commissar Theren has made an effort to strengthen ties between Orpheus Salient forces and the Adeptus Astartes fighting alongside them, particularly the Deathwatch. The need for strength and inspiration to aid in the defence against the Tyranids makes every Space Marine a valuable ally to the Imperial Guard forces Theren is responsible for—absolutely crucial to the ongoing war effort.

Similarly, as a proud and devout servant of the Imperium, experienced in the field of battle as well as the politics of high command, Theren is well regarded by many of the Space Marines he has dealt with.

ADVENTURE HOOKS

Below are a number of possible adventure hooks relating to Lord Commissar Theren and the forces under his authority:

Much Needed Support: Commissar Theren frequently petitions Space Marine commanders and the Deathwatch for aid within the many warzones covered by the Orpheus Salient, seeking their aid in repelling the assaults of mankind's enemies—most frequently Tyranids, although other foes have also used the opportunity to strike against the beleaguered defenders of mankind. Kill-teams frequently serve such duties, their prowess and reputation normally sufficient to bolster the defences long enough to find a more permanent solution, such as the assassination of an enemy leader.

Eliminate the Vanguard: In the last month, several vanguard organisms have been intercepted trying to assault Lord Commissar Theren's command post on Hethgard. While none have managed to breach the heart of the fortress as of yet, they push deeper with each assault. Should Theren fall, then the Orpheus Salient would soon crumble without his iron will to drive it. The Kill-team has been tasked with opposing these probing attacks and finding some way to prevent future strikes.

Arbites, Adeptus Ministorum, and Adeptus Mechanicus, while endeavouring to win an extremely costly war. In short, it is Theren's iron will that is the greatest factor in both the deception that General Curas still lives, and rallying the Crusade forces that the General once commanded.

It should come as little surprise that Theren seems withered and exhausted to those who meet him in person. The cost of the Orpheus Salient's seemingly inexorable collapse weighs heavily on any man, and like his compatriots in the Triumvirate, the strain is taking a toll. Amidst this pressure, Theren is gladdened by the increased Space Marine presence within the Salient, and the more widespread deployment of Deathwatch Kill-teams, for every Space Marine who stands beside the mortal guardsmen and shipsmen of the Orpheus Salient lessens the weight upon his shoulders and those of every officer under his command.

WATCH CAPTAIN MARIUS AVINCUS

"Brother-Sergeant Avincus, you have served this Chapter honourably and solemnly for many long years, and I have no doubt that you would continue to do so under other circumstances; instead, you honour our Chapter and Primarch greatly by choosing to serve as our ambassador in the distant reaches of the galaxy, to spread our experiences and insights to our brother Chapters. I salute your endeavour and your devotion."

–Brother-Captain Agemman

Born to a noble family on Prandium, Marius Avincus Caeso was recruited into the Ultramarines with his twin brother Gnaeus, and both served together for centuries. After more than three hundred years in service to the Ultramarines, the brothers faced a horror the likes of which none could imagine—the Tyranids attacked Prandium. Gnaeus was slain, crushed by a Carnifex while trying to defend refugees being evacuated from their home world.

Avincus was furious at what the Tyranids had done, and he was given the opportunity to strike back against them during the Battle for Macragge, where he fought valiantly amongst the 3rd Company, seeing many of his Battle-Brothers slain during the brutal tunnel fighting. In the years that followed, he was amongst those survivors who were chosen to join the 1st Company as one of Chaplain Cassius' Tyrannic War Veterans. Twelve years later, he was nominated for Deathwatch service, and he gladly swore the Apocryphon Oath in order to share his experiences with those outside the Ultramarines, to give them a fighting chance should the Tyranids return.

In the sixty years since beginning his long Vigil, Avincus has fought countless xenos threats and proved his dedication and prowess time and again, being elevated to the rank of Watch Captain in 792.M41. When word came of the Tyranid onslaught, Avincus relocated to the Orpheus Salient immediately, selecting the swiftest ship available and the surest Navigator he could find to brave the smothering influence of the Shadow in the Warp. His loathing for the Tyranids is unending, and he is unwilling to allow them to freely prey upon yet more worlds.

At present, Avincus remains mobile, employing his chosen ship—the Nova-class Frigate *Hallowed Sword*—as a mobile command centre from which he directs the Kill-teams under his auspices, leading on the ground as frequently as the opportunity allows. His presence has been instrumental in dozens of missions against the Tyranids, but it has been costly as well. During the battle for Trimalov Hive on Castobel, Avincus confronted the infamous Dagon Overlord synapse-beast, suffering grievous injuries at the talons of that terrifying creature, which left him crippled and forced him into a sus-an coma from which he did not wake for eleven months.

Using Watch Captain Avincus

As one of the Jericho Reach's Watch Captains, and a veteran Space Marine with a particular loathing for the Tyranids, Avincus is an ideal superior officer for a Kill-team operating within the Orpheus Salient. His devotion to the war against the Great Devourer is unending, and he expects the Kill-teams under his command to match his fervour and righteous loathing of the Tyranids.

Having fought the Tyranids since the first Tyrannic War, and having studied them extensively in the decades since, Avincus understands the strategies required to successfully fight them, teaching his Kill-teams those strategies to better their chances of survival.

For any Kill-team that reports to Watch Captain Avincus, missions against the Tyranids gains an additional Target of Opportunity: Slay at least one Synapse Creature.

In addition, any Battle-Brother who reports to Avincus may purchase the Tyranid Hunter Talent, described below, for 500xp:

New Talent: Tyranid Hunter

Prerequisites: Hatred (Tyranids), Hunter of Aliens
The Battle-Brother is well versed in the ways of slaying Tyranids, having studied their strengths and weaknesses extensively and putting this knowledge into practice almost instinctively. The Battle-Brother gains a bonus degree of success on all Forbidden Lore (Xenos) and Tactics (any) Tests that pertain specifically to fighting the Tyranids, and when in combat with Tyranid creatures, any Fate Point the character spends grants two of the possible benefits (which must be different benefits—you cannot select the same benefit twice).

With his body rebuilt by the efforts of Forge Master Mac Zi Ven, Captain Avincus returned to the field almost immediately, slaying the Dagon Overlord when it appeared on the world of Zurev's Rest a year later. In spite of having slain the beast, its continued presence in the Jericho Reach haunts him, and he loathes it with a passion.

Avincus is an embittered veteran of countless wars who has had both his homes ravaged by the Great Devourer, and lost much more besides. Even with extensive bionic replacement, he still feels the pain of his crippling injuries, and the only thing that keeps him going in spite of all he has suffered is his hatred for the Tyranids. He regards the war against Hive Fleet Dagon to be the last one he will fight, and he has bent every fibre of his being to crushing the Tyranid threat.

Watch Captain Marius Avincus

WS	BS	S	T	Ag	Int	Per	WP	Fel
56	52	77 (14)	54 (10)	47	55	46	50	61

Movement: 5/10/15/30   **Wounds:** 25

Skills: Awareness (Per) +10, Charm (Fel) +10, Ciphers (Chapter Runes) (Int) +10, Ciphers (Deathwatch) (Int) +20, Climb (S), Command (Fel) +20, Common Lore (Adeptus Astartes) (Int) +10, Common Lore (Deathwatch) (Int), Common Lore (Jericho Reach) (Int) +20, Common Lore (Imperium) (Int), Common Lore (War) (Int) +10, Concealment (Ag), Demolition (Int), Dodge (Ag) +10, Drive (Ground Vehicle) (Ag), Drive (Skimmer) (Ag), Evaluate (Int), Forbidden Lore (Adeptus Astartes) (Int), Forbidden Lore (Xenos) (Int) +10, Forbidden Lore (Deathwatch) (Int) +10, Intimidate (S), Literacy (Int) +20, Navigation (Surface) (Int), Pilot (Personal) (Ag), Scholastic Lore (Codex Astartes) (Int) +10, Search (Int), Silent Move (Ag), Speak Language (High Gothic) (Int), Speak Language (Low Gothic) (Int), Tactics (Assault Doctrine) (Int) +20, Tactics (Orbital Drop Procedures) (Int), Tactics (Void Combat) (Int), Tracking (Int) +10.

Talents: Air of Authority, Ambidextrous, Astartes Weapon Training, Bolter Drill, Bulging Biceps, Call to Vengeance, Combat Formation, Duty Unto Death, Hatred (Tyranids), Heightened Senses (Hearing, Sight), Hip Shooting, Hunter of Aliens, Iron Discipline, Iron Jaw, Killing Strike, Master Orator, Mighty Shot, Nerves of Steel, Quick Draw, Rapid Reaction, Resistance (Cold, Heat, Psychic), Sprint, Storm of Iron, True Grit, Two Weapon Wielder (Ballistic, Melee), Tyranid Hunter, Unarmed Master, Unarmed Warrior, Unbowed and Unbroken.

Traits: Size: Hulking, Space Marine Implants, Tactical Expertise, The Flesh is Weak (2), Touched by the Fates (2), Unnatural Strength (x2), Unnatural Toughness (x2).

Armour: Artificer Armour and The Flesh is Weak (2) (Head 14, Body 14, Arms 14, Legs 14).

Weapons: Exceptional Astartes Bolter/Flamer Combi-Weapon with Fire Selector (100m; S/3/5; 2d10+8 X; Pen 5; Clip 28; Rld Full; Reliable, Tearing, and 20m; S/–/–; 2d10+5 E; Pen 3; Clip 1; Flame), Astartes Master-Crafted Plasma Pistol (30m; S/2/–; 1d10+12 E; Pen 8; Clip 12; Rld 3 Full; Never Jams, Volatile), Master-Crafted Power Sword (1d10+20 E; Pen 6, Balanced, Power Field), Combat Blade (1d10+14 R; Pen 2; Balanced), 3x Frag Grenades, 3x Krak Grenades.

Gear: Back Banner, Codex Astartes, Master-Crafted Bionic Left Arm, Master-Crafted Bionic Locomotion, Master-Crafted Bionic Respiratory System, Master-Crafted Bionic Heart.

MASTER APOTHECARY KREGOR THANN

"Suffer no impurity of flesh, above all things. Suffer not the mutant whose form blasphemes against mankind. Suffer not the alien whose nature mocks the sacred human form. In all cases, these impure things must be eliminated without hesitation."

—Commander Leonym Antir, Red Scorpions 5th Company, before the Purging of Castillium

A senior Apothecary of the Red Scorpions Chapter, Kregor Thann has only relatively recently begun his Vigil and entered the Jericho Reach. A veteran of countless warzones and a master of biological weaponry, Thann gained renown as the mastermind behind the geno-tailored toxins that made the Purging of Castillium possible, defeating the horrific Thazeme when no other weapon could slay them. In the aftermath of the Purge, Commander Antir petitioned Lord High Commander Ortys to consider Thann for Deathwatch service.

In 815.M41, Thann arrived at Watch Fortress Erioch and was given the details of his Vigil. Unlike most who step through the voidlocks of Erioch, Thann was not assigned to a Kill-team, but rather remains as part of Watch Commander Mordigael's command staff, tasked with engineering a virus or toxin that could be used to combat the Tyranid menace. Nonetheless, his command experience—for Thann, like many Apothecaries in the Red Scorpions Chapter, has served as a Sergeant as well as in his role as a medic—is useful to less-experienced Kill-teams deployed to the Orpheus Salient.

Thann's duties have taken him across much of the Orpheus Salient, and he has served alongside a dozen Kill-teams in the prosecution of his duties, taking samples of various Tyranid flora and fauna, or testing recently developed concoctions in the field. To date, he has not yet found a substance that works for more than a single generation, the Tyranids adapting to overcome his creations swiftly, though his tests have still provided numerous opportunities for other Imperial forces to drive back the crippled swarms.

Most recently, Thann has been operating towards the Spinward edge of the Orpheus Salient, pushing deep into the heart of the Tyranid advance. He is working under a theory that worlds beyond the vanguard will contain less-evolved or otherwise purer creatures that are closer to a theoretical genetic baseline that can be exploited. Several Kill-teams are operating deep behind the enemy lines, and Thann coordinates with each of them to gather samples and deploy newly developed bio-weapons.

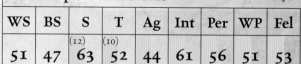

Watch Captain Kail Vibius								
WS	BS	S	T	Ag	Int	Per	WP	Fel
51	47	63 (12)	52 (10)	44	61	56	51	53

Movement: 5/10/15/30   **Wounds:** 22

Skills: Awareness (Per) +20, Chem-Use (Int) +20, Ciphers (Chapter Runes) (Int), Climb (S), Dodge (Ag), Command (Fel), Common Lore (Adeptus Astartes) (Int), Common Lore (Deathwatch) (Int), Common Lore (Imperium) (Int), Common Lore (War) (Int), Concealment (Ag), Drive (Ground Vehicles) (Ag), Forbidden Lore (Xenos) (Int) +10, Intimidate (S), Literacy (Int) +10, Medicae (Int) +20, Navigation (Surface) (Int), Scholastic Lore (Chymistry) (Int) +10, Scholastic Lore (Codex Astartes) (Int), Silent Move (Ag), Speak Language (High Gothic) (Int), Speak Language (Low Gothic) (Int), Tactics (Defensive Doctrine) (Int), Tracking (Int).

Talents: Air of Authority, Ambidextrous, Astartes Weapons Training, Bulging Biceps, Deathwatch Training, Exotic Weapon Training (Astartes Needle Pistol), Hardy, Hatred

(Mutants, Tyranids), Heightened Senses (Hearing, Sight), Hunter of Aliens, Killing Strike, Nerves of Steel, Quick Draw, Resistance (Poisons, Psychic Powers), True Grit, Tyranid Hunter, Unarmed Master, Unarmed Warrior.

Traits: Size: Hulking, *Master of Poisons†*, Space Marine Implants, Unnatural Strength (x2), Unnatural Toughness (x2).

†Master of Poisons: Kregor Thann is extremely skilled in the art of poisoncraft, having studied the physiologies of a great many foes and the deadly toxins that are employed by xenos reavers like the Scythians and the Dark Eldar. There are few creatures his concoctions cannot slay. Kregor Thann has the Create Toxins Special Ability from the Deathwatch Apothecary Speciality, and consequently has the Toxic Quality on all his weapons. In addition, any weapon that gains the Toxic Quality due to his Create Toxins ability may affect creatures (though not Daemons or Machines) that are normally immune to poisons.

Armour: Mark VII Astartes Power Armour (Arms 8, Body 10, Head 8, Legs 8).

Weapons: Astartes Bolter with Fire Selector (100m; S/2/4; 2d10+5 X; Pen 5; Clip 28; Rld Full; Tearing, Toxic), Bolt Pistol (30m; S/3/–; 2d10+5 X; Pen 5; Clip 14; Rld Full; Tearing, Toxic), Exceptional Chainsword (1d10+14 R; Pen 4; Balanced, Tearing, Toxic), Combat Blade (1d10+12 R; Pen 2; Balanced, Toxic), 3x Frag Grenades, 3x Krak Grenades.

Gear: Narthecium, Needle Precipitator, Reductor, 3 doses of Deadlock, 3 doses of Delay Agent, 3 doses of Genophage.

USING MASTER APOTHECARY THANN

As an itinerant specialist, Thann can be added to any Tyranid-focussed campaign for a short space of time, providing expertise in poisons, effective even against Tyranids, as well as healing ability that may be absent in Kill-teams that lack their own Apothecary. Rather than being a deadly combatant in his own right, Thann bolsters any Kill-team he fights alongside, allowing them to keep fighting longer and to slay more readily.

POISONS AND THE GREAT DEVOURER

Tyranids are not, strictly speaking, immune to poisons, toxins or venoms. Rather, each generation of Tyranids is engineered to overcome the weaknesses of those that came before, and thus a toxin that functions against the Tyranids during one engagement may be completely useless during the next one.

As a result, a newly developed, specifically tailored poison (such as those created by some Apothecaries, or the Genophage toxin), never before encountered by the Tyranids may function normally at GM's discretion, with the next generation of Tyranids (typically spawned between 24 and 48 hours apart) being immune to that poison. Each generation requires new, specifically created toxins.

III: THE GREAT DEVOURER

Extract from Dissection Report Theta-55.7.9
Submitted by Deathwatch Apothecary Kregor Thann

At last, I have breached the carapace around the incubation chamber. Its armour is as obdurate as the hunger of its hellish race, and I was nearly forced to resort to measures that could have damaged the innards. I have never been one to gamble with such a precious sample, bought with the blood of my Battle-Brothers, but I will admit these unyielding plates provided temptation towards those foolish risks. The Emperor provides all His servants need to triumph, however, and I was able to brew a corrosive agent to weaken the plates out of the ancillary samples provided.

My caution has been well rewarded, as I see within what would have been otherwise obliterated by heedless folly. The incubation chamber is filled with a veritable legion of dormant Termagants, fully formed and ready for combat. It appears they just await a signal from their progenitor to awake and swarm the battlefield.

I had expected to find the yet-unborn progeny further developed. That they can develop from this state of waxy flesh and limp muscle so quickly is yet further evidence of the monstrous nature of the xenos—something never in doubt, but rather always affirmed and compounded by every specimen I have gazed upon.

[Recording pauses]

My initial count finds nearly three-score larvae in the final stage of development, where they are recognizable as Termagant vermin. Eighteen more are budding forth from the chamber walls in lumpen sacs of fluid. This may be what I am seeking. The broth that nurtures these beasts to life is likely to contain a purer strain than the gene-samples I have been working with thus far. The sacs appear surprisingly delicate for Tyranid life, however. Perhaps the Hive Mind is reluctant to expend bio-mass reinforcing internal structures under such formidable external protection—a line of inquiry worth pursuing later…

[The recording trails off at this point into the visceral noises of Thann's work. Observations continued in File Theta-87.5.76]

ORPHEUS SALIENT SPECIAL ABILITIES

"The Tyranids are a canny foe. Overcoming their ever-changing abilities requires a careful examination of the Codex to reveal the most appropriate techniques."

–Chaplain Cassius, Ultramarines Master of Sanctity

Deathwatch Space Marines active within the Orpheus Salient have the opportunity to live the very essence of the organisation's mandate: They slay xenos. The forces of Hive Fleet Dagon are vast and are revitalised with each successful conquest. The only hope for success lies in completely overwhelming these forces and then cleansing the worlds they have savaged of their taint. This conflict is more than a battle for individual survival. It is truly a vital battle that could be necessary for the preservation of the Imperium and humanity as a whole.

ORPHEUS DEMEANOURS

The Crusade forces within the Orpheus Salient are stretched far too thin. Only on those occasions when the Salient's leadership can consciously focus their defences are there ever anything close to enough resources available for a conflict. As a consequence, Deathwatch Kill-teams are crucial not just for their expertise but for their efficiency as well. Though many may not realise it, the Crusade is very nearly dependent upon the Deathwatch to wage an effective war against Hive Fleet Dagon.

Many of the Battle-Brothers who serve within this region have come to realise this fact. As a consequence, their outlooks have begun to change. Some acknowledge this additional responsibility and embrace it. Others become ever more reckless as they distrust the interactions with the Crusade forces. A few begin to weight of the seemingly endless battle against the Tyranid Swarm, while others enter a state of near-ecstasy at the opportunity for unending conflict. These different philosophical outlooks can represent new Personal Demeanours. For players considering a change of Demeanour for their characters, this section offers several that are particularly suited to activity within the Orpheus Salient. There is no XP cost required for a shift in Demeanour. Refer to Deathwatch p. 32 for more information on Personal Demeanours.

APPALLED

As the Tyranid swarm continues to infest the worlds of the Orpheus Salient, it brings with it endless abominations. These foul xenos are offensive in virtually every imaginable way to the Imperium. There is no opportunity for communication with these hostiles. Rather, they ceaselessly consume and incorporate all life that stands before them. Over the course of this consumption, they spread their filth everywhere. Once beautiful vistas are choked out by their presence. A world's very atmosphere becomes impossible to breathe as it fills with their spore. All the pleasures of a planet may be quickly replaced with the nightmares, filth, and biological contagions that represent the very essence of the Tyranid host. Soon, even these foul plagues are gone. The hive fleet consumes everything of value and beauty, leaving nothing but dust in their wake.

Some Battle-Brothers become utterly disgusted by the horrible waste of life the Tyranids leave in their wake. Their consumption of innocent human lives along with the beauty of the galaxy is an offence that they cannot accept. Where humanity uses resources to develop a world, the Tyranids devour all that is good leaving nothing but barren rock behind. As the Battle-Brother redoubles his efforts to defeat these xenos, he also embraces the notion of complete extermination. There is no time for study, analysis, or even careful planning. These Space Marines view the continued existence of the Hive Fleet as an inexcusable offence. Any measure is acceptable to eliminate it, as long as it is eliminated swiftly so that humanity need no longer share its galaxy with the foul Hive Fleet.

CAUTIOUS

As worlds are subject to Tyranid infestation, their very ecology begins to change. New organisms sweep through and transform the landscape into a lethal environment filled with creatures focussed on devouring the planets bio-mass. While most of these creatures are aggressive animals, such as the various Gaunt strains and Ripper swarms, others, like the Capillary Towers, appear more planet like. However, even these plants can be unexpectedly deadly, as they ooze toxins and acids capable of penetrating even the most protective of the Imperium's designs. At the same time, many of these xenos are particularly adept at concealment. Horrors constantly lurk within concealed tunnels, over hills, or in the branches of trees. Watching for these deadly threats requires additional time and care on any journey behind enemy lines.

This continuous exposure to unexpected threats can begin to wear upon even a hardened veteran Space Marine. For some, the only reasonable approach is to be conservative in all of their actions. Prior to treading into unfamiliar territory, necessary measures must be taken to minimise the risks. Battle-Brothers who embrace this philosophy believe in carefully identifying and testing unknown threats prior to interacting with them. For in these hostile alien ecologies, there are countless organisms that appear harmless that may conceal untold dangers. Such seemingly innocuous dangers must be overcome, or else a Mission might fail with little justification. These Space Marines insist that all reasonable precautions must be taken.

Eager

Hive Fleet Dagon continuously rolls through the Orpheus Salient. With each new conquest, it grows in size as new vessels are spawned. Among these vessels are drones that identify new sources of bio-mass to temporarily satiate the unending hunger of the Tyranid swarm. This constant growth—extending across numerous systems—dictates that the Crusade forces must be ever vigilant for new incursions. At the same time, planets that are engaged by the swarm engage in constant warfare; the opposition grows as fast as they can consume new bio-mass from the planet itself. At any moment, there are dozens, if not hundreds of different skirmishes fought within the Orpheus Salient.

A few Space Marines revel in the constant battle with these xenos. Each additional conflict is an opportunity to fulfil their lust for physical conflict. The vast Tyranid hordes provide a wealth of opportunities to face skilled opponents that are capable of adapting to overcome even a Space Marine's prowess. Only by continuously overcoming such foes can some Battle-Brothers feel fulfilled. For these warriors, the call to battle is almost an addiction. They readily volunteer for the most dangerous of assignments, knowing that these provide the greatest challenges. Such battles are more than an opportunity to defend the ways of the Imperium. Instead, they are a way for the Space Marine to enjoy the conflict; a rush that he wishes to never surrender.

Furious

The call to hate the xenos is an integral part of the Imperial Creed. When a xenos is as virulent and destructive as Hive Fleet Dagon, this hatred is second nature. Millions of humans—both bystanders and combatants—have had their lives destroyed by the Tyranid host. Few even had an opportunity to try to escape the wrath of the xenos forces. Rather, they were consumed within their homes often before they were fully aware of the assault. Those who became aware of the incoming assault seldom had means to attempt to escape it. Some of those who could flee only escaped the attack in time to reach another system already under assault. A thirst for vengeance against the creatures responsible for such actions is simple human nature.

However, some Space Marines take this hatred even further. For them, the existence of a species that could successfully perpetrate such heinous acts upon the Imperium of Man is an affront against the Emperor and the Primarch. Their bodies and souls are consumed with a burning fury that compels them to take the most extreme actions possible. For these Battle-Brothers, the call to action is immediate. Measures must be taken that focus on eliminating this threat with extreme prejudice. They can focus on little but their anger at the xenos, and they must take immediate and ongoing actions to eliminate it.

Reserved

During the course of a Tyranid planetary assault, the battle lines often blur and shift. Imperial strongholds may be struck by incoming Mycetic Spores or Trygons may tunnel from deep beneath the earth to compromise the facilities. In other cases, an overwhelming push may split a line, leaving two or more pockets of Crusade forces isolated as they continue their stalwart defence. Often, Deathwatch Kill-teams are sent deep behind enemy lines to try to identify and eliminate Tyranid breeding grounds or rare specimens credited with leading particular assaults. In any of these circumstances, Space Marines can be dependent upon their abilities to remain concealed from the overwhelming numbers that Hive Fleet Dagon presents.

For some Battle-Brothers, this mode of operation becomes second nature. This is particularly true if they have been involved in Missions behind enemy lines for months or even years. Many Tyranid strains have enhanced physical senses that can detect far more than those of unaugmented humans. Overcoming these perceptions requires intense training to learn and extreme care to implement. Due to the efficiency of the Hive Mind, a single brief encounter can soon lead to hundreds of additional Tyranids answering a call. Space Marines deployed upon such missions often take this approach deeply to heart. They continue to follow a path of silence and stealth no matter the situation. For these characters, the idea of aggressive and direct action is not necessarily the first and most appropriate response to every situation.

VIGILANT

Hive Fleet Dagon constantly sends out additional drones, many of which carry Lictors and Genestealers to untainted worlds. Long empty Space Hulks or unsuspecting transport ships may also allow these xenos to spread their foul contamination. As a consequence, the Tyranid swarm may appear on virtually any planet within the Jericho Reach at any time. Even on those worlds where the Tyranid invasion has begun, assaults seldom follow any preordained timetable. Rather, the Tyranid host descends upon location with waves of creatures on a timetable that is known only to the Hive Mind. Because of this, all Imperial forces, especially those within the Orpheus Salient, must be constantly prepared for another Tyranid assault.

Some Battle-Brothers devote their lives to this state of preparedness. They rely upon their physiological enhancements to delay rest, keeping themselves at full alert at all time. Further, these Space Marines often take care to insure that their brethren and Crusade allies maintain comparable states of readiness for any attack. Weapons must remain prepared at all time. In their minds if a vital piece of equipment must be shut down for maintenance, then a redundant version should be ready in case of another attack. Of course, such vigilance comes with a cost in terms of both Imperial resources and troop morale. However, such a cost is far more easily borne than the loss of a vital facility to an unexpected attack.

ORPHEUS SOLO MODES

The Tyranid forces of the Orpheus Salient constantly assault the Imperial defenders with seemingly endless waves of biological monstrosities. These xenos assault the human defenders with a massively integrated force that uses their overpowering telepathic presence to coordinate actions with split-second precision. While the Tyranids are hardly triumphant in every battle, their superior numbers, rapid adaptation, and ever-growing resources continuously place them in an advantageous position relative to the defenders of humanity.

Deathwatch Space Marines constantly strive to solve this disparity. Even in the face of the xenos nightmares, they push their bodies and equipment to the limit so that they can become the inspirational heroes that the Crusade forces desperately need. This is partially done through the development of new battle techniques specifically designed to address the Tyranid threat. While a few of these were pioneered by Ultramarines who fought against Hive Fleet Behemoth, the majority are novel and distinctive to those operating within the Orpheus Salient.

INGENERI

CRUCIAL TARGET

Cost: 250 XP
Type: Active
Required Rank: 4
Effects: Tyranid forces are extremely dependent upon their link to the Hive Mind for coordination. Without its influence, many of the Tyranid life forms lose the ability to effectively contribute to an engagement. While others may remain effective combatants, they may still lose the ability to carry out plans in concert with forces located far from visual or auditory range. These situations are clearly favourable for the Imperium, as the odds often tilt sharply against the xenos.

This limitation has been well documented by the Inquisition as have the organisms most commonly associated with transmitting the will of the Hive Mind to the lesser organisms. Some Space Marines have begun to selectively identify these targets, so that they can be swiftly eliminated in combat. The most daring of these Battle-Brothers go so far as to selectively bypass lesser entities so that they can attack these greater manifestations of the Tyranid psyche directly in melee combat.

Space Marines who learn this technique gain the ability to safely manoeuvre up to their charge distance directly through hordes of lesser Tyranids to engage Elite or Master Rank Tyranid creatures. This movement may only be taken if they complete their movement adjacent to an appropriate foe and complete a Charge action. However, due to the sheer audacity of their action, these characters may not be attacked by any Tyranid Hordes until their action in the next combat round.
Improvement: At Rank 6, the Battle-Brother increases his charge bonus on a Crucial Target attack to +30. At Rank 8, he gains an additional Reaction for use during the same turn that he made the initial charge.

DISTRACT THY ENEMY

Cost: 250 XP
Type: Active
Required Rank: 2
Effects: The Tyranid ecosystem is filled with creatures that epitomise animal ferocity. These xenos slaughter and devour anything that can contribute to their bizarre lifecycle so that it can serve as additional fuel for their Hive Fleet. With few exceptions, these creatures are constantly driven by an overwhelming urge to acquire new bio-mass for the swarm. Their biological adaptations are extremely well suited for overcoming defenders and adding their genetic information to the xenos resources.

Because of this drive to consume, it is not uncommon for Tyranids to fixate on a single source of bio-mass. In some cases, Space Marines attempt to exploit this tendency. The most common way to do this is by selecting a volunteer to provide a distraction so that others might make a killing blow—often from range.

Battle-Brothers who serve as such a distraction must be capable of defending themselves against the relentless and often overpowering attacks of the Tyranid swarm. To do this effectively, some Space Marines hone their defensive skills, focusing entirely on their defensive abilities. When those who learn this technique take a Defensive Stance Action, see Deathwatch p. 238, against a Tyranid opponent they gain three additional Reactions instead of one.
Improvement: At Rank 6, the Battle-Brother becomes particularly adept at parrying Tyranid attacks after taking a Defensive Stance Action. All parry attempts against Tyranids receive a +20 bonus until the character's next action.

EMBRACE THE SHADOWS

Cost: 250 XP
Type: Passive
Required Rank: 3
Effects: During a planetary assault, the Tyranid Swarm often quickly dominates much of a world's surface. When this happens, Imperial forces and assets are often isolated far from any support elements. Even worse, additional xenos may rapidly grow within unassailable Brood Nests, far from regions secured by the Crusade's defenders. In isolation, these nests have ample time to expand and grow a vast array of creatures while consuming all of the planet's bio-mass.

Deathwatch Kill-teams are often dispatched on missions that require journeys and even extended observational assignments deep within Tyranid-held regions. During these missions, it is essential for the Battle-Brothers to remain hidden from the xenos. If even one creature of the Hive Mind were to be come aware of the intruders, wave upon wave of horrors could be dispatched against the Space Marines.

In order to increase survivability, Inquisition forces have worked closely with the Adeptus Mechanicus to assess the capabilities and limitations of Tyranid sensory organs. With this knowledge in hand, some Deathwatch members within the Orpheus Salient have begun to follow techniques specifically adapted to overcome the sensory limitations. Marines trained with these techniques ignore the -30 penalty to all Silent Move or Concealment Tests from their Power Armour when the Tests are taken against Tyranids.
Improvement: At Rank 5, the Space Marine's study has extended to identifying consumables within the Tyrnaid environs. When working behind Hive Fleet Dagon lines, these Battle-Brothers gain a +20 to all Survival Tests.

IMMUNITY OF FAITH

Cost: 250 XP
Type: Passive
Required Rank: 3
Effects: While the forces of Hive Fleet Dagon are more than capable of physically overwhelming most opposition, their brute strength is not their only offensive weapon. In addition to their deadly might, the vast majority of these forces are also carriers for a broad array of toxins and pathogens. The majority of these substances can swiftly reduce a healthy organism to little more than a puddle of protoplasmic sludge. However, some of these are even capable of infecting a host, turning the unsuspecting victim into an incubator for Tyranid growth.

Space Marine physiology is particularly well designed for dealing with these sorts of physiological threats. However, many of these substances are so virulent that they may even overcome a Battle-Brother that has been caught unawares. Some members of Deathwatch Kill-teams are deliberately subjected to minute quantities of Tyranid strains, so that they can develop a gradual immunity from these biological toxins. These treatments are rare, as safely acquiring the toxins and correctly identifying them requires a substantial effort and risk. Those Space Marines that complete this treatment receive an additional +20 bonus to resist any toxin or pathogen of Tyranid Origin.

Improvement: At Rank 6 or higher, the Space Marine's biology has begun to effectively identify and adapt to expected variations of the Tyranid toxin families. At this point, the toxin resistance bonus is increased to +40.

KNOW THY FOE

Cost: 400 XP

Type: Active

Required Rank: 4

Effects: Hive Fleet Dagon employs a seemingly endless variety of different Tyranid strains as part of its effort to devour the Orpheus Salient. Identifying these different variations is further complicated by the fact that, in many instances, a significant change in appearance may not be representative of a significant change in physiology or function. As a consequence, identifying a target so that its weak points may be easily identified is a challenging task that may require substantial battlefield experience to fully master.

Some Space-Marines have studied the records of Hive Fleet Behemoth and correlated those data with the additional information available to the officers of the Orpheus Salient. Through careful study and analysis of both Hive Fleets, they have been able to identify common organisms based upon function and extrapolate physiological weak points that are associated with these different strains. This research grants them a near intuitive grasp of Tyranid physiology and vulnerabilities. Through this study, these Battle-Brothers earned a +20 bonus on any called shots taken against Tyranid creatures.

Improvement: At Rank 6, this technique becomes increasingly precise. At that rank or higher, any time the Battle-Brother successfully takes a Called Shot action against a Tyranid creature, the target's armour for the region hit is halved (rounding up).

PREPARE FOR THY ENEMY

Cost: 250 XP

Type: Passive

Required Rank: 1

Effects: The Tyranid planetary assault is a battle fought upon every frontier. Some specimens fly, others swim, and a number of strains burrow beneath the earth or fly through the void. The different specimens exploit their diversity so that they can be certain to extract every bit of bio-mass from a planet, but also to be certain that their prey is under constant attack. By using specialised troops in these different fronts, the xenos forces manage to expand through virtually all portions of a planet's biome even during the earliest stages of their assault.

As these horrors expand throughout the planet, they are able to launch their attacks against Imperial forces from any of these battlefronts. Regions thought safely secure—even within mines, hives, or space stations—become targets for Tyranid incursion. In short order, the xenos may be found virtually anywhere on the planet.

With this expansion and their extended presence, an assault can come at any time. Many Battle-Brothers respond to this constant threat by remaining constantly prepared for any such incursions. They maintain their gear in a state of readiness and focus constantly on any changes in their surroundings. As a consequence of their vigilance, in any situation where these characters would normally be surprised, they may make a **Difficult (–10) Awareness Test**. On success, they are not surprised.

Improvement: At Rank 4, it becomes a **Challenging (+0) Awareness Test**. At Rank 6, characters who use this Solo Mode are immune to Surprise.

ORPHEUS SQUAD MODES

The Hive Mind provides a constant network of communication for all of the Tyranid creatures that fall within its reach. During any planned conflict, creatures that serve as nodes for this psychic phenomenon are well distributed, insuring that the various xenos function as the cogs of a well oiled machine. In this way, the Tyranid operates as a single mind, coordinating all of its actions so that the every action is complemented by

a host of actions from supporting creatures. Even the well honed Imperial forces are limited in their abilities to compete with such a thoroughly orchestrated attack.

As part of an effort to effectively overcome this, Deathwatch Kill-teams operating within the Orpheus Salient have developed a series of specialised techniques focussed on overcoming the Tyranid invasion. A single squad of Space Marines are limited in their potency against the assembled might of Hive Fleet Dagon, but their example and their talents serve as inspiration to other Crusade elements. As individual Kill-teams master these techniques, they also spread them to other Deathwatch members as part of their training regimen between missions.

See the Using Salient Squad Modes sidebar on page 84 for more information on how these Modes may be integrated with Oaths.

ATTACK PATTERNS

These techniques are focussed on breaking the advance of the Tyranid swarm. Through these abilities, Deathwatch Kill-teams can more easily preserve Imperial worlds, preventing them from becoming a part of Hive Fleet Dagon's bio-mass.

Purge with Fire

Cost: 100 XP
Action: Full Action
Activation Cost: 2
Sustained: No
Effects: The forces of Hive Fleet Dagon often employ overwhelming numbers in the course of their battles. When the swarm is gathered, their flying creatures blacken the sky and their ground units carpet the ground in a layer of xenos flesh that extends for kilometres. These alien terrors are often densely packed, as they clamour atop one another in search of fresh bio-mass for the swarm. In regions where the fighting is exceptionally intense, broods of the lesser Tyranid creatures may advance in closely packed waves of tens of thousands of creatures, seeking to overwhelm even the most advanced Imperial weapons with the sheer might of their numbers.

For situations like this, Space Marines often select flamers as their weapons of choice. When the enemy are so tightly packed, the fonts of promethium flame can scarcely miss their targets. Tissues burn, exoskeletons pop, and their ichor boils as the intense heat cleanses the world of the xenos taint.

When a Space Marine activates this ability he, and all squad members within Support Range, may immediately make an attack with any flame-based weapons they carry, even if they currently had another weapon readied. Because of the overlapping fields of flame, all targets hit by the attacks are lit on fire unless they succeed at a **Hard (–20) Agility Test**.
Improvement: If the Battle-Brother is Rank 4 or more, the difficulty for targets lit on fire by this action to act normally is increased to a **Hard (–20) Willpower Test**. If the Battle-Brother is Rank 6 or higher, the field of fire for all of the flame weapons used in this attack is increased to 45 degrees.

Selective Targeting

Cost: 250 XP
Action: Half Action
Activation Cost: 1
Sustained: Yes
Effects: Under the influence of the Hive Mind, the lesser xenos among the Tyranid swarm become a directed force that can devour their opposition, taking advantage of their ready self-sacrifice and incredible coordination. Without that direction, these aliens often lose their cohesion and will to fight. An undirected swarm can be easy prey for the attacks of the Achilus Crusade, quickly blunting the effectiveness of the swarm's initial attack.

The Inquisition agents active within the Orpheus Salient are charged with identifying unknown specimens observed within the region's battlefronts. Imagery of these varied xenos is compiled into recognition guides, which include favoured combat strategies and counters. These guides specifically identify all aliens that are believed to contribute to the Hive Mind and are provided to Deathwatch Kill-teams for reference.

When a Battle-Brother activates this ability, he and all squad members within Support Range may immediately make a Standard Attack against a Tyranid creature that has the Synapse Creature Trait. All weapons used for this attack recieve +2 Penetration during the attack, addtionally, if the attack hits a location that would be protected by cover, the attacker may reroll the hit location.
Improvement: If the Battle-Brother is Rank 4 or more, all weapons used for this attack receive +4 Penetration during the action instead. If the Battle-Brother is Rank 6 or more, characters may choose to make a Full Auto Burst, Semi-Auto Burst, or All Out Attack instead of a Standard Attack for this action.

Tunnel Advance

Cost: 250 XP
Action: Full Action
Activation Cost: 3
Sustained: Yes
Effects: Many of the forces of the Tyranid swarm spawn and dwell deep beneath the surface of the planet they invade. These horrors are native to the darkness and cramped quarters of the tunnels they create as they devour the planet's bio-mass. The Imperium has no easy way to find, much less defeat these creatures. Instead, Crusade forces must venture into a foreign and hostile environment so that they can identify and engage the xenos that possess every territorial advantage.

When Deathwatch Kill-teams travel into these tunnels, they lose any advantage that their ranged weapons provide. As the tunnels twist and turn, xenos targets are often found only when melee combat is engaged. The complete lack of light and the oppressive stench of the alien permeate the passages, further limiting the effectiveness of their senses.

When a Space Marine activates this ability, he and all squad members become far more attuned to fighting within tunnels. Characters receive an additional reaction each round while fighting within these dark confines. In addition, their practice in navigating these tight confines confers a +20 bonus to any Contortionist Tests required to travel through the tunnels.
Improvement: If the Battle-Brother is Rank 4 or higher, the

Kill-team has become so adept at battling within these tight confines that they receive a +10 Weapon Skill bonus to any attacks within a tunnel. At Rank 6 or higher, the squad members become immune to Surprise when fighting in tunnels.

DEFENSIVE STANCES

When a swarm of Tyranids rush an Imperial battle line, mounting a defence is as much about directing the flow as it is killing the xenos.

Fire by Ranks

Cost: 300 XP
Action: Full Action
Activation Cost: 1
Sustained: No
Effects: In order to maintain a constant and high rate of fire against the incoming swarm, Imperial units in the Orpheus Salient often rank their forces so that a second line of attackers may fire as the first line reloads. This can create a devastating firestorm that is more focussed upon directing the Tyranid advance away from a location than it is upon actually killing any members of the xenos.

While Space Marine weaponry is far more capable than those used by most Crusade forces, Space Marines found that the core tactic is sound. As a consequence, they often mimic this strategy by pacing their bolter fire so that a fellow squad member's volley is timed to hit the latter ranks in a charge, effectively devastating a unit as it charges forward.

When a Battle-Brother activates this ability, he and any squad members within Support Range may immediately execute a Full Auto Burst action. When determining the number of hits in the burst, calculate two hits per Degree of Success instead of one, limited by the weapons Rate of Fire.

Improvement: If the Battle-Brother is Rank 4 or higher, all characters receive an additional +10 bonus to the Ballistic Skill Test on the Full Auto Burst action. If the Battle-Brother is Rank 6 or higher, characters attacked must resist Pinning.

Hold the Line

Cost: 100 XP
Action: Reaction
Activation Cost: 2
Sustained: Yes
Effects: When arrayed to defend a vulnerable asset against Tyranid attack, Imperial assets willingly make whatever sacrifice is required in order to preserve that resource against the ravenous swarm. At times, this may require a noble loss of lives. In other situations, jury-rigged explosives, chemical toxins, or even biological contaminants may be used to sterilise a region against the oncoming xenos.

Though the Deathwatch is devoted to slaughtering the alien, this is not always immediately possible within the Orpheus Salient. At many times, blunting Hive Fleet Dagon's advance may mean that the Crusade forces can survive and live to fight another day. Because of this, some Battle-Brothers have begun to employ techniques that are focussed upon stopping the swarm for a set length of time, often providing allies an opportunity to trigger explosives, begin long-ranged shelling, or complete the evacuation of a region.

When a Battle-Brother activates this ability, he and any squad members within Support Range may each physically barricade a region from advance. While they may not take any actions or reactions, including defensive reactions or movement, any time an opponent attempts to pass within 3 metres of their location, the Marine may immediately make an opposed Agility Test. If the Space Marine succeeds, the opponent's movement immediately stops. The Space Marine may make this Test among any number of opponents for any round that the Ability is sustained.

Improvement: If the Battle-Brother is Rank 4 or higher, all squad members receive +10 to their Agility Tests. At Rank 6, all characters may take a single Reaction each round that Hold the Line is active.

Lure

Cost: 250 XP
Action: Full Action
Activation Cost: 2
Sustained: No
Effects: Because of the Hive Mind, knowledge is readily shared between different members of the Tyranid swarm. This includes shared battlefield memories. With this information, the aliens can quickly discover the vulnerabilities of Imperial assets, enabling the xenos to more effectively compromise such targets. This information sharing remains available to Hive Fleet Dagon even if the organisms that discovered it is slain. Because of this, swarm tactics are often quite consistent and accurate. This plays an even more significant factor if the Tyranids are engaged in combat by Imperial units that have fought against the swarm previously. Memories of general tactics and even those favoured by individual soldiers may benefit the overriding Tyranid strategy.

As part of an effort to prevent his, some Space Marines attempt to deliberately draw the attention of Tryanids, so that other units may be preserved. In this way, Imperial tactics remain effectively in play and units that are more vulnerable to direct Tyranid attack may continue to assist the battle in a less direct manner.

When a Battle-Brother activates this ability, he and any squad mates within Support Range may immediately make a Deceive Test against a Tyranid target with a bonus of +5 for each squad member within Support Range. On success, the Tyranid must move to engage the Space Marine who successfully used the Lure ability for at least 1 combat round.

Improvement: If the Battle-Brother is Rank 5 or higher, the bonus to the Deceive Test increases to +10 for each squad member within Support Range. If Rank 7 or higher, all characters receive a +20 bonus to their next Reaction test, due to their expectation of attack in this situation.

ORPHEUS OATHS

Hive Fleet Dagon's advance into the worlds of the Orpheus Salient is implacable. With each new world overcome, the Tyranid Swarm gains in potency and the Crusade forces lose resources necessary for their desperate defence. The Deathwatch has become an essential asset to the Imperial forces, as their focussed abilities provide the Crusade with necessary reprieve from the most hazardous of duties.

The Deathwatch are often used when all other options have been exhausted, forcing the Space Marines to solve situations that have become truly dire. In several cases, Battle-Brothers have been martyred trying to preserve the lives of others. To cope with these extreme conditions, the Kill-teams within the Salient have learnt to refocus their abilities so that other units might survive to fight another day. At the same time, these Space Marines have developed means of coordination to improve their own chances of survival.

OATH FOR THE FALLEN

When facing the might of Hive Fleet Dagon, even the might of the Imperium can prove an insufficient defence. Millions have been devoured by the Tyranid swarm that rushes through the systems of the Orpheus Salient. For many, there are no survivors to recount their memories. For others, friends and comrades recall how their lives were snuffed out far too soon by the xenos invaders. Even a few of the elite Deathwatch Space Marines have succumbed to this brutal assault.

Cost: 300 XP

Prerequisite: Tactical Marine, Apothecary, or Assault Marine

Effect: As the Kill-team prepares for the mission, they share their memories of those who have fallen in battle against the Tyranid swarm. These meetings are carefully archived, so that the memories of those martyred may be added to the Deathwatch archives and retold to future members. With the tragic tales fresh in their hearts, the Battle-Brothers vow to not fail the memories of those who have gone before. They focus on both vengeance and their sacred duty. For the duration of the mission, each member of the kill team receives 5 Temporary Wounds. Unlike normal Wounds, these bonus Wounds are removed when affected by the Damage of any successful attack, and are always removed first before applying Damage to the Battle-Brother's normal Wounds. When the Mission is completed, these bonus Wounds are lost.

Squad Mode Abilities: Lure, Tactical Spacing, Soak Fire

OATH OF CLEANSING

Once a system has become tainted with a Tyranid infection, overcoming that disease is a virtually impossible task. These xenos infest a world from the microbial level, and virtually every organism is capable of growing, mutating, and developing to eventually replicate most other strains of the Tyranid swarm. To eliminate this threat, any portion of a system that has played host to Hive Fleet Dagon must be thoroughly cleansed. In fact, some portions must be sterilised, before native forms of life may be safely reintroduced.

Cost: 250 XP

Prerequisite: Devastator Marine, Techmarine, or Librarian

Effect: Kill-teams that are assigned a mission to completely eliminate a Tyranid force often choose to swear an Oath of Cleansing. These Space Marines typically choose weapons that are capable of inflicting massive amounts of damage over a large area. When facing the Tyranid swarm, collateral damage is rarely a concern. Instead, it is far more important that the xenos be cleansed before they have time to expand further. Kill-teams that choose this Oath are devoted to thoroughly annihilating all vestiges of Tyranid infection. They may reroll their damage on any successful attacks made with Blast weapons.

Squad Mode Abilities: Purge with Fire, Strongpoint, Tunnel Advance

TABLE 3-1: ORPHEUS OATHS

Oath	Prerequisite	Benefit	Squad Mode Abilities
Oath for the Fallen	Tactical Marine, Apothecary, or Assault Marine	+5 Bonus Wounds	Lure, Tactical Spacing, Soak Fire
Oath of Cleansing	Devastator Marine, Techmarine, or Librarian	Reroll damage on Blast weapons	Purge with Fire, Strongpoint, Tunnel Advance
Oath of Illumination	Librarian, Devastator Marine, or Tactical Marine	Penalty for Long Range and Extreme Range Targets reduced to 0 and –20.	Selective Targeting, Fire by Ranks, Fire for Effect
Oath of Preservation	Assault Marine, Tactical Marine, or Apothecary	+10 Bonus to Dodge or Parry Reactions	Dig In, Hold the Line, Go to Ground

OATH OF ILLUMINATION

Hive Fleet Dagon's forces are certainly capable of effective ranged combat, but their capabilities in this regard pale next to the awesome might of the Imperium's artillery. Crusade forces are most likely to win engagements against the Tyranid swarm when they can turn a battle into a protracted long range fight. As a consequence, it is essential for these units to begin firing at the most extreme range possible, and maintain a blistering rain of explosives to stop the horde from further advance.

Cost: 250 XP

Prerequisite: Librarian, Devastator Marine, or Tactical Marine

Effect: Space Marines that expect to support an Imperial stronghold against Tyranid assault often expect to assist in both the long ranged and short-ranged portions of the battle. As expert marksmen, a Kill-team can often eliminate huge swaths of Tyranids before the xenos have an opportunity to fire their bioweapons. If the Battle-Brothers choose to swear an Oath of Illumination, they undergo extensive rights of cleansing upon their eyes and other sensory organs. Visual acuity is temporarily enhanced with the addition of neurochemicals at the same time as fragile enhanced sights are requisitioned for their standard armaments. With these additional enhancements in play, the Kill-team reduces the penalty for Long Range fire to 0 and the difficulty for Extreme Range to –20.

Squad Mode Abilities: Selective Targeting, Fire by Ranks, Fire for Effect

OATH OF PRESERVATION

On worlds under the assault of Hive Fleet Dagon, it is often vital to preserve some Imperial assets so that they may be used for future battles. In these instances, it may be acceptable to sacrifice raw materials, replaceable stores, or even some military forces so that a vital manufactory, specialised combat unit, or command staff might survive to fight once more. The officers of the Orpheus Salient are forced to make these decisions on a daily basis as the Hive Fleet continues to grow in size and potency.

Cost: 250 XP

Prerequisite: Assault Marine, Tactical Marine, or Apothecary

Effect: Deathwatch Kill-teams that expect to be inserted into an extremely hostile environment may choose to swear an Oath of Preservation. Under this Oath's direction, they focus all of their efforts on keeping themselves and their allies alive, by whatever means are necessary. While slaying the enemy remains a focus, diverting it is generally a higher priority. In these circumstances, the enemy often has substantial advantages over even the most stalwart of Kill-teams, so they must focus on insuring survival. For the duration of the mission, all Kill-team members receive a +10 bonus to any Dodge or Parry Reactions taken.

Squad Mode Abilities: Dig In, Hold the Line, Go to Ground

Orpheus Salient Campaigns

"The Orpheus Salient is a blade in the back of the Achilus Crusade, each day sinking deeper into its flesh and inching ever closer to its heart."

–Lord Militant Solomon Tetrarchus

From the promise of victory to the shadow of complete collapse, the Orpheus Salient has, over the course of a few short years, become the greatest threat to the stability and success of Crusade. This reversal of fortunes lies squarely at the feet of a single fearsome entity: Hive Fleet Dagon. Almost overnight the arrival of the hive fleet changed the nature of the war on the rimward edge of the Sector, crashing down upon the unprepared Imperial forces and halting their rapid conquest of its worlds as they ran headlong into a wall of alien horrors. What was at first a rapid advance against inferior foes and isolated renegade worlds, became a holding action against the Tyranid vanguard, and then a retreat from the ponderous bulk of the Dagon swarm. Lord Tetrarchus rushed forces to the Salient to prevent its complete collapse, however it may be that he has only forestalled the inevitable, for each day the swarm inches closer to Well of the Night and the Crusade's command worlds.

This is what it means to fight within the Orpheus Salient, to struggle desperately to hold back an endless foe, which despite every defeat, every set back or massacre, continues to claim worlds and produce fresh hive fleets from the depths of the eastern fringe. Those that stand against Hive Dagon do so with the vain hope that their efforts will somehow halt the Tyranid advance, that the next battle or the next campaign will break the will of the beast and scatter its forces. Most know the futility of their actions but fight on anyway because they have no choice. This is either because they fight for their home worlds and have nowhere else to run, because their faith in the God-Emperor will not let them falter or, as often as not, because of the Commissar's bolt pistol pointed at their back. Unknown to these desperate forces, the Deathwatch acts as an invisible deterrent against the foe, their missions and actions often dealing telling blows against the swarm. As the strength of the Imperium's armies wane, the Deathwatch have quickly become the spear tip against the hive fleet, striking again and again at its tendrils as the Tyranids tighten their grip across the Sector.

Running Orpheus Salient Campaigns

The Orpheus Salient offers both players and GMs a rich and exciting locale for their adventures and a myriad of missions against not just the endless Tyranid swarms but also against the opportunists, renegades and repercussions of Dagon's arrival. What really sets this area apart from the other regions of the Jericho Reach is the air of desperation and doom that pervades it, colouring every world the players will visit and every NPC they will meet, giving the place a sense of a final stand or the last days against an encroaching and unavoidable cataclysm. Of all the Imperium's foes, only the Tyranids seem to be able to create this air of finality and apocalypse, the spectre of worlds stripped bare and whole populations consumed leaving only dead space and empty systems in their wake.

To bring the Orpheus Salient to life, regardless of the nature of the GM's campaigns and missions, there are a number of themes that can be used to capture the feel of the region and impart the presence of the swarm. When creating campaigns, GMs can consider these themes and draw inspiration from them.

Shadow of the Beast

Hive Fleet Dagon is coming. Wherever the Battle-Brothers travel within the Salient, this thought should be their constant companion. If a world has not been touched yet by the swarm, it is only a matter of time, or perhaps even now advanced vanguard organisms are prowling its forests or hiding in the sewers of its cities. Once such organisms are detected, decline is almost always rapid and soon the skies will darken and spores will choke the atmosphere as Hive Fleet Dagon adds another planet to its tally. Guardsmen and naval ratings sent to the Orpheus Salient pray to the God-Emperor that they will be stationed to a world far from the action and survive their tour to be sent elsewhere. They know in their hearts, however, that when the time comes it will be their regiment or their ship that is called to the defence of a dying world, where they will face their doom at the claws and maws of the Great Devourer like so many before them.

The GM can use this oppressive feeling of impending doom to build tension long before the PCs ever lay eyes on a Tyranid creature. While the majority of Imperial citizens are kept completely ignorant of their impending doom, there are an unfortunate few who are aware of the Great Devourer lurking ever closer. This can range from the defeatist talk of a hysterical guardsman all the way up to nervous planetary governors trying to bargain their way out of the annihilation of their worlds. While Battle-Brothers will not suffer from such doubts, the presence of these kinds of NPCs can have an effect on their allies and also the players themselves, who may well begin to wonder about the strength of their enemies if everyone they meet is almost mad with fear at the thought of their arrival.

STALKERS IN THE DARK

Fear is among the Tyranids' greatest weapons and paradoxically it is never so great as when they are not present. A dozen Genestealers charging down a corridor at the Battle-Brothers is merely a threat (albeit a dangerous one) waiting to be dealt with, whereas a lone Genestealer somewhere in the ventilation and reclamation systems of a ship is a lurking horror and a massive demoralizing factor for its crew. Like the unseen presence of rats in the walls of an old building, the GM can use unseen Tyranids to create a hostile environment for the Kill-team without actual combat. Whether it is in the back alleys of a hive city, the depths of a death world jungle or the corridors of a space station, simply knowing such creatures are lurking nearby will keep the Battle-Brothers on edge. The presence of unseen enemies also forces the PCs to be more creative in dealing with their foes if they must first find them before they can kill them, and it will also draw out an encounter or produce a more interesting outcome than a simple stand up fight would offer.

LENGTHENING SHADOWS

While Hive Fleet Dagon is in theory a single entity pouring into the Sector from the Eastern Fringe, it is in reality spread across a broad front with dozens and dozens of lesser swarms spreading out in all directions. This means there is no clear frontline or "safe zone" against the swarm and Tyranids can strike anywhere and at any time within the Orpheus Salient (or even beyond). The GM can use the erratic nature of Dagon's advance to add to the sense of doom and fear that presses down upon the Imperial forces and also the tactical nature of the Tyranids, which confounds elite organisations like the Deathwatch. No one knows for sure why the swarm will bypass some worlds to strike at others, though both the Inquisition and the Adeptus Mechanicus have spent long years studying the nature of the Hive Fleets so far without much insight into the alien mind driving them. What is known is that no matter how remote a world, how far it might be from the nearest confirmed sighting of the swarm and how unimportant it is, its citizens may still look up one day to see the swarm blot out their sun.

FEW AGAINST THE MANY

The swarms of Hive Fleet Dagon almost always outnumber the Imperium's forces, often many times over. For every score of Tyranids struck down, three score take its place and worlds drown in tides of chitin and claws. Even the most heavily defended worlds of the Salient can only hope to slow the Tyranid advance unsupported, the highest walls and staunchest defenders only buying a little more time for beleaguered populations before the inevitable fall to the swarm's endless warriors and implacable advance. Even though in some places the Imperium has turned back the tendrils of Hive Fleet Dagon, deflected its attacks on worlds or met it in open naval engagements in the depths of the void, it has yet to make a measurable blow against the swarm. While the swarm continues to press in from the void, new fleets appear to replace the blasted remnants of the old, from some seemingly endless column of alien advance, and every victory costs the Imperium dear, leaving ruined worlds and decimated formations in their aftermath.

As members of the Deathwatch, the players will always be outnumbered by their foes. In the Orpheus Salient this is even more pronounced, and the GM can use the endless overwhelming nature of the hive fleet to cast it in to stark relief. There should never be enough of anything in the war against the Tyranids; even well defended worlds should struggle to hold back the swarm's advance, often barely able to counter the Tyranid vanguard before the hammer blow of the main fleet falls upon them. The GM can use this situation to add to the desperation of the players' missions, as they are rushed to warzones or arrive in the final days before an invasion to demoralised faces and the thin green line of the Imperial Guard trying vainly to protect an entire world with only a handful of regiments. Hopeful and ignorant nobles and governors will look upon the arrival of the Deathwatch as their salvation, even though the Kill-team will know better. NPCs can be used to convey this delusion to the players and add to the sense of impending and final annihilation as tacticians and commanders bravely speak of their orbital defences or elite soldiers stopping the swarm in its tracks, surely now a certainty with the arrival of the Deathwatch. What the Kill-team knows is that most worlds they visit are already lost, and even the most stubborn of defences cannot hope for victory, only delay and the hope of buying a world's citizens a few more hours of existence.

A LAST STAND

With complete victories against the Tyranid swarms few and far between, it is far more likely for the Kill-team to find themselves as part of a holding action or last stand while they struggle to complete their mission. Quite often Imperial forces will be crushed in a matter of hours by the arrival of a full strength swarm. Orbital defences will expend months worth of ammunition in minutes before being overrun, their magazines empty and their power cores drained, while entire regiments will simply vanish beneath a tide of alien shock troops as they futilely try to hold their ground. The GM can use these events to add a real sense of pressure and time to a Deathwatch mission, the players aware that Imperial defences will only hold for so long, and sooner rather than later the Tyranid vanguard will be knocking on their door. A good way to bring this to life, without going into excessive detail or overly plotting out the stage-by-stage fall of a world, is to have the Battle-Brothers privy to the Imperial vox net and local command channels. The GM can then throw in vox transmission between naval ships, PDF companies and to and from the planetary governance as the swarm advances. Typically this will be cries for reinforcements, or tactical data and final messages from forward units as they are overrun (often laced with gunfire and alien screams in the background).

By Our Deaths Shall the God-Emperor Know Us

More often than not it is the fate of Imperial forces to give their lives to slow the advance of the hive fleets or simply because they have no other choice but to go down fighting. Even the most ignorant of guardsmen or Planetary Defence Force conscripts have heard the horror stories and dire rumours of the fate of worlds that fall to the Tyranids. They know all too well what their chances will be when the swarm darkens the skies of their world, and the grisly fate that awaits them personally at the claws and fangs of a xenos bio-horror. This knowledge, as much as Commissars and captains may try to stamp it out, leads to an air of fatalism among those facing the swarm, a sense that they are already dead and living on borrowed time. Many of the NPCs the players come into contact with in the Orpheus Salient will share this fatalism and, even if their faith in the God-Emperor is strong, it will affect the way they respond to crisis and conduct their attacks and defences. For some this fatalistic air will lead to depression, and the GM can have some NPCs seemingly "give up" when the hive fleet arrives on their worlds, overcome by the inevitability of the situation. Others however will see their death as a chance to prove their worth to the God-Emperor, and may even become reckless in their attempts to take as many xenos with them as possible. The Adeptus Astartes almost always fall into the latter category with varying degrees of fanaticism.

Fall into Darkness

At their current rate of advance, it is only a matter of time before the Tyranids wipe out all life but their own within the Orpheus Salient. The pressure to halt them lies firmly on the back of the Crusade, and unless the tide somehow turns against the swarm, defeat is inevitable. What makes this even worse is that there is no going back against the Tyranids; no retaking of fallen worlds or rescue of prisoners. This is the finality of the presence of Hive Fleet Dagon as it devours everything it touches and leaves nothing but cold rock and empty space in its wake. In the mind of man, the Tyranid represents the death of entire sectors and is the deadliest of all the alien horrors encountered. Worlds that fall to Orks, Tau or even heretic forces can always be reclaimed, their cities resettled, their forests, mountains and oceans purged of alien taint. Those taken by the Tyranids, however, are gone forever, consumed and regurgitated into more alien monsters, slavering and hungering for more.

The finality of the Tyranid advance though the Orpheus Salient is a very important theme, which will have an effect on everything that happens within the region. Players should feel the gravity of it when their characters look at strategic maps or listen to reports and see worlds vanishing from charts one by one. Hive Fleet Dagon does not just represent a temporary shift in the fortunes of the Crusade but the icy hand of death itself reaching for its throat, enveloping systems, fleets and whole armies as it creeps in across the galactic gulf. The war against the Tyranids is not a war of ideology or faith, it is not a war to free humanity from alien masters or right an ancient wrong, it is a war of survival plain and simple: either mankind will prevail or it will perish.

DEAD BUT NOT FORGOTTEN

The Orpheus Salient is a place of ghosts and memories, where the living remember the dead, and contemplate their own fate. So far, dozens of worlds have fallen to Hive Fleet Dagon, wiped from the Sector and consumed utterly, each one a unique culture, prosperous human world or staunch Imperial ally. The memory of these lost worlds still haunts the surviving worlds and peoples of the Salient, as once thriving trade routes die and close friends are lost. The GM can remind the players of these lost worlds by having them encounter survivors or rare items (now often unique given the demise of their world of origin), bringing with them stories and legends of places that are no more. Perhaps most tragic among the lost are those worlds that survived the Age of Shadow and had only just heard of the Imperium's return, and stood ready with open arms to welcome back the light of the God-Emperor only to be washed away by Hive Fleet Dagon. Such worlds and peoples are also a good source of mysteries and missions, as when the swarm scours a planet they will leave behind the ruins of its civilisation in the form of broken cities and many of the secrets they hide. Returning to such places is never easy, however, as many remain toxic for years after the touch of the swarm, and inevitably some Tyranid organisms are left behind like so much meat between the teeth of the monster.

SCAVENGERS

There are those, both among humanity and its lesser foes, who attempt to benefit from the presence of Hive Fleet Dagon. Opportunists and renegades, these scavengers play a dangerous game and shadow the swarm, waiting for it to strike a rich and bountiful world. Then during the chaos and carnage of the invasion, they undertake their own dark design, be it the theft of Imperial wealth, the stealing of secrets or some other purpose such as the taking of slaves. Often these scavengers are simply bold human pirates or renegade Imperial formations turned mercenary by the breakdown of order and communication, though sometimes they are much worse and can include alien aggressors. Eldar corsairs especially have been observed striking amidst the first thrusts of the Tyranid invasion in the Orpheus Salient, though with so few survivors of such battles, reports are almost impossible to verify. The GM can use scavengers to complicate already perilous situations for the players, having allies turn on them in a bid for their own greed or a third enemy enter the fray when they are fully engaged with the swarm. The presence of other alien forces can also be used to turn a mission on its head, certainly in the case of powerful xenos such as the Tau and Eldar. The arrival of these aliens can bode no good for the Imperium, and as members of the Deathwatch, the players must then decide if this new xenos presence supersedes the Tyranid presence and might just have more far reaching consequences than the loss of a single world.

NO QUARTER GIVEN, NO QUARTER ASKED

Tyranids don't take prisoners. In the eyes of the swarm, all non-Tyranid life is simply more bio-matter for the hive ships, more raw material for its fleet and more fodder to fuel its endless war of annihilation. This is a painful lesson the Imperium has learnt time and again against the hive fleets and at the cost of countless billions of lives. The tally of these past encounters and the relentless, pitiless nature of the swarm has created a special hatred for the Tyranid in the Imperium, a hatred that goes even beyond the normal xenophobia of aliens and the teachings of the God-Emperor to repel them. The warriors of the Orpheus Salient know that when the fight is taken to Hive Fleet Dagon, it is a fight that promises only victory or death. The Deathwatch also approach the Tyranid threat differently to dealing with other aliens, focusing less on understanding or manipulation and more on simple uncomplicated extermination, much as one might deal with a disease or any other unthinking, unreasoning entity.

The unreasoning aspect of Hive Fleet Dagon can make it even more terrifying to face and the GM can explore the theme in his adventures to add to the tension of facing the swarm. Even the brutish mind of an Ork or the corrupt philosophies of the Tau can be understood to an extent, but not the alien hunger of the Tyranids. Players should feel truly hunted when facing the full force of the swarm, small insects in the path of an unstoppable juggernaut of alien horror. The best way to capture this bestial nature is often though the actions and reactions of NPCs who will always be more afraid or unsettled than the PCs. As the shadow of the swarm falls upon a world, those defending it will know there will be no surrender, no prisoners taken and no reasoning with the enemy. It is a primal fear, shared by all mankind, of predators, things which hunt man not to capture his cities or usurp his governments but to feed upon his flesh until there is nothing left.

A SPARK OF INTELLIGENCE

It is easy for Battle-Brothers and Imperial commanders to forget the intelligence that lurks within the depths of the Hive Mind. Such is the typical behaviour of the swarm and its animalistic assault on worlds that it can often be seen as little more than a rabid beast driven only by hunger. This is not true, of course, for a feral and deep intelligence guides all Tyranids, especially vanguard organisms like the Lictor and Genestealer, which must make their own decisions far from the caress of the Hive Mind. The GM can explore this theme to keep the players off balance and add to the horror of the alien hordes. Tyranids might change their tactics or outsmart human defenders during an assault, making feint attacks or infiltrating through supposedly secure tunnels and passages. The GM can even have seemingly mindless Tyranids like Hormagaunts or Rippers exhibit this behaviour with the guidance of the Hive Mind, cutting power to buildings, exploiting blind spots in defences and even destroying or damaging cogitators to disrupt communications. The GM can alternate such behaviour, having the swarm seem mindless only until making an act of intelligence, to take the PCs by surprise.

DEATHWATCH ACTIVITY

"Ours is a sacred duty to the armies of the Achilus Crusade. While guardsmen may toil against the endless legions of xenos and naval ships burn the sky, we are the needle's tip, slipping past the scales of Hive Fleet Dagon and piercing its beating black heart."

–Watch Captain Marius Avincus

The Deathwatch has been active in the Orpheus Salient long before the arrival of the Achilus Crusade, Kill-teams from Watch Fortress Erioch carrying out the will of the Chapter Masters, Ordo Inquisitors, and the Emperor who guides them all. Even during the Age of Shadow, the eyes of the Chapter were keenly fixed on worlds within what would become the Salient, as if anticipating the horrors to come. After the arrival of the Crusade and the influx of Adeptus Astartes, the Deathwatch became significantly more active, aiding the crusaders to push back the boundaries of the Jericho Reach along the rimward edges and deal with the ambitions of xenos empires and alien interlopers. While the vanguard of the Crusade pushed forward, claiming world after world, the Deathwatch moved both ahead and behind it, weakening alien and rebel resistance. Often unknown to the soldiers of the Crusade, powerful foes and xenos plots would be dealt with swiftly and brutally before even a single crusader set foot on a world, and paving the way for Imperium conquest.

Everything changed with the arrival of Hive Fleet Dagon. Almost overnight, the Tyranids fell upon the Salient like a hammer blow and the Imperium was forced to retreat on all fronts and dig in on key worlds, clinging desperately to forward systems against the alien assault. The eyes of Watch Fortress Erioch immediately turned to the Orpheus Salient, and as Lord Militant Tetrarchus enacted a rapid redeployment of men and material, the Deathwatch sent dozens of Kill-teams to Watch Stations on the rimward edge to help stem the tide and support the Imperial forces from the shadows. In those first, dark days of the swarm's arrival, the Battle-Brothers of the Deathwatch performed precision strikes on the Hive Fleet in areas where the Imperium was weak, rushing to systems teetering on the edge of collapse and worlds where uprisings and the terror of impending annihilation were tearing apart Imperial rule. In time, Hive Fleet Dagon's advance was slowed, worlds fortified and a frontline established against the swarm; all in no small part due to the invisible efforts of the Deathwatch.

Even now, as war drags endlessly on against the Tyranids and worlds continue to be consumed, the Deathwatch has a vital role to play within the Orpheus Salient. Under the command of Watch Captain Marius Avincus, a veteran of the Tyrannic Wars, Deathwatch Kill-teams undertake some of the most dangerous and audacious missions within the region, man for man dealing more damage against the Tyranids than any other force. It falls to the Kill-teams to go where other larger forces cannot and even a company of Space Marines could not strike and return alive, often delving deep within Tyranid infested space to tear at the heart of the beast. Over the course of the war against the Tyranids, the Deathwatch have executed this duty with exceptional skill, and if the Hive Mind is aware of such things then surely it would count the black armoured warriors among the greatest threats to its survival.

ASSASSINATIONS

Kill-teams (as their name suggests) excel at taking out individual targets. More reliable than anything short of an Imperial Temple Assassin, the Inquisition frequently calls upon the Deathwatch to eliminate specific threats within the Orpheus Salient. Currently there are a number of most wanted "Targets of Opportunity" which the Ordo passes on to Kill-teams operating in the area. These usually include high profile foes, such things as the creature known as the Dagon Overlord or the Eldar Syndilian, but can equally extend to rogue Imperial commanders or Tau spies and sympathisers. The Deathwatch maintains a standing order to eliminate these threats as they are encountered, often overriding lesser objectives. In addition to these high profile threats, many of the missions the Deathwatch undertake in the Salient are assassinations, even in the midst of invasions. Watch Captain Marius Avincus knows well the benefits of taking out key Tyranid synapse creatures, and in battle, this honour will usually fall to a Kill-team.

RECOVERY

The Orpheus Salient is often a chaotic place where frontlines can shift in an instant and whole armies find themselves cut off from support. There are also countless worlds of interest to the Imperium and the Inquisition, which were cut off or overrun before the Crusade could reach them. For this reason, Kill-teams, usually at the behest of the Inquisition, may be called upon to undertake recovery missions. These can range from investigation and retrieval of artefacts to actual rescue missions where important Imperial personnel need to be saved, often from the impending advance of Hive Fleet Dagon. Given their robust and resourceful nature, the Kill-team may sometimes find themselves sent into places where other specialist teams could not hope to survive. The ruined hives of Castobel are an example of this, and more than one Kill-team has been covertly deployed to the beleaguered world to search the radioactive remains of Hive Tyralos, which seem for some reason to be of interest to the swarm—all without the knowledge of Lord Castellan Ortarna Lokk of course.

TOTAL WAR

The Kill-teams of the Deathwatch are exceptionally efficient, capable of striking at a dangerous xenos target and extracting long before the enemy has time to react. Their systematic approach keeps their presence all but completely secret from the forces of the Achilus Crusade, allowing them to move about the Reach with relative ease. But as Hive Fleet Dagon descends on more and more worlds, and the Shadow in the Warp obscures all communications, the necessity for Kill-teams to perform operations alongside the forces of the Imperium increases. Often, in the Orpheus Salient, Kill-teams have inserted directly into pitched planetary battles to strike critical blows against the Tyranids. Such is their prowess in battle that their presence in a warzone can easily tip the balance in the Imperium's favour. After a battle, surviving Imperial Guardsmen tell whispered tales of the black-clad Space Marines, blazing a glorious trail to victory before vanishing as quickly as they came.

Areas of Interest

It is the Deathwatch's primary mission to counter xenos threats within the Orpheus Salient, often working on the intelligence and direction of Ordo Xenos Inquisitors. Unlike the blunt attacks of the Imperial Guard and Imperial Navy, or even the surgical strikes of the Adeptus Astartes, the Deathwatch are usually only dispatched to deal with the most significant targets at the most critical times. It falls to the elite Kill-teams to deal with tasks which either cannot or would not be dealt with by the larger more ponderous elements of the Crusade military. As such the Deathwatch do not usually concern themselves directly with such things as planetary assaults or naval engagements with the swarm, instead first considering carefully the nature of their foe before choosing the most telling place to land a blow. To conduct this manner of warfare, the Deathwatch often calls upon the Inquisition (or vice versa) to gather intelligence on the Tyranid hive fleets, chart their movements and the influence they exert over worlds. Watch Captain Marius Avincus is especially adept at judging the disposition of the swarm, long years fighting the Tyranids giving the old Space Marine a keen sense of the Hive Mind's instincts and allowing him to direct his Kill-teams to where they are needed most.

A result of these focussed areas for the Deathwatch within the Salient is that quite often Kill-teams will be operating around the edges of the Tyranid assaults rather than charging into them head on. As the Deathwatch knows well, a world is not only at threat from the swarm when it darkens their skies but often long beforehand. Harbinger organisms and alien infection can cripple a world, often under the nose of Imperial forces, setting off the flames of rebellion or destruction far too quickly for the local defences to respond. It is in these cases that the eyes of the Inquisition and the firepower of the Deathwatch are all that stand between survival and ruin. Curtailing the influence of the hive fleets in this way means constant vigilance, however, and while many of a Kill-team's missions may be to lay waste to a brood or vanquish an infiltrator creature, just as many will be either to gather intelligence or test the reactions of the foe, poking the beast to see how it stirs.

Swarm Movement

Plotting the movements of Hive Fleet Dagon is of considerable interest to the Imperium, and a vital part of planning which worlds to fortify and where a swarm might be engaged in the void before it even reaches a world. For the most part this responsibility is shared by the Adeptus Mechanicus and the Inquisition, agents of both organisations spreading out across the Salient, looking for clues to the Tyranids' movements. The Deathwatch is also active in this endeavour and where lesser agents would have little chance of survival, Kill-teams are sent in. One of the most notable examples of this is in the identification and neutralisation of space hulks, a favoured method of the Hive Mind to spread its spore far ahead of the advance of its fleets. Along the edge of the eastern reach, beyond the frontier worlds of Herisor and Atonement, space hulks have become more numerous in recent years. Some speculate that this is a result of recent losses to the Imperial Navy or the number of Rogue Trader, explorator and other long-range ship that have been lost. Some whisper that the truth is more sinister than this and that many of the vessels are in fact the remains of Lord General Mikal Curas' fleet, raising questions about both its fate and the fate of the Lord General himself.

Ancient Alien Ruins

The Deathwatch's primary concern within the Orpheus Salient is combating the advances of Hive Fleet Dagon. While this takes the lion's share of their resources and the time of its Kill-teams, they are not blind to the actions and movements of other kinds of xenos, or to other more ancient concerns. The Tau, Orks, and, to a lesser extent, the Eldar are all active within the Orpheus Salient even if their activities are overshadowed by the presence of Hive Fleet Dagon and do from time to time demand the attention of the Deathwatch. In addition to these lesser threats, the Deathwatch also maintain a close eye on numerous worlds within the Salient, worlds scattered with ancient ruins that were old even before the man set foot within the Jericho Reach, and long before the Age of Shadow cast a pall upon the region. Watch Captain Marius Avincus knows the importance of vigilance, just as do his superiors in Watch Station Erioch, so sometimes Kill-teams are deployed to such worlds to ensure their continued silence.

ORPHEUS MISSIONS

"A darkness has fallen over the rimward edge of the Reach, its deep shadows blotting out the holy gaze of the God-Emperor. We are the light in this dark place, and by our actions and the actions of our allies will we draw His grace once more to this forsaken place and cast out the night once and for all."

–Inquisitor Kalistradi of the Ordo Xenos (Deceased)

Across the length and breadth of the Orpheus Salient, Imperial forces struggle to hold back the advance of Hive Fleet Dagon, fighting desperate battles on dozens of worlds to save dozens more. Amid this raging conflict, the Deathwatch dispatches Kill-teams to help tip the balance and turn the tide against the swarm. These are often covert missions, based on Inquisitorial intelligence, and intended to do the most harm to Dagon by striking hard and fast against any weakness it can find. While the greater Imperial command, and even the Chapters of the Adeptus Astartes, may be unaware of Deathwatch operations, they are often vital to the survival of a world or the destruction of a hive fleet. Such missions are also extremely hazardous even for Space Marines, and Kill-teams often face the swarm unsupported, a handful of Battle-Brothers alone on a hostile world against the wrath of the Tyranid advance.

There are a variety of missions and adventures GMs can base within the Orpheus Salient; both against the forces of Hive Fleet Dagon and against other perils created by the constant Tyranid threat. Common types of missions include recon and scouting operations to learn more about the nature of a hive fleet or the Dagon genus, search and destroy operations to kill or recover certain Tyranid bio-forms, or assault operations where Kill-teams aid other Imperial forces, or Adeptus Astartes Chapters, in all-out war against the swarm. Below are some examples of different takes on these kinds of missions and how, even in the war against Tyranids, they can have shades of grey and unexpected complications. The GM can use these mission overviews either as the jumping off point for a more detailed adventure or use some of the ideas and themes presented within them for his own unique adventures.

EYE IN THE STORM

"A good hunter learns how his prey thinks, how it acts and reacts so that he might become more adept at killing it."

—Magos Biologis Melkov Kreel, Precept of the Eye in the Storm

Since the first reports of Hive Fleet Dagon from the surface of Herisor, the Magi Biologis of the Adeptus Mechanicus in the Jericho Reach have been studying the creatures. They are trying to determine how their behaviour and biology differ from those Tyranids encountered previously throughout the Imperium. For many, this understanding has been limited, restricted to weapon systems and tactical data. For a few, though, the scope has been much larger and the plans far more grandiose in design. The Magi have delved deep into the building blocks of this genus and its very nature, in an effort to understand how Dagon thrives and evolves at such a terrifying rate. In some cases this has led to potent virus weapons or toxic munitions, both of which have had mixed effects on the creatures of Hive Fleet Dagon, ranging from deadly potency to abject failure. In other cases, the Magos have learnt to manipulate Tyranid organisms, either by disrupting the controlling influence of the Hive Mind or by confounding their natural instincts, once again with mixed success.

Among these Magos is Melkov Kreel, an ancient and brilliant adept of the Adeptus Mechanicus and a member of the Crusade since it first crossed the Well of Night. Kreel saw the arrival of Hive Fleet Dagon in the Orpheus Salient not as the great disaster it was widely perceived as, but rather a rare opportunity to study a fascinating xenos organism and learn its secrets. At first, Kreel's efforts were restricted to gathering and studying samples of Tyranid creatures recovered in battle, but soon he and many of his colleagues were conducting their own experiments to better understand the swarm. Under the remit of the Mechanicus, he conducted expeditions into the region's warzones or to worlds left in the hive fleet's wake. More recently Kreel and some members of the Ordo Xenos have been developing a new weapon to use against the Tyranids, a method of detecting the Shadow in the Warp long before it falls by reading the tiniest ripples in the Immaterium caused by Dagon's passing. To this end the Magos has created the Eye in the Storm, a vast void station permanently situated in the depths of the warp, to monitor and report on the movements of "Dagon's Shadow."

Kreel, in attempts to develop a device to detect the approach of the Shadow if the Warp, uses captured Tyranid organisms, especially vanguard bio-forms like Lictors and Genestealers. Hooked up to complex cogitators and tended by med-servitors, the Magos can observe the brain activity and metabolism of the creatures and has come up with a method of determining how to read the approach or retreat of the Shadow through them. Such experiments have taken their toll, and some of the creatures imprisoned within the Eye have killed their attendants and tried to escape, forcing Kreel to exterminate whole batches. Of more concern to the Magos, however, is that recently these escape attempts have become more co-ordinated, and often creatures in different parts of the station will rebel simultaneously as if somehow in communication with each other, despite the absence of the Hive Mind. Kreel knows he is close to unlocking a reliable way to track the Shadow and so has refused to eradicate the creatures on board despite the warnings of his peers, instead sending out teams to bring back more, convinced he has everything under control.

OVERVIEW

The Ordo Xenos and Adeptus Mechanicus have lost contact with the Eye in the Storm, a secret research facility deep within the warp. The Eye was conducting research into ways to track the movements of the hive fleets and predict the imminent fall of the Shadow in the Warp. While the station contains numerous important Mechanicus personnel (such as Magos Biologis Melkov Kreel), of upmost importance is the recovery of the data already collected on the Shadow. The Kill-team will be briefed on what the members of the Inquisition and Adeptus Mechanicus know about the facility, but given the lack of recent contact, they have no idea about the Eye's current condition or even the status of its crew. Elements of the Inquisition and Adeptus Mechanicus both have concerns over Kreel's research and it has been decided that once the data is recovered, the station should be destroyed, the experiment officially ended and all trace wiped away.

Getting to the station will require the Kill-team to travel on a Mechanicus Explorator vessel, tasked to make contact with the station. Its crew will not be able to aid them, for they are under strict orders not to venture onto the station for fear of contamination. Thus the Battle-Brothers will need to cross the gulf of boiling warp space between vessels in a small shielded shuttle. Getting into the station should not be a significant challenge, its Gellar Field is still functioning and its plasma reactor is still online. Once inside, though, the real test begins, as they will discover much of the station has fallen to the Tyranids and only a small group of Tech Priests are holding out, though they themselves may have become tainted.

PRIMARY OBJECTIVES

Recover the Data: The Eye is a mess, a maze of corridors and chambers overrun by Tyranids. The Kill-team should have to work their way down from the station's docking ring to get into its primary medicae level and from there to the cogitator-core where the data on Kreel's experiments are stored. The GM can have them encounter lone hunting creatures but the bulk of the Tyranids (a Genestealer Brood) will wait until they are as far from the docking ring as possible (probably during the agonizing minutes they are downloading the data from the cogitator-core). In the lower levels, near the reactor, there is also a group of tech-priests holding out, who may or may not help the Kill-team. If they choose to ignore the tech-priests' cries for help, they might find themselves sealed into the cogitator level to draw the Tyranids' attentions while the tech-priests make a break for it.

Destroy the Eye: There are two ways to destroy the Eye; either overload the plasma reactor or shut down the Gellar Field. The first will require the Kill-team to enter the lower levels, and either do a manual override or simply enough damage to the reactor to trigger a cascade and eventual overload. The second is harder but can be done from the operations centre on the medicae level if the station's cogitator codes can be broken. Unfortunately, there is no way to delay the Gellar Field shutdown, so when it is triggered, the Kill-team will have only a few moments to return to their vessel before the warp begins to invade the station and they are contending with more than mere xenos...

SECONDARY OBJECTIVES

Find Melkov Kreel: Kreel has been taken by the Alpha Brood but not killed. For reasons unknown the Genestealers have not devoured him and instead he is sealed in the middle of their nest, along with other members of the crew. Quite mad, Kreel still believes there is hope for his experiment and believes he has a rapport with the Tyranids. The Kill-team will be able to find him if they either try to clear out the medicae level or if they can hack into the station's auspexes and get pic feed of the chambers taken over by the brood. Getting to Kreel and killing the brood guarding him is not necessarily the hard part. Once there the Battle-Brothers will have to convince him to leave (he thinks the Genestealers respect him and would never harm him) or drag him away under protest. They must also decide what to do with the

dozen or so crew with him, some of which have been driven completely mad by the horrific things they have seen, if allowed to live they will begin to wreak havoc around the station in their panicked insanity (sealing or opening doors, destroying lights, dragging off Kreel, etc.).

TERTIARY OBJECTIVES

Exterminate Any Surviving Tyranid Organisms: The GM can have as many or as few Tyranid creatures aboard the Eye as he likes. Lictors and Genestealers are most likely, but in his experiments, Kreel has worked on anything he could get his hands on. Many of the Tyranids have also been modified (plates and wires still attached to skulls and chests or limbs missing, replaced with bionics to monitor internal processes), and could have traits like Armour Plates or Machine if the GM chooses. The GM should also make use of the twisting corridors and vents of the station, and have the Tyranids stalk the Battle-Brothers, striking and then disappearing beneath floor plates or wall panels.

COMPLICATIONS

Geller Field Destabilisation: If the GM wants to increase the challenge for the PCs, he can have the Eye's Geller Fields begin to fail. Flickers in the field's protection could allow daemons to access the station, as well as the corrupting influence of the warp to play with the Battle-Brothers' minds. The PCs could find the Geller Field generator and attempt to stabilise the device, or alternatively they could simply race against time to escape before the field fails entirely, engulfing them in the deadly energy of the warp.

Servitor Malfunction: In addition to the failing Geller Fields, the GM can have the servitors on the station begin to malfunction, and attack the Kill-team. This can make a good ambush situation where "dead" servitor corpses litter a floor as the PCs pass only for the servitors to rise up in their midst and attack them. Servitors can also add some ranged combat challenges to the Kill-team who might otherwise think themselves safe as long as they keep their distance.

OUTCOMES

The Ordo and Mechanicus will consider the mission a success if they recover the data or destroy the station (though both will be considered a better outcome). The return of Kreel will also be regarded as significant, though the Magos will likely disappear into an Inquisition interrogation cell for some time. Finally, if the PCs do bring back the data on Kreel's research, the GM may allow them to benefit from it in the future and gain information into the movements of the hive fleets from their Adeptus Mechanicus allies.

A TWISTING PATH

"I don't know what's worse, the naked aggression of the Tyranids or the plots and schemes of the Eldar. At least you'll probably see the Tyranids coming..."

–High Envoy Kaydon

The Ordo Xenos has been aware of the presence of the Eldar in the Jericho Reach since the arrival of the Crusade. At first, encounters with Eldar pirates and corsairs, especially along the rimward edge of the Sector, raised little concern among the Imperial command. Such opportunists and raiders are encountered in systems and regions across the Imperium and pose little threat to well armed Imperial forces. Encounters were also infrequent and far below those with heretic worlds, Tau scouting forces and even indigenous xenos empires. It was officially reasoned by some within the Inquisition that the Eldar had no significant stake in the Jericho Reach, no Craftworld was located nearby and no worlds seemed to be under the ancient alien's protection, as had been found in other parts of the Imperium. Those Eldar pirates who were encountered seemed to melt away before the advance of the Crusade, as if they had been expecting its arrival and already knew the path it would take. Unknown at the time, Eldar forces had taken an interest in the Sector and even before the first Imperial vessels crossed the warp gate and gulfed the Well of Night, agents of the Eldar were already moving among the worlds of the Reach, manipulating events and changing the course that the Crusade would eventually take.

In time, Inquisitors of the Ordo Xenos have gained the barest sense of these sinister plots, as agents of the enigmatic aliens have come to light. Among them, the Eldar Pathfinder Syndilian Shanyr has been identified by the some Inquisitors as key to the Eldar's interests, her name becoming synonymous with the Eldar's covert operations in the Orpheus Salient. Frustratingly for the Inquisition, and despite the work of their best agents and most skilled interrogators, they have practically no knowledge of Syndilian's motivations, what her mission is or even what she looks like beyond a handful of blurry pic captures from installations and worlds she has visited. In fact the Inquisition has yet to find any pattern in the Pathfinder's actions, much of which seem to have little or no short term effect on the Imperium's presence in the Sector or the advance of the Crusade. Without any great understanding of this dangerous foe, the Ordo Xenos has sealed much of the information on Syndilian and kept knowledge of the existence of these Eldar raiders, and the successes of their missions, from much of the rest of the Inquisition and the Deathwatch, at least until they know more. Assassinations, sabotage, and acts of rebellion instigated by Syndilian are, as a result, often blamed on other enemies such as heretics and xenos sympathisers, lest too many unanswerable questions be asked.

The reality, largely unknown to the Ordo Xenos, is that Syndilian is following a path laid out by the Farseers of her Craftworld long ago to subvert the advance of Hive Fleet Dagon and steer the swarm away from key worlds which will, in times to come, be vital to defeating an even greater and more ancient foe. As part of her mission, the Pathfinder has spent years with a small group of elite Eldar Rangers, travelling across the Sector and altering events with timely interventions. Sometimes this will mean killing an important figure, or fomenting an uprising, other times it can be as simple as delaying a shipment of promethium by a few days or stealing a seemingly unimportant document or device.

Recently Syndilian has arrived in the Iantos system, a remote Imperial outpost orbiting a massive blue giant star. Close to the Iron Collar, and separated by unstable warp routes from any world touched by Hive Fleet Dagon, Iantos is not considered a likely target for the swarm. It is little more than an Imperial listening post, settled around an ancient human habitation and only supporting a merger population of relevantly content citizens. It is Syndilian's intent to instigate the first seeds of rebellion here and begin a cascade of events that will drive the Imperium out and turn the system against the God-Emperor.

OVERVIEW

The Iantos system was settled long before the Age of Shadow and comprises a tiny world held in a shifting elliptical orbit by its massive blue star. It skips in and out of the system's narrow and weak primary bio-zone, which, combined with its thin atmosphere and poor mineral content, means it has never thrived or expanded much beyond those early days of settlement. With the arrival of the Crusade and the return of the Imperium, the world fell quickly back into the fold with negligible resistance. Iantos, bathed in the harsh radiation of its star, is an inhospitable place almost entirely covered by hydrogen seas, dotted with rocky islands wrapped in crumbling stone hives. Governed by the Sapphire Council and advised by High Envoy Kaydon, the Imperium's reprehensive on Iantos, the world and its few million inhabitants are largely given over to mining operations and hydrogen refinement plants. Only a small planetary defence force garrison, the Iantos 3rd Sapphire Guard, provide any protection against external or internal threats.

Aboard her ship the *Memory of Solace*, Syndilian and a half dozen of her Pathfinders have arrived in-system. Given the background radiation and the world's ancient orbital sensor-net, they have had no trouble avoiding detection. Syndilian plans to first create a crisis on Iantos using several captured Genestealers (which she is bringing to the system held in stasis) to infect the population and foment an uprising. She will then capture or kill the Sapphire Council's astropath, cutting the world off from the rest of the Imperium and the chance of assistance. Then, at the point local forces are about to be overrun and Imperial help is not forthcoming, she will intervene by aiding and arming a local anti-Imperial cult known as the Azure Sons, helping them (behind the scenes) to drive out the infestation and setting them up as the savours of the world.

The PCs will arrive in Iantos at the behest of High Envoy Kaydon, just as the first reports of the Genestealer infection are taking hold. Unknown to Syndilian, Kaydon is an agent of the Ordo Xenos, deployed to Iantos ironically to hunt for Tau sympathisers believed to be spreading out to remote areas of the Reach in the hopes of setting up pockets of rebellion and

descent. Recognizing the Genestealer threat for what it is, he has been quick to call in a Kill-team, not just to put down the Tyranid vanguard creatures before they spread their infection, but also to find the reason behind their arrival. Kaydon is no fool and hardly any vessels come or go between Iantos and the Imperium, and certainly none for months, begging the question of where the brood came from. Kaydon will want the PCs to find the real alien threat on Iantos and destroy it if they can. He will also advise discretion, the Genestealers have only just begun infecting the populace and the local council will react badly should the Kill-team cause unnecessary harm to the locals. Ideally the Kill-team's actions will prove the importance of the Imperium on Iantos and improve relations with the locals, provided the PCs think before they act.

PRIMARY OBJECTIVES

Identify the Xenos Threat: The Kill-team will need to do some investigation to find the source of the true xenos threat to Iantos. Syndilian has released Genestealers in all the major settlements on the planet and, when the Kill-team arrives, is in the process of having her agents take action to expedite the spread of the Tyranids' infection. Kaydon's own agents have only just detected the presence of the creatures and only know the location of a few of the Genestealers deep within the stone hive cities. The PCs will need to first hunt down the Genestealers in the depths of the hive cities, and from there they will find the first clues as to the existence of another xenos threat (tell-tale signs that the Genestealers where transported in stasis, markings on the Tyranids that indicate they were captured rather than merely spawned). Syndilian and her Pathfinders will then react accordingly and attempt to assassinate the Kill-team and ensure the continued infection. At first the Eldar will be subtle and careful to avoid detection or identification (using accident or manipulation to turn locals and environments against the PCs), but as time goes on she may show her hand and take more direct action to destroy them. Only when the hand of the Eldar has been revealed and Syndilian forced to retreat (only in the most extreme of circumstances will she face the Kill-team herself without a sure method of escape), will Kaydon be convinced the threat is identified.

Maintain Imperial Control of Iantos: How the PCs conduct their investigation into the Genestealer presence, and subsequently the Eldar behind them, will have a lasting effect on the stability of Iantos and the will of its people to support the Crusade. While Iantos is not likely to fall into open rebellion, there is already discontent among the stone cities as to the treatment of its people and should the Kill-team rampage through their streets, destroying property and gunning down citizens in their efforts to hunt the Tyranids, then extreme groups may move against them. Principle among these are the Azure Sons of Iantos, a brotherhood which during the Age of Shadow fell to the worship of the system's massive blue star as the sole source of power and awe in their world's life. The Azure Sons have long resented the Imperium's return, though thus far have been firmly in the minority. Syndilian is also aware of the group as a likely tool to destabilise the populace and has brought weapons to arm them. Even if the Genestealers are defeated and the Eldar driven off, the Azure Sons will need to be addressed, either wiped out (a lengthy and difficult task and one which is largely beyond the remit of the Deathwatch) or better still, integrated into the Sapphire Council and Imperial control of the system.

SECONDARY OBJECTIVES

Eliminate the Tyranid Infestation: The Kill-team will not need to destroy every Genestealer to gain enough leads to guide them to the Eldar, though even one left behind could spell disaster for Iantos in the long run. The PCs can either try find every Tyranid creature during their investigations into the real xenos threat (in fact if they get distracted in their elimination of the brood, Syndilian will conceal some brood members as backup stock to work with later), or once the Eldar have been dealt with they can hunt the Tyranids down. Genestealers are notoriously resilient and the GM can have them pop up in all manner of places, even forcing the PCs to go deep beneath the stone cities of Iantos and hunt them through the hydrogen flooded tunnels of the island cities.

TERTIARY OBJECTIVES

Improve Relations with the Sapphire Council: Quite apart from the glory of uncovering the Eldar plot and destroying the Tyranid creatures, this mission offers a chance for the Imperium to improve relations with Iantos and its peoples. The GM, though Kaydon, should make the PCs aware of the shaky nature of Imperial control on the planet and factors like the Azure Sons that are a constant source of disquiet. Kaydon will also ask them to tread with care when pursuing the brood and be mindful of what the heavy hand of the Imperium may stir up. The PCs do not have to consider any of this to complete their mission, however if they act with political savvy, speaking to the council for its "advice," working with local planetary defence force and agents, or evacuating areas before they strike, they will leave a lasting impression of respect and strengthen the Imperium's hold on Iantos.

COMPLICATIONS

Covering Her Tracks: Syndilian is a skilled and cunning Eldar Pathfinder with countless successful missions behind her. She has never been cornered by the Imperium and so careful is she in covering her tracks that even the Ordo Xenos only barely know of her existence. Her mission on Iantos will be no different and if things go against her and her plans come undone, she will lay waste to whole sections of the world (using the *Memory of Solace* for a swift orbital strike) to cover her escape. Her fellow Pathfinders would also sell their lives for her if need be, though this is not the Eldar way and is only used as a last resort. When playing Syndilian, the GM should have her largely act off screen, planting false clues or laying traps for the PCs. She will only attack them directly if she has a solid escape route, and even then, she and her followers will likely engage at a distance using their long rifles.

Ancient and Unstable: The Tyranids, the Eldar, and the Azure Sons are not the only threats to the PCs on Iantos. The world itself can be a dangerous place, its crumbling rock islands and the unstable deep tunnels below them collapse all the time, worn away by time and the constant movement of the oceans. When the PCs are forced to follow the creatures (or the Eldar) into the older sections of the stone cities, there is always a chance that the environment may turn against them. Sidewalks might fall away, walls can collapse and walkways will sag. This is exacerbated by the fact that a fully armoured Space Marine weighs considerably more than a lithe Eldar ranger or agile Genestealer, and there are places the xenos can go that the Battle-Brothers will have trouble following.

OUTCOMES

If the Kill-team discover that it was the Eldar who brought the Tyranids to Iantos, and that they are hoping to destabilise the world, then Syndilian will retreat, falling back to return another day. Depending on their actions, relations with the world might be improved and Kaydon's position strengthened. There are, however, many loose ends to tie up and the PCs may find themselves hunting down rogue Genestealers or members of the Azure Sons even after the Eldar are unmasked. More likely, the Deathwatch will recall them, leaving Kaydon to clean up the mess they leave behind and repair any damage they might have done, both physical and political.

BEYOND THE NIGHTMARE'S EDGE

"God-Emperor alone knows what lurks beyond the rim; the eastern wilds stretch out towards the desolation of the galaxy's edge, a tangled web of xenos worlds and warp spawn. All we know for sure is it is where the swarm comes from and that alone should make us tread with care."

–Rogue Trader Jargus Pale, Captain of the Lament of Castobel

Precious little is known about the far reaches of the Orpheus Salient, its eastern fringes and the worlds that lie beyond the reach of the Crusade. Records indicate that once the Imperium's boundaries stretched far beyond its current borders and included worlds right out to the edge of the Sector, further even than the most far flung of the current outposts. During the Age of Shadow, this region was cut off from both the Imperium and the core worlds of the Jericho Reach, fading into darkness and languishing for centuries far from the light of the God-Emperor. With the arrival of the Achilus Crusade, the worlds of the Orpheus Salient were in the process of being gradually reunited with the forces of mankind, each one brought back into the fold as the soldiers of the God-Emperor marched deep into the rimward reaches of the Sector. Tragically, before these areas could be completely reclaimed and these lost worlds restored, Hive Fleet Dagon arose from the Eastern Fringe, pushing the Crusade back and once more cutting off these systems and their peoples from salvation.

Even in the dark days of the swarm's advance and the fall of dozens of worlds to the Tyranid fleets, there are those who have made efforts to reconnect to the far east of the Orpheus Salient. Rogue Traders seeking profit and Adeptus Mechanicus Explorator fleets have undertaken perilous journeys to find untouched worlds which may yet have escaped the Hive Fleet Dagon. These bold individuals and their crews have plunged into the depths of the void, beyond the Slinnar Drift Star Cluster and even the most far flung Crusade worlds such as Jove's Decent and Zanatov's Harbor. Though few of these intrepid explorers have returned, those that have paint a picture of dozens of human worlds stretching out to the galactic east. Some have tragically been swept away by the swarm but others still cling to life in the darkness, hungry for contact with mankind, many holding to the ancient memory of the God-Emperor, taken away from them so long ago by the Age of Shadow and the catastrophic warp storms it brought. So far, however, only the reckless and the brave have been able to reach them, and as long as Hive Fleet Dagon continues to press down upon the Salient, hope of reunification remains a forlorn dream.

Not all of those who have braved the eastern reaches have done so for profit or exploration, and sifting through the scraps of information returned to the Crusade, the Inquisition has taken an interest in some of its charted worlds. Recently the Ordo Xenos Inquisitor Dragur Gan and his retinue departed on a mission to recover data from some of these worlds and the void which separates them. Dragur believed there was a reason that the Tyranids had avoided these worlds, something about their populations or about the planets themselves. In some cases he even found evidence that Tyranid organisms had indeed visited these worlds, thus strengthening his belief that Hive Fleet Dagon had not simply missed them during its advance. Unfortunately for the Ordo Xenos and the promise of what could be vital information in the war against the swarm, Dragur and his team vanished shortly after crossing into the eastern reaches and sent a final astropathic communication indicating promising leads but no hard data. Now, over a year later, astropaths at listening posts along the fringe of the Crusade have picked up a fragmented message from Dragur, or at least someone using his codes and ciphers. The message seems to indicate that Dragur has uncovered something, something unexpected about the fringe. Primarily, though, it is a cry for help, a desperate missive requesting rescue from somewhere deep within the claws of the swarm.

OVERVIEW

The Ordo Xenos has decided that the information Dragur is carrying could be of vital importance to the Crusade's efforts in the Orpheus Salient and a rescue mission has been assembled. The Kill-team's mission is to make the long and perilous journey into the eastern reaches to find the lost Inquisitor and his team, or what remains of them, and recover whatever information they can. Unfortunately there was no mention of a location in the message and astropaths have only been able to narrow down its point of origin to a broad stretch of space, somewhere to the galactic northeast of the Slinnar Drift Star Cluster. Given that the mission will involve potentially searching multiple systems in the region, the Deathwatch has made an alliance with a local Rogue Trader Jargus Pale, Captain of the *Lament of Castobel*, and a veteran of the fringe. Pale and his crew have agreed to help the Inquisition and the Deathwatch to find Dragur, for an exchange of information (the details of which will not be shared with the Battle-Brothers).

Travelling to the area where the astropathic message originated will be dangerous in itself, even discounting the chances of an encounter with elements of the swarm, and should take weeks if not months to complete depending on the ebb and flow of the warp and the skill of Pale's Navigator. Once beyond the northern edges of the Slinnar Drift, the Kill-team will then need to commence a search pattern of at least half a dozen systems, some home to lingering human civilisations, others bare stripped rocks still reeking from the touch of Hive Fleet Dagon. Pale's own astropath will be alert for signs and signals, but the Rogue Trader will be reticent to send out any astropathic calls to Dragur so deep within the domain of the swarm, lest it draw Tyranid organisms to their location. As a result the Kill-team and their allies must tread lightly, following the trail of the missing Inquisitor as they negotiate the lion's den, looking for clues to his location.

PRIMARY OBJECTIVES

Find Dragur and his Team: There are five worlds in the region where Dragur's astropathic communication originated, each with a chance of being the location of the Inquisitor, or the surviving members of his retinue. The five worlds include:

- KV85, a blasted airless moon in orbit around a faded red giant star and the home of an ancient Imperial penal colony lost long before even the Age of Shadow cut it off.
- Yanris Secondus, a death world covered in a single living fungal jungle, connected by millions of kilometres of roots and warrens which react as one to animal life.
- Vorl's Rest, a dead world stripped clean by Hive Fleet Dagon, left only with the skeletons of its feudal cities and continent-wide grain mills to attest to its once thriving life.
- Devil's Gate, a volcanic world and home to an abandoned Adeptus Mechanicus Explorator mission which was documenting an indigenous race of sentient silicoid creatures.
- Ayrisa, another world devoured by the Tyranids, still covered in spore chimneys and brood pools as the last organisms strip away its once thick atmosphere.

Dragur has visited each of these worlds until his vessel was destroyed in orbit by vanguard droneships. The GM can either choose which world to place him on, or have him on the last world the PCs arrive at (ensuring they visit each world first to find clues of his passing, such as camp sites or the corpses of his team). In either case Dragur is only barely alive and has been hiding in the wilds of the world for months, hunted by Tyranid vanguard organisms.

Recover Dragur's Data: Dragur was gathering data on why the swarm bypassed some worlds but fell upon others. So far he has amassed significant research from the five worlds he has visited and his travels within the eastern reaches. He is also deeply paranoid (likely the result of months on the run) and will need to be convinced of the Kill-team's motives before he turns anything over. He will also try to press the Kill-team into aiding him in continuing his research, forcing the PCs to decide between following him across the five worlds or keeping to their original orders and dragging him and his information back to the Orpheus Salient. In either case it will mean traversing Tyranid infested space and the very likely chance of an encounter with the swarm, either in the void or while they are on the surface of one of the worlds.

SECONDARY OBJECTIVES

Gather Intelligence on the Eastern Worlds: Dragur's data is not complete and, when they find him, he will insist that they return to each of the five worlds to recover intelligence he left behind (in his paranoid flight from the Hive Mind). Visiting each of the worlds, either with Dragur or for the first time, carries its own risks:

- KV85 is a warren of cellblocks and detention centres operating with an ancient and barely functioning life support system. In the dark tunnels of the installation are clues to the passage of the Tyranids, gathered by the world's long-range sensors (which have never ceased to function) but also tribes of ghoul-like humans, the cannibalistic ancestors of the prisoners.
- There is something about Yanris Secondus and the nature of the single organism which covers its surface which seems to be repellent to the Tyranids (after all, what other reason could there be for avoiding it). The Adeptus Mechanicus Biologis would be very interested in samples, though gathering them may be difficult as it is a massively hostile environment where the very world itself will fight the PCs.
- Vorl's Rest is a place of ghosts and despair, a barren rock with the cold remains of a once prosperous human world. Somewhere in the airless cities are records scrawled on parchment and persevered by vacuum which chart its last days and clues to how the hive fleet devoured it. The world is not without danger, however, and many un-sprung mechanical traps remain, left by its long lost population.
- Devil's Gate is a hostile world where an unprotected human would be quickly burnt alive by the raging fires in its atmosphere. This factor alone though is not a clear reason for the Tyranids to bypass it, especially as records seem to indicate the presence of a silicoid xenos species living in the lava tunnels and rock of the world. If this race somehow has a weapon to turn away the swarm, it must be investigated, whether or not they turn out to be hostile to the Imperium.
- Ayrisa was once a garden world with only a handful of scattered human tribes living in its lush mountains and valleys. Now it is in the last stages of consumption by the swarm, a nightmare of poisonous atmosphere and rippers. Somewhere on the world, though, a few examples of its flora and fauna survive containing clues to the genetic makeup of its biosphere and why it attracted the Tyranids.

Discover Jargus Pale's Ulterior Motives: Quite aside from recovering Dragur and visiting the five worlds, the PCs may have to contend with Pale and his crew. He has not come to the eastern reaches for love of the Imperium, and certainly not for love of the Inquisition or Deathwatch—he is looking for profit. Once he meets with Dragur, he may decide that the data the Inquisitor carries is worth more than the good will of the Ordos, after all Kill-teams are lost all the time. This places the PCs in a position either to make a deal with Pale or take him out, the latter possibly causing more problems than it solves as it leaves them stranded aboard a hostile ship far from any hope of recovery.

TERTIARY OBJECTIVES

Weaken the Swarm: While recovering the Inquisitor, the Kill-team will have a chance to weaken Hive Fleet Dagon, or at very least claim glory in the destruction of more Tyranids. Ayrisa is an especially good place for this and if they can convince Pale to help them, they could conduct a hit and run attack on the Tyranid fleet at high anchor as it feeds on the dying world. Dragur will advise against unnecessary risks, but the GM should reward the PCs if they go out of their way to cause as much damage as they can on the swarm while deep behind enemy lines.

COMPLICATIONS

A Few Thrones More: Pale's loyalty is a fickle thing, ruled as much by profit as it is by fear of reprisals. If the Kill-team tries to steer his vessel into danger too often he might begin to lose faith in helping them. If Dragur is on board, he might also side with Pale to get back to the Crusade as quickly as possible, even going so far as to make a side deal that could leave the Kill-team stranded on one of the five worlds while the Inquisitor and the Rogue Trader sail off into the void without them.

Infested: Every time the *Lament of Castobel* visits a world touched by the Tyranids, there is a chance Tyranid organisms might come on board. The GM could even have one of Dragur's team bring something on board under the nose of the Inquisitor, by carrying tiny organisms on his person. If

this happens, the ship itself might become a battlefield and quite apart from the treachery of Pale, the PCs might find themselves putting down a vessel-wide rebellion or hunting creatures though its warren-like depths.

OUTCOMES

With luck and courage, the Kill-team will return to the Crusade with Dragur, or at very least his data. If they have acquitted themselves well it will mean great glory for them and improved relations with the Inquisition. If they have had a falling out with Pale or killed him (even to save their own lives), then there will be consequences, for the death of a Rogue Trader cannot go unanswered. While the Deathwatch will consider the matter beyond its direct concern, the Inquisition may try to make amends, even using the Kill-team in a roundabout way to aid the interests of the Pale Dynasty. At the very least the Battle-Brothers will earn the enmity of the dynasty, which may come back to haunt them in the future, especially if they travel beyond the reach of the Crusade again.

Orpheus Salient Complications

Complications are a way for the GM to alter the nature of a mission, potentially change its objectives and add further challenges for the PCs. They offer a chance for the GM to represent the fog of war and the general maxim that no plan survives contact with the enemy. They also force the PCs to think on their feet as the nature of their mission changes around them, and they must adapt and survive if they are to be successful. More details on Complications and their uses can be found on page 231 of the DEATHWATCH rulebook.

Presented here are a selection of complications specific to the Orpheus Salient, focussed on the massive impact the presence of Hive Fleet Dagon has upon the forces and operations of the Imperium within the region. GMs should feel free to use this as he sees fit, either adding them to his own missions, any of the missions in this chapter or simply taking elements from them to further develop his adventures.

Table 3-2: Orpheus Salient Complications

1d10	Complication
1	Doom and Despair
2	Evolution
3	False Dawn
4	Foes without Number
5	Hunters Hunted
6	Position Overrun
7	Putting out Fires
8	Sacrifice
9	The Shadow Falls
10	Xenos Cults

Doom and Despair

Poor morale can be as deadly to the strength and defence of a world as the claws and fangs of Tyranid bio-forms. In the face of almost certain extinction and the pressing darkness of a full-blown swarm invasion, men can lose their spirit, their minds broken and their wills crushed by the despair of the annihilation all around them. Though Battle-Brothers are not affected by such weakness, their altered nature and their duty sustaining them in even the most nightmarish of situations, they can suffer from the weakness of their allies and the madness such fear can bring. The GM can use this complication to make allies of the Kill-team act unpredictably, their courage stolen by the terrible majesty of the hive fleet. This could include such things as mass retreats, suicides, gates being sealed and bridges destroyed (blocking the Kill-team's advance or retreat) in a futile attempt to slow the swarm, and even Imperial forces detonating reactors or setting vessels for self-destruct rather than let them fall to the Tyranid assault.

Evolution

The hive fleets are always evolving to deal with new worlds and new Imperial weapons. No sooner has a reliable method of killing a swarm been perfected than the Tyranids adapt, making it redundant and twice as hard to defeat in a similar way again. Despite years of conflict, the Imperium still struggles every time it tries to defend a world or vanquish a hive fleet in deep space, and must often expend prodigious amounts of resources for what are only partial successes and near victories. Deathwatch Kill-teams are also in danger of suffering from the evolutionary leaps the Tyranids can make, and even during the course of a mission they may face a creature that adapts to their methods and renders some of their tactics obsolete. The GM can use this complication to change the nature of the PC's enemies, altering a well know Tyranid organism with different traits or skills or changing the way it fights. This could be something simple and fundamental such as a Genestealer Broodlord, which regenerates or a Tyranid warrior, which flies. It could also be a change in behaviour like Gargoyles that rather than attacking with ranged weapons, sacrifice themselves by flying into the engines of the Kill-team's lander, or a Ravener, which tunnels under a guard tower rather than trying to assault it, destabilising the ground and causing it to collapse.

False Dawn

Tyranids have a nasty habit of coming back from the dead. Often a creature that was thought destroyed, riddled with lasgun holes or even partially dismembered, will rise up to make a final attack. Large Tyranid creatures are especially suitable for this kind of final revenge, their ponderous bulk plodding forward in the face of withering fire and refusing to die no matter how much damage they take. These monstrous resurrections can be used to create a false sense of security or a false dawn where a few moments of respite lead the Kill-team to believe that they have completed their mission or downed their foe. The GM can use this complication to string out an objective and make a mission more challenging. A false dawn can either be a creature that won't die, or a victory which turns out to be only the tip of a large and more brutal conflict. In the first instance, the GM can have a creature return time and again, forcing the PCs to expend large amounts of firepower on it or literally hack it to pieces to make sure it is dead (perhaps even calling in an orbital strike or otherwise vaporising an entire area). The second can see the Kill-team defeat a substantial Tyranid threat or vanquish a massive swarm, only to see another crest the horizon, reminding them of the endless nature of the hive fleets.

FOES WITHOUT NUMBER

Tyranids seldom attack in small numbers, preferring to swamp a foe in bio-horrors spawned from the seemingly endless birthing sacs of the hive fleet. Often, encounters with the swarm can become battles of attrition for a Kill-team, a simple engagement turning into an all-out fire-fight just to hold their ground, while more and more foes stream into the battlefield. Unlike a false dawn, however, this is a fight the Kill-team will have been expecting and which they can also win if they are stalwart and determined. The GM can use this complication to make the enemies in an encounter recurring, effectively regenerating their number and continuing to attack until the PCs achieve an objective or something changes (i.e. allies arrive, citizens manage to escape or enough time elapses). Hordes are especially suitable for this manner of mission complication, by their nature comprising an indeterminate number of individuals and assaulting as a single mass organism. The GM can also use this complication in time sensitive encounters, forcing the PCs to choose between the glory of a long and brutal combat or the difficult decision to retreat if it means completing a mission objective.

HUNTERS HUNTED

Kill-teams are used to hunting their prey as small elite teams sent on missions of assassination, or to seek out and destroy enemy combatants. Against the Tyranids, though, things can change in an instant as a bio-form detects their presence and begins to stalk them itself. Lictors, Genestealers and Raveners are all skilled hunters and difficult prey for a Kill-team to surprise or run to ground. More likely, if such creatures are in the Kill-team's area of operation, then it is the Battle-Brothers who will be the hunted, regardless of what they might believe to the contrary. The GM can use this complication to turn the tables on the PCs and have one or more of the creatures they are hunting detect their presence and stalk them instead. Alternatively, there might be more than one of the creature or brood they are hunting and while they think they are sneaking up on the unsuspecting Tyranid creature, another is following their progress with its beady eyes. If their mission does not involve the direct destruction of Tyranid creatures and instead has other objectives, then this complication means they have picked up a stalker, a Lictor, Genestealer brood or Ravener brood, which will dog their steps and then strike when they are at their weakest.

POSITION OVERRUN

When the Tyranids assault a world, they often strike from many sides at once, pressing down from the sky and establishing multiple landing zones which blossom like boils on the planet's surface. For forces on the ground, this can be chaotic and alarming as front lines are overrun or outflanked before they can be established and defenders find themselves suddenly isolated in pockets of resistance cut off from their allies. Even Deathwatch Kill-teams, which usually operate independently, can suffer from this fate as the tides of war shift around them and extraction routes or objectives become untenable. If the GM uses this complication, it can make an objective more challenging and more dangerous by having the area in which it takes place overrun by Tyranids. This can be an area that would otherwise be safe (or relatively safe) for the PCs to traverse, such as an Imperial base, city hab block or stretch of wilderness. Now it has become infested with vanguard Tyranid organisms and the Kill-team must either sneak or fight their way through. Not yet fully organised, the Tyranids should not present a serious threat to the PCs and should only be encountered in isolated pockets, but can nevertheless slow them down or force them to expend resources to destroy the xenos.

PUTTING OUT FIRES

Things can change quickly in any battle, and even more so during an attack by a hive fleet or a Tyranid assault on a world. Imperial forces can find themselves under attack from unexpected avenues or fronts, fortified lines can collapse or logistics break down, and commanders must rush troops to shore up weaknesses in their defence. Kill-teams (and all Adeptus Astartes) are prized for their ability to respond quickly to these kinds of situations and deal with anything they must face. This complication adds a secondary objective to the Kill-team's mission as they receive an impassioned call for assistance from Imperial forces, or, if they are working alone or far behind enemy lines, a message from local forces. The PCs can then choose to complete this new objective for additional glory and potentially the good will and favour of the force they are coming to aid. If they fail to complete the objective, or if they simply choose not to, it will not impact on their own mission but might be remembered later by those they chose to abandon. The nature of the objective is left up the GM, but should involve some time sensitive aspect and the peril that if left unattended, it could spiral out of control and lead to a significant weakening of the Imperial attack or defence.

SACRIFICE

Not all victories against the Tyranids bring honour and glory to a Kill-team. Sometimes, in the course of defeating the swarm, the Battle-Brothers will suffer too much or cause too much damage to a world, making any pretence of victory hollow at best. Worse still is when a Chapter of the Adeptus Astartes suffers loss at the hands of the Tyranids, vital equipment and precious Space Marines vanquished without hope of replacing them. This complication should be applied to one of the mission objectives, introducing an element of sacrifice to complete it, forcing the PCs to choose between completing their objective or failing it but saving lives or material, even if it means a loss of glory. These choices could include a variety of things, such as a local population of valuable artisans or adepts which must be eradicated to ensure the destruction of a virulent Tyranid organism. A vessel can be used as a weapon to ram a hive ship, ensuring mutual destruction. Another Kill-team might require extraction, though taking the time to do so would risk the PCs own mission. The loss or sacrifice of Adeptus Astartes should present some especially hard choices to the PCs, and can also have lasting effects on their relations both inside and outside the Deathwatch.

THE SHADOW FALLS

It is likely that if the Kill-team enters a warzone to face the Tyranids, then the Shadow in the Warp will have already enveloped the area and smothered communication though the warp. Sometimes though, the Kill-team will arrive on the cusp of such an event, as the psychic event horizon from the approaching hive fleet crashes down across the world and closes in around the minds of psykers and the psychically sensitive alike. While this does not necessarily adversely affect the manifesting of powers by those members of the Kill-team (or their allies) with psychic powers, the moments just after the arrival of the shadow can be traumatic for psykers. The GM can use this complication to make psykers, and their powers (especially divination), unstable and produce unusual results. More appropriate for NPCs than PCs, this could mean that for a time the Kill-team will be cut off from using psychic intelligence gathering or that their own Librarians might not be able to aid them to their full potential. Such difficulties will pass with time, typically by the end of the mission, as the shadow settles over the region and the warp stabilises, local psykers getting used to the constant oppressive presence of the Hive Mind.

LURKING DANGER

Ahead of the Tyranid Hive Fleet, Vanguard Drone Ships drop creatures to scout out planets potentially high in bio-mass. These creatures, such as Lictors and Genestealers, stay hidden in the shadows, preying on and sampling the planet's creatures—and population. Even after the Tyranid swarm arrives, vanguard creatures stalk the shadows, striking out at vulnerable targets to aid the swarm in the consumption of the planet. This complication should be used to add an invisible adversary to antagonise the Kill-team, stalking through the shadows and disrupting their mission. This creature should attempt to separate the Kill-team and catch them alone, picking them off one by one.

CRUSADE ASSETS

"We are the dam wall against the xenos flood, holding back the foul alien advance with our guns, our ships and our very lives. Should we fail, the Crusade will surely drown beneath the Tyranid assault, washed away on a tide of blasphemies and nightmares."

–Master Tactician Vermillion Class, Horance Talt

The Deathwatch seldom work completely alone within the reaches of the Orpheus Salient, for they are usually supported by local Imperial forces, advance elements of the Crusade and a myriad of organisations and allies from the Inquisition to the Adeptus Mechanicus. In many cases this support is vital in reaching a warzone or enjoying safe passage across the warp, the Kill-teams of the Deathwatch working alongside other warriors of the God-Emperor in the endless battle against the advance of Hive Fleet Dagon. In others it is more subtle, more circumspect, as the Inquisition or Salient worlds provide information or advanced intelligence on the swarm, gathered at the cost of countless lives, which the Kill-team can then call upon to complete its own missions. Equally a Kill-team may also take on obligations to the worlds of the Salient, either at the behest of the Ordo Xenos or their Deathwatch superiors, completing objectives and sharing their experience with planetary governors and commanders as part of a joint operation against the Tyranids.

At the GM's discretion he can allow players to acquire assets for their missions from **Table 3-3: Orpheus Salient Assets**. These assets represent Salient allies, specialised equipment and even obscure information that the Kill-team can acquire using Requisition in the same way that they would select weapons and armour from the Deathwatch. Each asset has its own description and game effect as detailed below and has a set Requisition cost and a Renown requirement. For more details on Requisition and Renown, see page 138-139 of the **DEATHWATCH** rulebook.

ADEPTUS MECHANICUS BIOLOGIS TEAM

The agents of the Machine God have gathered more technical lore and biological data on the Tyranids than any other arm of the Imperium, the efforts of the Magos uncovering countless hidden secrets about the xenos and the nature of their species. In times of need, the Adeptus Mechanicus will share this knowledge with frontline Imperial forces and agencies such as the Inquisition and the Deathwatch, so the Crusade might better combat Hive Fleet Dagon. A Kill-team can even call upon the specialised knowledge and skills of an Adeptus Mechanicus Biologis Team should their mission warrant it. Depending on the nature of the Kill-team's mission, the Biologis Team, consisting of several tech-priests and their medicae servitor attendants, will be on hand to help. If they are present, the Biologis team can use their Medicae knowledge to give members of the Kill-team a +20 to all their Medicae Skill rolls. Also with their help, whether they are present or not, the information they provide will grant the Kill-team members +10 to all Toughness Tests to resist or overcome Tyranid toxins (such as damage from the Toxic special quality).

CASTOBEL VENGEANCE COMPANY

The world of Castobel has had a long and brutal struggle against Hive Fleet Dagon and millions of its citizens have perished against the creatures of the swarm. Formed from the grieving families and rage filled survivors of the populace, the Castobel Vengeance Company is a citizen militia that throws itself into the path of the swarm with a reckless disregard for their own lives, simply to vent their hatred of the creatures that took their world. Since its creation, the company has also been used in Imperial armies in other parts of the Salient, valued for the fearless ferocity they show the hive fleets. In special circumstances, even the Deathwatch can make use of the Vengeance Company. A Kill-team with support from the Vengeance Company can use it to counter a Tyranid horde once during their mission. The GM has final say in whether or not a horde can be countered in this way (though unless it is vital to the plot that the Kill-team fight the horde themselves, it should be permitted). The Vengeance Company can either fight alongside the Kill-team or the battle can take place "off screen."

TABLE 3-3: ORPHEUS SALIENT ASSETS

Asset	Requisition Cost	Renown
Adeptus Mechanicus Biologis Team	15	Respected
Castobel Vengeance Company	20	Distinguished
Charts and Tides	10	—
Deep Scout Group	20	Respected
Experimental Ammunition	15	Respected
Forward Assault Group	25	Distinguished

CHARTS AND TIDES

The movements of Hive Fleet Dagon and the ragged nature of the Crusade in the Orpheus Salient mean that many of the stable warp routes between its worlds have been cut off. In addition, much of the eastern reaches of the Salient were never explored or claimed after the arrival of the Crusade and have not seen contact with the Imperium since before the Age of Shadow. This means that it often takes far longer for a Kill-team to reach its destination (especially worlds beyond the Crusade's frontlines) than normal. It is possible for the Inquisition and the Deathwatch to make an alliance with Rogue Traders, if not for direct passage then for the knowledge they have, greatly speeding up transit. The Kill-team can use this asset to improve the speed at which they are deployed and extracted from missions, effectively halving the time it takes to reach their destination. If time is not a factor in the mission, this asset can be used to call in the assistance of a Rogue Trader (or a ship from his dynasty) for quick extraction, if Imperial forces are unable to come to the Kill-team's rescue.

DEEP SCOUT GROUP

Scouts from all the major Crusade Space Marine Chapters are active in the Orpheus Salient, such as the Wolf Scouts of the Space Wolves or the legendary Storm's Warning of the Storm Wardens. Like Kill-teams, these small groups of Adeptus Astartes will range ahead of the Crusade, looking for signs of the swarm or setting up supply drops and ambushes for forces that come after. With cooperation between the Deathwatch and these other Chapters, the Kill-team can make use of one of these scout group to aid them in their mission, either providing information beforehand or softening up a target for them. A Deep Scout Group can be used on one of two ways depending on the wishes of the PCs. In the first instance they can reduce the number of Kill Markers on any single mission objective by half (rounding up); it can be imagined they reduce the number of foes the Kill-team must deal with or disable or destroy some of the enemy's logistics. In the second instance they can provide intelligence and the PCs can ask the GM any one question about the mission. It is up to the GM if the scouts can provide an exact answer for them, but they should give them some piece of information they would not have otherwise had.

EXPERIMENTAL AMMUNITION

As the Tyranids are always evolving to face the Imperium, the forces of the Achilus Crusade must change their tactics, weapons and troops to meet the variety of threats posed by the swarm. Part of this evolution includes the development of toxins and viruses to better attack the Tyranid biology or antipersonnel weaponry better suited to cutting through chitin and bone. While the Adeptus Mechanicus is largely responsible for these creations, the Inquisition and the Deathwatch also make use of them, or benefit from the specified ammunitions produced. A Kill-team can make use of experimental ammunition on its mission, field testing either a creation of the Adeptus Mechanicus or something developed by the Inquisition or Deathwatch. Experimental Ammunition can be used instead of normal ammunition in any Bolt or Solid Projectile ranged weapon. It does not change the stats of the weapon but adds the Toxic special quality when used against Tyranids. At the start of each encounter, the Kill-team should roll a d10: on a 1-4 the Toxic quality functions as described on page 144 of the DEATHWATCH rulebook for the duration of the encounter, on a 5-7 it inflicts 2d10 extra damage rather than just 1d10 and on a 8-0 it counts as only regular ammunition.

FORWARD ASSAULT GROUP

When working closely with Imperial forces, the Deathwatch can make use of assault groups to clear an area before the insertion of Kill-teams, either drawing away the bulk of enemy forces or punching a hole in their defences which the Kill-team can then exploit. The nature of these forward assault groups can vary widely depending on the warzone in which they are used, but could include Stormtrooper companies, Space Marine Tactical squads or even Skitarii heavy infantry. A Kill-team can use a forward assault group to reduce the number of enemies protecting one of their objectives, using the assault group to take some of the pressure off their own attack. The PCs can choose one of their mission objectives and reduce the enemies protecting that objective by half (not including special enemies such as NPCs or unique enemies such as war engines or single creatures). The GM has final say in which forces the forward assault group has dealt with, but they should reduce the combat difficulty of the objective by roughly half, thinning out the numbers of foes the PCs need to take out.

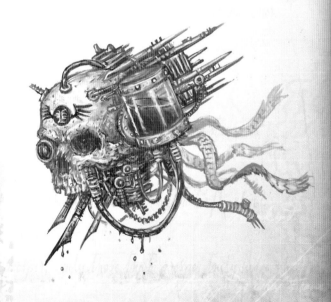

Hive Fleet Dagon

"The Tyranid swarm must not be viewed as a foe set to destroy us, but as a tool. Our challenge is to learn to use that tool, so that it may not be used against the Imperium, but rather to assist the Imperium in fulfilling our manifest destiny."

—Inquisitor Evaine Cartier

This section is devoted to providing further information regarding the Tyranid threat that opposes Achilus Crusade elements within the Orpheus Salient. Initial contact with the Tyranid foe suggested that the xenos forces were little more than a minor splinter fleet. However, over the years since first contact, the Tyranid forces have shown little signs of abating. Instead, they have advanced into the Jericho Reach to an extent that may be triggering additional growth and expansion.

After the discovery of Freya's ruination in early 814M41, Deathwatch forces became aware of the Tyranid incursion. Since that time additional worlds have fallen prey to the swarm. Astropathic communications have been limited as the Hive Mind has spread its Shadow in the Warp. The relentless swarms of the xenos continue to grow, as each new triumph expands their available bio-mass. The stalwart vigilance of the Deathwatch in concert with the near-boundless sacrifices of the Achilus Crusade has blunted the pace of the xenos advance. However, the tide has not yet turned and the final outcome remains in the balance. The size of Hive Fleet Dagon has not yet been determined, but the forces of the Crusade and the Deathwatch are being struggling to compete.

Throughout the Hive Fleet's advance, it has continuously evolved new Tyranid creatures and alternative tactics. Imperial forces are thus challenged to identify new effective ways to respond to these threats. This section presents a number of the Hive Fleet's more extreme innovations, while disclosing a few of the Imperium's attempted responses. To date, neither side has enjoyed tremendous success from their alternative methods, but the tipping point continues to grow ever closer.

The Orpheus Salient's advance was once rapid. System after system fell before the might of the Imperium's return to the Jericho Reach. So great were there successes that Crusade command chose to reassign many of the Salient's forces so that they might be utilised to fulfil more desperate needs. With the xenos incursion, the remaining forces have become overstretched. Substantial ground has been lost, and the Salient is in desperate need of reinforcements that are no longer available. As the individual battles stretch on longer and devour resources through attrition and loss, Crusade command has grown ever more frustrated. Unless the Imperium manages to somehow regain control, the Tyranids may overwhelm the Imperial armies that remain committed to the Orpheus Salient's battlefronts.

DAGON OVERVIEW

"We have begun to encounter some communications difficulties within the Salient. These seem linked to activity near the Phonos system. I am personally taking Battlegroup Argo there, to identify the issue and get it quickly sorted. I am confident that it is not a matter of serious concern."

—General Mikal Curas, in his last dispatch to the Lord Militant

Imperial forces have continued to analyse Hive Fleet Dagon, but any measurement based upon Tyranid activity is confounded by the Shadow in the Warp. As the xenos presence prevents Imperial forces from effective communication, it is likely that additional worlds have fallen to the alien threat without the Crusade or even the Deathwatch becoming aware of the attacks. Consequently, any analysis that depend upon such data collection must be carefully considered in light of this imposed limitation.

Though Herisor was the first world to fall to the Tyranid threat, attacks upon Freya and Zanatov's Harbour also occurred in short order. Timing of these early attacks is difficult to gauge, as there was little contact during the attack and substantial time may have passed before investigations revealed the Tyranid activity. Best estimates suggest that all three of these worlds were under assault at the same time.

Since these initial attacks, reports have begun pouring in from worlds all across the rimward edge of the Reach. Much of this information comes from bedraggled survivors who managed to escape on warp-capable vessels just as their worlds were being consumed, and Crusade leadership has struggled to sort through the mountains of contradictory reports. Some headway has been made in stalling the relentless advance of the Hive Fleet, but most of it has been due to the efforts of the Triumverate who are operating deep within the Shadow in the Warp.

The agents of the Deathwatch and the Ordo Xenos have had much more luck than the overwhelmed Crusade leadership. Making use of their array of rapid strike vessels, the Deathwatch has sent Kill-teams into the swarm to collect samples for analysis, scout the Hive Fleet's progress into the system, and to strike at high-value targets when the opportunity rises. However, even the elite and well organised Deathwatch Space Marines have difficulty contending with the complete communications blackout imposed by the Shadow in the Warp. Watch Fortress Erioch will go great lengths of time hearing nothing from the rimward edge of the Reach, unsure if the Watch Stations there are even still standing.

ADDITIONAL RESOURCES

This section features some of the most horrific xenos found among Hive Fleet Dagon. However, some GMs may want even more Tyranids to inflict mayhem upon their Battle-Brothers. In addition to the xenos featured in the DEATHWATCH rulebook, there are a variety of creatures also presented in MARK OF THE XENOS.

HIVE FLEET DAGON TACTICS

"There is no evidence that these so-called "Tyranids" are a reasoning opponent. The xenos are surely incapable of using any sort of advanced tactics. Rather they are little more than an all-consuming organism. Overcoming them should be a simple matter of applying thought and leverage to determine their vulnerabilities."

—Bishop Josef Daven to Inquisitor Kryptman

Because of the limitations imposed by the Shadow in the Warp, Imperial analysts believe that Hive Fleet Dagon was identified only after it had completed several successful assaults within the Jericho Reach. As a consequence, it is uncertain whether the Tyranid forces are the spear tip of a much larger force, or if they simply represent the surge in growth that would occur after absorbing the bio-mass from several of the region's planets. If these xenos began their intrusion with a limited force, it may be that the earliest attacks exhibited were undertaken in a conservative manner.

Unfortunately for the Achilus Crusade forces, it is clear that the Hive Fleet has met with a great deal of success. At this time, the Hive Fleet's resources are generally well supplied with bio-mass. As a consequence, the Tyranid incursion represents a substantial threat to all other life within the Jericho Reach. These xenos are capable of exploiting the raw materials that they have captured to launch attacks that utilise near overwhelming force against prey worlds. With each triumph, their resources are renewed and their capacity for destruction becomes further enhanced.

Crusade and Deathwatch forces have confirmed intrusions by Tyranid Drone ships within more than twenty systems of the Orpheus Salient. Imperial forces fear, but have not confirmed, that the majority of these intrusions coincide with insertions of Genestealers or Lictors to habitable planets. Imperial analysts have thus far had no luck in tracing a pattern of how Hive Fleet Dagon's Vanguard Drone ships have been scouting the Reach. This, combined with a lack of knowledge regarding the lifespan of the Vanguard Drone ships, leaves Imperial forces helpless to defend against these forward scouts of the Hive Fleet. If each such creature is capable of identifying and infecting multiple targets, a single vessel surviving could soon draw Hive Fleet elements to dozens of planets.

Deathwatch agents are currently monitoring reports that could indicate the earliest stages of Tyranid scouting activities within more than a dozen systems. Based upon current data, the Deathwatch believes that this substantially exceeds the number of planets that the Hive Fleet is currently capable of engaging. While Deathwatch agents have confirmed Tyranid activity in all systems that have been attacked by the full might of the Hive Fleet, not all systems that exhibited a scouting presence have been attacked. This suggests that the Hive Fleet may be plotting out its travel through the Jericho Reach. The Hive Mind may be preparing for an extended incursion, carefully selecting which planets might offer the most bio-mass return, so that environments of less strategic value could be targeted after its resources are better established.

When the Tyranid Hive Ships enter a system, they have consistently demonstrated a specific focus upon immediately assaulting any habitable planets. While this may seem an obvious strategy, it is important to note that Hive Fleet Dagon has largely ignored Imperial space stations and outposts on otherwise barren planets and moons. Imperial vessels have generally only been attacked after they directly engaged the Tyranid void travellers. It might offer further evidence that the Hive Mind is operating in a conservative fashion, or might simply be that for some reason the Hive Fleet is unable to accurately identify these elements as worthwhile targets.

Once Hive Ships enter the orbit of a prey planet, they have consistently begun their attacks by launching vast numbers of Mycetic Spores towards the world's surface. In the earliest reported instances, this initial attack wave was so numerous that defenders were overwhelmed within days. More recently, Crusade forces have successfully survived this initial attack. On Castobel, Atonement, and Hethgard, Imperial defenders managed to repel enough of the spores that the battles for control of these planets have become protracted engagements. On Avalos and Treyen, Imperial defenders even managed to repulse the initial Tyranid attack, causing the void-faring Tyranid creatures to leave those systems. There are many speculations as to why the Tyranids fled, some Imperial analysts believe they moved on to easier prey, while more military minds speculate the creatures are attempting deliberate feints to draw Imperial defenders away from other worlds.

If this is the case, it may be that planets further from currently engaged systems could be attacked unexpectedly. The Orpheus Salient currently has a very limited number of defenders held in reserve. The vast majority of these are currently deployed upon those planets closest to the Tyranid incursion. In the event the Hive Mind chooses to bypass those planets, and instead targets worlds deeper behind enemy lines, the consequences could be catastrophic. Such a tactic might also explain the extensive number of systems where scouting activity has been confirmed.

The potential for this strategy is increased due to the absence of a Tyranid supply line. Once a Hive Ship leaves a system after devouring its habitable planets, nothing is left behind. A Hive Ship and its support vessels effectively carry all of its swarm into each new warzone. Once a system is engaged, it must triumph quickly or the vessels possess ever fewer creatures to commit to an attempt to consume an alternative target. While these failed and extended engagements could increase the chance of an ultimate Imperial victory, they might also provide evidence that Hive Fleet Dagon is actually carefully preparing to expend all of its resources upon an unsuspecting target.

DAGON MORPHOLOGY

"Before we can come to understand the threat presented by Hive Fleet Dagon, we first must come to grips with the organisms that comprise it. Only by studying their ontogeny can we begin to understand their capacity."

–Brother Codicier Taelon

The Tyranids of Hive Fleet Dagon are similar to those which encountered during Hive Fleet Behemoth's assault. However, additional Tyranid creatures have been observed among the forces of Hive Fleet Dagon. There have also been subtle changes within the appearance, but not the tactical role, of some of the previously identified strains. These variations have included exoskeletal structures, colourations, and the most commonly observed weapon symbiotes used by the different Tyranid strains.

The most distinctive change shown by Hive Fleet Dagon is a variation in the hues of the different Tyranid creatures. The carapace on specimens from Hive Fleet Behemoth typically ranged from jet black to a deep blue. The unprotected skin of those species was typically a bright red. In contrast, the exoskeletons of Hive Fleet Dagon are generally dark grey or a blue close to that used by the Ultramarines Chapter. In portions of the xenos where their flesh is unprotected, it is a burgundy colour.

Weapon symbiotes employed by the various Tyranids also show a substantial change in frequency from those observed during Hive Fleet Behemoth's forays into Ultima Segmentum. Specific instances within commonly encountered creatures are addressed below. Nonetheless, the consensus variants have been shown to be statistically different among parts of Hive Fleet Dagon. As this incursion has been in progress for less than five years, this may be an anomaly due to the environmental conditions and the defenders present on the worlds that have been invaded to date. This evidence suggests that Hive Fleet Dagon is a distinct entity, but does not definitively confirm a separation between the two incursions.

In addition to symbiote modifications, the Tyranids found within Hive Fleet Dagon have shown an increased propensity for toxicity. A substantial number of otherwise characteristic Tyranids have presented with venomous sacks near their claws and fangs. These toxins substantially increased the mortality rate among Imperial casualties within the Orpheus Salient. Further, these toxins have shown a substantial range of variation even within planetary environs. Imperial medicae personnel have been unable to identify an antiserum that works consistently against the toxins.

Distinctive Specimens

Several Tyranid variant strains have been observed within Hive Fleet Dagon that are believed to be completely novel. Of these, a few have generated legends and lore among the Imperial forces that oppose them. Tech-priests seem unable to discern whether these specimens are specific individuals of their species or variant strains. It is, however, clear that these examples are consistent in their tactical approaches and seem capable of learning from past encounters. Some reports indicate that members of these strain variants have returned to the battlefront after being slain in battle. It is unclear if this indicates that the Tyranids have a mechanism for resurrecting these specimens, or if the later encounters are evidence of additional specimens.

The Dagon Overlord

First encountered during the brutal warfare on Castobel, this specimen is believed to be a variant of the Hive Tyrant strain. The Dagon Overlord has been identified as active within many of the systems under assault within the Orpheus Salient. This monster is known for its malicious streak and its ability to drive lesser Tyranid strains into an even more hideous fervour than is typically observed. As is often seen amongst Hive Fleet Dagon strains, this specimen is exceptionally toxic, constantly dripping with venom.

The Mist Reaper

First observed on Xyan, this variant of the Lictor strain has been recently observed on other worlds of the Orpheus Salient. The Mist Reaper invariably works alone, generally long before Tyranid forces assault a prey world. This monster is responsible for the deaths of hundreds of Imperial citizens who believed that they were safe, far from any conflict lines. Members of the Divisionis Biologis postulate that the creature has a specific knack for overcoming Imperial security measures, though this has not yet been confirmed.

What Lies Beneath

First identified during a hive assault on Castobel, this horror is believed to be a variant of the Trygon bio-construct. Always accompanied by swarms of Hormagaunts, What Lies Beneath is characterised by attacks upon Imperial structures far from any battle lines. Reports indicate that this nightmare is capable of burrowing through even the thick fortifications of plasteel and ferrocrete required by the foundation of an Imperial Hive. Imperial analysts are currently attempting to identify what draws the creature to its targets, so that they might find a means to isolate and eliminate the threat it represents.

HARPY

"Scores of winged creatures are approaching the Hive complex. The larger ones are dropping organic missiles that burst on impact, and they seem to screech as they swoop down. The sound is becoming louder and louder. The screaming, Emperor preserve us, the screaming!"

—Vox recording recovered from Hive Cresson on Castobel

Harpies are monstrous, serpentine Tyranid creatures that resemble Trygons sporting large leathery wings and wide heads with armoured plates. Magos Biologis of the Adeptus Mechanicus have argued whether Harpies and Trygons are closely related bio-forms or separate genuses in their own right. However, few comparative studies have been made, and to date, phylogenetic categorization remains highly speculative.

Lending weight to the arguments of those taxonomists who classify the two life forms as distinct is the fact that, unlike the sturdy, heavily armoured carapace of the Trygon, the Harpy's frame is relatively fragile (though still quite resilient by human standards). The Harpy, like many avian and other airborne fauna catalogued by Codiciers throughout the Imperium, is hollow-bodied and thus unable to survive injuries that might not even faze other Tyranid creatures of similar size.

The Harpy, however, more than compensates for its lack of resilience with remarkable agility and manoeuvrability in the air. Reliable Imperial witnesses, including trusted members

HARPY

of the Aquilan Pluracy on the Tyranid-besieged planet of Castobel, have observed these creatures turning, climbing, and diving with far greater deftness and precision than even the most sophisticated fighter-craft of the Imperium.

Harpies typically appear in the early phases of a Tyranid invasion alongside Gargoyles and other flying organisms of the Tyranid host. Perhaps owing to their lightly armoured frames, Harpies favour strafing, hit-and-run attacks, rather than sustained assaults. Large cysts on the underside of the Harpy's abdomen produce clusters of spore mines, which the Harpy drops on its foes to deadly effect. The Harpy's arms boast a number of bio-weapons, such as Scything Talons and often a Stranglethorn or Heavy Venom Cannon. Survivors of attacks by Hive Fleet Jormungandr reported other bio-variants as well, though these accounts remain unconfirmed. In addition to this formidable arsenal, the Harpy can also stun and, in some cases, injure its opponents with the high-pitched shriek that gives this creature its name. Though Harpies generally eschew close combat unless the odds are stacked heavily in their favour, their scything talons make them terrifying opponents when they do engage in melee, particularly when their enemies are suffering from the disorienting effects of the Harpies' sonic attacks.

Author: Steward Militant Lukas Vierling, Governor's Installation, Hethgard
Recipient: Lord Admiral Arkelius, Battlegroup Cerebus in orbit around Hethgard
Subject: Possible Xenos Presence
Date: 342815.M41

My Dear Lord Admiral:
Greetings. It has come to my attention that members of the Adeptus Astartes garrison of Fortress-Installation Vanagandr have reported sightings of a flying xenos life form of unknown type or origin. While the representatives of the Adeptus Astartes have reassured me that they will respond to and destroy any threat these organisms pose, duty and prudence (as well as a few of the more alarmist voices among my staff) demand that I inform you of our status and recommend that you undertake whatever preparations you deem necessary in order to respond appropriately should these reported sightings escalate to a possible threat. Attached data files include the field reports of Commander Gaius, coordinates of the xenos sightings, and my personal threat assessments. May the God-Emperor protect.

Author: Steward Militant Lukas Vierling, Fortress-Installation Hrovitnir, Hethgard
Recipient: Lord Admiral Arkelius, Battlegroup Cerebus in orbit around Hethgard
Subject: Possible Xenos Takeover/Request for Evac
Date: 346815.M41

Lord Admiral:
Situation dire. I have confirmed reports of hostile xenos activity in multiple planetary sectors in our northernmost continent. Confirmed losses of Fortress-Installations Vanagandr, Stigandir, and Vali, as well as countless outposts in nearby sectors. The Ultramarines 35th under Commander Gaius and the 27th under Commander Britannius reported lost. I urgently request additional support and hereby authorise and request orbital bombardment of sectors E22-E55, F17-F66, G07-G114, H03-H166, I22-I79, and J35-J 42. Also, urgently request immediate evacuation of planetary executive staff to ensure continued and effective administration of planetary defence forces. May the Emperor save us.

Field reports indicate that Harpies played a significant role in Hive Fleet Dagon's initial attacks on the Fortress world of Hethgard, a key strategic location in the Orpheus Salient. Numerous Imperial combat personnel, including Adeptus Astartes of the Space Wolves and Storm Wardens chapters, recount witnessing skies all-but obscured by winged, screeching Tyranid creatures and entire mountainsides transformed into writhing, shimmering masses by untold thousands of gleaming carapaces of roosting Harpies.

As Harpies function as the vanguard of a Tyranid host, the Deathwatch takes reports of sightings of these bio-forms very seriously and investigates them with extreme prejudice.

Harpy (Master)

WS	BS	S	T	Ag	Int	Per	WP	Fel
32	55	50	50 (10)	42	15	42	30	––

Movement: 4/8/12/24 **Wounds:** 95

Skills: Acrobatics (Ag), Awareness (Per), Climb (S), Dodge (Ag).

Talents: Death from Above, Fearless, Heightened Sense (Vision).

Traits: Dark Sight, Fear 3 (Horrifying), Flyer (20), Natural Armour (Hardened Carapace), Improved Natural Weapons (Scything Talons), Size (Massive), Tyranid, Unnatural Toughness (x2).

Armour: Hardened Carapace (All 6).

Weapons: Scything Talons (1d10+20 R; Pen 3), Twin-Linked Stranglethorn Cannons (Heavy: 80m; S/–/–; 2d10+10 I; Pen 3; Clip –; Rld –; Blast (10), Deadly Snare, Devastating (2), Living Ammunition, Tearing), Stinger Salvo, Spore Mine Cysts.

Special Rules

Sonic Screech: The deafening high-frequency scream that gives the Harpy its name can disorient enemy troops, rupture eardrums, and in some cases, cause serious injuries and even fatalities. Pistol: 30m; S/–/–; 1d10 + 11 E; Pen 0; Clip –; Rld –; Concussive, Blast (6).

Biomorphs: At the GM's discretion, a Harpy may have Adrenal Glands (gaining the Furious Assault Talent), Toxin Sacs (gaining the Toxic (1d10) Trait on all melee attacks), and/or Regeneration (5) (gaining the Regeneration Trait); may replace the Twin-Linked Stranglethorn Cannons with Twin-Linked Heavy Venom Cannons (Heavy: 100m; S/–/–; 4d10+10 I; Pen 6; Clip –; Rld –; Blast (6), Living Ammunition, Toxic); and/or may replace the Stinger Salvo with Cluster Spines.

Stinger Salvo: Embedded in the Harpy's carapace are rows of metre-long, poisoned spines that the creature can fire by means of incredibly strong muscle contractions to rain a shower of deadly missiles into the ranks of the foe. Typical targets are enemy infantry. Basic: 50m; –/–/12; 2d10+3 R; Pen 6; Clip –; Rld –; Razor Sharp, Tearing, Toxic.

Spore Mine Cysts: Once per encounter, the Harpy may release a bombardment of Spore Mines on its enemies. Heavy: 50m; –/–/6; 3d10+4 X; Pen 4; Clip –; Rld –; Blast (4), Toxic.

Cluster Spines: Some Harpy variants possess Cluster Spines mounted in their carapaces in lieu of Stinger Salvo missiles. Cluster Spines are similar in appearance to the Stinger Salvo projectiles and are fired with the same type of powerful muscle contractions. However, instead of relying on toxins to slay the enemy, Cluster Spines explode upon impact, showering a large area with needle-like shards. Like Stinger Salvoes, Cluster Spines are effective anti-infantry weapons. Basic: 50m; –/–/4; 1d10+14 X; Pen 3; Clip –; Rld –; Blast (3).

Author: Steward Militant Lukas Vierling, Governor's Installation, Hethgard
Recipient: Lord Admiral Arkelius, Battlegroup Cerebus in orbit around Hethgard
Subject: Confirmed Xenos Threat
Date: 345815.M41

Dear Lord Admiral:

As more information arrives, I regret to inform you that the xenos threat appears more dire than the initial reports indicated. We have positively identified a number of Tyranid life forms: Gargoyles, Harpies, Genestealers, and others. Since my last communication, I have received multiple reports of increased xenos activity and sporadic attacks from outposts in planetary sectors G32-G64 and H28-H55. We have received no communication from Fortress-Installation Vanagandr for almost 32 hours, and the garrison is feared lost. My staff and I are relocating to Fortress-Installation Hrovitnir. I recommend the immediate intervention of Battlegroup Cerebus. I shall await contact from you before issuing further orders. The Emperor protects.

HARRIDAN

"That creatures exist with both the mass of the leviathan and the grace of the hawk on the wing is a testament to the necessity of the holy efforts of the Chamber Militant of the Ordo Xenos."

–Inquisitor Lok

The gargantuan Harridan, also known as a Brood Mother and Avius Terriblis, measures up to 30 metres in length with a wingspan of up to 40 metres. As such, the Harridan is by far the largest flying Tyranid creature ever encountered by citizens of the Imperium. The Harridan has a long, ophidian body and large bat-like wings, and its head closely resembles that of the serpentine Trygon.

The Harridan is capable of soaring at great altitudes where it glides on thermal winds. In fact, the seemingly effortless flight of the Harridan has prompted some Magos Biologis to argue that the legless Harridan, once airborne, may never again land. Others argue that the Harridan is capable of a snake-like locomotion on the ground. In any case, the Harridan is capable of flights of indefinite duration and tens of thousands of kilometres in length.

In battle, the Harridan manoeuvres with startling speed and dexterity. The large creatures can dodge enemy fighter-craft as well as surface-to-air ordnance. While these enormous Tyranid flyers do not have the maximum straight-line speed of mechanised aircraft, Harridans can intercept flying vehicles by attacking them with their powerful claws. Field reports also indicate that Harridans make occasional suicide ram attacks to destroy enemy fighters. The Harridan's scything talons can cut through the plates of even the most heavily armoured Imperial tanks, and the creature's twin biocannons enable it to make devastating strafing attacks as it swoops down over enemy positions.

Though Harridans resemble Harpies, curiously, they share an almost symbiotic relationship with Tyranid Gargoyles. A brood of as many as 20 Gargoyles can cling to the belly of the Harridan who acts as a "carrier" of sorts to transport the smaller Tyranid flyers, who, according to many experts, are incapable of long-distance flight. As the Harridan nears the battlefield, the Gargoyles detach themselves from the larger creature and fly off independently to attack the enemy. It is because of this unique relationship that Harridans are called Brood Mothers.

In 814.M41, Deathwatch forces fighting to cleanse Herisor of the Tyranid menace reported devastating initial losses due in large part to attacks from Harridans and associated Gargoyles. While the smaller flyers distracted ground troops with swooping attacks and strafing runs, the Harridans crippled Imperial aircraft, thereby preventing effective air-transport of ground troops. It is well known throughout the Orpheus Salient that less than half of the Space Marines who fought on Herisor survived. Many of the those who fell in these battles lost their lives to Tyranid Harridans.

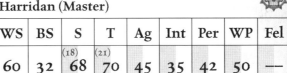

Harridan (Master)								
WS	BS	S	T	Ag	Int	Per	WP	Fel
60	32	(18) 68	(21) 70	45	35	42	50	––

Movement: 1/1/2/4 **Wounds:** 175

Skills: Awareness (Per), Dodge (Ag), Survival (Int).

Talents: Death from Above, Fearless, Furious Assault, Heightened Senses (Vision, Sound), Iron Jaw, Swift Attack.

Traits: Dark Sight, Fear 4 (Terrifying), Flyer (20), Improved Natural Weapons (Scything Talons), Natural Armour (Hardened Carapace), Size (Immense), Tyranid, Unnatural Strength (x3), Unnatural Toughness (x3).

Armour: Hardened Carapace (All 6).

Weapons: Scything Talons (1d10+20 R; Pen 3), Twin-Linked Biocannons (Heavy: 200m; S/–/–; 4d10+6 X; Pen 6; Clip –; Rld –; Blast (4), Devastating (3), Felling (2), Toxic).

Special Rules

Biomorphs: At the GM's discretion, a Harridan may have Acid Blood (when wounded in melee combat, all non-Tyranid creatures in melee with the Harridan must make a **Challenging (+0) Agility Test** or suffer 2d10 Damage with a Pen of 5), Toxin Sacs (gaining the Toxic (1d10) Trait on all melee attacks), and/or Regeneration (5) (gaining the Regeneration Trait).

Brood of Gargoyles: At the GM's discretion, a Harridan may be accompanied by a brood of up to 20 Gargoyles (see **MARK OF THE XENOS**, page 41). Treat the Gargoyle brood as a Horde with a Magnitude of 40 (see **DEATHWATCH**, pages 359-360). If the Harridan is carrying the Gargoyle brood at the beginning of the first Round of combat, make separate Initiative rolls for Harridan and Gargoyle Horde. The Gargoyle Horde may detach from the Harridan brood mother in its normal Initiative Order and act normally and independently thereafter. Should the Harridan be struck with a blast weapon while carrying Gargoyles, then the Gargoyle Horde will be hit as well.

ADVENTURE SEEDS

Aerie Assault: Reconnaissance by Adeptus Astartes forces has identified a concentration of winged Tyranid creatures on a remote mountaintop on a planet under Tyranid attack. The Kill-team is dispatched via Drop Pod to reconnoitre the area, gain any available intelligence on the spawning and life-cycle of the avian Tyranids, and finally to cleanse the area of Harridans, Harpies, Gargoyles, and any other xenos creatures.

Harridan Down: Little is known about the Tyranid Brood Mothers. When the intact corpse of a Harridan is discovered on a Tyranid-besieged planet, the Kill-team receives orders to escort a group of Magos Biologis to study the creature, to assist and protect the scientists, and to evacuate them if hostile xenos should threaten the task force. As Tyranid creatures approach, scholarly and military objectives may into conflict, particularly as the xenobiologists begin to question the ambiguous wording of the Kill-team's orders.

Seek and Destroy: Imperial forces have detected a brood of Harridans carrying Gargoyles en route to a strategically significant battlefield where their numbers could tip the balance of the fight in the Tyranids' favour. Can the Kill-team intercept and destroy the Harridan brood before it reaches the battlefield?

Record 094-01665-875-0132/DA9 : 56 : 01C/ADDENDUM 3E

Field Report, 9846814.M41

ORDO XENOS

Battle Brother Aelianus
++Deathwatch++

A Genestealer horde was threatening to overrun a Deathwatch-held position on the southern landmass of Herisor. Four Tactical squads, each in a Rhino, were despatched from orbit in two Thunderhawk transports to support Space Marine forces on the ground. The drop went off without difficulty. As we entered the atmosphere, the squad prepped for disembarking. At 3500 metres to target, our paired Thunderhawk, The Acanthus, experienced a mid-air collision with a flying xenos, which Brother Martinus identified as a Harridan. Thunderhawk Acanthus plummeted to the ground and exploded. We later confirmed that none aboard survived.

Our Thunderhawk, The Eligius, began to veer and jink rapidly. I assumed our pilot was engaging in evasive manoeuvres. Soon after, I heard the ship's heavy bolters open fire, and through the gun port periscope, I could see at least two Harridans flying nearby. At about 1000 metres to the target, our pilot pulled up suddenly. I felt an impact, and The Eligius went into a spinning dive. I saw the other Rhino tear free from the Thunderhawk's grapple arms and fly away from us. Moments later, we hit the ground sideways, crashing and sliding for a few hundred metres. Only three of my ten-man squad survived the crash, myself, Brother Lucianus, and Brother Marinus, who was badly injured in the crash. We spent several minutes extricating ourselves from the wreckage.

We emerged to find ourselves about 1.5 kilometres from our drop target. About 150 metres from the wreckage lay the injured body of the Harridan that must have hit us. It was writhing in its death throes, its left wing and shoulder a devastated ruin. We had just enough time to confirm that the pilots of The Eligius were dead before the Genestealers attacked. We took cover in the wreckage and thereby managed to hold off the Genestealers for several minutes with sustained bolter fire. The Genestealers attacked relentlessly, and Lucianus fell. Marinus shot the Genestealer who killed Lucianus but was in turn slain by yet another Genestealer. Falling back further into the wreckage, I was able to gun down the remaining three Genestealers.

HIVE GUARD

"The armour of a Land Raider, the strength of a Thunderfire Cannon, the accuracy of a veteran Devastator, and the discipline of the Emperor's Finest—this is the Tyranid Hive Guard."

–Aloysius at the Battle of Macragge, 745.M41

Hive Guard function as sentries for Tyranid capillary towers and spore chimneys. The lower body of the Hive Guard resembles that of a sturdy canid or squat horse, while the upper body of this centaur-like creature is not unlike that of a Tyranid Warrior. Its head and back benefit from the protection of a large armoured hood. Fused with the forearms of the Hive Guard is a large biological weapon known as an Impaler Cannon. The Hive Guard's two pairs of stout legs enable the creature to contend with the Impaler Cannon's enormous recoil.

Hive Guard play a crucial role in the final stages of a Tyranid invasion, when all of the planetary bio-mass the xenos have harvested and partially digested must be transported to the Hive Ships. In these last stages, enormous capillary towers and spore chimneys emerge from the ground, the former growing with astounding speed past the upper reaches of the planet's atmosphere, to channel the processed organic soup to orbiting Hive Ships. As these towers and chimneys enable the Tyranids to achieve the ultimate goal of their planetary invasions, the Tyranids take particular care to defend these structures well. Indeed, the Hive Mind seems to have developed the Hive Guard specifically to fulfil the important function of standing watch over these towers.

ADVENTURE SEEDS

Synaptic Study: The complex telepathic relationships between the Hive Mind, synapse creatures, and Tyranid life forms of all kinds have long baffled both the Magos Biologis and the Ordo Xenos. Recently, an Inquisitor of the Ordo Xenos hypothesised that he might obtain profound insights into the functions of the Hive Mind by studying the theoretically less complex psychic communications between Hive Guard and shard-beast. To this end, the Kill-team must escort the Inquisitor and his retinue, which includes a powerful psyker, to a Tyranid-infested planet where the Inquisitor hopes to conduct psychic field experiments. Will the psyker be able to understand the telepathic commands of the Hive Guard, or in making the attempt, will the psyker expose himself to the potentially dangerous synaptic powers of the Hive Mind?

Tower Assault: In hopes of crippling a Hive Ship, Deathwatch officers order the Kill-team to destroy the emerging capillary towers before they can funnel the harvested bio-mass off a Tyranid-infested planet. Equipped with powerful explosives devices, the Kill-team must avoid Tyranid organisms, plant the explosives, exit the blast radius, and remotely detonate the bombs. However, recently spawned Hive Guard interfere with the Kill-team's mission. Alternatively, the Kill-team's mission could involve obtaining biological specimens from the capillary towers instead of (or in addition to) destroying them.

Typical of the ever-efficient Tyranids, Hive Guard have a very short incubation period and are spawned only when needed in the final stages of the harvest and only when the capillary towers and spore chimneys face an enemy threat.

Xenobiologists have determined that Hive Guard have some capacity for telepathy, though not to the extent of the more sophisticated synapse creatures like Hive Tyrants. This low-level psychic capacity enables the creatures both to see through the eyes of their fellow xenos in order to target enemies with their Impaler Cannons and to communicate with the shard-beasts that are fused to the Cannon's projectiles, long bony spikes up to 2 metres in length. Through the psychic link that Hive Guard and shard-beast share, the Hive Guard can direct the symbiotic organisms to alter the course of the projectiles in mid trajectory, by moving membranous fins to act as wing flaps or rudders that steer the missiles. As such, Hive Guard need not make direct visual contact with enemy targets to fire upon them. Field reports from Imperial troops indicate that the Hive Guard can target unseen foes with uncanny accuracy even over moderate distances.

Unlike most Tyranid creatures, which advance upon any non-Tyranid life forms with seemingly reckless abandon, Hive Guard instinctively function as sentries who seldom charge or pursue their foes. The Hive Guard's task is to stand sentinel over the capillary towers, and only in moments of desperation will the Hive Mind prompt these stalwart guardians to advance upon the enemy.

Hive Guard (Elite)

WS	BS	S	T	Ag	Int	Per	WP	Fel
40	52	62	64 (18)	25	25	45	45	––

Movement: 6/12/18/36 **Wounds:** 46

Skills: Awareness (Per), Climb (S), Concealment (Ag), Swim (S).

Talents: Fearless, Marksman, Mighty Shot, Stalwart Defence†, Target Selection.

Traits: Dark Sight, Fear 2 (Frightening), Instinctive Behaviour (Lurk), Natural Armour (Hardened Carapace), Natural Weapons (Teeth and Claws), Unnatural Senses (30m), Unnatural Toughness (x3), Size (Hulking), Tyranid.

Armour: Hardened Carapace (All 6).

Weapons: Teeth and Claws (1d10+3 R; Pen 3), Impaler Cannon.

†Stalwart Defence: Hive guard count as having two Fate Points for the purposes of activating Stalwart Defence. These Fare Points may not be used for any other purpose.

Special Rules

Limited Synapse Creature: The Hive Guard's limited psychic abilities enable it to telepathically "see" through the eyes of nearby Tyranid creatures, including the Living Ammunition fired by the Hive Guard's Impaler Cannon. As a result of this singular ability, Hive Guard may shoot at any target within weapon range, even if they cannot see it directly. Further, when shooting, Hive Guard may ignore Difficulty Skill Modifiers for shooting at a target at long or extreme range; at a prone target; at targets in melee combat; and/or at a target in fog, mist, shadow, or darkness.

Impaler Cannon: The Hive Guard's Impaler Cannon fires a bony spike 1 to 2 metres in length that is powerful enough to penetrate even Space Marine power armour and the strongest Imperial armoured vehicles. The psychic bond the Hive Guard shares with the shard-beasts melded to the Impaler's missiles bestows these weapons with uncanny accuracy, even when the Hive Guard cannot directly see its target. Heavy: 100m; S/2/–; 2d10+5 R; Pen 8; Clip –; Rld –; Accurate, Felling (1), Living Ammunition, Razor Sharp.

Personal Log

Author: Watch Captain Marius Avincus, currently serving aboard Nova-Class Frigate *Hallowed Sword*, Orpheus Salient

Date of Original Vox-Log Entry: 9132745.M41

Title of Log Entry: The Last Days of Prandium

+++ TRANSCRIPTION CODE 122568ELS : JBGS6570 : ALS080205 +++

+++ VOX-RECORDING OF ORIGIN INDEX RAS : BAL: 320glw +++

Just days before, I had lost Gnaeus, my battle brother and twin, to the Tyranid menace. Though I did not realise it at the time, I would soon lose my home world of Prandium, a world the Ultramarines had sworn to protect, to the foul xenos as well.

Thus, with my grief and hate as raw as a fresh wound, I deployed with my squad in the sector that had contained one of Prandium's largest forests. The Tyranids had debased the awe inspiring landscape that had made Prandium one of the Wonders of the Imperium. Where once clear pools of the purest water reflected the land's lush foliage, degenerate swamps of half-digested organic sludge festered obscenely. Where once stood majestic trees, grotesque towers erupted from corrupted ground and stood ready to pump the harvested bio-mass of my home world to the Hive Ship that orbited the jewel of Ultramar.

+++ PASSAGE FRAGMENT DELETED BY ORDER OF THE INQUISITORIAL REPRESENTATIVE +++

We advanced per the tactics decreed by the Codex Astartes and prepared to set promethium incendiary devices at the base of the capillary tower that was our target. Before we advanced to within 250 metres of the base of the tower, my squad began taking fire. Bony spines more than a metre long rained down. Battle-Brothers Benedictus and Dacian fell in the initial salvo. We laid down suppressive fire, though none of us could establish visual on our enemy.

Per orders, we continued to advance under fire and lost four more of our squad before laying eyes on the xenos defending the towers. Large centauroid Hive Guard defended the chimneys with long-range biological cannons apparently capable of remarkably accurate indirect fire. Heartened by having confirmed targets, we continued our advance, which was hampered further by the increasingly gelatinous surface of the ground upon which we trod. Bolter fire eventually brought down two of the Hive Guard as we neared the base of the first capillary tower. However, we lost all but two members of our squad, Brother Corbin and myself, to enemy fire by the time we reached the minimum effective distance of our ordnance.

Sighting five more Hive Guard taking up position on a nearby ridge supporting the next capillary tower, our secondary target, I, with regret, ordered Brother Corbin to deploy the ordnance and retreat with our secondary and tertiary objectives uncompleted.

TYRANNOFEX

"As the Tyrannofex fell back, we detected a burning, almost sulphurous smell, which we initially assumed was the odour of biochemical discharges from the creature's injuries. However, the scent seemed to attract smaller Tyranid life forms, and soon a swarm of Hormagaunts descended upon us with the savagery of slavering wolves."

—From a field report filed by Sergeant Aurelius, Ultramarines 34th Company, Stationed on Hethgard

The Tyrannofex is an enormous Tyranid creature protected by multiple layers of chitinous armour and propelled towards the battlefield by six powerful legs the size of temple columns. This walking, nigh-invulnerable battle fortress can bring to bear a deadly arsenal of bio-weapons against its foes.

The Deathwatch and other Imperial troops have encountered Tyrannofexes with a wide variety of biomorphs, and Codiciers have catalogued the following Tyrannofex weapons. When engaging infantry, many Tyrannofexes defend themselves by firing a Stinger Salvo, a volley of poisonous spikes a metre long. Other Tyrannofex variants have evolved with Cluster Spines, explosive quill-like missiles that can devastate foot troops.

Bloated cavities in the Tyrannofex's thorax serve as breeding chambers for small Tyranid swarm creatures that the Tyrannofex can unleash upon the enemy at will. Perhaps the most common swarm creatures observed to date are

ADVENTURE SEEDS

To Battle the Goliath: Tyranid hordes engage Imperial forces in a terrible melee. A few kilometres away, a Tyrannofex lumbers forward and threatens to join the battle. In desperation, Deathwatch commanders dispatch the Kill-team to destroy or, failing that, delay the Tyrannofex to give the forces of the Imperium a chance to rally and win the day. Under the circumstances, the Kill-team must rush to deploy against the Tyrannofex. As such, the Kill-team cannot requisition any special equipment or heavy ordnance and must defeat the creature and any lesser Tyranid creatures it may summon with cleverness and guile rather than brute force.

Bad Samples: The Kill-team is tasked with accompanying a Techmarine working for Harl Greyweaver onto a planet in the midst of a Tyranid invasion, to collect samples. The Techmarine is incredibly powerful, and easily forges a path deep behind the battle-lines in search of a Tyrannofex from which to collect samples to bring back to Watch Fortress Erioch. After hunting and killing the Tyrannofex with the Techmarine, the Kill-team must stand watch while he collects samples from the Fleshborer Hive writhing in the creature's belly. Something goes horribly wrong during the collection process and the Techmarine is swarmed by the host of different creatures living inside the Tyrannofex. The Kill-team is now stranded deep behind Tyranid lines, and must extract themselves as well as the incapacitated Techmarine and his samples.

Electroshock Grubs, squat worm-like creatures protected by small armoured plates that generate static electricity as the teeming organisms flow through the enemy ranks. This energy is sufficient to electrocute those caught in the arcing electrical discharges that accompany the writhing grubs' movements. The forces of the God-Emperor have also witnessed thorax swarm creatures such as Desiccator Larvae, slug-like organisms with hollow fangs that latch onto their victims and drain them of all moisture within seconds, and Shreddershard Beetles, insectoid organisms that are covered in needle-like spines and that instinctively crawl into tight spaces such as gaps in armour and body orifices. Shreddershard Beetles cannot survive for long outside of the Tyrannofex host and explode after a few moments' exposure to an aerobic environment, thereby showering those nearby in a blast of spikes.

Finally, the Tyrannofex is equipped with a massive biological cannon capable of firing deadly missiles at its enemies. Cannon types vary from creature to creature, but the most common are Acid Sprays, which shower the enemy in caustic fluids that rapidly break down organic tissue as well as armour plating and other substances. Another primary-weapon biomorph is the Fleshborer Hive, a pullulating nest of the same small Tyranid creatures fired from Termagant weapons. Yet another is the Rupture Cannon, which fires two projectiles, the first of which is a bloated tick that erupts and covers the point of impact with a sticky, oily substance, and

the second of which is a hard seedpod whose armoured shell dissolves instantly in the tick's remains and then implodes with enough force to destroy even a tank's armour.

Savvy commanders have determined that the Tyrannofex, however formidable, is vulnerable to massed attacks by infantry troops disciplined enough to weather the volleys of stinger projectiles or cluster spines. However, the Tyrannofex has a powerful defence against this tactic. When threatened by close combat opponents, the Tyrannofex emits a Pheromonal Distress Signal that attracts lesser Tyranid creatures such as Hormagaunts and Termagants that rush to the Tyrannofex's aid and overwhelm attacking foot troops. As such, Imperial troops are advised to engage the Tyrannofex in close combat only with a supporting reserve that can guard against the smaller Tyranids that will attempt to defend these deadly bio-fortresses.

Tyrannofex (Master)

WS	BS	S	T	Ag	Int	Per	WP	Fel
35	37	(24) 65	(24) 64	25	28	35	48	—

Movement: 6/12/18/24   **Wounds:** 128
Skills: Awareness (Per), Climb (S), Swim (S).
Talents: Crushing Blow, Fearless.
Traits: Dark Sight, Fear 4 (Terrifying), Natural Armour (Bonded Exoskeleton), Natural Weapons (Teeth and Claws), Size (Immense), Sturdy, Swift Attack, Tyranid, Unnatural Strength (x4), Unnatural Toughness (x4).
Armour: Bonded Exoskeleton (All 10).
Weapons: Teeth and Claws (1d10+27 R; Pen 3), Acid Spray, Stinger Salvo, Thorax Swarm.

Special Rules

Pheromonal Distress Signal: Once per encounter, a Tyrannofex that is engaged in melee combat and that has been reduced to half its starting number of Wounds or less may, in lieu of making melee attacks, emit a Pheromonal Distress Signal to summon a Horde of Termagant or Hormagaunts with a Magnitude of 2d10+20. In the next combat turn, the Horde will charge any enemies engaged with the Tyrannofex, enabling the larger creature to Disengage from combat and still shoot.

Biomorphs: At the GM's discretion, a Tyrannofex may have Adrenal Glands (gaining the Furious Assault Talent), Toxin Sacs (gaining the Toxic (1d10) Trait on all melee attacks), and/or Regeneration (5) (gaining the Regeneration Trait); may replace its Acid Spray with a Fleshborer Hive or a Rupture Cannon; may replace its Stinger Salvo with Cluster Spines.

Acid Spray: The Tyrannofex's primary weapon typically fires a shower of caustic and corrosive chemicals that can eat through flesh, bone, plasteel, and metal with ease. Heavy: 40m; S/–/–; 2d10+8 I; Pen 8; Clip –; Rld –; Blast (6), Devastating (2), Felling (1), Toxic.

Fleshborer Hive: Fleshborer Hives are variant weapons that replace the Tyrannofex's Acid Spray. These weapons fire clusters of the same sharp-fanged beetles that fly from Termagant weapons. Heavy: 50m; –/–/15; 1d10+5 R; Pen 3; Clip –; Rld –; Living Ammunition, Tearing.

Rupture Cannon: One of the most devastating bio-weapons ever encountered by the Imperium, the Rupture Cannon fires two missiles. The first is a tick that ruptures on impact covering the target area with an oily, corrosive substance. The second is a seedpod that almost instantly dissolves in the tick's residue and then explodes. Heavy: 150m; S/–/–; 4d10+10 I; Pen 13; Clip –; Rld –; Blast (6), Concussive, Devastating (2).

Stinger Salvo: Embedded in the Tyrannofex's carapace are rows of metre-long, poisoned spines that the creature can fire by means of incredibly strong muscle contraction to rain a shower of deadly missiles into the ranks of the foe. Typical targets are enemy infantry. Basic: 50m; –/–/12; 2d10+3 R; Pen 6; Clip –; Rld –; Razor Sharp, Toxic.

Cluster Spines: Some Tyrannofex variants possess Cluster Spines mounted in their carapaces in lieu of Stinger Salvo missiles. Cluster Spines are similar in appearance to the Stinger Salvo and are fired with the same type of powerful muscle contractions. However, instead of relying on toxins to slay the enemy, Cluster Spines explode upon impact, showering a large area with needle-like shards of spine. Like Stinger Salvoes, Cluster Spines are effective anti-infantry weapons. Basic: 50m; –/–/4; 1d10+4 X; Pen 3; Clip –; Rld –; Blast (3).

Thorax Swarm: The thoracic cavity of the Tyrannofex provides a hospitable environment for a variety of smaller Tyranid life forms. A Tyrannofex hosts one of the following types of Thorax Swarms, which it may eject as a shooting attack.

Electroshock Grubs: These armoured, worm-like creatures generate static electricity that can electrocute infantry. Basic: 20m; S/–/–; 2d10+6 E; Pen 2; Clip –; Rld –; Blast (10), Living Ammunition, Shocking.

Desiccator Larvae: These fanged, slug-like creatures latch on to infantrymen and drain them of bodily fluids. Basic: 15m; –/–/12; 1d10+1 I; Pen 2; Clip –; Rld –; Felling (2), Living Ammunition, Tearing.

Shreddershard Beetles: These insectoid creatures covered in needle-sharp quills instinctively seek out vulnerable areas of enemy infantry and vehicles and, after a few moments of exposure to the air, explode, skewering those nearby with a shower of sharp spines. Basic: 10m; –/–/6; 2d10+5 I; Pen 5; Clip –; Rld –; Living Ammunition, Scatter, Tearing.

Field Journal

Author: Master Apothecary Kregor Thann
Red Scorpions Chapter, Deathwatch
Subject: Biochemical Analysis of Tyrannofex Bio-weapons (samples collected from a single Tyrannofex specimen and associated symbiotic organisms on Castillium)
Date: 9432815.M41

Stinger Salvo. Initial field analysis of the residue coating Tyrannofex projectiles, collected approximately 90 minutes after the creature fired them, reveal a complex poisonous cocktail of highly concentrated polymerised toxins [specific chemical compounds are detailed in Attachment 5-ALS2-33GLW], which cause most humanoid life forms to release neurotransmitters, resulting in nearly instantaneous severe pain in local muscle groups. As these toxins enter the bloodstream, they quickly affect muscular nerves, resulting in tetany (i.e., painful muscle contractions), paralysis, and often death within a few moments. Further study is required to determine the effects of these toxins on Space Marine physiology and the oolitic kidney's ability to process them.

Shreddershard Beetles. I have long been curious about the chemical or biological mechanism by which Shreddershard Beetles explode after a short exposure to aerobic conditions outside of the Tyrannofex host. Chemical residues collected from Adeptus Astartes casualties a few hours after the Beetles exploded contain trace amounts of a variety of flammable chemicals [specific chemical compounds are detailed in Attachment 1-RAS8-51BAL]. I hypothesise that the beetles somehow produce these compounds biologically, though it is possible that they are coated in these chemicals by the Tyrannofex host. As Shreddershard Beetles explode moments after leaving the Tyrannofex's thoracic cavity, obtaining a living, intact specimen will prove difficult. Samples collected directly from the Tyrannofex thorax may prove illuminating.

Acid Spray. Early tests reveal that the term "Acid Spray" is something of a misnomer, as the weaponised fluid produced by the Tyrannofex includes not only acids but also a variety of corrosive and caustic substances [specific chemical compounds are detailed in Attachment 6-ELS4-17JBG]. Note that tests detected other agents that my field equipment could not identify. Further laboratory testing will be required to determine the precise nature of the Tyrannofex's "acid" weapon. However, given the polymorphism associated with Tyranid life forms and particularly the high-degree of mutability observed in the Tyrannofex, I suspect that the Tyrannofex genus, if not individual Tyrannofex organisms, is capable of producing "acid" weapons with a variety of chemical compositions tailor-made for particular enemy targets.

BIOVORE

Most Tyranid bioforms thus far encountered by mankind have been ravening horrors of tooth and claw, eager to rend their prey limb from limb in a deadly flash of talons. These simple tactics sufficed when the horror of the Hive Fleets was still fresh, and the defences of the Imperium reeling under its onslaught. Staunch defenders across the Eastern Fringe sought to rally against these assaults, from the proud Ultramarines to regiments of hard-bitten Imperial Guardsmen. The hordes of the Great Devourer were kept from close quarters by the relentless bombardment of artillery, only for a new horror to make itself known on the battlefield.

The spawning of the Biovore showed that the Hive Mind could match mankind's best strategies stroke for stroke, and improve on them with a horrific alien genius. Even the most learned scholars of the Ordo Xenos do not know if the Biovore's creation was an act of new, malefic creation, or if these terrible living weapons were simply waiting to be deployed all along. Ultimately, another question takes precedence—how to defend the forces of the Imperium from their depredations.

A Biovore is a squat, misshapen creature, but thickly corded with muscle and covered in a plated carapace. Its reflexes are sluggish compared most of its kind, but this matters little. The true threat of a Biovore is not in its claws, but in the huge mortar-like symbiote on its back. These beasts carry within them foul offspring known as Spore Mines, which are among

the simplest of Tyranid life-forms: floating sacs of gas and bile, plated in a rigid shell of bone. They hibernate within the Biovore's recesses until launched towards a distant foe by a spasm of twisted muscle. When leaving their host, Spore Mines quickly awaken and extend their alien senses in search of a foe. They then quickly register the presence of whatever target they were fired at and explode in a shower of hardened bone shrapnel or corrosive acid. But even an off-target Spore Mine can prove deadly, as it drifts onwards, ready to explode as soon as it senses a new enemy.

Kill-teams are most likely to encounter Biovores when operating within a warzone where the Hive Fleet is fully engaged. The amount of bio-mass a Hive Ship must expend to create a Biovore and its clutch of living bombs is not insignificant, and few planetary assaults merit the kind of extended warfare at which the Biovore excels. As such, Biovores are more likely to be an obstacle to Kill-teams than their target, especially once they have been active long enough to blanket the battlefields with a living minefield.

The exceptions tend to be of two sorts. Firstly, when the Deathwatch cooperates with the Achilus Crusade in overt military action, the broods of Biovores often become high priority targets. The Deathwatch also sometimes seeks to capture living or at least relatively intact Biovore specimens on behalf of research-minded Ordo Xenos Inquisitors, for study or dissection in the most secure research chambers of Watch Fortress Erioch. The principles of Tyranid weapon symbiotes are still poorly understood by the Imperium, and the Biovore stands out as one of the purest examples of such creations. Some in the Inquisition hope to find some

Departmento Munitorum Internal Report

For the Attention of the Commissariat Committee on Morale and Discipline
Compiled by Scrivener Second Class Publius Naso, on behalf of Commissar Octavian

Thought for the day: Mercy is not for a man, not for a city, not for a nation, not even for a world. Mercy is for the whole of the Imperium, and never less.

To the esteemed Lords of the Commissariat,

The cancer of the alien spreads its subversion ever deeper into the forces here in the Jericho Reach. We came expecting the most malign xenos horrors of the galaxy, and we have certainly not been disappointed. But it is more than ordinary fear that poisons the resolve of the Imperial Guard.

I write this letter to bring to your attention the case of Captain Zacharias of the Monrass 25th, upon whom I have recently passed judgment in my function as guardian of regimental discipline. This Captain, lauded for his courage in many other campaigns, refused a direct order to send men to secure an important shrine being desecrated by the claws of xenos monstrosities. The shrine was surrounded by a field of Tyranid Spore Mines, which his men were to clear out, bodily if necessary. But such was the craven proclivity of this Captain that he refused to sacrifice his men for even so noble a goal.

I have since resolved the matter, sentencing the former Captain to personally head the charge he protested. But if the fear of these Tyranids, this so-called "Great Devourer," has so claimed our fighting men, more extreme measures will doubtless be necessary in the future. The Tyranid is but a ravening beast, and yet the officers of our regiments fear it more than the fear of failing the Emperor's sacred trust. I will send them to Him to deliver an accounting in person, long before I let fear of these vermin claim hold of the men I safeguard.

The Emperor Protects,

Commissar Octavian, attached to the Monrass 25th "Scythewind Recon"

Fools, both of them the Captain and the Commissar alike. Only the greatest of sacrifices will suffice to keep the Great Devourer's jaws at bay. It is a threat we cannot underestimate. The hesitance of Zacharias and the blindness of Octavian may have already cost us more than we can afford, if my reports are to be believed. The alien's reach is long indeed.

— Inquisitor Ghraille

underlying principle at work that would assist in the creation of an anti-Tyranid weapon or strategy. Thus far, the endless mutability of the Hive Fleet has frustrated such efforts.

Biovore (Elite)

WS	BS	S	T	Ag	Int	Per	WP	Fel
35	40	40 (8)	45 (8)	15	10	40	35	—

Movement: 3/6/9/18   **Wounds:** 40

Skills: Awareness (Per) +10, Swim (S).

Talents: Combat Sense.

Traits: Auto-Stabilised, Dark Sight, Fear 2 (Frightening), Improved Natural Weapons (Claws and Teeth), Instinctive Behaviour (Lurk), Multiple Arms, Natural Armour (Hardened Carapace), Size (Enormous), Sturdy, Unnatural Strength (x2), Unnatural Toughness (x2), Tyranid.

Armour: Hardened Carapace (All 6).

Weapons: Spore Mine Launcher (Heavy; 300m; S/–/–; 2d10+6 X, Pen 8; Clip –; Reload –; Blast (8/Special), Devastating (2), Tearing), Teeth and Claws (1d10+8 R, Pen 3).

Special Rules

Biomorphs: At the GM's discretion, the Biovore may be "loaded" with a variant species of Spore Mine, providing the following alternate profiles for the Spore Mine Launcher:

Bio-acid: These Spore Mines are filled with caustic fluids capable of melting through even adamantine and ceramite plates, but their viscous payload provides a smaller spread than the more standard fragmenting variety. (Heavy; 300m; S/–/–; 2d10+10 E, Pen 12; Clip –; Reload –; Blast (4/Special), Devastating (1), Tearing).

Poison: A spray of deadly toxins is released when a Poison Spore Mine detonates, of such potency that even the slightest trace penetrating through an air-filtration system can spell a man's death. (Heavy; 300m; S/–/–; 2d10+2 X, Pen 10; Clip –; Reload –; Blast (6/Special), Devastating (1), Toxic).

Living Bombs: When the Spore Mine Launcher fires and misses its target, the shot may release an unexploded Spore Mine onto the battlefield. Consult the Scattering diagram on page 248 of the **DEATHWATCH** rulebook, but roll 2d10 for the number of metres scattered. If there would be a non-Tyranid creature within the Blast radius of the Spore Mine at this new point, the shot resolves normally. Otherwise, the Spore Mine land and begins to drift about. It will move 1d5 metres in a random direction each turn until a non-Tyranid creature is within its blast radius, then detonate as if resolving a direct hit. Spore Mines can be detonated prematurely by making a Challenging (+0) ranged attack against them with any weapon. Fields of Spore Mines function identically, except that the Mines drift in clustered groups of three to six at a time, which always detonate simultaneously.

PYROVORE

The Pyrovore is little more than an ambulatory digestive system set in a squat and vicious body, containing nothing that does not serve it in sating the Great Devourer's hunger. Its role within the Tyranid swarms is to find the choicest morsels of the worlds the Hive Fleet consumes, from living flesh to exotic minerals required by the strange leviathans in orbit above it. Serving the Pyrovore in this function are several unique biomorphs, all of which stem from the volatile and caustic chemicals flowing throughout its alien system.

It is this vile arsenal that makes the Pyrovore best engaged at a distance, even by the boldest of Kill-teams. The plumes of corrosive flame sprayed from the weapon-symbiote atop the Pyrovore's dorsal ridge are mercifully short ranged, but deadly to those caught within. More deadly still is the caustic bile dripping between the Pyrovore's fangs, which can melt through even the blessed plates of Terminator Armour.

Those few who have successfully braved close combat with a Pyrovore rarely repeat the experience, as even the death spasms of this beast can be deadly. An ill-placed final blow will rupture the gastric sacs of the beast and release its chemical payload in one deadly torrent. Some call this the Hive Mind's revenge for slaying its progeny, but others doubt whether so understandable a motive can truly be ascribed to this most alien of foes.

Quenching: A Techmarine working in the forges of Erioch believes his research into ancient weapon-tech will produce a blade equal to the mightiest relics in the armoury of the Watch Fortress. To finish his work, it must be quenched in the blood of a deadly foe, and the Techmarine believes that of a Pyrovore would be ideal. Surviving that caustic bath would prove the weapon's perfection beyond doubt. The Kill-team has been assigned to protect the weaponsmith as he seeks the ultimate test of his forge-craft amidst the teeming Tyranid swarm.

Pyrovore (Elite)

WS	BS	S	T	Ag	Int	Per	WP	Fel
40	30	45 (8)	45 (8)	15	10	35	35	—

Movement: 3/6/9/18   **Wounds:** 45

Skills: Awareness (Per), Swim (S).

Talents: Cleanse and Purify, Combat Sense, Crushing Blow.

Traits: Auto-Stabilised, Dark Sight, Fear 2 (Frightening), Improved Natural Weapons (Acid Maw), Instinctive Behaviour (Feed), Multiple Arms, Natural Armour (Hardened Carapace), Size (Enormous), Strange Physiology, Sturdy, Unnatural Strength (x2), Unnatural Toughness (x2), Tyranid.

Armour: Hardened Carapace (All 6).

Weapons: Acid Maw (1d10+10 E, Pen 15, Tearing), Flamespurt (Heavy; 30m; S/–/–; 2d10+5 E; Pen 8; Clip –; Reload –; Flame).

Special Rules

Acid Blood: The blood of a Pyrovore is a vile, caustic fluid nearly as deadly as its digestive juices. Any attacker inflicting Wounds on a Pyrovore with a melee weapon must make a **Challenging (+0) Dodge Test** to avoid being caught in the spray. Note that using Dodge in this manner does not require use of a Reaction. Failure inflicts 2d10 Energy damage on the attacker, ignoring Armour.

Flamespurt Weapon-Symbiote: The Pyrovore's Flamespurt weapon is, as with many Tyranid armaments, a separate creature bonded to its wielder. However, in the case of the Pyrovore, the weapon retains a greater independence and cunning than its carrier. The Flamespurt has occasionally been known to attack foes without its host so much as noticing their presence. As such, the Flamespurt may fire when the Pyrovore is Stunned or Grappled.

Volatile Death: When a Pyrovore reaches zero Wounds, there is a chance the precarious balance of chemicals inside it will react violently. As it dies, roll 1d10. On a result of 8 or higher, the Pyrovore explodes in a foul plume of corrosive acids, dealing damage to targets with five meters as if they were struck by the Pyrovore's Acid Blood.

MAWLOC

The great worm-like Mawloc is a perpetual threat to Imperial operations in any world with an established Tyranid presence. Once the Hive Fleet is able to commit enough captured bio-mass to the creation of these huge monstrosities, the very concept of a safe house, stronghold, or fortress is invalidated. No adamantine-plated bunker or mountain-walled command centre is spared the depredations of the subterranean threat now running rampant throughout the hallowed ground of the Imperium's worlds.

The unrelenting pervasion of the Mawloc threat owes much to the creature's simple construction. Bone and muscle arranged on a massive scale allow the creature unrivalled access to the deep earth of even the densest planetary surfaces. This massed array of brawn and sinew also serves as the Mawloc's sole weapon, allowing it to smash through the armour of battle tanks with its fluked tail, or crush a fully armoured Space Marine in its constricting gullet.

The ground rumbles and shakes at the passing of a Mawloc, as if the soil itself rebels futilely against the xenos menace. But the Mawloc is a cunning hunter, aided by a "ground sense" that is barely understood by the most learned xenobiologists. Using their alien sense they can home in on their target, whether the thrumming of a tank division's engines, or the frantic beating of a terrified Guardsman's heart.

The cunning of the Mawloc shows most clearly in their patterns of engagement, more hunting behaviour than tactical doctrine. The serpentine beast will erupt from the

MAWLOC

ground beneath an unsuspecting target, throwing everything into disarray. After doing as much damage as it can fit in a few frantic minutes, it will seize a final morsel and burrow down again, collapsing its old tunnel behind it. The process is continued and repeated until whatever great convoy or battalion once opposed it is reduced to a few desperate survivors huddled atop the highest vantage they can find.

Mawloc (Master)

WS	BS	S	T	Ag	Int	Per	WP	Fel
38	––	(18) 60	(12) 60	40	15	25	45	––

Movement: 4/8/16/32   **Wounds:** 160

Skills: Awareness (Per) +10, Swim (S), Tracking (Int) +20.

Talents: Ambidextrous, Combat Master, Fearless, Furious Assault, Heightened Senses (Touch), Swift Attack.

Traits: Burrower (4), Crawler, Dark Sight, Fear 4 (Terrifying), Improved Natural Weapons (Claws and Teeth), Instinctive Behaviour (Feed), Multiple Arms, Natural Armour (Thickened Scales), Size (Massive), Unnatural Strength (x3), Unnatural Toughness (x2), Unnatural Senses (Ground Sense)†, Tyranid.

Armour: Thickened Scales (All 10).

Weapons: Claws and Teeth (1d10+23 R, Pen 5).

Special Rules

Biomorphs: At the GM's discretion, Mawlocs may have any of the following biomorphs:

Adrenal Glands: The Mawloc gains the Furious Assault Talent.

Toxin Sacs: The Mawloc gains the Toxic (1d10) Trait on all attacks.

Regeneration (5): The Mawloc gains the Regeneration Trait.

†Ground Sense: A Mawloc can detect enemies while burrowed, through the vibrations they make. It can easily detect anything in contact with the ground within 15 meters and receives a +10 bonus to tracking prey in constant motion. Large vehicles and similar give greater bonuses.

A Tricky Foe

The Mawloc, as well as the Ravener and Trygon presented in **MARK OF THE XENOS**, present unique opportunities and challenges for a Game Master. While most foes engaged by a Kill-team operate in two dimensions, these Tyranids operate in three, and not in the open sky like flyers (who are in some ways similar). Burrowing creatures have the freedom to engage and disengage without easy reprisal, a trait that can make for fun or frustration, depending on how it is handled.

There are several issues it is best to consider ahead of time when including burrowing creatures in your Missions. For example, the Deathwatch usually attempts to strike first in any engagement, but when your target is buried beneath thirty meters of solid rock, this can be difficult! The flipside of this is that a Mawloc or any similar creature can strike with almost no warning, turning the tables of standard Deathwatch operations. They can also flee into tunnels when wounded,

only to return later, bearing the scars of their previous encounter, or even healed by the Regeneration Trait.

Some players will not enjoy what feels like losing control over the game, while others may embrace the sense of a constant threat to keep them on edge. Here are some good guidelines to keep in mind:

Don't create untouchable objectives. If the players need to kill a Mawloc, make sure they have a way of reaching it without relying on the beast to overextend itself. This also applies to anything that escapes the Kill-team. Space Marines are not known to let enemies who have challenged them live, and so you should allow your players to exact the revenge they may be seeking.

Don't make things too easy. This may seem like a contradiction to the previous point, but it needs to be said for the same reason. Your tunnelling terror isn't going to impress anyone if the players can just chase it down the hole it leaves behind—and your players won't feel nearly as accomplished either. The deep places burrowing Tyranids operate in are not standard theatres of operation, even for the Deathwatch, and the Kill-team should have to deal with that fact. Adeptus Mechanicus breaching engines or traps laid in deep-set mining tunnels make exciting set-pieces for a final showdown with the Kill-team's quarry.

Consider how everything fits together. A Mawloc with the Regeneration biomorph can come back from the edge of death if it escapes, and even a small brood of Hormagaunts becomes a threat when they can traverse the tunnels left behind by their larger cousins to strike at will.

++Life is the Emperor's currency. Spend it Well.++

+++CLASSIFIED+++

///Document Desc.: Field Report from Throne Agent Cell Sanctus Sarcina, stationed on Hethgard///

Assessment of Laboratory Equipment Prior to Mawloc Intrusion Event:
  7x class 3 cogitator banks, supporting a Mars-Pattern logic engine
  5x reinforced plasteel specimen cages (empty), enclosed by power fields
  2x adamantine dissection tables, with triple-bonded restraints
  Eighty-gallon tank, for acid bath treatment and disposal of specimens
  Apothecarium unit equipped with full array of toxins and sedatives (Alpha-level supply)
  12x Mezoa-pattern Heavy Bolter turret security emplacements

Length of Mawloc Intrusion Event (best estimate, based on security footage):
  One minute, twenty-four seconds.
  Assessment of Laboratory Equipment After Mawloc Intrusion Event:

Intact:
  1x steel aquila pendant, formerly belonging to the chief researcher
  Salvageable:
  1x weapon tripod from Heavy Bolter turret security emplacement
  2x reinforced plasteel specimen cages (empty)

Estimated Losses:
  127,000 Calixis-standard Thrones value of research equipment
  Full security complement (two squads)
  Full research complement (three Vermillion-clearance Adepts, Magos Xenologis Anchises)

Conclusion:
  This is an intolerable situation. A lone Tyranid beast breached the tunnel network for under two minutes, and destroyed a secure facility more thoroughly than the Guard could have done with a squad of demolition specialists and half an hour. Furthermore, this is hardly a lone incident, see attached files [REDACTED]. If these breaches continue, there will be little left of Hethgard, much less its planetary defences.
  I recommend a full re-working of the tunnel security network to allow for remote detonation of any area where a Tyranid may be lurking, preferably followed by a thorough sweep of the rubble by the deployed Adeptus Astartes forces. Those areas we cannot afford to lose should be surrounded by promethium tanks and ignition arrays ready to flood the access tunnels with cleansing fire. If progress on this project appears unlikely to be completed within ten days, conscript all available units of the Guard to manual labour—they won't survive without it, in any case.

TERVIGON

The massive Tervigon is a horror even among the chitinous hordes of the Hive Fleet. They tower above the battlefield, dwarfing even fearsome Hive Tyrants and Carnifexes. To support their tremendous bulk, they scuttle forward on all limbs at once, deceptively seeming free of the fearsome talons and claws that define so many other Tyranid bioforms. This illusion is crushed the moment the Tervigon reaches its prey, as, with a deftness none would believe from such a behemoth, it brings to bear its front limbs, trading locomotion for the ability to scythe its font claws out in front of itself, killing all those too foolish to flee. Flight buys only a few scant seconds of life, however, as serried rows of spines are embedded in the Tervigon's carapace, ready to launch forth at a more distant foe.

Despite all the terrible might of this xenos abomination, the true reason to dread the Tervigon lies not in its claws or spines, but beneath the unyielding plates of its carapace. Nestled deep in the Tervigon's abdomen is an incubator for scores of dormant Termagants. When the Tervigon's attention in drawn to fresh prey, the Termagants awaken and swarm forth to assail the Tervigon's target. As the beast advances, its path churns with the progeny constantly being birthed.

As the progenitor of this skittering brood, the Tervigon acts as a potent nodal relay to the Hive Mind for the Termagants it spawns. Its presence keeps them calm and organised as they ruthlessly hunt down their prey. This potent symbiotic relationship acts to make the Tervigon an even more deadly opponent, but it also creates a grave weakness. If the enemy commander can keep his wits about him in the face of the horrifying swarm and command his troops to focus fire, the symbiotic backlash from the Tervigon's death will kill all its surrounding young, striking a devastating blow against the swarm.

Deathwatch Kill-teams must not only contend with Tervigons on the battlefield, as an obstacle in some of the deadliest missions it is possible to undertake. There have been times when the Deathwatch was called upon to board a living Tyranid Hive Ship, to deliver toxic payloads or seize pure gene-samples. The survivors, when there were any, always reported that though most Tyranids slumbered within the belly of the ship, or were recycled for bio-mass, Tervigons were found patrolling the capillary tunnels of the leviathan ships, observing an obscene vigil in the depths of space.

Tervigon (Master)								
WS	BS	S	T	Ag	Int	Per	WP	Fel
38	38	(12) 60	(18) 65	15	40	35	(12) 65	—

Movement: 4/8/12/24   **Wounds:** 180

Skills: Awareness (Per), Climb (S), Swim (S).
Talents: Ambidextrous, Combat Master, Crushing Blow, Fearless, Heightened Senses (All), Psy Rating (6), Two-Weapon Wielder (Melee), Swift Attack.
Traits: Auto-Stabilised, Dark Sight, Fear 4 (Terrifying), Natural Armour (Bonded Exoskeleton), Multiple Arms, Unnatural Strength (x2), Unnatural Toughness (x3), Unnatural Willpower (x2), Improved Natural Weapons (Claws and Teeth), Shadow in the Warp, Size (Massive), Synapse Creature, Tyranid.
Armour: Bonded Exoskeleton (All 10).
Weapons: Claws and Teeth (1d10+14 R, Pen 3), Stinger Salvo.

Special Rules

Biomorphs: At the GM's discretion, a Tervigon may have any of the following biomorphs:
Scything Talons†: The Tervigon gains the Lightning Attack Talent and the Improved Natural Weapon (Scything Talons) Trait. Replace the profile of its attacks with the following: Scything Talons (1d10+16 R, Pen 3).
Crushing Claws†: The Tervigon gains the Flesh Render Talent and the Improved Natural Weapon (Crushing Claws) Trait. Replace the profile of its attacks with the following: Scything Talons (1d10+18 R, Pen 6, Tearing).
Adrenal Glands: The Tervigon gains the Furious Assault Talent.
Toxin Sacs: The Tervigon gains the Toxic (1d10) Trait.
Regeneration (5): The Tervigon gains the Regeneration Trait.

†A Tervigon may have Scything Talons or Crushing Claws, not both. Note that these biomorphs are the only way for the Tervigon to make use of its Ambidextrous and Two-Weapon Wielder Talents.

TERVIGON

ADVENTURE SEEDS

Mostly Dead is Insufficient: Reports have reached Erioch of a heavily wounded Hive Ship that escaped an engagement in the depths of space, and is limping towards an unguarded world rich in bio-mass. Should it reach the planet, it will not only be able to seal its wounds, but perhaps spawn new creatures to extend the reach of the Hive Fleet. The Kill-team is assigned to one of the fastest vessels of the Deathwatch in order to intercept the Hive Ship and kill it from the inside. However, while the Hive Ship is heavily wounded, the unceasing watch of the Tervigons over its vital organ-systems has not abated.

Decapitation Strike: A powerful Tyranid force is sweeping aside the Imperial war machine, necessitating the intervention of the Deathwatch. The Synapse web guiding it is produced not by Warrior broods or a Hive Tyrant, but by several Tervigons. Not only would defeating these Synapse creatures weaken and confuse the swarm, but it would cost the Hive Mind dearly in bio-mass to replace the huge beasts.

Behind Friendly Lines: A major victory against the Tyranids has been tarnished by reports that a Tervigon thought to be fatally wounded has escaped, and has made its way behind the cordon of Imperial forces. If left unchecked, the broods it produces could destroy vast swathes of territory, but the Imperium's forces cannot abandon their defensive line. A Deathwatch Kill-Team must hunt down and destroy the beast.

Stinger Salvo: Embedded in the Tervigon's carapace are rows of metre-long, poisoned spines that the creature can fire by means of incredibly strong muscle contractions to rain a shower of deadly missiles into the ranks of the foe. Typical targets are enemy infantry. Basic: 50m; –/–/12; 2d10+3 R; Pen 6; Clip –; Rld –; Razor Sharp, Tearing, Toxic.

Spawn Termagants: A Tervigon may spawn Termagants as a Free Action each turn, creating a Horde of Magnitude equal to a 2d10 roll. If it spawns Termagants in the presence of an existing Horde, instead increase that Horde's Magnitude by 2d10. If any double is rolled when spawning Termagants, the Tervigon's incubation chamber has been emptied, and it will be unable to spawn more until it has had a chance to consume and digest fresh bio-mass.

Brood Progenitor: A Termagant Horde with any members within 15 meters of a Tervigon may use its Willpower characteristic in place of their own. They also gain the benefits of the Adrenal Gland and Toxin Sac biomorphs if the Tervigon possesses them. However, should a Tervigon be slain, all Termagant Hordes with any members within 15 meters immediately suffer 2d10 Magnitude damage from psychic backlash.

Monstrous Tyranid Psyker: Tervigons are Psykers, but draw power from the Hive Mind rather than the direct manipulation of the warp. A Tervigon follows all the normal rules for Psykers as detailed in Chapter VI: Psychic Powers of **DEATHWATCH**, with the exception that if it suffers Psychic Phenomena or Perils of the Warp, it does not roll on either table. Instead, it suffers 1d10 Energy Damage, not reduced by armour or Toughness, as it loses control of the power and the immense strength of the Hive Mind backlashes upon it; otherwise, the power has no effect. A Tervigon automatically has the Dominion power, and may have the Onslaught and Catalyst powers at the GM's discretion.

PSYCHIC POWERS

Tervigons are Tyranid Psykers, and have access to the three Tyranid Psychic Powers listed below.

Dominion
Action: Half
Opposed: No
Range: Special
Sustained: Yes
Description: The Tyranid creature reaches into the depths of the Hive Mind and strengthens its links to the indomitable alien will, projecting a blanket of control and purpose through its synapse to all Tyranid bio-forms nearby. While this power is in effect, the Tyranid creature's Synapse range (see Deathwatch page 135) is doubled. In addition, the hardened resolve of the Hive Mind gives both the creature and all other creatures with the Tyranid Trait affected by the power +10 to all Willpower tests for its duration.

Onslaught
Action: Half
Opposed: No
Range: 25 metres x PR
Sustained: Yes
Description: The Tyranid creature infuses a nearby brood with burning energy and the pitiless drive of the Hive Mind to devour all in its path. The creature chooses a single Master, Elite or Troop Horde within range, allowing it to either make a Full Move, Standard Attack (Ranged or Melee), or Charge Action as a Free Action once per Round. The warrior or brood continues to benefit from the effects of this power as long as the creature sustains it and they remain in range.

Catalyst
Action: Half
Opposed: No
Range: 75 metres
Sustained: No
Description: This power functions as described under the Hive Tyrant's special rules in **DEATHWATCH** page 370.

MYCETIC SPORE

When a Tyranid fleet first attacks a planet, the initial assault stages are typically begun by launching several waves of Mycetic Spores. Each wave is launched simultaneously from the ships of the invading fleet, into the planet's atmosphere. Even the most comprehensive of planetary defence systems are overwhelmed by the sheer quantity of incoming Tyranid creatures. From the ground, this rain of hungry intruders resembles the twinkle of a meteor shower, as their fleshy outer shells burn up in the atmosphere.

Soon, the xenos alter shape to slow their descent, landing precisely through the guidance of the Hive Mind. Typically, shortly after impact, the Mycetic Spore perishes as it completes its life cycle. Though it may survive long enough to launch a few salvoes from any bioweapons it possesses, by landing intact the organism has fulfilled its genetically programmed duty. As it completes its transformation, the remaining layers of insulation unfurl. In short order, a brood of invading Tyranids emerge from belly of the beast. Typically Hormagaunt or Genestealer broods are found within, but in some cases Warriors or even a dreaded Carnifex might be found.

Within Hive Fleet Dagon, Mycetic Spore strains have begun to show some variation. Those of more recent invasions have physiologically enhanced sensory nodes. These nodes are believed to work in conjunction with pheromone markings left by Lictors on the planet's surface. By following the trails that the Lictors plant, in conjunction with Hive Mind directives, the Mycetic

ADVENTURE SEEDS

Verify and Eliminate: Recent reports have found their way to the Deathwatch of Mycetic Spore sightings deep within the Orpheus Salient's secure worlds. These reports arrived through secure and trusted Inquisitorial channels. Sources include acolytes stationed in systems where there is no known Tyranid presence either on the planet or within the void. The Battle-Brothers must verify the reports, and eliminate any infestations that they find. Crusade elements are not yet appraised of this information. The Watch Captain has decided that it should be kept from them until confirmation becomes available. If these reports are accurate, this may represent a substantial threat to the Crusade's supply lines. In that instance, word of the incursion must be passed on to the Crusade so that elements may be reassigned.

Interception: Imperial forces have successfully defended the planet from the first wave of attack. Unfortunately, the Imperial Navy has been less successful. As Hive Ships dominate the system, another wave of Mycetic Spores is likely to be released in short order. These must be defeated before they have an opportunity to land and disperse another wave of lethal cargo. The Space Marines are assigned to perform as gunners and pilots on any available aircraft to stop those Mycetic Spores that get past the planet's static defences. Once the majority of the wave is overcome, they may also be called upon to identify and eliminate any broods that successfully made landfall.

Spores are capable of targeting key defensive elements far more accurately. To counteract the spread of these enhancements, Crusade forces have begun to take additional precautions against Lictor incursions. Other Mycetic Spores have shown enhancements to the bioweapons carried, with a few even replacing their cargo with additional resources to keep the armaments active. Spores of this variant have been exploited to provide additional support to broods deploying in closely contested regions.

Mycetic Spores play a crucial role in the Hive Mind's early assault upon prey systems. In addition to offering a mechanism to overwhelm the system's defences, they also offer a means for the Tyranid forces to quickly deploy reinforcements as needed. This is especially true for invasions where the system has been inadequately scouted by Tyranid organisms. The brutal impact from a landing Mycetic Spore, backed by the deployment of the transported Tyranid creatures deep behind enemy lines can be an overwhelming combination. The only truly effective strategy to counteract this has been extensive aerial defences.

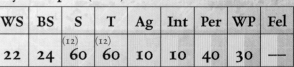

Mycetic Spore (Elite)								
WS	BS	S	T	Ag	Int	Per	WP	Fel
22	24	(12) 60	(12) 60	10	10	40	30	––

Movement: –/–/–/– 　　　　　　　　　　　　**Wounds:** 52

Skills: Awareness (Per) +10, Dodge (Ag) +10, Pilot (Mycetic Spore) (Ag) +20, Survival (Int) +10, Swim (S), Tracking (Int) +20.

Talents: Fearless, Heightened Sense (Hearing, Smell).

Traits: Dark Sight, Natural Armour (Hardened Carapace), Unnatural Strength (×2), Unnatural Toughness (×2), Improved Natural Weapons (Lash Whip, Ripper Tentacles), Size (Massive), Tyranid.

Armour: Hardened Carapace (All 6).

Weapons: Lash whip (1d10+15 R; Pen 3), Ripper tentacles (10m ; –/–/10, 1d10+6 R, Pen 0, Clip N/A, Reload –; Living Ammunition, Tearing).

Equipment: None.

Special Rules

Plummeting Spore: Mycetic Spores are incapable of movement once they impact with the planet's surface. While falling, some may have the ability to angle various spines and protrusions to slightly modify their flight path. As a consequence, if encountered during flight, the Game Master should consider using the Vehicle Movement rules from RITES OF BATTLE. If using these rules, the Spores are considered to have a Tactical Speed of 100 AUs. The only actions they may perform are Dodge, Tactical Manoeuvring (Half Action), or Ram. As the Spores lack a propulsion system, they may not actively adjust their speed.

Brutal Impact: These Tyranid creatures are specifically designed to survive their impact with a prey planet. As a consequence, they do not suffer any falling damage when they impact with the ground. Further, as it approaches the planet's surface, a Mycetic Spore may attempt to impact directly upon a nearby target. To hit the target, it must make a **Challenging (+0) Pilot Test**. If it succeeds, it deals 4d10 +6 damage to whatever it strikes. Targets struck by this attack become buried beneath the Mycetic Spore.

Limited Sentience: Mycetic Spores have extremely primitive minds, even by Tyranid standards. Further, they are immobile once they make impact. On the ground, these creatures are insufficiently advanced to possess an instinctive behaviour. Rather, they simply attack any non-Tyranid creature that comes within range of their weapons.

Transport Spore: Mycetic spores are capable of transporting other Tyranid creatures from the Hive Ships to the planet's surface. Each spore's cargo may include a single Master, up to five Elites, or a Horde of up to 20 Troops. As long as the Mycetic Spore is not slain prior to landing, the transported creatures arrive unharmed and capable of disembarking for immediate combat.

Ripper Tentacles: Under its ablative chitinous shell, Mycetic Spores typically trail bundles of thickly corded tendon and muscle. These are used to guide its descent prior to its surface impact. Once upon the surface, these lengthy tentacles sway wildly towards any non-Tyranid life forms that they can detect. The Mycetic Spore uses these swathes of muscular tentacles to mercilessly bludgeon any prey it can identify. Because they are heavy enough to aid in landing, they are not prehensile enough to be used as a melee or grappling weapon.

Classification: Achilus Crusade Code Scarlet
Date: 148813.M41
Author: General Derian Arkelius
Subject: Xenos Landing Pods
Recipient: All Orpheus Salient Field Commands

This notification is served to address strategies regarding the landing pods utilised by the xenos intrusion within the Orpheus Salient. All commanders are directed to review the attached files immediately, so that they may be properly prepared to follow newly revised protocols when combating the foul creatures. The xenos appear to have changed their tactics. If we do not implement effective new stratagems to address these revisions, we are likely to suffer unacceptable losses. The attached directives are specifically organised so that we may more quickly vanquish our foes in the light of the God-Emperor.

Among the attached files are images and analyses provided through the grace of Adeptus Mechanicus analysts. Please exercise discretion prior to sharing this iconography. These materials are poorly suited for general dissemination. Rather, commit them to memory so that you might know the true horrors that we face, and then destroy all copies.

In contrast, take care to distribute those files marked "For Field Units." These data include the specific strategies that our analysts have identified as most appropriate for overcoming the xenos threat. Please note that these strategies are designed for general dissemination. Some field commands may have specific environmental challenges that make them inappropriate. At your discretion, you may attach an addendum to further clarify the tactics with any necessary modifications. Know, however, that if these modifications are directly responsible for Imperial losses, officers issuing them face serious repercussions.

In brief terms, these directives encourage units to remain aware at all time for orbital insertion attempts. The numbers observed have substantially increased since the earliest planetary assaults. These insertions have also been identified as playing more of a key role in latter parts of the invasion than previously expected. In addition, analyst reports now believe that some of these insertions may be linked to sightings of the xenos creature designated the Lictor. All Imperial units assigned to systems within the known incursion zone must be proactive in dealing with any signs of orbital insertion or Lictor reconnaissance efforts. Recommended procedures are included for methods to maintain high levels of alertness during extended watches and also to increase recognition efforts for both of these threats. By enhancing our ability to confront both of these threats at the earliest possible stages, the data suggests that we may decrease our cost per kill by as much as 0.7%.

MALANTHROPE

Repeatedly, Deathwatch agents have had to take actions in support of the Achilus Crusade. In the Orpheus Salient, many of these actions have drawn the Space Marines far behind enemy lines, either to rescue Crusade elements or to recover Imperial resources that the Crusade has chosen to abandon. Regardless of the reasons, these Deathwatch members have identified Tyranid creatures that were not previously recorded. While a number of those observed may be unique or unrecognisably modified organisms, some of these creatures have been observed repeatedly and therefore represent distinct species.

In select instances, records of these findings have been provided to Adeptus Mechanicus agents associated with the Achilus Crusade for further analysis. The classified nature of the Crusade has required that these findings be kept confidential. As a direct consequence, these findings have only been accessible to organisations and individuals directly involved in the Crusade. Some Inquisitorial and Administratum members have chafed at these restrictions. In spite of these objections, providing this information to other Imperial organisations could risk compromising the Crusade's chance for success within the Jericho Reach.

The Malanthrope is a prime example of an instance in which this confidentiality is restrictive. A very limited number of sightings of these Tyranid creatures have been recently confirmed. Initial images and field reports were disregarded by analysts. The Magos Biologis concluded that the reports were simply Zoanthrope

ADVENTURE SEEDS

Slay the Reaper: On a planet that verges on being lost to Tyranid forces, the Watch Commander has issued an edict that Malanthropes must be targeted with extreme prejudice. Deathwatch teams are being sent behind Tyranid lines to identify and eliminate these threats. Other Tyranid creatures are to be ignored, in favour of eliminating the greater threat—one that could lead to even more capable xenos forces in the short term. Deathwatch teams may be deposited on the surface using drop pods, gunships, or teleporters. Upon their arrival, they are directed to use whatever means necessary to avoid the vast swarms of Rippers so that they may survive to eliminate Malanthropes. Even after these targets are destroyed, escaping to a recovery zone is a major challenge.

Protect the Geneseed: A Storm Warden Apothecary, with geneseed recovered from two fallen squads, has been trapped behind Tyranid lines. He has holed up in a bunker with a few other surviving members of his unit. These Space Marines must be recovered before the swarm has an opportunity to devour them and incorporate their genetic materials. Due to the occupying Hive Fleet, the Battle-Brothers have no Imperial Navy support. They must fight their way to the bunker either on foot, or through the remnants of the planet's security tunnel network. Either option requires that they overcome front line Tyranid forces, then disengage so that they can battle their way through to the trapped Battle-Brothers. Once they arrive, they must safely escort the wounded and exhausted forces back to an Imperial stronghold.

sightings, exaggerated or poorly pictographed by the viewers. However, as additional reports continued to come in, these early reports were reviewed in conjunction with the newer data.

In point of fact, a Deathwatch team assigned to extract a Mechanicus outpost that was trapped deep behind Tyranid lines confirmed a Malanthrope sighting. Their imagery, in conjunction with specimen samples that they were able to recover, enabled the Mechanicus agents to perform a more thorough genetic analysis. Their findings have confirmed that this is a previously unknown species.

Further analysis of recordings from this incident and earlier ones have concluded that the Malanthrope is a synapse creature that operates in conjunction with Ripper swarms to selectively devour the genetic resources of a prey world. In several confirmed instances, a Malanthrope is identified as accompanying and apparently directing the actions of these Ripper swarms. The Malanthrope's role seems to be to selectively collect and process genetic material from fallen enemies, before itself being reabsorbed, along with the Ripper swarms, into the Tyranid bio-mass. The bio-mass is then used to create more complex creatures. The Malanthrope's full role is not yet understood, but some Magos Biologis believe that it is seeking out unique genetic material for use in creating new Tyranid creatures.

This suggests that these creatures could play a direct role in the hive fleet's genetic adaptability. As a consequence, Deathwatch teams have been reassigned to eliminate any sighted Malanthropes with extreme prejudice. Any further genetic enhancements that these creatures could incorporate pose additional risks to the Imperial presence. The Achilus Crusade can ill-afford for the Tyranid Hive Fleet to become any more capable than it already is.

Malanthrope (Master)								
WS	BS	S	T	Ag	Int	Per	WP	Fel
62	36	(18) 62	(18) 64	35	38	42	54	––

Movement: 4/8/12/24 **Wounds:** 124

Skills: Awareness (Per) +10, Climb (S), Dodge (Ag), Psyniscience (Per) +10, Survival (Int) +10, Swim (S), Tracking (Int) +10.

Talents: Fearless, Heightened Sense (Hearing, Smell), Improved Warp Sense, Psy Rating (6), Sprint, Warp Sense.

Traits: Dark Sight, Fear 4 (Terrifying), Hoverer (8), Natural Armour (Bonded Exoskeleton), Multiple Arms, Unnatural Strength (x3), Unnatural Toughness (x3), Improved Natural Weapons (Toxic Tendrils), Shadow in the Warp, Size (Massive), Synapse Creature, Tyranid.

Armour: Bonded Exoskeleton (All 10).

Weapons: Toxic Tendrils (1d10+16 R; Pen 3, Toxic).

Special Rules

The Horror (Psychic Power): As a Half Action, the Malanthrope may unleash a wave of horror that gnaws at the resolve of its enemies. This power may be used to target a Kill-team within 75 metres. Each member of the Kill-team within the range of this power must take a Willpower test with a –30 modifier. The Kill-team takes one point of cohesion damage per member that fails this test. All other non-Tyranid (and non-Space Marine) NPCs within range of the Malanthrope must pass a fear-based Willpower Test with a –30 modifier or flee in panic.

Warp Field: Malanthropes are protected from harm by a powerful psychic warp bubble. This functions as a Force Field (see page 166 in the DEATHWATCH rulebook) that counts as having a protection rating of 65 and overloads on a roll of 01-05. If a Malanthrope's Warp Field overloads, the creature can spend a Full Action to restore it, the effects coming back into effect at the start of its next turn.

Anaphylactic Shock: The Malanthrope's tendrils carry a highly venomous, cardiotoxic, neurotoxic, and dermatonecrotic poison that, when injected through the skin of just about any living creature, causes excruciating pain. It counts as having the Toxic Trait, but the damage is 3d10 + 5, ignoring Toughness and Armour. The Toughness Test to resist the poison is Arduous (–40).

Feeder Tendrils: This creature gains the Crippling Strike and Sure Strike Talents against enemies belonging to a species that it has previously slain, and confers these Talents to other Tyranids within 10 km of it against those same enemies, even if the other Tyranids do not possess the prerequisites for those Talents. It is at the GM's discretion as to what species the Malanthrope has previously encountered and slain for the purposes of this ability.

Classification: Jericho Xenos Code Saffron
Date: 205814.M41
Author: Lord Commissar Vance Theren
Subject: Xenobiologist Rahjid
Recipient: Administratum Command; Calixis Sector

My Lords,
   I believe it is my responsibility to inform you that the forces operating within the Orpheus Salient of the Achilus Crusade have encountered internal resistance. This comes in the form of one Xenobiologist Rahjid of the Adeptus Mechanicus. I do not doubt her zeal to destroy the dread xenos. However, I question the decision that placed this woman within our zone of conflict.
   The xenobiologist has a near obsessive interest in the biology and psychology of the Tyranid forces. We believe that she has accumulated a substantial wealth of information regarding their tactics, strategies, and physiology. However, she steadfastly refuses to share any of this information with Imperial Guard forces.
   Recently, our agents discovered that she had even confirmed the existence of a new Tyranid creature. In spite of this, Rahjid steadfastly keeps her findings from our agents. We have reason to believe that targeting this creature—designated a Malanthrope—could be highly beneficial to the Imperial war effort. However, until her information is recovered, we lack the necessary data to even identify these monsters in the field. The xenobiologist has consistently taken draconian measures to insure the confidentiality of her information.
   At this time, our forces must exploit any opportunities that we might find to overcome the xenos threat that has intruded upon our battlefront. Based upon her extensive analysis and the work of her acolytes, our intelligence operatives are convinced that her latest findings represent information that might be used to substantially impact the Tyranid threat. Even if we could study a limited subset of her findings, the value could be immense.
   We believe that by identifying these creatures and eliminating them at every opportunity, we could stretch the Crusade's resources in this front substantially further. This could both substantially reduce the time required to secure success for the Crusade, and substantially reduce the necessary resources required for success. Though no sacrifice is too great for those in the God-Emperor's service, it would be a blessing if we might maintain some reserves for use in the Crusade's other fronts. I would regard it as a personal favour, if you could please exert any influence you might have to obtain this information.

BROOD NEST

After the initial wave of attacks, Tyranid forces begin to subjugate the planet, seizing control of the bio-mass in regions where defences are lightest. In many cases, the more combat capable Tyranid creatures are not necessary in these environs. Instead, Capillary Towers and Ripper swarms are adequate to devour all life from the region and then transport those materials back to the waiting void-capable members of the Hive Fleet in orbit.

For these regions, Mycetic Spores represent an inefficient means to distribute Tyranid creatures to the planet's surface. Instead, the Hive Mind maintains slower growing options, which can utilise the planet's resources, rather than depending upon the materials that the Hive Fleet has retained from prior conquests. These are introduced to the planet's atmosphere through rains of nearly microscopic spores. Some may be spread by Tyranid flying organisms, while others drift from spore chimneys spouting alien contaminants into the atmosphere.

Brood Nests are one of the products of these spores. From a single malignant spore, an enormous structure can grow under the planet's surface. As these caverns extend, the nest produces incubator-like structures that fill with growing Tyranid creatures. These are nurtured to near maturity within them, and then kept in a state of hibernation. If the nest is threatened or the Hive Mind requires additional units, these bio-killers complete their maturation within moments and awaken.

Just seconds after they mature, these creatures rush out of the Brood Nest's entrance. In short order, they burst upon the

planet's surface, glistening with amniotic slime and mucus, fully grown and ready to kill in the service of the Hive Mind. In this way, the Tyranid swarm has devised a mechanism to maintain reserve units as protection for regions far from enemy lines, without costing the swarm significant resources.

Imperial reports indicate that Brood Nests can vary wildly in size. Some have just a few creatures, and some are dedicated to the production of only a single Tyranid creature. Agents of the Adeptus Mechanicus theorise that some nests may grow large enough to produce Hierodules or even Hierophants.

With its accelerated biological processes, Tyranid creatures grow at a terrifying rate and gestation periods are short. In a matter of just a few days, a Brood Nest may develop from a single spore into a large complex packed with fully grown monsters. They may then wait in hibernation for months until needed, but once born they are instantly under the Hive Mind's control. Magos Biologis who have studied the development of Tyranid organisms note that they do not have the equivalent of a human growth cycle, from infancy to adolescence to maturity—Tyranids are always birthed fully mature.

Status Report: Inquisitor Cartier
ATT: Watch Commander Mordigael; ++Priority Citrine
FROM: Watch Captain Avincus
Date: 132815.M41

Today's force reconnaissance mission has been completed in accord with Inquisitor Cartier's request. While I can only respect the woman's devotion to the Emperor, I have grave reservations about the path she has chosen to follow. My personal experience has clearly shown that the Tyranid threat is not one to be taken lightly. Nonetheless, Cartier and her puppet explorator lackeys remain intently focussed on using experimental methods to turn the Tyranid threat against itself. I maintain that the risks her methods require are unacceptable over the short term.

Our squad was under orders to attempt to secure a Brood Nest for study. While the Inquisitor chose to accompany us to the location, she remained safely behind in the Land Raider with her entourage. My squad approached and descended directly into the nest. The Inquisitor provided Battle-Brothers Cassiel and Marnk with experimental armaments that were intended to incapacitate, but not kill the xenos. Fortunately, both chose to carry their bolt pistols with them as well.

From first contact, things at the nest went poorly. As we approached, a Lictor assaulted the squad. Though we dispatched it without incident, its activity apparently triggered a Brood Nest response. Just as the Lictor fell, a stream of Hormagaunts began to emerge from the nest. As these were already separated from the nest, I directed my men to employ lethal measures. Inquisitor Cartier attempted to override my commands by vox, but my squad was wise enough to ignore her directive.

When the last of that batch of xenos fell, we hurriedly drove forward into the nest, through the opening from which the Hormagaunts had emerged. Brother Marnk took point, armed now with the weapon that Inquisitor Cartier had provided. After only a few steps, several Raveners appeared in the darkness within the murky depths of the Brood Nest. Marnk fired his experimental weapon, but it sputtered and froze his right arm in a block of ice. Cassiel's met with no greater success.

Through the providence of the Emperor, the remainder of my squad reacted in a timely fashion. We were able to eliminate the Raveners, several further waves of Hormagaunts, and a brood of Genestealers. At that time, ammunition was running low, and we were forced to withdraw from the site. I deployed the melta bombs that I had kept in reserve. As we withdrew from the structure, a remote detonation triggered a collapse, and I believe effectively eliminated the Brood Nest threat.

Inquisitor Cartier has strenuously objected to the use of lethal force at the site. Under the conditions that we faced, I do not believe that we had another acceptable option. I have refused her directive to perform further field tests with her pet explorator's weapon designs.

I have directed Brother Marnk to return to the Watch Station so that his right arm may be replaced. We lose some efficiency, but my squad remains battle-ready despite his absence.

HIEROPHANT

More than thirteen metres tall and massing over fifty tons, the Hierophant is one of the largest Tyranid creatures to have been observed within the Jericho Reach. There have, mercifully, only been a handful of battlefields where these enormous creatures have been used against the Achilus Crusade. In all instances, the creatures devastated the Imperial forces that they opposed, even in those instances where the Imperium eventually triumphed. Between their broad range of weapons and their inordinate defences, the Hierophant represents a threat that requires extreme solutions.

Analysts believe that the Hierophant represents the largest shock troop the Tyranid forces have produced to date. Its huge form is covered in thick, chitinous armour, but it is also protected by warp fields, created by the overwhelming psychic potential of the Hive Mind. These armoured plates bristle with sharp edges and spines, presenting a lethal proposition for anything that might attempt to engage it in melee or come close enough to plant explosive munitions.

These close defences are further supplemented by its natural armaments. Each of the Hierophant's four enormous legs terminates in a razor sharp claw. In many instances, the Hierophant has destroyed Imperial vehicles by the simple expedient of stepping on them. The monster's two forelimbs terminate with scything talons on a scale far larger than any others observed. These are capable of penetrating the armour on anything but the largest Imperial Titans or the most secure fortifications. Even against these types of structures, given time the Hierophant can eventually rend the armour apart.

For foot soldiers—or even smaller vehicles—that dare to engage the bio-Titan, it offers two additional close-quarters threats. Its underbelly is littered with dozens of spine covered tendrils that are similar to the lash whips employed by lesser Tyranid creatures. These symbiote weapons can swiftly entangle and rend the monster's attackers. Wielded by the enormous strength of the massive creature, they can rip through the defences of any personal armour or light vehicle.

The bio-Titan also constantly emits a dense cloud of toxic spores from the millions of small pores on the underside of its bony armour plates. With each motion it makes, some of these are exposed, and the spores are launched into the air, forming a cloud around the creature. These are lethal to all non-Tyranid creatures, forming a drifting vapour about the Hierophant that chokes and burns anyone without proper protection. Any attacker whose armour is pierced by the creature's flailing whips may then suffer exposure to this airborne threat.

The Hierophant is well equipped for confrontations with ranged attackers as well. Two lengthy bio-cannons are mounted just above its forearms, alongside the creature's head. These symbiote weapons are triggered by a massive electro-chemical shock from the host creature. The bio-cannon spews forth a hail of highly corrosive, maggot-like organisms. When these venomous and highly acidic organisms impact upon the target, they splatter gobbets of bio-acid and poison over an enormous area. The biochemicals can melt through plasteel, ferrocrete, ceramite, and unprotected flesh in seconds. Targeted structures and victims are swiftly reduced to smouldering puddles of their component materials.

Several different variants of the Hierophant bio-Titan have been observed. It is believed that these alternative strains are simply carefully constructed combinations of known biomorphs applied to the much larger framework. Some of these variants have been identified with huge rending claws, enormous bone swords, and other bio-weapons. The development of these enormous Tyranid creatures remains a mystery to the Imperium's Biologis. A Hive Tyrant or Carnifex could easily be an alternate growth variant of a Tyranid Warrior, but there are no clear associations between the Hierophant and any other known strains.

Within the Orpheus Salient, Hierophants have only been observed on planets where Imperial forces had already committed Titans to the battle. It is unclear if this was simply a coincidence or if the Hive Mind has deliberately reserved creation of bio-Titans for instances where it has deemed them necessary. When used, Hierophants are often encountered alone, though a few reports have observed up to three bio-Titans within a Tyranid swarm. These comparatively low numbers seem to support the theory of limited use of the creature.

Imperial command has had mixed reactions to this theory. The proposed solution is to avoid fielding Titans in new battlefronts. However, the strategic value of the Titans to the Imperial war machine cannot be easily dismissed. Many commanders seem to feel that the presence of Hierophants may be an acceptable consequence of the opportunity for a representative of the Titan Legions to accompany Imperial forces to battle.

ATT: *Inquisitor Evaine Cartier; ++Priority Aquamarine*
FROM: *Master Apothecary Kregor Thann*
Date: *085815.M41*

As requested, I have performed a field analysis of the Hierophant slain by the forces of Legio Venator, after recovering and securing its remains under Inquisitorial sanction. Due to the nature of the armaments employed, the creature's corpse was severely damaged. Many of its injuries were distributed across its carapace and are unlikely to have proven individually fatal. It may even be that a combination of these lighter injuries would not have been fatal to the monstrosity. In fact, our limited knowledge of complex Tyranid physiology proves extremely limiting in this regard. As such, it is impossible to confirm a single cause of death through necropsy.

However, the scale of the creature offered its own set of opportunities. While the creature was surely slain, many of its tissues remained very much alive. Secondary or even tertiary organ complexes still provided a flow of ichor through many sections of the creature's mutilated form. As my unit made our way across the Hierophant's torso, we were initially surprised to discover that the lashing tendril symbiotes remained very active. Fortunately, my Battle-Brothers avoided serious injury in the resultant conflict. We also managed to recover one of the still living tendrils. It has been preserved in a stasis field and will be forwarded on to the Watch Fortress for more thorough analysis.

The musculature of the Hierophant's left hind leg appeared to have survived the conflict, suffering only minor damage. I have assembled an extensive pictographic record of the dissection I conducted of this limb. Chainfists were used to saw through the monstrosity's armour plating and then lever it away from the underlying muscles. The scale of its muscle tissues is extraordinary. Chitinous structures, interwoven with complex metallic alloys, are required to hold the tendon analogues into place. These tissues were discovered to have an extraordinary tensile strength. Cutting through them required extensive work with Chainfists, and even after death, the stretched muscles recoiled explosively. Specialised ammunition might be synthesised to target them in the future.

In the course of the limb dissection, we discovered a large neuronal mass near the joint with the bio-Titan's torso. This mass is reminiscent of Tyranid brain-analogues that have previously been identified. This sample has also been preserved and returned to the Watch Fortress for more detailed analysis. Based upon the scale and positioning, my preliminary theory is that this structure was primarily devoted to coordinating the adjacent limb. As there was no evidence that the mass had suffered physiological damage prior to my dissection, I believe that the organ is reasonably intact and should withstand strenuous tests.

While we did succeed in obtaining many samples of the Hierophant's spores, we were unable to positively identify any of the organs involved in their production. The spores are clearly launched from many regions throughout the bio-Titan's central core, but they appear to be produced by a single internal organ. After manually tracing the vessel network that transferred the spores throughout the bio-Titan's body, I discovered that the source region had been struck by a blast from a Volcano Cannon. Another specimen must be recovered before the origin of these spores may be confirmed and studied. Detailed analysis of the spore samples will require additional assets beyond those available in the field.

Requested tests to confirm the origin of the Hierophant's void shield analogue or the construction of its Bio-Cannons were also impossible using the available materials. Unfortunately, the head region had been the primary target for the Titans of the Legio Venator. The frontal, dorsal section of this Hierophant was largely atomised. I will continue to remain in the field, hoping to identify further samples for analysis. I will also continue to attempt to resolve the issue of target selection with the Titan units. Unfortunately, requests to speak with the ranking members of the Legio Venator have gone unanswered.

Adventure Seeds

Repel the Threat: Hierophants have been particularly effective in engagements with the Titan Legions on Jove's Descent. They have been so successful, in fact, that the last functional Imperial Titan has been withdrawn for repairs. Without Titans to deploy against the bio-Titan threat, Crusade forces have begun to falter against the oncoming Tyranid horde. The Battle-Brothers have been tasked with identifying an alternative solution to fell these vast monstrosities. They must deploy to the warzone, locate the targets, and determine the best available weapons to eliminate the threat. They have been granted full Inquisitorial authority to requisition any Crusade resources necessary to eliminate the bio-Titans, but that does not mean that the officers within the warzone are anxious to cooperate. In addition to a squadron of Baneblades, the Imperial forces have a variety of heavy weapon squads, artillery vehicles, and tank units in a variety of configurations. None of these have successfully overcome a Hierophant to date, but perhaps the Battle-Brothers have an alternative strategy to employ.

Bomb Them: A valuable munitorium is directly in the path of an incoming Tyranid attack. Two Hierophants are at the centre of the oncoming swarm. The Battle-Brothers are tasked with defeating the Tyranid swarm at any cost. While sacrificing the munitions within the structure may be a necessary option, the facility must be preserved. If it is lost, Crusade supply chains would be stretched far too thinly. Future engagements might be lost when units run out of necessary munitions. The Battle-Brothers must devise a strategy to exploit the available resources and then out manoeuvre the Tyranids, so that the Hierophants might fall into their trap. Timing, stealth, and a careful selection of the most appropriate bait are all crucial to a successful engagement. The munitorium includes a variety of shells, energy charges, and the raw materials necessary to synthesise additional equipment or to create a sizable bomb. Of course, triggering such an explosion, if not done directionally, could result in certain destruction for the munitorium as well.

The Big Guns: Land-based methods for dealing with a Hierophant have failed miserably. The only surviving weapons near the planet with the necessary range and stopping power to halt the Tyranid incursion are those mounted upon orbiting cruisers. The Battle-Brothers are tasked with getting close enough to a Hierophant to supply targeting coordinates. If successful, an orbital bombardment might be sufficient to eliminate the threat. Of course, if they get too close, they could fall prey to elements of the Tyranid swarm as well as risk becoming collateral damage from the bombardment. If necessary, Crusade elements could be used as a distraction to attempt to draw the Tyranid forces towards a specific location, but Imperial units must not be unduly sacrificed. The time window for the attack is razor thin. Orbiting Tyranid assets are likely to identify and launch their own attack against the supporting voidcraft in short order. If the Space Marines are delayed in acquiring their target, they might discover that their fire support is unavailable.

Hierophant (Master)

WS	BS	S	T	Ag	Int	Per	WP	Fel
66	34	(36) 90	(32) 84	35	20	35	45	—

Movement: 8/16/24/48 **Wounds:** 220

Skills: Awareness (Per), Climb (S), Swim (S), Tracking (Int).

Talents: Ambidextrous, Berserk Charge, Combat Master, Fearless, Furious Assault, Heightened Senses (Sound, Smell, Touch), Lightning Attack, Swift Attack, Two weapon Wielder (Melee), Two weapon Wielder (Ballistic).

Traits: Dark Sight, Fear 5 (Paralyzing) †, Instinctive Behaviour (Feed), Multiple Arms, Natural Armour (Impenetrable Carapace), Improved Natural Weapons (Scything Talons), Regeneration (15), Size (Gargantuan)† †, Spore Cloud†††, Tyranid, Unnatural Strength (x4), Unnatural Toughness (x4).

Armour: Impenetrable Carapace (All 12).

Weapons: Scything Talons (1d10+38 R; Pen 3, Devastating (8)), Lash Whips (1d10 + 39 R; Pen 3, Devastating (8), Flexible, Snare), Claw Stomp (1d10 +37 R; Pen 4, Devastating (8)), Two Twin-Linked Biocannons†††† (Heavy: 200m; S/–/–; 4d10+6 X; Pen 6; Clip –; Rld –; Blast (4), Devastating (3), Felling (2), Toxic).

Special Rules

Warp Field: A Hierophant is protected from harm by a powerful psychic warp bubble. This functions as a Force Field (see page 166 in the **Deathwatch** rulebook) and counts as having a protection rating of 65 and overloads on a roll of 01-05. If a Hierophant's Warp Field overloads, the creature can spend a Full Action to restore it, the effects coming back into effect at the start of its next turn.

Claw Stomp: Each of the Hierophant's legs terminates in a massive bony spike, which is interwoven with threads of complex alloys. As the Hierophant strides through a battlefield, it may deliberately target an object for destruction by stepping down with one of these claws upon its prey.

Lash Whips: The Hierophant has as many lash whips descending from its lower torso as are necessary to engage each foe within range with a single attack.

Discretionary Targeting: A Hierophant's multiple redundant neuronal systems are capable of acting independently. Because of this, each weapon system may act of its own accord. Each of the Hierophant's ballistic and melee weapons may independently attack the same or multiple targets each turn, with no penalty.

†Fear 5 (Paralyzing): Due to its massive size, immeasurable armaments, and additional threats, the Hierophant exceeds the values presented in the standard Fear Chart (see page 277 in the **Deathwatch** rulebook). The Hierophant imposes a −50 Fear Test modifier.

††Size (Gargantuan): Creatures in this Size category are even larger than those described as Massive. Attacks targeting a Gargantuan sized creatures receive a +40 Modifier to hit, and these creatures receive a –40 penalty to concealment. Their movement is calculated based upon Agility Bonus +4. In addition, all of their Natural Weapons are imbued with the Devastating Quality at a rating equal to their base Toughness attribute.

†††Spore Cloud: The Hierophant emits a thick and choking spore cloud from vents in its armour, that exposes all non-Tyranid beings within 20m of the creature to a poison attack. Unless foes have an airtight system, they are subject to an inhaled Toxic attack. This attack damage is increased to 2d10. This cloying vapour partially obscures the Hierophant, imposing a –10 penalty to all shooting attacks made against it.

††††Bio-Cannon: The symbiote that launches this lethal hail of highly corrosive, maggot-like organisms is triggered by a powerful electrical blast. When these venomous and highly acidic organisms impact upon the target, they splatter gobbets of bio-acid and poison over the targeted region.

Distress Call: Jove's Descent
ATT: Adeptus Mechanicus Forces; ++Priority Crimson ++349815M41
From: General Derian Arkelius

Tyranid forces within this system continue to pose a substantial threat to Imperial success. Most recently, the last of the Titan Legions assigned to work with my command were withdrawn from active duty. Without the support of the Titan Legions, our forces have no resources that are capable of directly confronting the bio-Titans that the xenos employ in the ongoing confrontation. Our casualty numbers have risen at a substantial rate without their aid. We need at least a small unit of Titans deployed to this system as a direct counter to the Tyranid bio-Titan threat.

We further believe that the bio-Titan strains observed on Jove's Descent may include novel variants. A few of the creatures have been measured at over 14 metres in height. Some of these specimens have a central body structure that seems broader or narrower than is observed in the picts that have been provided for threat recognition. The primary armaments observed were also not consistent with those observed during the earlier stages of the conflict. While those were universally armed with massive talons that could slice through our support elements, several of the newer sightings include examples where the creatures' forelimbs terminated in massive claw structures. These claws appear to be utilised to pick up, and in some cases hurl, Imperial assets towards other Imperial units. The psychological effects of such a display of power are nearly as devastating as the damage that it inflicts.

With the frequency of these sightings and our inability to counteract their advance, we believe that Tyranid forces may be constructing bio-Titans at a rate that eclipses our ability to defeat them. By analyst counts, there may be as many as fourteen Hierophants currently active within the system. We are unclear as to whether this is an indicator of Tyranid production capacity or if some of the specimens may be changing their weapon symbiotes, such that analysts are identifying the same specimen multiple times. In either case, these production numbers and variations may be of tremendous interest to Adeptus Mechanicus investigators. In addition to the tremendous opportunity for Titans to earn glory for their name, these conflicts may offer a hidden opportunity for a Magos Biologis to uncover crucial information on the Tyranid life cycle and growth process.

I have attached pict imagery of several of the specimens that we have identified. I have also included reference imagery of sample creatures from a variety of other Tyranid strains. I believe that by superimposing some of this imagery, it may be possible to identify the source genetic materials used to create the Hierophant strain. I would very much like to discuss this analysis with any available Adeptus Mechanicus experts, so that we might be able to identify armaments better suited to combat the Hierophant. For if we know a weapon is particularly effective against a source strain, it might retain its efficacy against the derived species.

HIERODULE

Recently, observations have begun to filter in from several planets of a new front-line Tyranid creature. Dubbed the Hierodule, the creature is substantially larger than the Carnifex, though it is being deployed in comparable numbers and roles. This monstrous killing machine is armed with four enormous claws, and protected by massive chitinous plates. Field reports indicate that these claws are sharp enough to slice cleanly through the front armour of a Land Raider. Its armour plating has been observed to deflect fire from a Leman Russ Battle Tank's main cannon. Combined with a mouth filled with forty centimetre fangs and a broad range of spines and barbs spread across its massive frame, the creature represents a significant physical threat.

In addition to its melee and defensive capabilities, the Hierodule also bears a weapon symbiote mounted within the armoured plates of its dorsal side. The creature is capable of emitting a devastating jet of mutagenic acid at will. The torrential eruptions from this symbiote have devastated unprotected Imperial units and have even caused substantial damage to vehicles and Space Marine power armour. Samples of the acid have been exceptionally difficult to analyse. It is believed that there may be Tyrannic pathogens present within the bio-acid that contribute to its potency.

Field reports suggest that the Hierodule is not a focal point for the Hive Mind. Rather, known synapse creatures are typically found directing the monster's actions. However, the creature is most commonly found working in close concert with broods of lesser Tyranids. Termagants, in particular, often accompany the Hierodule. This has proven an alarmingly effective strategy. The massive Hierodule draws a storm of weapons fire, which it can typically ignore. At the same time, the smaller creatures rapidly advance, as defenders dismiss them as a lesser threat. Unfortunately for Imperial forces, this grants the lesser xenos ample opportunity to prove their effectiveness.

Imperial analysts are anxious to recover Hierodule remains, or even a still living specimen, for research purposes. In cases in which one of the monstrous killers was defeated, the heavy weapons necessary for its destruction left little available for examination. To date, there have been a limited number of attempts to capture a living specimen, all of which have met with failure. The creature is simply too massive and capable to be contained by typical methods. It has also proven resistant to anaesthetics that had been effectively used against lesser Tyranid creatures.

Hierodule (Master)

WS	BS	S	T	Ag	Int	Per	WP	Fel
64	23	(24) 82	(24) 81	35	20	35	45	—

Movement: 7/14/21/42   **Wounds:** 180
Skills: Awareness (Per), Climb (S), Swim (S), Tracking (Int).
Talents: Ambidextrous, Berserk Charge, Combat Master, Fearless, Furious Assault, Heightened Senses (Sound, Smell, Touch), Lightning Attack, Swift Attack, Two weapon Wielder (Melee).
Traits: Dark Sight, Fear 4 (Terrifying), Instinctive Behaviour (Feed), Multiple Arms, Natural Armour (Impenetrable Carapace), Improved Natural Weapons (Scything Talons), Regeneration (5), Size (Gargantuan)†, Tyranid, Unnatural Strength (x3), Unnatural Toughness (x3).
Armour: Impenetrable Carapace (All 12).
Weapons: Scything Talons (1d10+26 R; Pen 3, Devastating (8)), Bio-Acid Spray†† (Basic; 30m; S/–/–; 3d10+6 E; Pen 4; Clip –; Rld –; Living Ammunition, Tearing, Toxic).

Special Rules

†Size (Gargantuan): Creatures in this Size category are even larger than those described as Massive. Attacks targeting a Gargantuan sized creatures receive a +40 Modifier to hit, and these creatures receive a –40 penalty to concealment. Their movement is calculated based upon Agility Bonus +4. In addition, all of their Natural Weapons are imbued with the Devastating Quality at a rating equal to their base Toughness attribute.

††Bio-Acid Spray: The symbiote that launches this potent spray of lethal acid maintains an astronomical respiration rate. In this manner, it isolates reducing agents from the planet's atmosphere, which can be used to generate the extremely potent acidic spray. The acid's component elements are then stored in separate vesicles within the symbiote. When it launches its deadly stream, these reagents are combined with pathogenic microbes from several biological passages constructed near the symbiote's surface. The various components only combine into their lethal form during an exothermic reaction as the stream leaves the Tyranid creature's body. This weapon uses the Flame Quality rules (see page 142 in the DEATHWATCH rulebook) for targeting purposes, but does not set anyone on fire.

Status Report: Unidentified Creature
ATT: Watch Captain Virgil; ++Priority Aureus
FROM: Master Apothecary Kregor Thann
Date: 564815.M41

My squad has successfully completed our analysis of the remains found at the outpost. The site designated Epsilon-472 appeared to be consistent with the reports forwarded to the Deathwatch. As expected, the remains were in very poor condition, due to additional degradation that has occurred between the time the reports were issued and when we arrived upon the scene. However, we were able to obtain biological samples from the remains of the victims as well as material that I believe is linked to the Tyranid creatures involved in the attack.

I have compiled a set of preliminary findings, which are included in the attached files. Please note that these data are very rough, as I was limited to using field equipment to perform the analyses. Once I return to the Watch Fortress, I expect to provide a revised version, using the complete resources of our well equipped Medicae. However, as there are pressing concerns, I felt that it was only appropriate to provide data that could be distributed immediately.

In short, the outpost was assaulted by a Tyranid creature armed in a manner that is not consistent with any known creatures. Analysis of the resultant devastation indicates that it was far stronger than any known species, save for bio-Titan variants. A thorough study of the scene suggests that no organisms of that scale were present. However, our squad did identify footprints embedded in the ferrocrete surfaces near the destroyed structure. Based upon the depth of the impressions, the creature that damaged the roadways must have been at least twenty tons. Estimates of its stride length suggest that the creature is a quadruped at least twelve meters in length, though this measure has a very low degree of confidence.

Damage to the outpost's walls indicate that a creature whose vertical reach exceeded six meters used massive sheering claws to rip through and pull down the ceramite-armoured walls. Given that these walls bore twenty centimetres of plating, it is safe to assume that the Tyranid creature poses a substantial threat to well fortified outposts and military vehicles. The resultant opening suggests that the creature is less than ten metres wide, but this estimate seems excessive based upon footprint spacing measurements.

Either this creature or one working in close concert with it was equipped with a weapon capable of discharging a potent bio-acid, with a range of at least twenty metres. I was unable to recover intact samples of the solution due to the site's deteriorated state, though I have obtained samples of surfaces which were exposed to it. Spectrographic analysis may reveal additional properties of this substance, though visual inspection indicates that it is capable of dissolving ceramite, ferrocrete, and, of course, exposed human tissues.

I recommend that these data also be provided through discrete channels to analysts affiliated with the Orpheus Salient. The Crusade forces need to make adjustments to weapon distribution in order to counter the presence of these monstrosities. As things stand, there are a very limited number of fortifications and units capable of withstanding a direct confrontation with one of these Tyranid creatures. The Crusade must reassign those units best suitable for facing them to the systems where there are confirmed sightings.

"WHAT LIES BENEATH"

"I'm confident that those seismic tremors are just the plasma coolant system acting up again. We can safely disregard it."

—Gideon Hyland, Overseer of Hive Trimalov before its fall

Confirmed reports of this specimen were first obtained during the early stages of Castobel's invasion. Just days after the first wave of Mycetic Spores descended upon the planet, one of the planet's massive hive cities was fatally crippled by Tyranid invaders. Recovered security recordings from the ruins of Hive Trimalov indicate that an exceptionally large Trygon burst through the hive's lower levels. Within hours of its arrival, there was a major explosion within the hive's central plasma core, irrevocably collapsing the city's power supply and slaying all of the xenos attackers. Without power to maintain internal ventilation, lighting and water systems, let alone defensive weapons, the hive's doom at the claws of the oncoming swarm was assured.

A low ranking tech-priest who worked within the plasma core maintenance system was among the few survivors of the explosion. Mech-Wright Tolber endured extensive debriefings with Inquisitorial agents recounting the fine details of the event. Through these interviews, Inquisitorial agents discovered that the plasma core was in the process of a long overdue retrofit when the attack struck. As the Trygon burrowed beneath the imperial hive, creating a tunnel for its attack, its passage severed the massive pipes that carried the

Distress Call: Depot Epsilon-Z019
ATT: All Respondents
++Priority Amaranth
++452815M41

This depot has come under unexpected xenos attack. Promethium and ammunition reserves have been compromised. All stationed units have suffered casualties in excess of seventy percent. We have no surviving medical personnel nor do we have any surviving followers of the Adeptus Mechanicus. Ninety percent of the depot's structures and all vehicles have been destroyed. Extensive Tyranid forces are active deep behind formerly secure lines. Immediate support is requested from any able units.

All bases receiving this should take appropriate actions to prepare for attacks coming from beneath the planet's surface. An enormous worm-like creature was accompanied by hundreds of Hormagaunts. The xenos assaulted from below ground without triggering any of our standard security alarms. Before the active duty guards could even trigger the manual alarm system, we suffered more than 200 casualties in an explosion of the depot's promethium storage tanks.

The attack struck at night, shortly after a supply vessel had completed its delivery of supplies. All of our security records appear to be compromised. The depot cannot currently send any additional imagery or information regarding the forces we encountered.

energy core's coolant fluid. The sacred fluids drained into a deep underground chasm in short order. Without any coolant, the plasma reaction soon escalated beyond the capacity of its containment vessels, leading to the explosion.

The presence of Tyranids within the hive city, far from the known battlefronts, was terrifying to the population. However, the damage to the plasma core was directly responsible for the Imperial loss. It seems extremely unlikely that a Tyranid monster could comprehend the complexities of the plasma reactor. Further, as the creature was unquestionably slain in the resultant blast, there was no reason to expect a recurrence of this tactic. Consequently, the loss was explained as a tragic coincidence.

During the battles upon Credos, a similar Trygon attack took place deep behind lines that were believed secure. In this instance, the monstrous Tyranid creature led an assault upon a supply depot, where Imperial assets were stored and refitted. The base commander had violated standard Imperial deployment regulations and established the temporary promethium storage tanks far too close to the facility's field munitorium.

Again, this may have been a tragic coincidence. The foul xenos just happened to strike shortly after the depot had undergone a full resupply. An orbital resupply run had just topped off the promethium tanks. The munitorium had also recently completed a manufacturing cycle devoted to artillery

ADVENTURE SEEDS

Ambushed!: The Battle-Brothers are in the midst of a clandestine surveillance mission, close to a Crusade supply depot. Several platoons are at the station, refitting vehicles and in the process of resupplying ammunition, promethium, and additional standard requisitions. Many of their field vehicles are disassembled for routine maintenance when the ground rumbles and "What Lies Beneath" bursts from the ground into the midst of the encampment. Within moments, two swarms of Hormagaunts also emerge from the hole the Trygon created. The Battle-Brothers must decide if it is acceptable to break their cover to save their Imperial Guard allies, or if it is more important to keep their presence on the world a secret. This also offers an opportunity to study the tactics of this rare Tyranid specimen in the field from a comparatively safe location, as it proceeds to destroy the Crusade depot.

Vengeance of the Emperor: A veteran Deathwatch Kill-team was recently slaughtered when they were unexpectedly attacked by "What Lies Beneath." The Watch Captain, in a rage of righteous fury, commands the Battle-Brothers to find this creature, eliminate it, and to slay any others of its kind, so that the xenos might experience the full wrath of the Emperor. The team must first travel to Castobel, or another infested world. Once there, they must travel the tunnels burrowed by the Tyranid creatures to find and eliminate "What Lies Beneath." If there are similar specimens, they must destroy them as well, along with any Brood Nests capable of producing this monstrosity. As they follow this path, they are likely to encounter Mawlocs and other Tyranid creatures prowling the tunnels beneath the surface. The Battle-Brothers must take care to track their ammunition usage, as their travels take them far from Imperial resources.

units. Hundreds of thousands of potent explosive shells were awaiting transfer to an overdue transport shuttle. In combination with the thousands of kilolitres of promethium, the depot was a lethal combination.

The consequence of this timing was predictably disastrous. When the Trygon made its attack, a massive bioelectric pulse ignited the fields of promethium storage tanks. In short order, the intense fire spread to the munitorium. Then, the artillery shells detonated in a cataclysmic fashion. Between the detonations and the walls of flames, the depot was a near total loss. Hundreds of Imperial tanks and crews, thousands of trained support staff, and a crucial resupply facility were all lost in a few moments. The only positive to be gleaned from the incident was that the Tyranid creature responsible was surely slain in the explosion as well.

After that incident, several Imperial analysts noticed the similarities between the events upon Credos and Castobel. Since that time, several similar instances have been recorded. In all cases, an unusually large Trygon emerged amidst a seemingly secure location. In an instant, the monstrosity would trigger a disastrous explosion that vaporised substantial Imperial assets as well as the Tyranid responsible. Weeks or months later, a similar incident would occur on another world, often systems away.

Between pictographic records and sketches compiled from survivor interviews, additional elements began to crystallise a complete story. The Trygon, which has been dubbed "What Lies Beneath," was somehow capable of targeting Imperial stores of volatile substances. Once this information was deduced, further investigation linked the creature to additional attacks upon Imperial fortifications. In all instances, the facilities had received substantial chemical stores or had altered the mechanism by which its volatile chemicals were contained.

Further analysis revealed that the creature was consistently accompanied by several Hormagaunt broods during the attacks. None of the confirmed incidents included any other Tyranid strains as part of the assault. Another point of interest was that many of these attacks occurred during the earliest stages of the Tyranid invasion. These events were identified as anomalous, because they preceded the usual time point at which Trygons would appear as a part of the ecological invasion. Analysts have suggested that this particular variant is either capable of travelling within a Mycetic Spore or that it has an altered genetic prioritisation so that it appears at a time point earlier than the norm. Additional evidence must be acquired before either mechanism may be confirmed.

Almost as debilitating as its attacks have been upon Imperial supplies, they have also been devastating to Imperial morale. Survivors of the horror's previous attacks have spread word of the nightmares it incurred. Crusade command has attempted to stifle these rumours, but as necessary procedural changes have been made to counter its actions, the stories have circulated ever faster. Because some recount stories of seeing "What Lies Beneath" slain in a massive fireball, later confirmed sightings have also added legends of immortality to the creature's reputation.

Some commanders have taken extreme reactions to the horror's presence. These include cutting fuel and ammunition reserves to extremely minimal levels, keeping supplies within transports, and repurposing armour for tank repairs as additional plating beneath structures. Several have even requested their Adeptus Mechanicus allies to install seismographic equipment, so that they might be aware of any unusual motions beneath them at all times. These reactions are, of course, frowned upon as their expense limits Crusade capabilities even further.

Analysis of compiled imagery and witness reports has met with limited success to identify specific characteristics of this specimen. While it appears that "What Lies Beneath" is larger than other representatives of the Trygon species, a very limited number of additional identifying traits have been found. In the majority of instances, the creature bore a distinctive ventral stripe, but this trait was not confirmed in all attacks. This specimen has also never been confirmed as active on a battlefront within a more traditional engagement. However, it remains possible that field units were unable to distinguish "What Lies Beneath" from a typical Trygon during the course of a battlefield encounter.

A limited number of orbital images include evidence of a Trygon that is twenty percent larger than the median size. In all instances, this specimen was observed behind the swarm's front lines. However, these Tyranid creatures seldom spend a substantial time upon a planet's surface. As a consequence, consistent scaling information is exceptionally difficult to obtain and may be inaccurate. Further, any ventral markings are generally obscured from orbital cameras.

There are numerous reports of this specimen dying in engagements. Many of these reports come from different systems. Further, there have been a number of attacks that match the creature's tactical profile on different worlds, which are estimated to have occurred within days of one another. These data call into question whether it is a unique specimen or just a variant strain specific to Hive Fleet Dagon. While either explanation could offer a valid conclusion, neither possibility is one that appeals to Orpheus Salient command elements.

"What Lies Beneath" (Master)

WS	BS	S	T	Ag	Int	Per	WP	Fel
55	35	(18) 64	(18) 62	40	32	43	52	—

Movement: 4/8/16/32   **Wounds:** 160

Skills: Awareness (Per), Psyniscience (Per) +10, Swim (S), Tracking (Int).

Talents: Ambidextrous, Combat Master, Fearless, Furious Assault, Heightened Senses (Hearing, Touch), Lightning Attack, Psy Rating (5), Swift Attack, Two weapon Wielder (Melee), Warp Sense.

Traits: Burrower (3), Crawler, Dark Sight, Fear 4 (Terrifying), Improved Natural Weapons (Scything Talons), Multiple Arms, Natural Armour (Thickened scales), Size (Massive), Shadow in the Warp, Synapse Creature, Unnatural Strength (x3), Unnatural Toughness (x3). Unnatural Senses (Ground sense, Smell)†, Tyranid.

Armour: Thickened Scales (All 10).

Weapons: Scything Talons (1d10+20 R; Pen 3), Bio-Electric pulse (Basic; 60m; –/–/12; 2d10+6 E; Pen 4; Clip –; Rld –; Storm, Living Ammunition).

Special Rules

†Ground Sense: "What Lies Beneath" can detect enemies while burrowed, through the vibrations they make. It can easily detect anything in contact with the ground within 15 metres and receives a +10 bonus to tracking prey in constant motion. Large vehicles and similar give greater bonuses.

Catalyst (Psychic Power): As a Half Action, "What Lies Beneath" may send out a signal from the Hive Mind that infuses lesser Tyranid creatures with an unnatural vitality. This power may be used on a single Tyranid Horde within 75 metres: until the beginning of the "What Lies Beneath"'s next turn, the Horde gains 10+1d10 Magnitude.

The Horror (Psychic Power): As a Half Action, "What Lies Beneath" may unleash a wave of horror that gnaws at the resolve of its enemies. This power may be used to target a Kill-team within 75 metres. Each member of the Kill-team within the range of this power must take a Willpower test with a –30 modifier. The Kill-team takes one point of cohesion damage per member that fails this test. All other non-Tyranid (and non-Space Marine) NPCs within range of "What Lies Beneath" must pass a fear-based Willpower Test with a –30 modifier or flee in panic.

Classification: Achilus Crusade Code Ruby
Date: 524816.M41
Author: General Derian Arkelius
Subject: Volatile Supply Storage
Recipient: All Orpheus Salient Field Commands

Analysts believe that xenos forces may have identified a method for tracking volatile supplies, including promethium, ammunition, and explosives. There have been two incidents in which critical stores were lost due to unexpected attacks within purportedly secure regions. These losses are completely unacceptable and must not be permitted to recur.

To eliminate this threat, elements within the Orpheus Salient are hereby ordered to cease storage of volatile reserves on any planetary surface. Moving forward, no depot is to maintain more than a three day supply of fuel or ammunition for the units under its jurisdiction. Any substances in excess of this quantity are to be transferred to Imperial Navy resources in planetary orbit at the earliest opportunity. Surveys are already being conducted to compare utilisation ratios with current storage capacity.

Navy resources have already been informed of this tactical revision. They are in the process of reconfiguring and reallocating transport shuttles to accommodate the increased workload necessary for the additional resupply flights. To offset this new drain on Imperial resources, Guard units are to restrict their use of naval assets for troop movements. Instead, troops are to use ground-based transport for reassignment whenever possible. Further, additional ground-based reconnaissance efforts are now required. Naval manpower used for aerial reconnaissance has been reassigned to assist with the increase in supply shuttle flights.

I have requested Adeptus Mechanicus agents to begin an investigation and review to identify any modifications that might be made to our existing storage facilities. If their efforts bear fruit, they may identify additional protective measures specifically for the types of attacks that have previously caused our resource loss. In that eventuality, such changes may be implemented, and this order may be rescinded, so that standard resupply procedures may be resumed.

FALL INTO DARKNESS

IV

DEATHWATCH

CHAPTER 4: FALL INTO DARKNESS

"We cannot live through this. Mankind cannot live through this. In a single day they have covered the surface of this planet with a flood of living blades and needle-fanged mouths. Kill one and ten takes its place. If they are truly without number then our race is doomed to a violent death, before every shred of our civilisation is scoured away by a force more voracious than the fires of hell themselves! Death! By the Machine God, Death is here!"

–Last words of Magos Varnak at the fall of Tyran

Wherever the Shadow in the Warp descends upon the Domains of Man, the Great Devourer reduces entire worlds to barren rocks. Every scrap of biological matter is rendered down into a steaming nutrient gruel, collected in vast digestion pools and siphoned into orbit by grazing hive ships, their hideously writhing feeding tubes descending through the clouds to suck the pools dry. So efficient are the Tyranids that many of those warrior-creatures initially bred to take the world are themselves rendered back into the raw material from which they were created, the final stage of the death of a world being a spectacle that no human can surely ever have witnessed. Every Tyranid creature remaining on the surface migrates to the last digestion pool, and throws itself into its churning depths. Thus dissolved to its essential matter, the remains are returned to the hive fleet, to be reused over and over again. At the last, not a single cell of biological origin remains.

To date, the Imperium's energies have been directed towards holding the Tyranid menace at bay, and on occasion to baiting the hive fleets into committing their resources attacking a world that is then immediately destroyed by Exterminatus. Such a drastic tactic sacrifices one world for dozens, and denies the hive fleet an incalculable measure of raw bio-mass.

Numerous worlds have fallen in such a manner, some formerly populated by countless billions of souls, others host to small populations existing beyond the note of the Imperium at large. Some are all but uncatalogued, yet possessed of a human presence of some kind before the coming of the hive fleets. One such world in the Jericho Reach is known to the Deathwatch as Khnum, the seventh sphere in a system that appears in scant few of the Imperium's archives.

Though Khnum supported abundant plant life, it had never birthed autochthonic life. At some point in the distant past however, Khnum must have been marked for potential settlement, for it was host to a small human population. It is probable that the maelstrom of the Age of Strife descended upon the galaxy before the main wave of colonists could be dispatched, for the numbers of the first group were too small to support a viable population. Millennia later, the distant descendants of these settlers lingered still, though regressed to a primitive state far removed from how their own ancestors must have lived. How many more generations this population might have lasted cannot be known, and the Imperium at large was certainly ignorant of their existence. When Hive Fleet Dagon wrapped its tendrils about the world, the Imperium had precious little reason to expend resources defending it, the fleets and armies falling back upon other, more valuable locations.

The fall of the world, known to most in the Crusade's command echelons by no more than a Cartographicae code, passed with barely a comment from the Imperium's planners and commanders. It served as little more than another scrap of data to be fed into the cogitation protocols on which the battles of the Orpheus Salient are built. The war soon passed over Khnum, and the attentions of the planners were drawn to other, more pressing warzones.

Thus, it was something of a surprise when an astropathic distress canto was received, its source somewhere on the surface of Khnum. The signal triggered long dormant and rarely initiated cogitation routines, Crusade command initially rejected the data as flawed or corrupted in some way. Nonetheless, the signal continued, and the tech-priests overseeing the data-mills insisted their cogitation engines were outputting the correct data. Thus confirmed, the signal was shunted up the chain of command, until it appeared on the desk of General Curas' chief of operations. By that time, the Deathwatch was aware of the signal, though how they knew of the cogitation protocols would not be revealed. The Chamber of Vigilance convened, and Watch Captain Avincus was tasked with investigating the source as a matter of urgency. If someone had somehow survived the death of an entire world at the hands of the Great Devourer, the Imperium needed to know how. Rescuing the sender of the distress canto would be secondary to gaining that knowledge, it was ordered.

LINKING FALL INTO DARKNESS
WITH OTHER PUBLISHED MISSIONS

Several published adventures pitch the Space Marines against the creatures of Hive Fleet Dagon, notably Extraction (see the **DEATHWATCH** Rulebook) and Final Sanction (which can be downloaded from the Fantasy Flight Games website). If the Kill-team has played either or both of these missions, Fall into Darkness would serve well as a continuation of the ongoing theme of the battle against the Great Devourer. In addition, both of these missions explore events leading up to and during the early stages of a Tyranid invasion. Fall into Darkness, however, describes events taking place in the final stages of planetary consumption, and as such would make an ideal climax to a string of missions against the Tyranids. After Fall into Darkness, the focus of the campaign might shift to other enemies, as discussed in the section headed "Further Adventures."

GM's Brief

Fall into Darkness is a Deathwatch adventure that pitches the player characters straight into the nightmarish environment of a world all but consumed by the Tyranids. Though once a living planet, complete with forests, oceans, an atmosphere and rudimentary animal life forms, Khnum is now a desiccated, violated husk, the last of its vast resources of bio-mass rendered down into steaming digestion pools. Even the air is fast vanishing, and the landscape is covered with obscenely pulsing, root-like matter transferring the last of the planet's chemical resources to the pools. If the landscape is perilous, those Tyranids that yet stalk it are doubly so. Every manner of genetic nightmare rules the wastes, ever watchful for some intruder foolish enough to set foot upon the surface of a world dying in the most horrendous manner possible.

The player characters are tasked with locating the source of the distress signal, which has been traced to someone on, or below the surface of Khnum. They must penetrate the atmosphere, avoiding or defeating numerous airborne creatures, locate the source, and ascertain its nature. Their orders are to rescue anyone they might find on Khnum, though in truth this is no mercy mission. If someone has found a way of surviving the death of a world, the Imperium needs to know about it, at any cost.

The Kill-team have no idea as to who the source of the signal might be, only that it includes a high level clearance code and as such must be investigated fully. The source is in fact a highly ranked tech-priest of the Adeptus Mechanicus, a member of an obscure order of xenobiologists who have made it their business to turn their expertise towards the defeat of the Tyranid menace. The tech-priest has constructed an impenetrable bunker so far beneath the surface that it is suspended in the world's superheated mantle. Though he intended only to observe the processes by which a world is consumed, the tech-priest has found what he believes to be a weakness, and one that with the help of Imperial forces he could exploit. He has synthesised a unique gene-keyed toxin, which he claims could slow or even halt the advance of Hive Fleet Dagon if it can be introduced into the digestion pool from which the hive fleet is even now replenishing itself. And that is where the Kill-team comes in…

Introducing the Mission

Fall into Darkness can be used as a "standalone" adventure that has little or no connection to previous adventures, as, after all, the Kill-teams of the Deathwatch are routinely dispatched to every corner of the Jericho Reach and beyond, following the orders passed down to them from the Chamber of Vigilance.

Fall into Darkness would work especially well in the context of a series of battles set in the Orpheus Salient, especially if the Kill-team is based, for a time at least, at Watch Station Arkhas. The following are several ideas the GM could use to tie the mission into a wider campaign:

War Without End: If the Kill-team has already fought any battles against the leading forces of Hive Fleet Dagon, the Kill-team might find itself passing through the Khnum system, perhaps aboard Watch Station Phaedas. The mission briefing could therefore take the form of a transmission from Watch Station Arkhas, or it could take place via a messenger, or even Watch Captain Avincus.

Cry in the Night: The mission is precipitated by the astropathic distress canto transmitted from the world of Khnum. It is possible that instead of this signal being detected elsewhere, it is the Kill-team itself that discovers it, perhaps during a preceding mission. Upon their return to base, the message can be passed on, resulting in the Kill-team being immediately re-tasked with investigating.

Unanticipated Allies: Some groups like to include characters other than Space Marines in their Kill-teams, perhaps having an Inquisitor, Assassin or other such player character join the Kill-team. If this is the case, it could be the character in question who has been contacted by the institution they represent, and that communication leads to the mission being launched. Perhaps an Adeptus Mechanicus tech-priest has been informed of the possibility of hereteks operating in the region, or an Inquisitor has learned of Magos Klute's activities in other sectors and traced him to the Jericho Reach.

SYNOPSIS

Fall into Darkness is organised in three parts, each of which presents a set of encounters and challenges. Between them, the three segments represent a range of challenges, from investigation and evasion, to interaction and combat.

PART 1: RUINS OF A WORLD

The Battle-Brothers arrive in orbit around the world of Khnum, and must pilot their vessel to the surface. In so doing they must avoid, outrun or defeat numerous airborne Tyranid constructs, and narrow down the location from which the mysterious distress signal is being broadcast. Having tracked the signal to a specific region, they must set down and continue the search on foot. Part 1 ends when the source of the signal is pinpointed.

PART 2: WHAT LURKS BENEATH

In the second phase of Fall into Darkness, the Kill-team discovers just who the source of the distress signal is, but only once they have overcome the numerous defences built into the approach to the bunker. The tech-priest is Adept Erlan Klute, and while he is not entirely forthcoming about it, he is in fact a virtual outcast from his order, due to the unorthodox nature of some of his theories. Klute petitions the Kill-team to deliver the toxic payload he has developed, and in so doing potentially end the Tyranid invasion of the Jericho Reach once and for all.

PART 3: BAD MEDICINE

The mission reaches a dramatic climax as the Battle-Brothers penetrate the heart of the Tyranid swarm and locate the last digestion pool, to which they must administer Magos Klute's gene-toxin. But events take an unexpected turn when the toxin has a far more dramatic effect than anticipated, and the adept's true loyalties are revealed, leaving the Kill-team fighting for their lives to escape a world of death!

KHNUM–WORLD OF DEATH

The world designated in the Codex Cartographicae as DXX738-1222-7/ was once a verdant orb swathed in lush, dense forests and fertile plains. The shallow, warm oceans supported an abundance of aquatic creatures, and the lands were host to sufficient grazers to support the dwindling human population that lingered from the Age of Strife.

While the world held no specific relevance to the Imperium at large, the Deathwatch have, for several centuries, had a name for it—Khnum. This name appears in but a single stellar archive of the Jericho Reach, held by the Deathwatch, having been recovered from the Omega Vault. The archive in question depicted the world at a very specific point in its progression through the local stellar group, allowing the Deathwatch to ascertain not only the place to which the coordinates related, but the time as well. Thus, when the astropathic distress canto was received, the Deathwatch were already scrutinising the region in question, the Chamber of Vigilance standing ready to react to unfolding events.

What none, including the Deathwatch, are aware of is that the archives are incorrect in their assertion that no human life is present on Khnum. In fact, the world is host to a clandestine Adeptus Mechanicus facility, and one created under such secrecy that even the adherents of the Cult Mechanicus active in the Orpheus Salient were ignorant of it. The facility is a magma-warded, armoured bunker, sunk fifty kilometres beneath the surface of Khnum. So deep is the bunker that it is not encased by solid rock, but by shifting, super-heated magma, marking it as a feat of engineering only seen in the most strategically vital command centres and strategiums in the entire galaxy. That such a facility was constructed at all was exceptional, but that it should have been built without the knowledge of other Adeptus Mechanicus members in the region is an indication that its creator was at once supremely secretive, and pathologically mistrustful of his peers.

That creator was a Magos Biologis called Adept Erlan Klute, and the construction of the facility was achieved only because the xenologis was an adherent of an obscure sub-order within the Adeptus Mechanicus. Erlan and many likeminded members of the Adeptus Mechanicus studied the work of Magos Varnak, the tech-priest who first catalogued the Tyranids and who fell on the world after which they are named—Tyran. Calling themselves the Circle Varnak, these individuals set about the formation of an order entirely dedicated to pursuing the most drastic of responses to the rapidly unfolding Tyranid threat. Through a mixture of secrecy, bitterness, and what they of course saw as necessity, the Circle Varnak soon found themselves operating beyond the pale of the Cult Mechanicus. They unlocked archives and vaults that had long been sealed, hunting down any possible weapon they could utilise against their extra-galactic foe. In so doing, Erlan and his peers have effectively set themselves up as outcast hereteks, and were their deeds known to the Cult Mechanicus, they would almost certainly be denounced as such.

With a prescience that speaks of knowledge obtained by methods bordering on the heretical, Erlan's facility was completed less than a month before the first vanguard organisms of Hive Fleet Dagon appeared on the world's surface. So well hidden was the bunker that even the preternatural senses of the Lictors and other creatures that moved unseen across the surface detected no trace of it. Erlan and his staff watched from their hiding place as the skies above the mighty primordial forests turned dark and Mycetic Spores rained down. He remained silent as clouds of Gargoyles descended and waves of Hormagaunts fell upon the primitive human population. Erlan lifted not a finger as the Tyranids butchered the natives, for their fate was none of his concern. Rather, he regarded the spectacle as an opportunity to observe the Tyranids harvesting a sentient population, his remote spy drones recording every detail of the battle.

Yet, the natives of Khnum put up a far stauncher defence than the adept had predicted, affording him the opportunity to observe how the Hive Mind adapted to such circumstances. While they suffered grievously in the first days of the invasion, the natives rallied well, the tribes uniting against the horrors that had descended from the stars. In response, the Hive Mind created more of the beasts needed to subdue them, and soon the forests of Khnum were bloody battlefields as the population fought for its very survival.

The natives were doomed of course, for the hive fleet's resources were all but unlimited and the primitive humans had no weapons more effective than spears and bows. Wave after wave of Tyranid warrior constructs overwhelmed the natives, until at last the main strength of their armies was broken. The last warriors went to ground, fleeing into forests mutated into the hyper-evolved vegetation of Tyranid consumption, there to continue a desperate guerrilla war they had no hope of winning.

Magos Klute was fascinated by the spectacle of these last holdouts launching all but suicidal attacks upon the Tyranids, and he watched in awe as the Hive Mind concocted ever more effective countermeasures to track them down. Every manner of beast was utilised in the hunt, and often used in ways that had never been witnessed before. Lumbering bio-Titans stalked the dying lands, crushing any potential hiding place, while Malanthropes used their own vile sensory abilities to track down the last of the population. Though their defence was worthy of the deeds of many of the Imperium's greatest heroes, the defenders were at last silenced. But Magos Klute had gathered numerous observations of the manner in which the Hive Mind operated in the closing phases of a world's consumption, especially as relates to the process by which the genetic material of those who resist is harvested and then used against them. The sights Erlan witnessed in Khoum's dying days would have driven a lesser man insane, but as a servant of the Omnissiah, and one dedicated to the defeat of the Hive Mind at any cost, there were no depths to which he would not descend. Formulating a plan, Klute ordered his astropath to transmit a distress signal and to call in aid, and somehow she succeeded in breaching the Shadow in the Warp, the canto ringing out across the Jericho Reach.

GM GUIDANCE: A WORLD OF DEATH

It is important that the players appreciate that their characters can never afford to let down their guard whilst operating in the surface of Khnum, for death awaits them at every turn and in hundreds of unfamiliar forms. The most innocuous of actions can lead to a Battle-Brother's armour being compromised, hordes of Tyranids being attracted or the very ground opening up beneath his feet. The GM should remind the players of this by keeping them on their toes, perhaps calling for Awareness Tests right in the middle of other actions, conversations or lulls in the mission. Some examples of the consequences of failing such tests follow:

MICROBIAL THREATS

Every square inch of the surface of Khnum is crawling with xenos microbes, and while they may not be visible, their presence can certainly be felt. Should a Space Marine be injured and his armour compromised, these microbes are likely to find their way into his armour, and potentially into his system, despite his superhuman physiology. At the least, a **Challenging (-0) Toughness Test** should be taken for every hour or so that a compromised suit of armour remains damaged, making the skills of a Techmarine in repairing such damage especially valuable. Failure of these Toughness Tests should not result in huge amounts of damage, but a cumulative –5 Penalty to any Skill Tests based on Strength, Willpower, Agility and similar characteristics would certainly be appropriate. If the armour cannot be repaired then an Apothecary could attempt to counter the microbes' effects using his own specialised Skills, as the GM deems appropriate.

CHOKING CLOUDS

The skies above Khnum are choked with spores, as well as the by-products of the planetary consumption process. Any Space Marine breathing in such air without the benefit of a rebreather or his helmet systems should risk taking damage, perhaps using the same mechanic as described above. Towards the end of the mission, such clouds might choke the land itself, and so instances when an exposed Battle-Brother might have to test to avoid their effects should get more frequent.

WRITHING ROOTS

The ground over which the Battle-Brothers must travel is in places alive with a mass of writhing, vine-like organisms, which harvest every last mineral and nutrient from the ground and transport it towards the vast digestion pools. Though ever-present and not especially dangerous most of the time, they should occasionally represent a threat by counting as Treacherous terrain (see page 206 of the DEATHWATCH rulebook).

QUAKES

Khnum is being consumed in every way possible, and the vast tendrils plunging into its surface in search of valuable organisms and minerals cause the ground to tremble in a manner that cannot be predicted. The GM should remind the players of this frequently, and every now and then ramp the tremors up so that they make movement across even open ground harder (see Table 7-6: Treacherous Environment Agility Modifiers on page 206 of the DEATHWATCH rulebook).

ACID STREAMS

The bio-mass of Khnum is being slowly rendered down into a bubbling, acidic gruel, and much of this vile liquid is present on the surface as streams, and even rivers, wending their way towards the vast digestion pools. Every now and then, the Kill-team might be presented with the need to cross such an obstacle. In most cases it is possible to cross without the acid coming into contact with the Space Marines' armour, but if they should have to wade across, or otherwise find themselves exposed directly to the liquid, each location contacted takes an automatic hit inflicting 1d10 Damage (Pen 4) every turn, reducing to 1d5 (Pen 2) for a further d5 turns after the contact ends.

UNNATURAL HAZARDS

Khnum is a world in the final stages of Tyranid consumption, and as such its surface is inimical to all but the hardiest forms of life. Any creature not exuding the pheromones of Hive Fleet Dagon will be assailed at every level possible, from ravaging microbes to gargantuan bio-Titans. Vile Malanthropes taste the air for traces of genetic material not emanating from a Tyranid creature, and myriad other threats face any foolish enough to intrude.

A LANDSCAPE OF DEATH

The surface of Khnum bears no resemblance to its former state. Where once mighty forests clothed the hills and plains, now a rampant mass of hyper-evolved vegetation is being rendered down by a sprawling mass of what appears a hybrid of root and vein. These structures range in size from the minute to the truly massive, the smallest easily crushed underfoot and the largest a considerable impediment to an intruder's progress. These pulsing roots are all interconnected, forming a planetwide network that penetrates the surface soil, harvesting every last shred of nutrient from the planet. When at last their work is done, the roots themselves will be consumed by bacterial action, the resulting sludge harvested by the grazer ships in orbit high above.

While the mass of root structures writhing across the desiccated surface are not dangerous in themselves, other features most certainly are. The ground beneath an intruder's feet might be solid rock, in which case it is of little interest to the Tyranids, but it might be nutrient rich soil. In that case, it may have been hollowed out into a honeycomb that might collapse at the slightest pressure, plunging the intruder down into a winding tunnel network if he is fortunate, or into a deep chasm filled with digestive acid if he is not.

Further hazards include the ever present spore chimneys and capillary towers that are scattered across the surface of Khnum, many of which constantly belch forth columns of choking gas. Others are possessed of vile womb-pods, from which a wave of Rippers or similar creatures can emerge having been hyper-gestated in response to an intrusion.

SERVANTS OF THE HIVE MIND

The natives of Khnum mounted a fierce resistance to what proved the death of their world. While initially many fell to the waves of Hormagaunts and Termagants sent against them, the primitives soon organised themselves into large armies, against which the Hive Mind was forced to send ever larger and more destructive beasts. Many of the same beasts that the forces of the Imperium have faced in the Orpheus Salient were fielded on Kknum, though in far different proportions than when the Hive Mind is presented with the extent of Humanity's arsenal. Against primitives armed with bow and spear, the Hive Mind fielded very different forces to when it engages troops armed with tanks and missiles. By focusing on creatures armed with rapid-firing, ranged weaponry, the Hive Mind decimated the defenders' forces, broods of Gargoyles as thick and black as thunderheads unleashing withering storms of fleshborer fire upon the tragically vulnerable natives.

Such tactics resulted in the skies over Khnum being overrun with Gargoyles and other airborne constructs, the result being the total collapse of the defending armies. When the natives devolved into smaller guerrilla bands, the Hive Mind reacted by fielded other types of beasts, and these too still infest the surface of the planet. Any intruder upon Khnum must first penetrate the Gargoyle-plagued skies, before avoiding the mighty beasts that are the undisputed masters of the desiccated wastes.

The Tyranid creatures present on Khnum are not massed into coherent swarms, for at this stage in the planet's consumption they are rarely required to face an organised foe. Instead, the Hive Mind has scattered them across the surface, searching out any lingering pockets of resistance and standing vigil against potential intrusion. As far as the Hive Mind is aware, the last of the native guerrillas has been slain, its genetic material harvested and its remains added to the acidic slurry of the digestion pools. Certainly, no such resistance has been encountered for several weeks, and so many of the Tyranid beasts have entered a semi-dormant state, not actively hunting yet ever watchful for enemies.

UNSEEN KILLERS

While it might appear to an intruder that the most numerous Tyranid beasts are the Rippers that swarm across the wastes and the Gargoyles that swoop through the clouds, these are outnumbered a trillion times over by the microbial life forms unleashed by the Hive Fleet. In the opening phases of the consumption, the primary function of these unseen creatures was to deliver hybridising payloads to native plant life forms, in particular the most abundant forms of flora covering the surface. In an instant, the most common of native plants were transformed into a hideous crossbreed, growing at a blistering rate to overwhelm natives and their settlements. Later on, the mutated flora itself was attacked by a second wave of Tyranid microbes, broken down into the nutrient rich gruel that is sucked up by the root structures sprawled across the land and massed at the vast digestion pools.

These microbes remain active long into the final phases of the consumption process, and they are present anywhere and everywhere an intruder might go. The very air is laced with their taint, and the ground carpeted by the invisible swarms. While not specifically created to attack intruders, the effects of these microbes are nonetheless incapacitating to most non-Tyranid life forms. Once they enter the system, the microbes begin to attack the host's body, and should any of the hybridising strain find their way in, the result is likely to be a rapid and hideous mutation in which the intruder's body is transformed into something resembling the capillary towers and spore chimneys already scattered about the wastes. Fortunately, very few intruders are likely to survive the attentions of the numerous warrior beasts roaming the land, and they are spared such a grisly death.

ENVIRONMENTAL HAZARDS

On a world rapidly approaching its final death throes at the hands of Tyranid consumption, even the weather is hazardous to everything but the constructs of the Hive Mind. The air is toxic and in places so blisteringly hot that to breath it would sear the lungs. The ground is threaded with rivers of digestive acid running towards the vast digestion pools and the surface is wracked by earthquakes as the subsoil is mined for every last nutrient. All that now lies in store for Khnum is the siphoning off of its oceans, followed at the last by the grazer vessels stealing its very atmosphere. By the end of it all, Khnum will be a barren, airless rock, with only those artificial constructs made of utterly inert and unusable materials left behind to bear witness that man ever dwelled there.

PART 1: RUINS OF A WORLD

While the action could begin earlier or later, the most dramatic way of beginning the adventure is to kick things off as the Kill-team begins its descent from orbit into what remains of Khnum's atmosphere. The player characters are travelling in a Stormraven Gunship, and as such one or more of their number might be able to play a direct role in the insertion, depending on what skills and specialisations the team has. Even if none of the Kill-team take a direct hand in the operation, the situation is sufficiently tense and dramatic that it would be a shame not to use it to set the tone of the mission to come.

Read aloud or paraphrase the following:

> *The interior of the Stormraven is filled with raucous sirens as the gunship's machine spirits warn of imminent planetfall. Your squad has completed last minute armour and restraint checks and recited the prayers of orbital deployment, and now the interior bucks and shakes as the gunship hits the target world's outer atmosphere. As the heat rises and flames lick the view port, you mouth the last lines of your prayers, surrendering yourself to the planetfall.*
>
> *The next ten minutes are all sound and fury as every surface vibrates violently. The heat rises and your helmet displays inform you that you are experiencing forces that would turn a normal man to boneless pulp. But you are Space Marines, and this is what you were created to do. All too soon, the tremors subside and the flames enveloping the gunship's exterior fade away, affording you your first glimpse of the surface of the target world.*
>
> *Truly, the Great Devourer has desecrated this place. A landscape once swathed in verdant forests and fertile plains is now reduced to barren wastes, the bilious yellow-green fog of the consumption process casting all in an actinic glow. Rivers of digestive fluid snake across the violated land, while twisting capillary towers stretch up into the air. Spore chimneys disgorge thick, noxious columns of vapour, and dark flocks of airborne creatures are visible in the distance.*
>
> *The time for prayers is over. Now is the time for bold deeds, for the mission is all.*

THE MISSION BRIEFING

The Battle-Brothers have been fully briefed on the mission they are undertaking, and are well prepared for whatever might await them on the surface of Khnum. The players, however, need to know what's going on before getting too far into the mission. This can be handled by informing the players before the mission gets underway, and a great way of doing this is to circulate a summary of the briefing to the players before the session even begins. That way, everyone knows what to expect and the GM can dive straight into the action without preamble. However, this isn't always possible or preferable, so once the orbital insertion is complete the main points of the briefing can be communicated. This could be achieved by way of a pause in the action where the GM oversees a "flash back" to the mission briefing, a cinematic technique entirely appropriate to the pace and tone of the mission, or he could simply seed various points in as the action progresses.

Whichever of the techniques is used, the key points that the players need to know are as follows:

A tendril of Hive Fleet Dagon has overrun the world of Khnum. The commanders of the Orpheus Salient allowed this to happen unopposed, as there were no assets on the world worth defending. However, an astropathic distress signal bearing high-level ciphers has been detected, emanating from the surface of the world. To penetrate the Shadow in the Warp, the astropath sending the message must be powerful indeed.

The Kill-team has been dispatched to investigate the source of the distress signal. Their primary concern is to discover how the sender survived the fall of the world, and if possible to recover any relevant details.

If possible, the sender of the message should be retrieved. The sender is to be treated with suspicion, as whoever he is, he was operating beyond the knowledge and authority of any of the Crusade's command structures.

The Kill-team is being inserted by Stormraven, and must locate the region the signal is emanating from before setting down.

GM GUIDANCE:
INFILTRIOL ENAMEL

Players with access to the **RITES OF BATTLE** supplement are likely to request the use of Infiltriol Enamel for this mission, and it would certainly be an appropriate use for this exotic material. By coating a sealed suit of armour in this especially formulated bio-masking substance, Space Marines can make themselves all but invisible to the lower orders of Tyranid constructs, allowing them to travel almost unchallenged across worlds such as Khnum. However, the use of this item could complicate the GM's plans for the adventure, so it pays to be prepared for its use.

Should the players use Infiltriol, the GM should keep two points in mind, but he need not communicate these to the players. Firstly, the Kill-team is likely to be operational on the surface of Khnum for quite some time—longer in fact than the substance has ever been tested for. Infiltriol must be reapplied every 1d10+10 hours, and doing so is no simple task that can be carried out on the battlefield. It is suggested that the Kill-team only be allowed to reapply the Infiltriol once they have reached Magos Klute's bunker, and doing so requires a **Hard (-20) Tech-Use Test**.

The second consideration is one of escalating threat. If the players are successful in their use of the substance they should be rewarded for their cleverness, but the GM should make it clear that when the Tyranids do eventually attack they may do so in far larger numbers. For example, the Kill-team might fool three broods of Tyranid creatures, only for a fourth to pass its Awareness Test and detect their presence—at that point, all four broods might attack at once, making the use of the substance a definite two-edged sword.

Having set down, the Stormraven will head back into orbit, to await the order to return and extract the Kill-team.

The precise source of the signal must be located on foot, whilst every precaution is taken not to alert the Tyranids of the Kill-team's presence.

Once the source of the signal is discovered, the Stormraven must be recalled and extraction undertaken.

The Deathwatch frigate *Silent Vigil* is holding station in the outer reaches of the system, but can only approach Khnum for long enough to insert and extract the Kill-team, due to the high density of Tyranid hive vessels. The Stormraven must evade these and rendezvous with the frigate.

OBJECTIVES

Before the mission progresses too far, the GM should oversee the preparatory stages, as described on page 226 of the **DEATHWATCH** rulebook. The team must decide upon a leader and an Oath must be taken. The GM must assign a Requisition level, (suggested 75 to 140 based on which tertiary objectives the GM intends to use) and Mission Complications can be determined if the GM wishes. Given the limited knowledge the Deathwatch has of the situation on the surface or Khnum, the objectives the Kill-team start out with are fairly straightforward. As the mission progresses, further objectives will present themselves. As with the mission briefing, a lot of this stage can be dealt with before the session begins, or handled as a "flash back" once the introduction is complete.

Primary Objective: Locate and identify the source of the distress signal. This is by far the single most important objective. The Deathwatch and the Inquisition need to know how the sender survived as long as he did, and while the Kill-team itself is not necessarily expected to ascertain this information, it can only begin to be gleaned once the source of the signal is located. (Veteran Objective, 30 Requisition)

Secondary Objective: Retrieve the sender of the distress signal. The Battle-Brothers are not angels of mercy and their mission is not to rescue the sender out of altruism. If possible, the sender of the distress signal should be retrieved alive so that the Inquisition can investigate matters further in their own way. (Veteran Objective, 25 Requisition)

Tertiary Objectives (and personal goals): Throughout the mission, numerous encounters are sprung on the players that can lead to the introduction of tertiary objectives or the fulfilment of personal goals. Some of these are explained in the sections that follow, while others can be expanded as the GM sees fit. Some suggested examples are:

Bear Witness: The Battle-Brothers are likely to see things that none have ever encountered and survived to recount. One of their number might be designated as responsible for maintaining an auspex log of events, to be passed on to the Inquisition and their savants upon the team's return. (Novice Objective, 6 Requisition)

Kill-count: While the primary and secondary missions must at all costs come first, the Kill-team should be on the lookout for targets of opportunity, especially during the extraction phase. (Novice Objective, 6 Requisition)

The Better Part of Valour: In the early phases of the mission, stealth is far more important than strength of arms.

Outwitting the enemy and suppressing the urge to open fire at the first opportunity should prove worthwhile. (Skilled Objective, 10 Requisition)

The Source: If a Librarian detects the region the signal is being transmitted from using his Psyniscience Skill, this should be counted as the attainment of a personal goal. (Skilled Objective, 10 Requisition)

Heretic: If a Battle-Brother determines that Magos Erlan Klute cannot be trusted, and acts to mitigate potential treachery, this should be rewarded. (Skilled Objective, 10 Requisition)

Re-tasking: If the Kill-team decides to deliver Klute's gene-toxin, and succeeds in doing so, this should garner additional reward. (Veteran Objective, 15 Requisition)

For your own good: Though not explicitly stated in their mission briefing, the Kill-team might take it upon themselves to rescue (or rather detain!) all of Adept Erlan's staff, not just the sender of the distress signal. (Novice Objective, 6 Requisition)

Astropath Xhenek: If any of the Battle-Brothers detect Astropath Xhenek's call at the end of the mission, they must decide on the appropriate response. (Novice Objective, 6 Requisition)

Magos Erlan Klute: Additional rewards should be granted if the Kill-team actually confronts the Magos and defeats him in combat. (Skilled Objective, 10 Requisition)

COMPLICATIONS

Orbital insertion under combat conditions is a perilous operation at the best of times, but the Kill-team has no idea what awaits it beneath the churning clouds covering the surface of Khnum. As soon as the Stormraven breaks through the clouds and into the open sky, it is likely to attract the attention of airborne Tyranids in the region. One of the player characters may operate the Stormraven's auspex array, or if the group prefers an NPC pilot can do so. This individual has two primary concerns throughout this phase of the operation. The most immediate is to warn of approaching Tyranids, and to avoid or defeat them as deemed appropriate. If a threat cannot be avoided or defeated, it soon escalates. A small brood of Gargoyles, for example, will swiftly attract more if it is not avoided or wiped out in short order. At length, more dangerous foes yet are likely to be attracted, and if that happens the mission may well be over before it has even begun.

The second, but ultimately more important task, is to locate the region from which the distress signal is being transmitted. This could be anywhere on the planet so the Battle-Brothers have their work cut out as they seek the target zone.

ESCALATING ENGAGEMENT

In order to avoid the attentions of the numerous broods of Gargoyles, and other larger beasts, the character responsible for the Stormraven's auspex array must make a series of Awareness Tests, with failure indicating an encounter as presented below.

When the Stormraven first enters the skies of Khnum, the Tyranids are not expecting intrusion and none are present in the gunship's immediate vicinity. The character manning the auspex array should take a **Challenging (+0) Awareness Test**. Success locates a brood of Gargoyles several kilometres distant and allows the pilot to steer well clear of it.

The test should be repeated every hour or so of narrative time. Keep a tally of how many times it is passed, as once this reaches a total of five passes, the source of the signal has been narrowed down to a broad region and the Stormraven must set down. However, each time the test is failed, consult **Table 4-1: Aerial Complications** to determine what complications arise.

AERIAL COMBAT

The following mechanics are used to resolve combat between the Stormraven and airborne Tyranid beasts:

The gunship is armed with a front-mounted, twin-linked assault cannon (Range 150m, −/−/10, 3d10+6 I, Pen 6, Clip 300, Reload 3 Full, Tearing, Twin-linked), twin-linked heavy bolters (Range 150m, Heavy, −/−/10, 2d10+10 X, Pen 6, Clip 400, Tearing, Twin-linked), and four missiles (Facing Front, Range 750m, S/−/−, 4d10+6 X, Pen 14, each missile can only be fired once). One character (player or NPC) pilots the gunship and operates the heavy bolters and missiles, while another mans the overhead turret and may also operate the other weapon systems. A third character may operate the auspex array from a position in the crew compartment, while all the remainder of the team can do is hold on tight.

While the gunship's movement is handled abstractly, the firing of its weapons should be handled by the characters themselves. The pilot or gunner may only fire one weapon system per turn, though the pilot may shoot and still make Pilot Skill Tests. Shooting is carried out using the firer's Ballistic Skill, and suffers an additional −20 modifier unless the firer has the Pilot Skill in regards to the gunship. The only firing options are Attack, Semi-Auto Burst and Full-Auto Burst (see pages 236-243 of the **DEATHWATCH** rulebook). These Actions provide their standard bonuses to shooting, which can mitigate the innate penalty (weight of fire often counting more than accuracy in a gunfight).

While the Gargoyles are themselves unable to damage the Stormraven, the real danger lies in the fact that combat against them is likely to attract larger beasts, such as a Harridan. Both types of beast will follow the gunship in to the landing zone, and present a significant threat once the Kill-team has disembarked.

TABLE 4-1: AERIAL COMPLICATIONS

Degrees of Failure	Complication
1	The augur returns inclusive readings, making the course ahead uncertain.
2	A brood of Gargoyles (see page 237) descends from the clouds. If the brood is not entirely destroyed within three Rounds, the next Awareness Test becomes one level of Difficulty harder.
3	Two Harpies (see page 174) descend upon the Stormraven. If they are not destroyed within three Rounds, the next Awareness Test becomes one level of Difficulty harder.
4	A Harridan (see page 177) appears at the extent of auspex range and veers towards the Stormraven. The pilot must make a **Very Hard (−30) Pilot (Flyer) Test** to avoid the beast, or it will attack the gunship next turn.
5	A Harridan appears right on the gunship's tail having swooped down from an unanticipated quarter. The beast remains on the Stormraven's tail (at around 100m) and cannot be shaken off, though it never quite gets close enough range to attack the gunship. If the beast is still following when the gunship lands, it (or indeed they) attack the Battle-Brothers as soon as they disembark.

VEHICLES IN DEATHWATCH

This mission presents a simple set of rules for evading or engaging the airborne broods and beasts using the sensors and weapons of the Kill-team's Stormraven gunship. Groups with access to the RITES OF BATTLE supplement might like to use the more detailed rules for vehicles presented there, though this is not necessary to resolve the encounter.

LOCATING THE LANDING ZONE

In addition to avoiding the attentions of the airborne Tyranid beasts and fighting off those that latch onto the gunship, the Battle-Brothers must scan the surface of Khnum to establish a landing zone close enough to the source of the signal to continue on foot. There are two ways of achieving this.

If the Kill-team contains a Librarian, he may make a **Challenging (+0) Psyniscience Test** in order to home in on the Astropathic signal. In order to pinpoint the landing zone, the Librarian must pass five tests, one per hour of narrative time spent in the air. Failing a test has no ill effect other than to delay the mission, which may in itself result in more enemy creatures detecting the gunship's presence.

If the Kill-team has no Librarian, the process is far harder—after all, if the Tyranids have not yet discovered the hidden bunker then it is likely to be far from easy for the Kill-team to do so. However, it should still be possible, by the application of the human logic that the Tyranids lack. After all, the Battle-Brothers know there's a bunker hidden somewhere beneath the surface, and that should prove a starting point. One way is the use of the gunship's auspex array to detect energy emissions, but as the bunker is well hidden, shielded, and masked by hundreds of metres of raging magma this requires a **Punishing (-50) Search Test**. The GM should allow this test to be retaken every hour, and near-fails (within one Degree of Failure) should result in the next test being one Difficulty level easier.

Obviously, the Kill-team has to find the bunker for the mission to proceed, but this should not be presented as a foregone conclusion. Instead, any delay or failed tests should result in an escalation of threat and tension, really putting the pressure on the group to locate the bunker. Ultimately, failure is entirely possible, for if the Kill-team attracts large numbers of Tyranids, they may simply be unable to defeat them all and proceed any further, or they may find themselves taking unsustainable losses. Such is the harsh reality of service in the Deathwatch…

TOUCHDOWN

Having landed, the first thing the Battle-Brothers need to do is secure their immediate perimeter. It is possible that a number of Gargoyles or even Harridans may have followed them in, in which case now is the time these beasts strike. Only when the immediate surroundings are cleared of the enemy is it safe to proceed on foot, and for the Kill-team to familiarise itself with the lay of the land.

At some point, the Kill-team leader must order the Stormraven to pull out to a safe distance. The plan calls for the gunship to assume a holding pattern in orbit, and to extract the team when the mission is complete. However, the team leader might decide to issue alternative orders, such as ordering the gunship to fly to a position nearby and await his signal, or to provide fire support should the team need it. The GM is encouraged to consider any such requests, but to keep in mind that there will always be consequences to deviating from the mission plan. If the gunship follows the plan and heads back to orbit, it may take a while to respond to the Kill-team's extraction request, but it will be safe while waiting. If it lands in a concealed position nearby, its hiding place may be discovered, and when it does finally respond it has lost weapons or sustained other damage as a result of the attacks it suffered whilst waiting. If the gunship is used to provide the team with fire support, the roar of its weapons systems undoubtedly attracts more enemy beasts, a fact that should soon outweigh the value of any support it can offer.

Once the team has fought off any pursuing beasts and sent the gunship on its way, read aloud or paraphrase the following:

> *Looking around at your surroundings, you find that the surface of the world of Khnum appears even more hellish from the ground than it did from the air. The ground is crawling with writhing, vine-like roots and tiny creatures, little more than stomachs on multiple legs gnaw away at what tiny scraps of bio-mass remain. The land is a blasted desert, columns of yellow-green vapour ghosting across your vision and making it impossible to see more than a hundred metres. Occasionally, the mists part, and you catch a glimpse of the true extent of the world's devastation, before the fog descends mercifully once more.*

The Kill-team is now at liberty to explore the general region from which the astropathic distress signal is being transmitted. Having described the surroundings, the exploration is resolved by way of the encounters that follow. Use as many or as few as is appropriate to keep the action going to everyone's satisfaction. Encounters One to Four are optional, while Encounter Five is used to resolve this part of the mission, and is therefore mandatory.

In addition to the following encounters, keep in mind that the environment itself is hazardous, using the additional rules on page 212 to make the Kill-team's task harder still. These encounters can be set some time and distance apart from one another, and it is important to communicate the fact that the Kill-team is searching across a wide, and very dangerous area.

RED HARVEST (OPTIONAL)

As the Kill-team passes through a jagged mass of rocks intertwined with the ever-present roots of Tyranid consumption, the lead Battle-Brother cannot help but detect movement within the creeping mists up ahead. How the team responds is a matter for the Battle-Brothers to determine, but should they decide to investigate, they discover a Malanthrope (see page 194) moving slowing through the aftermath of what must surely have been a battle to the death. Keep in mind that the Imperium was unaware that the world was host to any natives, human or otherwise, and that the remains cannot be investigated with the vile Malanthrope harvesting them for genetic material.

Should the Kill-team engage and slay the beast, the Battle-Brothers discover an area of ground strewn with the corpses of slain native warriors. It is evident from the patterns and positions in which the corpses are arranged that whoever these primitive warriors were, they died valiantly. The Battle-Brothers see instantly that the fallens' wounds are all to the fore and they died back to back in what must have been a heroic last stand worthy of any battle recounted in Chapter legend. The Battle-Brothers are disgusted to see however that the Malanthrope has reaped a grim harvest amongst the corpses, removing organs and limbs with surgical precision. Should the team contain an Apothecary, he may be able to make further observations regarding the methods these all but unknown Tyranid beasts employ, and pass them on to the Inquisition after the mission. Passing a **Hard (-20) Medicae Test** results in the Apothecary making sufficient observations to count this as the attainment of a Personal Goal. If the test is failed the Apothecary recovers a usable sample, but plays no part in its analysis (this thread might still feed into a future mission however).

Should the idea occur to any of the Battle-Brothers, they could decide to use their Omophagea Implant (see page 36 of the **DEATHWATCH** rulebook) to learn something of the world's fate and temporarily gain an advantage. Doing so grants any Battle-Brother using his implant a portion of the preternatural fieldcraft abilities the natives developed whilst fighting their guerrilla war against the invading swarm, counting as a +10 bonus to Awareness Tests taken to detect the presence of nearby Tyranids (for the duration of this mission only).

INTO THE VALLEY OF DEATH (OPTIONAL)

Crossing the central point of a three hundred metre wide crater laced with drifting mist, the Battle-Brothers detect faint vibrations in the ground beneath their feet. Soon, the vibrations increase until the ground is shaking and vents of noxious gas are spewing up all around, reducing visibility and searing the throats of any Battle-Brothers eschewing helmets. If the Kill-team does not react quickly, the ground is wracked with upheaval and jagged cracks appear across the surface of the basin.

If the Battle-Brothers have not evacuated the crater within five rounds, they may be caught in the eruption that follows. Scores of fountains of raw digestive fluid geyser into the air, showering everything inside the crater with foul and highly acidic liquid.

To escape the geysers of digestive acid, each battle brother must make a **Difficult (–10) Dodge Test** for every Round he is within the crater. Failure results in exposure to acid. However, the opposite lip is steep, and a **Hard (–20) Climb Test** must be made to escape under such circumstances.

The Survivor (Optional)

Passing along the base of a cliff, the lead Battle-Brother comes upon the entrance to a network of caves. Should the Kill-team investigate further, they may find what could very well be the last of the humans native to Khnum, slumped, wounded and dying beside a pool of clear water, the only such pool the Battle-Brothers have encountered this far. The man is garbed in primitive attire and his scar-laced skin is daubed with a mixture of warpaint and his own blood. He has suffered numerous wounds, and it is obvious that he is doomed, yet he is just about conscious and aware of the Battle-Brothers as they loom above him.

What the player characters make of this encounter is left fairly open. Should they attempt to communicate with the dying warrior, they must first identify the debased variant of Gothic he is speaking. A **Hard (-20) Speak Language Test** must be made to understand each statement the survivor makes, and another each time a Battle-Brother seeks to speak to him. Subject to these tests, the following broad points can be gleaned:

The people of Khnum (the natives used the same title by which the Deathwatch archives record the planet) have dwelled upon their world for countless generations. Though their legends tell of humans existing elsewhere in the universe, few took such tales literally.

The warrior fought in the great war against the invading beasts, taking part in the last stand (see the Red Harvest encounter). He was wounded and lost consciousness, later awakening and crawling away to avoid the Malanthrope, which he calls the "corpse-eater".

Should the Battle-Brothers ask him of the distress signal, he misconstrues the term and starts talking about nightmares and doom. However, this is not the raving of a dying man but a hint that the Battle-Brothers might miss should they dismiss him. The survivor talks about the "Vale of Dreams", which he refers to as a real location not far away. Should they press further, the Battle-Brothers discover that this place is located roughly ten kilometres due north. These dreams are actually a bleed-over effect from the "Valbaran Subjectivity Engine," a device being utilised by the Adeptus Mechanicus and explained in more depth later on.

Having communicated some or all of this information, the survivor is wracked with a coughing fit, affording the Kill-team one last opportunity to communicate before he passes away. At the last, the man takes hold of a bone charm tied about his neck, snaps the cord and thrusts it into the hand of the nearest Space Marine. The GM should make a note of which Battle-Brother was given the charm, as it may come into play in part three of the adventure (in the "Last of their Kind" encounter). Should any of the Battle-Brothers decide to use their Omophagea Implant, the importance and location of the Vale of Dreams is all but overwhelming, though no further useful information is gleaned.

Belly of the Beast (Optional)

This encounter can be run at any point during the search for the source of the distress signal. As the Kill-team navigates a seemingly innocuous area of wasteland, picking its way through the obscenely pulsating vein-like roots that stretch across the land, a previously undetected threat presents itself. Have each Battle-Brother make a **Very Hard (-30) Awareness Test**. Any that fail must make a **Very Hard (-30) Agility Test**, or plummet into the maw of a subterranean brood nest, while those that pass either test jump clear just before the ground opens up beneath them.

Any Battle-Brothers falling into the brood nest must fight for their lives to escape before they are overwhelmed by its vile spawn. The Space Marines find themselves inside a wet, pulsing birthing canal, the only light provided by the opening thirty metres overhead. They must climb up the tube, whilst fighting off the creatures the brood nest spawns in response to the intrusion. Each turn that the Battle-Brother is inside the brood nest, it produces a single Ripper (see page 236), which instantly attacks the Battle-Brother. Keep in mind throughout the ensuing combat that the Battle-Brother is fighting in near blackout conditions (see page 247 of the **Deathwatch** rulebook) whilst climbing (described on page 206 of the same book).

The Vale of Dreams (Mandatory)

At length, the Kill-team comes upon the source of the distress signal, or at least the area of ground from which it is emanating. This might come about because the Battle-brothers questioned the last survivor in The Survivor optional encounter, or because they formulated some other plan to narrow the location down even further. The GM may simply determine that the player characters stumble upon the location in the course of their search, though he should only do so if and when the characters have faced and defeated multiple Tyranid beasts and exhausted all other options.

However they come upon it, the Kill-team does not immediately recognise the area for the location from which the distress signal is being sent. This is because it appears to the senses to be a barren expanse of wasteland bordered on all sides by sheer cliffs, with several natural ledges running down to a boulder-strewn valley floor. A successful **Challenging (–0) Awareness Test** results in a Battle-Brother noting that the Tyranids do not appear to have subjected the valley to the consumption process—why would they when there are clearly no life forms present in the valley that can be harvested?

The reality of the situation is that a powerful device, unknown to the mainstream of the Adeptus Mechanicus, and even to the Inquisition, protects Magos Klute's bunker. The Adept and his peers amongst the Circle Varnak recovered the item from deep in the Hecaton Rift on the outer verges of the Koronus Expanse, plundering ancient catacombs within which nothing but dead tech and the shades of extinct beings rested. When interfaced with a living being with the mental fortitude to control it, the device can be used to emit a psionic effect field that manipulates the perceptions of living beings in the vicinity. This device is the key to Magos Klute's bunker remaining hidden from the Tyranids, and indeed from the

Kill-team: the area around the entrance to the bunker appears to be dead and worthless, to living senses at least. It is only if and when the Battle-Brothers use any form of machine technology to examine the area that they notice everything is not as it seems. What the Battle-Brothers see depends on what means they are using to examine their surroundings.

- A Battle-Brother not wearing a helmet only notices something odd if he passes an **Arduous (–40) Awareness Test**.
- A Space Marine wearing a helmet and linked into his armour's auto-senses notices that something is not quite right about his surroundings if he passes a **Very Hard (–30) Awareness Test**.
- A character equipped with one or more bionic eyes, or one gifted of exceptional senses (such as a Space Wolf) detects something wrong if he passes a **Hard (–20) Awareness Test**.
- A character equipped with an Auspex may use it in the normal way (granting +20 to any of the above Awareness Tests). If he can pass a **Difficult (–10) Tech-Use Test**, he sees the surroundings for what they truly are, albeit rendered as grainy forms on the scanner's pict-screen.
- A Space Marine detecting that something is awry (i.e. by passing one of the first three Awareness Tests mentioned above) senses the unusual effect, but cannot pinpoint its source. Instead, he gets the distinct impression that, instead of walking across a blasted plain of grit and dust, lush grass is beneath his armoured boots. He catches the odd glimpse of plant life and greenery, though when he looks closer these fleeting impressions are gone.
- A Battle-Brother using an Auspex (or similar device) to scan the area sees that it is indeed an oasis of life. Lush grasses carpet the ground and mosses cling to the walls of the valley. There are even trace signs of small animal life forms cringing in the shadows, something the Battle-Brothers have not witnessed anywhere else on the surface of Khnum.

Yet still, the Kill-team see no obvious means sign of the bunker. They must perform a detailed search of the valley in order to locate the bunker's entrance, which is a metal hatch only just large enough for a Space Marine to pass through. The entrance is hidden at the base of the northern cliff wall. To locate it, a Battle-Brother must approach within 20 metres and pass an **Arduous (–40) Awareness Test**.

As the Battle-Brothers begin searching however, they realise that the Tyranids are closing in. The GM should up the tension as the Kill-team searches for the entrance, by having first Gargoyles, then Harpies, then a Harridan swoop down from above as they scan the area. Once they have located the entrance, the numbers of Tyranids should be increased still further, so that those Battle-Brothers further away risk being overwhelmed as ever greater numbers of airborne foes assail them.

Even once the entrance is discovered, the tension should not let up. Opening the hatch requires a **Very Hard (–30) Security Skill Test**, and the Tyranids should be closing in on the Kill-team in an overwhelming wave of teeth and chitin as they finally slam the hatch closed behind them.

At the last, the hatch slams shut and the Kill-team finds itself in a dark tunnel, barely lit by guttering lumen bulbs receding into the distance. As the Tyranids scratch and claw at the outside of the hatch, we move on to the second part of Fall into Darkness.

PART 2: WHAT LURKS BENEATH

In Part 2 of Fall into Darkness, the Battle-Brothers must penetrate the defences of Magos Klute's bunker, before they finally meet him and his staff. Something of the truth is then revealed, and the xenologis makes a proposition. The Kill-team has a few hours to replenish expended ammunition and tend to any wounds they might have sustained, before proceeding to the unplanned final stage of their mission.

PENETRATING THE BUNKER

The Space Marines begin this part of the adventure at the outer limits of Magos Klute's bunker, and must evade a number of ingenious, automated defences before even nearing the core, where Klute and his staff reside. The occupants have no direct control over the defences, which have been designed to repel any and all intruders that make it past the psychic dampening field that disguised the entrance.

The Kill-team must pass through each of the following areas, bypassing or otherwise overcoming the inbuilt defences before proceeding to the next. If the GM wishes, one or more of these areas can be left out or passage through them described in terms of the narrative passage of time, but it is important that the players get a feeling of how well defended and cunningly wrought the bunker is.

OUTER PERIMETER TUNNELS

The tunnel in which the Kill-team initially find themselves is dark, cold and oppressive, and made of rough cast rockrete. Apart from the pale lumen globes set into the low ceiling every ten metres or so, the curved walls are crossed by snaking conduits and cables, none with any obvious function. The overwhelming sensation is of being inside the pipes of a huge engine.

The outer tunnels slope steadily downwards, branching off at numerous points before joining with the main trunk once more. Though they might be concerned about becoming lost, the Kill-team soon realises that by following the steady downward gradient they always come back to the main tunnel. The side passages are only just large enough to accommodate a Space Marine, and there are smaller tunnels yet so small that only a servo-skull could travel along them. The main tunnel is only just large enough for the Space Marines to travel along, so they are forced to proceed in single file.

As they proceed deeper, the Battle-Brothers may discern that they are travelling in a wide spiral, taking them deeper and deeper into the planet's crust. The tunnels intertwine about the main spiral trunk, yet always converge with it once more, meaning that as long as the Battle-Brothers keep marching downwards they cannot get lost. It takes the Kill-team around five hours to reach bottom of the spiral, and the temperature steadily increases throughout the journey.

Though not essential to the action, the GM could describe

the descent and increase the tension, or simply present a summary of it and move on to the next segment. Should he decide to add a little action, he could have the players make a series of Awareness Tests (without telling them why!) and hinting that they might not be alone in the tunnels. Could something have gotten through the entry hatch before they closed it? Could the Tyranids have forced the hatch open after the Kill-team passed through? Should the GM wish, minor threats such as individual Rippers, Hormagaunts or Termagants (the latter two are described on page 371 of the **DEATHWATCH** Rulebook) can be introduced, requiring the player characters to deal with them in any way they see fit.

Read aloud or paraphrase the following summary of the descent through the outer perimeter tunnels:

> *Descending through the outer tunnels of the bunker complex is like journeying to the centre of the world itself. Without the tactical data projected by your helmet displays you might have become disoriented long ago, even with the prodigious skills of the Adeptus Astartes. The tunnels are dark and all but featureless, yet every now and then strange echoes resound up and down their lengths. As the hours stretch on, the heat increases, until at length warning runes are flashing in your helmet display, informing you that the temperature is reaching dangerous levels that your suit's cooling systems might not be able to counter.*
>
> *And then, just as the heat reaches a level almost intolerable even for a Space Marine, the tunnel you are travelling upon opens up into a long, straight and wide passage. You halt, guns levelled into the featureless darkness, aware that this area offers considerably less cover from any attack…*

APPROACH TUNNEL

As the ground finally levels off, the Kill-team find the tunnel straightening out, the furthest of the ever-present lumen-strips disappearing into the distance. This is the approach tunnel, along which any intruder that has passed down the outer tunnels must proceed. The reason for this is that the tunnel is fitted with a deadly, automated defence system designed to gun down any creature setting foot within. The ceiling is lined with machine spirit-guided targeters, and the walls with dozens of concealed Heavy Bolters. If the Battle-Brothers wish to penetrate further into Magos Klute's realm, they have but two choices: brave the torrent of Heavy Bolter fire that awaits, or find some way to confound or override the targeters.

Before either of these options can be undertaken, however, the player characters must detect the presence of the automated defences. If and how the defences are triggered depends on whether or not the Kill-team suspects an ambush. If they decide to proceed without actively searching for traps or the likes, have the player characters make a **Very Hard (-30) Awareness Test**. Success results in some hint being detected, such as the glint of a spy-lens overhead or the barely audible sound of a whirring servo. Failure indicates that the Battle-Brothers are about to walk straight into a hail of mass reactive Heavy Bolter shells, and must suffer the consequences.

It is possible that the players are canny enough to suspect that the chamber is one great big trap, and declare their intention to scan it for signs of ambush, etc. This can be

achieved by taking a **Hard (-20) Search or Security Skill Test**, with success resulting in them finding some clue of the true situation. If the test is passed by a small amount, then the player characters aren't aware of any specific threat but are sure there is one, while a pass by one Degree of Success results in them spotting the targeters overhead. Passing the test by two or more Degrees of Success results in the presence of the concealed Heavy Bolters being detected, and the full extent of the threat is revealed.

How the Battle-Brothers make it through the chamber depends on whether or not the concealed heavy weapons have been detected. If they have, the player characters have two further choices. They can attempt to confound the targeters or the weapons themselves, or they can attempt to avoid the worst of the fire. Should they wish to interfere with the targeters or the Heavy Bolters, the best course of action is to listen to the players' proposals for doing so, and assign an appropriate Skill Test and Difficulty. No specific mechanics are detailed for achieving this, as there are so many potential methods the players might dream up, from overloading the targeters with an electromagnetic pulse, a Techmarine using his specialised sensors and unique abilities or a Librarian attempting to trick the targeters into shooting mind-forged phantoms.

The second option requires the Battle-Brothers to dodge a hail of Heavy Bolter rounds. The tunnel is 100 metres long, with a Heavy Bolter emplaced every ten metres (ten on each side, staggered so they are facing a blank stretch of wall). Should the player characters decide to weather this storm, resolve their courageous attempt by having them make a series of Dodge rolls as they power along the chamber. The Heavy Bolters are triggered by the ceiling-mounted targeters and, so long as the targeter is present, fire with a Ballistic Skill of 20. Each targeter controls a single Heavy Bolter, so if it is destroyed or confounded, the corresponding weapon cannot fire.

Should the Battle-Brothers blunder into the chamber not suspecting it to be booby trapped, the closest pair of Heavy Bolters open fire before they can react. Having suffered a Full Auto burst, the Battle Brothers can pull back out of the line and fire, or power onwards, as they decide best.

INCINERATION CHAMBER

At the end of the Approach Tunnel waits one final defence that the Battle-Brothers must breach before they come upon the entrance to Magos Klute's bunker. This is the Incineration Chamber, a last ditch defence for use if and when the enemy have defeated every previous measure. Short of collapsing the entire tunnel network and sealing the occupants inside the bunker forever, the Incineration Chamber is the bunker's last line of defence.

Once the Battle-Brothers have passed through the Approach Tunnel, read aloud or paraphrase the following:

> *Passing out of the previous chamber, you enter a large, rectangular space, the opposite wall dominated by a massive, armoured portal. It is clear from the portal's construction that this must be the entrance into the bunker itself, for it appears as well armoured as the prow of a mighty warship.*

The Incineration Chamber is a four-sided space, roughly thirty metres to a side. The tarnished, gunmetal grey walls are largely featureless, but a close examination reveals them to be pitted and ingrained with what appears to be some sort of scorched residue. The wall opposite contains a large, heavily armoured portal, with a small command terminal set into its frame, while a series of small, circular vents are set into the floor and ceiling. Furthermore, the point through which the Battle-Brothers have entered the chamber is set with a similarly armoured door, which slams down with a resounding metallic crash once the entire group has passed through.

The purpose of the chamber is to unleash a blast of melta energy upon any intruder the occupants of the bunker deem a sufficient risk. Whether or not this applies to the Kill-team depends upon their actions thus far, and while the Adept is hoping aid will be forthcoming, he also has sufficient cause to be suspicious of any intruder, no matter how human they appear to be. After all, the occupants have been monitoring the death of the planet above them, and have witnessed all manner of horrors. They have every reason to be cautious, as Tyranid creatures have been known to dominate other life forms, subverting them at a genetic level to the Hive Mind's own, unknowable ends.

Upon approaching the bunker entrance, the Battle-Brothers are halted as an armoured vox-grille blurts to life. Read aloud or paraphrase the following:

> 'Halt!' A deep, grating voice resounds about the chamber, emerging from a vox-grille at the portal. "Tread carefully, for you enter the domains of the Circle Varnak. Identify yourself, for I must be certain you are not compromised by the taint of the Hive Mind!"

While the threat of incineration should not be far from the players' minds, what follows is a brief exchange in which they must convince Klute that they are who and what they appear to be, and that they have come in answer to his distress signal. In truth, the Magos knows that the Battle-Brothers are what they say they are, but the sights he has seen these last weeks have driven him to take precautions that might at first appear paranoid or irrational.

The encounter can be taken as an opportunity to roleplay a tense situation in which the Battle-Brothers are forced, unusually, to talk themselves out of harm's way instead of relying on their Boltguns to save the day. As with some previous elements of the mission, the players should ultimately be allowed to proceed, but they should not be given the impression that they don't have to work for it. The longer they take to convince the Magos, the more potential there is for mission complication. Perhaps some Tyranid infiltration creatures have followed the Kill-team's trail right into the bunker complex, and the first the team know of it is when the Heavy Bolters in the Approach Tunnel start blazing away inexplicably.

The exchange can be handled entirely as dialogue, or it can be resolved using the Interaction rules found on page 276 of the **DEATHWATCH** rulebook. In the latter case, the Adept starts off at the worst possible Disposition (Disgusted/Mutinous/ Disbelieving/Foolhardy) and must be "talked down" to the Challenging level (Indifferent) or better before he decides to trust the Battle Brothers, and to Ordinary (Favourable/Loyal/ Accepting/Startled) before he decides to allow them to enter his bunker. Note that this level represents the extreme measures the Magos feels compelled to take to protect his works from being compromised by Hive Mind enslaved enemies, rather than him being genuinely aggressive or belligerent towards the Kill-team. When the exchange is resolved to the GM's satisfaction, read aloud or paraphrase the following:

> 'Omnissiah be praised,' the voice from the grille exclaims, some trace of humanity entering its tone. "We are delivered. Enter, my friends, and take refuge from the storm."

ENTERING MAGOS KLUTE'S BUNKER

Passing through the massively armoured portal, the Battle-Brothers are greeted by Magos Klute and his entourage. A group of combat servitors cover the open portal with heavy weapons while it is open, before standing down once all of the team is through and the hatch has ground shut once more. Exactly how the two groups react and interact with one another depends upon many factors, but broadly speaking, Magos Klute is welcoming and relieved that the distress signal has been received and acted upon. He ushers the Kill-team into the bunker's strategium and enquires if any of the Battle-Brothers require any medical attention or have any other immediate needs (see the "Medicae Bay" section on page 226 for details). Once these are attended too, he introduces himself and his staff, and answers any questions the Battle-Brothers inevitably want to ask.

At some point, the Adept will voice his request for the Kill-team's aid (described in the next section). Until then, however, the Battle-Brothers have the chance to interact with the Adept and any of his staff (should they wish to) and to avail themselves of the bunker's facilities. They are free to do so as they please, and Magos Klute himself or one of his staff are pleased to aid them in any way they can. This section of the mission is in effect a brief interlude before the action significantly escalates. It provides a dramatic pause and an opportunity for the player characters to prepare themselves for what happens next, though, as they are soon to discover, the mission is about to take a drastic turn. Depending on the pace of the mission so far and the nature of the characters undertaking it, this passage of the adventure need not be especially detailed. It can be summarised if needed, in which case proceed directly to the section below headed "Magos Klute's Proposition."

Should the player decide to interact with the occupants of the bunker and it to explore or take advantage of its facilities, the information on people and places presented below should provide sufficient detail.

MAGOS XENOLOGIS ERLAN KLUTE

Magos Klute is a senior Magos Biologis who has devoted his service to the destruction of the Tyranid threat ever since it was first encountered. Erlan devoted a large amount of his life to studying the works of the well respected Magos Varnak, the first tech-priest to have identified and observed the creatures of the hive fleet, at the worlds of Tyran. Klute and his peers seem motivated by a xenocidal hatred, their mechanically augmented hearts burning with the heat of the forge. The so-called "Circle Varnak" has pursued the destruction of the Tyranids ever since the fall of Tyran. Widely spread across the Eastern Fringe, these few individuals work tirelessly against the Tyranid threat. Klute has been active in the Jericho Reach region for just over four years, having arrived just before Hive Fleet Dagon appeared. Though he kept his suspicions well hidden, Klute had determined that a tendril or offshoot of Hive Fleet Behemoth would descend upon the area, and his prediction was astonishingly precise. Had he notified many of his fellow adherents of the Cult Mechanicus of his prediction, he may have been denounced as a crank. However, they might have condemned him as something even worse still after such predictions had proved correct, for they were so accurate Klute must surely have utilised otherwise forbidden methods to scry such events.

Those of Klute's fellow tech-priests not part of the Circle of Varnak would be quite correct to question his methods, for the Magos has strayed far indeed from the essential precepts of the Cult of the Omnissiah. The small group of which he is a part has deviated from the prescribed Quest for Knowledge driven by their xenocidal hatred and pursued lines of heretical enquiry long denied to the Adeptus Mechanicus. The members of Circle Varnak have trod the surface of forbidden worlds and desecrated long buried tombs. It is even said that some of their number, including Klute himself, have entered the sealed archives beneath Mars itself, accessing crumbling data-stacks and recovering details of forbidden technologies they believe will aid them in their battles against the Great Devourer.

Klute and the Circle Varnak have plundered vaults both human and xenos, and amassed a sizable armoury of potent and often abominable technology. While all of the members of this secretive coterie are specialists in the alien, each of them has pursued a different factor of this broad discipline. Some are masters of alien science, genetics and even physics. Magos Xenologis Klute's particular obsession is xenos genetics, in particular, those of the Tyranids. Over the last year in particular, he has gained insights into the methods the Hive Mind utilises to propagate itself that have stretched his sanity to breaking point, though he hides the extent of his rapidly dissolving mental state very well. He has recently formulated some highly esoteric theories regarding the Tyranids' harvesting of genetic material, and the methods by which useful elements are apparently taken advantage of. By constructing his bunker and being on hand to monitor the process by which a planet is consumed and its bio-mass rendered down, Magos Xenologis Klute has determined what he believes is a viable method of destroying the Hive Fleet from within. He has created an artificial virus (itself a heretical process), gene-keyed to the most common elements of Khnum's bio-mass. He is certain that by introducing his virus directly into the consumption process, every Tyranid creature that shares even a small portion of the genetic characteristics harvested from Khnum can be attacked and destroyed at the genetic level. And if the process works on Khnum, the adept believes, in can be made to work anywhere.

The only issue with Magos Klute's scheme is that his gene-keyed virus must be delivered directly into a digestion pool in the very final stage as the Tyranids complete the consumption process. He knows that he has no chance of succeeding in such a mission. Yet, by sending his distress signal when he did, and gaining the attention of the elite Deathwatch, it might still be possible to defeat Hive Fleet Dagon once and for all.

INGENERI

IV: FALL INTO DARKNESS

ASTROPATH XHENEK

Astropath Xhenek is a fearsomely powerful psykers, possessed of the all but unique power to project her mind-voice through the Shadow in the Warp. Without her, Magos Klute's mission on Khnum would have been limited in scope to weathering the planet's destruction from far below the surface and not being able to emerge until the tendril of Hive Fleet Dagon had moved on. With her, however, Magos Klute was able to alert the Imperium at large to his presence, and to call in the aid he needs to enact his plan and poison the digestion pools.

Xhenek was recruited by the Circle Varnak some three years ago, by somewhat unorthodox means. The young Xhenak had only recently come into her powers, undergoing the unknowable ritual of Soul Binding at the foot of the Golden Throne itself, before being shipped out to the Calixis Sector to take her place in an Astropathic Choir on the sector's capital world of Scintilla. Xhenek never reached Calixis, however, her vessel's course instructions being deliberately corrupted by an agent of the Circle to ensure that it found itself far from its intended destination. By way of a cunning series of code manipulations, the Circle Varnak ensured that Xhenek's vessel was assigned incontrovertible, high-level instructions sweeping it up in the clandestine troop and materiel convoys passing from the Calixis Sector, through the Jericho-Maw warp gate, and into the Jericho Reach. From there, it was a simple matter for the Magos to spirit the young Astropath away and into his service.

The reason the Circle Varnak went to such effort to ensure that Xhenek entered their service was that, having intercepted transcripts of the tests performed on her aboard the Black Ship that ferried her to Terra, they saw something special in her abilities that others missed. Xhenek's prodigious psychic powers appear to operate at, for want of a better word, a frequency that makes her able to penetrate the Shadow in the Warp, though this is far from a precise science. With the Circle Varnak so dedicated to defeating the menace of the Great Devourer, it is hardly surprising they should have sought out such an individual, though to date, Xhenek is the only astropath displaying the ability they have identified. Needless to say, should other bodies, in particular the Inquisition, learn of the astropath's skill, they are likely to take quite an interest, a fact that may or may not occur to the Kill-team if and when they encounter her.

In appearance, Astropath Xhenek is quiet and innocuous, and certainly gives no outward sign of harbouring any special qualities. She is in her twenties, small and unassuming. Her empty eye sockets are obscured by a headscarf wrought of shimmering silk, the only relic she keeps of the culture of her home world. Xhenek wears the green robes of her order, and for no known reason eschews the wearing of shoes or sandals. She carries a bronze staff capped with the eye-symbol of her order, and a small bag containing her few personal effects.

Should the player characters meet and interact with Astropath Xhenek, they find her timid, yet uncowed by them. She is resigned to her station in life serving Magos Klute, knowing that it is her lot to suffer whatever fate awaits her. She is unaware that her fate has been manipulated in the way it has, but even if she knew, she would simply accept it as the Emperor's ultimate plan for her. However, should the Battle-Brothers attempt to subvert Klute's authority in any way, Xhenek is likely to see them as closer to the Emperor than the Magos, and therefore follow their orders.

Astropath Xhenek's profile can be found on page 235.

ADEPT BHRAWK

It is Adept Bhrawk's task to maintain the psychic dampening field that keeps the Tyranids away from the entrance to the bunker (see the "Vale of Dreams" encounter on page 219). Brawk is an ancient tech-priest with very little in the way of organic matter left in his frame, which is almost entirely mechanical. Even his mind is all but replaced with augmetic upgrades, a mere scrap of grey matter left at the centre of his armoured cranium. Having long ago submitted to the Rite of Pure Thought, Bhrawk is coldly logical and devoid of almost every human emotion. There is one feeling he still knows however, and that is the ruthless drive to conquer alien technology, regardless of any moral or legal quandary doing so might present. Though he cares little for the obsessions of the Circle Varnak, Bhrawk is so driven by his unquenchable desire to master xenos science that he has willingly thrown in his lot with them, the result being that he has been granted the task of utilising the arcane device known as the "Valbaran Subjectivity Engine."

The machine that Adept Bhrawk is tasked with operating and maintaining is housed in an armoured chamber that the tech-priest himself never leaves. For all intents and purposes he is hardwired into the machine, his mind monitoring and moderating its every function. The Subjectivity Engine appears as a vast array of glass-enclosed valves, each aglow with pulsating, violet energy. At the heart of the machine is a large sphere etched with undeniably alien runes, and inside this sphere is the source of the psychic effect projected into the Vale of Dreams.

Aside from Magis Xenologis Klute, Adept Bhrawk is the only member of the Circle Varnak who knows the true details of what lies at the heart of the Subjectivity Engine, and it is significant that Bhrawk is the only individual Klute trusts with the knowledge. The source of the machine's power is a mass of brain matter harvested from a xenos sample gifted of prodigious psionic power. Neither adept is entirely sure what species of alien this matter was harvested from, or how long it has powered the engine. All they care about is that the engine continues to operate at peak efficiency, projecting the effect that maintains the secrets of the Vale of Dreams as directed by Adept Bhrawk.

Should the Space Marines have cause to interact with the adept, they find him a contradictory character. Most of the time, he is detached, unemotional and barely engaged with anyone or anything around him. It is only when talking about the Subjectivity Engine or other xenos technology that he shows any hint of his erstwhile humanity, becoming animated to the point of mania the longer such a conversation continues. Should any of the Kill-team be carrying any truly unusual items of xenos tech, he shows an interest in these, and may even ask to examine them and to repair them if they are damaged in any way.

One very important point to keep in mind is that the psychic field projected by the Subjectivity Engine relies on Adept Bhrawk remaining at its controls at all times. He has no need of sleep or external nourishment, so he can remain at his station indefinitely, but should some fate befall him that disables or counters his ability to operate the machine, the psychic effect ends immediately. If that happens, the Hive Mind becomes aware of the last oasis of life hidden in the Vale of Dreams, and sets about consuming it with voracious hunger. That could have dire effects later on in the mission, as the Vale will be swarming with all manner of Tyranid beasts and the hidden entrance may well be compromised.

Adept Bhrawk's profile can be found on page 235.

GM Guidance: If it all goes south

While Magos Xenologis Klute is not exactly forthcoming about his factional leanings, the GM should keep in mind that he needs the Battle-Brothers in order to destroy the Hive Fleet. Without them, he cannot deliver his gene-keyed toxin to the digestion pools, and so he will try to keep relations on an even keel even should any of the Space Marines act in an antagonising manner.

There is an outside chance, however, that for whatever reason, most likely due to the Kill-team's belligerence or suspicion, relations break down entirely. Should this occur, it is suggested that the GM oversee a tense standoff, during which the Magos presents his proposition, as detailed on page 227. Hopefully, the Space Marines will realise that the chance to destroy the Hive Fleet is far more important than whatever brought about the confrontation, and the situation can be brought back under control. Essentially, if the mission is to be completed to its fullest extent, the player characters have little choice but to work with the Magos. This might produce some very interesting and unusual moral choices, especially if the Space Marines become aware of how far the Magos has strayed into heresy. What happens after the mission is completed is another matter entirely of course, and some ideas are explored further in the "Further Adventures" section on page 234.

However, some players just never get the hint and may decide to attack Klute, touching off a full-scale gun battle in the chambers and corridors of the bunker facility. Should this happen, then the Kill-team must fight its way out of a bunker filled with enemies armed with a wide variety of lethal, exotic weaponry, and should any make it back to their Watch-Station they will discover a last transmission from Magos Klute, in which he laments the fact that the Battle-Brothers ruined his "fool-proof" plan to destroy Hive Fleet Dagon once and foe all. Needless to say, the Kill-team deserves whatever punishment their superiors decide to subject them to as a result of their failure…

Tech-Priests

The bunker is host to a cadre of around fifty tech-priests of various ranks and disciplines. Many pursue the same activities as their master Magos Klute, while others are artisans and enginseers responsible for the maintenance of the bunker's highly complex life support systems. Only a small number of these lesser-ranked tech-priests are privy to the secrets of the Circle Varnak, and most are ignorant of the full extent of Magos Klute's activities. Nevertheless, all have pledged themselves to the Adept's service and none have any reason to betray him. Should the true nature of all of Klute's deeds become known, it is possible that as many as half of these tech-priests might reject them, though this is unlikely to come about unless the player characters deliberately cause it to happen for their own ends.

The profile of the average tech-priest can be found on page 236. GMs should feel free to vary the skills and gear of each as they deem appropriate.

Menials

The bunker is served by a staff of around three hundred menials and lay-techs, each a man or woman born into the service of the Adeptus Mechanicus and bonded to a lifetime of service to their tech-priest masters. Though not subject to the mindwiping and neuro-monotasking of servitors, these lowly individuals are far from masters of their own fates and slaves in all but name. They are fitted with a range of augmetics appropriate to their role within the bunker, and most are organised into parties of ten to twenty, directly overseen by one or more of the tech-priests. The menials are unlikely to initiate contact with the Space Marines, and are visibly cowed by their presence. They are easily commanded to undertake tasks for the Battle-Brothers, so long as the orders do not run contrary to their allegiance to the Cult Mechanicus, for they fear the tech-priests more even than the Space Marines.

The profile for the average menial can be found on page 374 of the DEATHWATCH rulebook.

Servitors

Magos Klute has ensured his bunker is well served with servitors, especially battle servitors equipped with a range of heavy weapons. These are essential to the operation of any facility of the nature and size of Klute's bunker, while the armed variants are present to defend their masters should the need arise. In truth, even the one hundred or so battle servitors present in the bunker would be quite useless should the Tyranids become fully aware of the facility and launch a determined assault against it.

The profile for battle servitors can be found on page 376 of the DEATHWATCH rulebook, and the majority are armed with heavy bolters, plasma cannons and heavy flamers.

LOCATIONS AND EVENTS WITHIN THE BUNKER

While there is no specific necessity for the Battle-Brothers to explore the various locations within the bunker, the players may nonetheless decide to do so. In this case, the following locations and associated events can be used.

CENTRAL STRATEGIUM

The Strategium is Magos Klute's main control centre, and it takes the form of a large, circular chamber, every square metre of its walls mounted with pict-slates of every possible size and configuration. Many of these depict scenes from the surface, transmitted by the numerous spy-drones under the control of the dozens of tech-priests manning the control terminals that dominate the main floor. Other screens show reams upon reams of raw data, endless lines of text representing the collation and analysis of the vast amounts of information being collected by sensors hidden all over the surface of the planet. Around half of these have gone blank however, for the sensors themselves have been compromised, discovered by roaming Tyranid organisms and broken down into their constituent particles.

It is in the Central Strategium that Magos Xenologis Klute is most likely to interact with the player characters, and where he is most likely to be found should they need to locate him. It is permanently staffed by at least a dozen tech-priests and scores of menials, and many of its stations are hard-wired with mono-task cogitation servitors.

ARMING CHAMBER

This armoured chamber is located at the end of a long corridor, and anyone approaching it must pass through three separate blast proof portals to gain access to it. The chamber consists of a central space, around which numerous isles lined with stasis cells are arranged, each containing nigh endless stocks of equipment of all types. The chamber is attended by a staff of menials, who genuflect endlessly, but only carry out those orders authorised by their master Magos Klute.

Should they request it of Magos Klute, the Battle-Brothers are readily permitted to replenish expended ammunition, but should they wish to take away any of the numerous weapons stored in the Arming Chamber, they must petition for the Adept's permission. Like any tech-priest, Klute is jealous of his resources and must be convinced (by way of appropriate Interaction Tests) to supply anything unusual.

The exact contents of the Arming Chamber are left up to the GM to determine as best he sees fit, with reference to the mix of characters in the group and how he wishes to run the mission. However, there should be sufficient stocks of ammunition to re-arm all but the most unusual weapons. In addition, the chamber should contain at least a handful, and potentially huge stocks, of all types of equipment up to the Average level of Availability (see page 139 of the DEATHWATCH rulebook). Furthermore, it should have a handful of other, more unusual items, right up to Near Unique, though Magos Klute is loath to authorise their use, even by the elite warriors of the Deathwatch.

MEDICAE BAY

The bunker's Medicae Bay is an extensive facility, and it is designed to heal both the organic and the mechanical components of the human body (as the majority of the staff are fitted with augmetics upgrades). The bay is a large network of work spaces and cells, and is staffed by several dozen menials and tech-priests.

So advanced are the facility's systems that Extended Healing times (see page 102 of the DEATHWATCH rulebook) are reduced, so that any treatment that would normally require a Medicae Test each day can be tested for each hour, and treatments tested for each week are rolled for each day. Unlike the use of the Arming Chamber, Magos Klute does not object to his staff healing any wounds the Battle-Brothers might have sustained.

In addition, the Medicae Bay has the resources to replace lost limbs with bionics, to repair damaged bionics and even to upgrade them to superior types. The extent to which this is possible is left up to the GM to determine, but Magos Klute must be convinced of the necessity to expend valuable resources before any such procedure is undertaken.

The staff of the Medicae Bay are mostly menials (see page 374 of the DEATHWATCH rulebook), all of whom have the Medicae (Int) Skill. The more senior of the staff are fully fledged tech-priests (see page 236) and as they follow the Biologis' discipline, they all have the Medicae (Int) +20 Skill.

SEALED ARCHIVUM

This area of the facility is strictly off limits and accessible only by Magos Klute himself. Within is a repository of the most valuable items of archaeotech in the Adept's possession, items too valuable or damning for him to leave unattended elsewhere. The Archivum is a spherical chamber, thirty metres in diameter. The inner surface is lined with stasis cubes accessible by an articulated, controllable gantry in the centre. Each of the stasis cubes contains an individual item, many of which are a mystery to the Adept, their origins and function as yet undetermined.

From the GM's point of view, Klute's Archivum and its contents can be used, if needed, to provide the player characters with an insight into the Adept's character and philosophical leanings. He does not announce himself as a virtual heretek (like most heretics, he views everyone else as the radicals) but may be revealed as such by clues such as the Archivum. In theory, the Deathwatch are above such notions and besides, the fine points of the doctrines of the Cult Mechanicus are beyond the Kill-team, though a Techmarine would soon grow suspicious.

Should the GM wish to develop the contents of the Archivum further, he could do so by inventing weapons profiles and the likes for key items. Furthermore, supplements such as EDGE OF THE ABYSS for the ROGUE TRADER roleplaying game contain plenty of items of xenos tech that could be utilised if needed.

Magos Xenologis Klute does not invite any of the characters to view his repository, and it is only if he is followed or tricked in some way that the players are likely to become aware of it.

COGITATION CORE

At the heart of Klute's bunker complex is a powerful cogitation engine. This is necessary not only to regulate the bunker's arcane life support systems, but also to process, analyse and store the flood of data gathered regarding the planet's consumption. The cogitation array holds a staggering amount of information, the likes of which have never been accessible before, because no one has attempted to record the consumption process in the way Klute has. Every possible scrap of information has been gathered, covering every stage of the consumption from the moment the first vanguard organisms inserted in their Mycetic Spores, to microscopic observations of the action of Tyranid-spawned hybridising bacteria.

While such a wealth of data would be supremely valuable to the ongoing war against the Great Devourer, the tragedy is that the Circle Varnak intends to keep it entirely to itself. Jealous of the intentions of other bodies, Klute and his peers aim to utilise the data they gather to their own ends, regardless of the value it might provide to the wider fight for survival. Needless to say, if any of the Space Marines come to realise the value of the information being gathered, processed and archived in the bunker's Cogitation Core, they might well decide to do something about it.

Magos Xenologis Klute is highly unlikely to allow the Battle-Brothers to find out the true extent of the data he and his staff have gathered, though he is willing to present them with an overview of the process. Only should a Techmarine successfully access the Cogitation Core (by gaining access to the core and passing a **Very Hard (–30) Tech-Use Test**) does he realise the sheer wealth and nature of the data being gathered. In order to ex-load more, the Techmarine must make a **Difficult (–10) Tech-Use Test** every ten minutes in order to gather around 1% of the useful data the cogitator has stored in its eidetic coils. Should the Magos learn of this activity, he is likely to become extremely antagonistic, yet regardless, he still needs the Battle-Brothers to fulfil his plan to destroy the Hive Fleet from within.

MAGMA-WARDS

The bunker facility Magos Klute has constructed is situated so far below the surface that it is actually submerged in a lightless ocean of molten rock. Needless to say, keeping any such structure intact and keeping the occupants alive is a prodigious undertaking, and one that draws upon engineering techniques very rarely utilised. The bunker itself takes the form of a spherical structure, which is surrounded by a halo of magma-wards. These devices utilise all but lost technologies that project an esoteric field effect into the surrounding mantle, manipulating the magma in such a way that it ceases to present a threat to the bunker. Exactly how this is achieved is a matter of debate, even amongst those who constructed the facility, and while some claim the field interrupts the local flow of space-time, others hold that it alters the laws of physics in such a way that the enormous heat and pressure simply do not come into play.

From the interior of the bunker, the magma-wards appear as huge, hemispherical blisters lined with arcing brass nodes and seething with arcane power. The air inside is charged and filled with a roar so loud that conversation is all but impossible. These magma warding chambers are staffed at all times by a crew of tech-priests and attendant menials, for should even one fail, the entire facility is doomed.

MAGOS KLUTE'S PROPOSITION

Whether or not the Space Marines seek to explore and take advantage of any of the bunker's facilities, Magos Xenologis Klute eventually seeks to explain to them the real reason he had Astropath Xhenek project her distress canto. While they might have supposed that the distress signal was intended to draw the attention of rescuers so that the staff of the bunker could be taken to safety, they soon discover that the Adept had something very different in mind indeed. This passage of the adventure leads ultimately to Part 3, so it should only be played when the group have completed any explorations or interactions they wished to pursue. When the time comes for Magos Xenologis to present his plan to destroy the Hive Fleet, have the group gather in the main strategium, and read aloud or paraphrase the following.

'Fellow servants of the all-prescient Omnissiah!' the Magos addresses you, his arms and numerous mechadentrites spread wide. "The time has come for me to avail you some of the findings we have gathered here, and of a plan I have devised that might spell the doom of Hive Fleet Dagon and its vile kin, once and for all."

As hush settles on the Strategium, the Magos Xenologis continues. "Such wisdom have we gathered, such weaknesses have we discovered, that it is my belief that I have successfully synthesised a gene-keyed, hybridising toxin with which we can slay this beast from the outer dark!"

Holding up a heavy, gunmetal cylinder, Klute continues. "I beseech you for aid, honoured Battle-Brothers of the Adeptus Astartes. This cylinder contains the toxin that, once introduced into the main digestion pool, shall be transferred into the genome of Hive Fleet Dagon and, in time, disassemble their very genetic structure. I have not the means to deliver the toxin, for such a task might only be executed by warriors such as you. Will you aid me?"

If the Battle-Brothers accept Magos Klute's plan and agree to deliver the gene-toxin, the Magos orders a servitor forward, bearing a large, heavy cylinder fitted with a carrying handle at one end and a control panel on its side. The cylinder contains the payload, which must be activated by lifting the cover on the panel and striking the payload rune. Following the activation, the Magos explains, the cylinder must be hurled into the digestion pool. The Magos calculates that the toxin is unlikely to take effect immediately, and that the Battle-Brothers should be able to return to the bunker by the same route they used to reach the objective.

The cylinder is a heavy object requiring at least one free hand to carry. This is likely to affect how the carrier uses two-handed weapons, so it is worth keeping track of who is carrying it and how.

PART 3: BAD MEDICINE

The third and final segment of Fall into Darkness presents the Battle-Brothers with the opportunity to deliver Magos Klute's gene-keyed toxin into the heart of the Great Devourer, and potentially to destroy it from within. There are no guarantees of course, and the Battle-Brothers might have decided that the Magos Xenologis is in the thrall of xenos archaeotech and not worthy of their aid.

OPTIONS

Magos Klute has presented the Battle-Brothers with the opportunity to strike a deadly blow against Hive Fleet Dagon, and while it should be obvious that his scheme is far from certain to succeed, the plan has obvious merits. Should the Kill-team decide to deliver Klute's toxin to the digestion pool, the objective is obvious. The execution, however, is a lot less clear, and it is up to the Space Marines to formulate a plan to traverse the Tyranid-infested wastes, reach the digestion pool and successfully extract. There are several potential plans the players might formulate, several of which are addressed below. It is always possible that the players will come up with some plan not covered here, in which case the GM will need to react accordingly. Conversely, if nothing occurs to the players, they could make Logic or Tactics Skill Tests to come up with some of these ideas, or parts of them could be suggested by Magos Klute or other members of his staff.

In addition to the issues presented here, the next section includes a number of specific encounters that can be played, regardless of which approach the Kill-team decides upon.

LEAVING THE BUNKER

Whichever method the Battle-Brothers plan to utilise to reach the objective digestion pool, there is only one way out of the bunker (that the player characters know of!), and that is through the Vale of Dreams. When they emerge, read aloud or paraphrase the following:

> *Setting foot upon the surface of Khnum once more, you see immediately that the consumption process has continued apace and must surely be approaching its hideous conclusion. The Vale of Dreams is as you left it, the psychic field still intact so that the Tyranids have been kept at bay. Those few beasts that pursued you into the entrance when last you were here appear to have dispersed, but in the distance you can see all manner of furtive movement, suggesting the dying world is now literally crawling with Tyranid monstrosities.*

Note that this description assumes that the Valbaran Subjectivity Engine is still active and keeping the Tyranids from stumbling upon the bunker entrance. In the event that the engine has been disrupted in some manner, alter the description accordingly.

TACTICAL ADVANCE TO BATTLE

The most obvious means of getting to the digestion pool is on foot, a method of insertion that has both advantages and disadvantages. Though a lot of ground must be covered, the Battle-Brothers can at least proceed with caution, scouting the path ahead and avoiding the worst concentrations of Tyranid beasts. The obvious downside is that the longer it takes to cross the wastes, the greater the chance that a small engagement could escalate out of control, forcing the Kill-team to fight its way through ever greater number of Tyranids.

Should the players decide to proceed on foot and brave the horrors of the dying landscape, they should decide whether to travel slowly but cautiously, or to take a more aggressive approach. Should they proceed stealthily, the journey should take around ten hours, with a Concealment Skill Test being made every hour until the Kill-team reaches its destination (in addition to any of the encounters presented in the next section). Whenever such a test is called for, roll on **Table 4–2: Wandering Tyranids** to determine which creatures are nearby. If the creatures have any reason to suspect an intruder is nearby (such as a noisy gunfight after the last test) then the Battle-Brother's Concealment is rolled against the Tyranids' Scrutiny as an Opposed Roll, while if there is no particular reason for the Tyranids to be suspicious, the Opposed Roll is made against their Awareness

TABLE 4–2: WANDERING TYRANIDS

D10	Tyranids Encountered
1	A single Hive Tyrant (see page 369 of the **DEATHWATCH** rulebook). Roll again to determine what creatures are accompanying it.
2	Three Tyranid Warriors (see page 370 of the **DEATHWATCH** rulebook).
3–4	A Magnitude 30 Horde of Hormagaunts (**DEATHWATCH** rulebook page 371).
5–6	A Magnitude 30 Horde of Termagants (**DEATHWATCH** rulebook page 371).
7–8	A Magnitude 30 Horde of Gargoyles (see page 237).
9	A single Mawloc (see page 187), lurking beneath the ground as the Kill-team passes by.
10	A single Hierodule (see page 202).

In addition to presenting the player characters with these threats, keep in mind the Unnatural Hazards presented on page 212. Also consider that if one of the above threats is not defeated quickly, others may be attracted via the Hive Mind or just by the sound of gunfire.

GUNSHIP DUST OFF

Another way of reaching the objective digestion pool is to call in the Stormraven and use it as transport. If the gunship is waiting in orbit it may take a while to get to the player characters' location, but this should not present a problem. It will, however, take a **Very Hard (–30) Tech Use Test** to contact the pilot. If the test is failed it may be attempted again, but each time the Difficulty is increased by a level, and once it passes Hellish (–60) may not be attempted again—the atmospheric disturbances caused by the consumption process are causing too much interference at this time.

If the Stormraven is waiting on the planet's surface, a **Difficult (–10) Tech Use Test** is needed to call it in, with the same complications as above. However, the gunship only takes ten minutes to home in on the Kill-team's signal. As stated in the first part of the adventure, if the gunship has been ordered to wait on the surface, the pilot will have spent much of his time fending off the attentions of prowling Tyranid organisms and continuously relocating to safer hiding places. As a result, the Stormraven has suffered some damage. All Piloting Tests as well as shooting actions it makes suffer a –10 penalty for the remainder of the adventure.

The journey from the Vale of Dreams to the objective is a matter of twenty minutes by air. However, the flight is very likely to attract the attention of airborne Tyranid beasts, and the skies are now swarming with Harpies and similar creatures. Use **Table 4–1: Aerial Complications** (on page 216) to determine the presence of such beasts, testing not every hour, but every minute of flight time.

CUNNING ROUSES

While the above are the two most probable methods the players are likely to concoct to reach the objective, they might invent some cunning ruse to distract the Tyranids, drawing them away from the digestion pool while the Kill-team approaches it. They might utilise some technological ploy using Magos Klute's staff and resources, or perhaps come up with a means of exploiting Astropath Xhenek's powers. They might even convince Magos Klute, and (somehow) Adept Bhrawk to disengage the Valbaran Subjectivity Engine long enough for the Tyranids to notice it and swarm in to investigate. Any such proposals should be considered on their own merit and, subject to the requisite Skill Tests, given a chance to succeed.

LAST MINUTE HITCHES

Whichever method the Kill-team uses to reach the objective, it is inevitable that a few last minute hitches will present themselves. The following encounters represent optional events taking place just before, during or after the journey to the digestion pool. The GM is free to play as few or as many of these as seems appropriate to the mission. The descriptions are not specific on the exact circumstance of the encounter, because the Kill-team might be travelling on foot or by Stormraven gunship. The GM should therefore ascertain the exact details based on the situation at hand.

GM GUIDANCE: OVERWHELMING ODDS

The Wandering Tyranids Table should be used with caution—after all, the Kill-team might have suffered injuries that slow it down, be accompanied by members other than Battle-Brothers, or have sustained losses. Another large variable is the skill level of the group as well as their wargear, all of which should lead GMs to adjust combat oriented encounters accordingly. Needless to say, characters can, and when appropriate should, die in combat, but only in circumstances in which they have a genuine chance to fight or think their way out, and in such a way as to enrich the narrative for all involved.

One way to moderate these encounters is by going easy on the players with regards to the escalating threat represented by additional Tyranids being drawn into a fight. The GM can use the first few encounters to judge the player characters' ability to fight them off, and adjust future ones accordingly.

In addition, if the combat encounters generated by rolling on the Wandering Tyranids Table become overwhelming or simply repetitive, feel free to swap them out with one or more of those presented in the next section, in particular "Last of Their Kind", which could, with a small amount of tweaking, be used several times.

LAST OF THEIR KIND

If the Kill-team met the wounded native in the opening part of the mission, they may have thought he was the last of his race. This proves not to be the case however, as the Battle-Brothers come upon a group of natives engaged in deadly battle against a horde of Termagants. There appear to be only a dozen or so warriors left standing and they are on the brink of being overwhelmed. If the Battle-Brothers can intervene in the next few minutes, they can save the natives from certain death, though what happens next is far from predicable.

If the Battle-Brothers attempt to communicate with the survivors, they find the warriors on the very edge of insanity, having witnessed their entire world turned into a living nightmare. If the Space Marines attempt to use any Interaction Skills, the natives start out at the worst possible Disposition (Disgusted/Mutinous/Disbelieving/Foolhardy) and are just as likely to flee in panic as to attack the Space Marines in unreasoning anger. However, should any of the Battle-Brothers be in possession of the charm given to them by the survivor in Part 1 (assuming that encounter was used) and have the presence of mind to produce it, that player character gains a +30 modifier to any Interaction Skill Tests. If the players simply forget that one of their number has the charm, the GM might consider having one of the natives see it, and take things from there.

If the players wish, they can ally themselves with the native warriors, for a time at least. The men are the strongest of their tribes and veterans at fighting the Tyranids. Subject to a suitable rapport being established by way of a **Hard (–20)**

Speak Language Test being made each time an order or request is made (reduced by a Difficulty level each time the test is passed) the warriors are willing to fight alongside the Space Marines, and able to guide them towards the digestion pool, their field craft skills granting a +10 modifier to any Awareness Tests to detect hidden or nearby Tyranids.

The profiles of the native warriors can be found on page 236.

DESTROYER OF WORLDS

Approaching the midpoint of their journey towards the digestion pool, a dark form appears at the horizon, its vast limbs moving with a stately, if hideous, grace across the devastated landscape. A low-slung head tracks back and forth as it scans the landscape for enemies, a low, droning challenge echoing across the wastes. The creature is a Hierophant, a massive Tyranid bio-Titan, and unless they take action to avoid it, the Battle-Brothers soon find themselves facing this most terrifying of foes.

In all likelihood, the player characters have no desire to face a Tyranid bio-Titan in combat, especially when they have their objective to carry out. However, especially headstrong Battle-Brothers or ones with personal goals or oaths to fulfil might find themselves unable to resist such a challenge. If that's the case, it is suggested that the GM allow the Battle-Brothers to indulge themselves… their fate is in their own hands!

In the event that the player characters are warlike or headstrong enough to go up against the Hierophant, its profile can be found on page 200.

THE HEAVENS OPEN

As the final hours of the world of Khnum draw near, the skies turn even darker and the black clouds part. A mass of vast, writhing feeder coils descend from the skies, unravelling slowly as they seek to suck up the remaining bio-mass. Each tendril is dozens of metres across and visible from many kilometres away, so on the whole they are not hard to avoid. However, every now and then one will descend from directly overhead, affording the Kill-team only seconds to get out of its path. Even if they avoid the initial surprise of such an encounter, the tendrils can be a hazard as they thrash about, sucking every scrap of matter into their vile maws.

Having observed several feeder tendrils descend from the sky at some distance away, have the Battle-Brothers make a **Difficult (–10) Awareness Test**. Success indicates the character catches sight of the feeder tube descending from the heavens directly overhead and is able to leap clear, while failure indicates that he saw it too late to get out of the way and risks

being sucked into the hideously questing sphincter-maw.

The surprised characters must make a Challenging (–0) Dodge Test, and consult **Table 4–3: Death By Feeder Tendril**.

INSTINCTIVE BEHAVIOUR

The xenologists of the Adeptus Mechanicus and the xenosavants of the Inquisition have long surmised that one of the final phases of Tyranid planetary consumption must surely be the re-absorption of the Tyranid creatures on the surface of the target world. While most are quite certain that such a process must take place, none, in the Jericho Reach at least, have witnessed it (and lived). As they close on the digestion pool however, the Battle-Brothers find themselves in a unique position. Read aloud or paraphrase the following:

> From out of nowhere, a sound like a mountain collapsing to the ground fills the air, and you turn in time to see a dark line appear at the horizon behind you. Before you can react, the line resolves into a vast stain that seeps across the landscape at impossible speed, and soon you realise that it is by far the largest swarm of Tyranids you have ever seen. Mouthing a silent prayer, you commend your souls to your Chapters as the first of the Tyranid beasts bears down upon you…

While the players should not find it out until the Tyranids are right on top of the Kill-team, this wave of beasts is acting according to the indomitable will of the Hive Mind, obeying the all-consuming command to head towards the nearest digestion pool and to throw themselves in so that every last scrap of bio-mass can be re-absorbed into the Hive Fleet's vast reserves. As such, every single Tyranid creature in the wave is attuned to one thing only—obeying the Hive Mind. Not a single one of the Tyranids is aware of the Space Marines, even when they are bearing right down on them, and they only way they become so is if the Battle-Brothers take any action that causes the beasts' natural instincts to kick in and override the Hive Mind's command.

Give the players a moment to consider their actions as the Tyranids close in, but make it clear that none of the creatures appear to be aware of their presence. If the players catch on that shooting will draw the Tyranids attention and they wisely hold their fire, read aloud or paraphrase the following:

> Like an avalanche of huge boulders breaking all about, the swarm envelops you, but incredibly, not a single one of the Tyranid beasts pays you any heed. Every type of creature, including dozens you have never before seen or heard of, swarms past, all heading in the same direction.

If however the Kill-team decides to fight, they will soon find that every Tyranid they shoot or otherwise attack becomes instantly aware of their presence, and directs its full attacks against the Battle-Brother that attacked it. As the Kill-team is by now entirely surrounded by a vast sea of Tyranid monstrosities, they should be given the chance to ascertain that only those Tyranids they attack become aware of them, meaning each must be fought to the death. While the majority of the creatures in the swarm are Rippers, Hormagaunts, Termagants and the likes, every variety of Tyranid is present. Whatever cause of action the player characters take, the swarm eventually passes over them. Read aloud or paraphrase the following:

TABLE 4-3: DEATH BY FEEDER TENDRIL

Degrees of Failure	Effect
2 or more	A mass of writhing tendrils lashes at the Battle-Brother, causing 1d10+5 (Pen 0) damage for each degree of failure.
1	A massive tendril slams into the Battle-Brother, inflicting a single hit at damage 2d10+5 (Pen 0).

Finally, the swarm passes you by, the last of its numbers receding into the distance. Following its progress across the landscape, you watch as the leading edge comes upon the sickly shores of a vast digestion pool at the horizon, the very pool you yourself are making for. Even from a distance, the spectacle that ensues is nothing short of horrific. The lead creatures, whether Ripper or Carnifex, throw themselves into the digestive juices, the chitin and flesh sloughing from them as they are reabsorbed by the Hive Fleet. In minutes, the entire stretch of shore is a vast, boiling vat of thrashing claws, deafening screeches and fountaining geysers of acid. Soon, it is all over, the entire swarm having pitched itself into the digestion pool, leaving nothing but a stinking yellow-green smog creeping over the blasted landscape.

THE LAST HOURS APPROACH

As the Kill-team finally approaches the objective, a vast sea of bubbling digestive juices, the Battle-Brothers' armour systems alert them to a change in the atmosphere. Two events appear to be happening at once, and both are equally portentous. Firstly, the nearer the Space Marines travel towards the objective, the higher the concentration of airborne contaminants of a highly acidic nature. The warning runes blinking in the Battle-Brothers' helmet displays inform them that these acid spores are getting denser, and are likely to reach concentrations potentially dangerous to the integrity of their armour seals very soon. The second event unfolding is that the air pressure is slowly dropping, suggesting that one of the very final stages of planetary consumption is underway—the harvesting of the atmosphere itself. As they proceed, the air begins to fog with bilious yellow-green haze, and the distant forms of writhing proboscis tubes are visible as they drop down through the clouds to harvest the air. Read aloud or paraphrase the following:

As the air pressure drops, so too does the temperature, and the skies overhead appear to fade to black as if night is falling, the pin-pricks of stars twinkling against the black. But this is no dusk—it is the very atmosphere of Khnum being sucked away by the bloated Tyranid grazer vessels just visible in the skies overhead. The only parts of the world not yet harvested are the distant oceans, and the vast digestion pool up ahead.

DELIVERING THE TOXIN

Having completed the journey to the objective digestion pool, the Battle-Brothers find themselves at the shores of a vast sea of boiling digestive acid. Such a sight has never been described, for no warrior of the Imperium has ever seen it and lived to tell the tale. It is truly the worst end a world could meet, the once great forests, the abundant animal live, even the proud natives and the minerals in the ground reduced to the abhorrent bubbling gruel stretching towards the horizon. Even as the Tyranid grazer vessels move into position to suck away the last of Khnum's oceans, the sky grows even darker still and the land all about is plunged into shadow. Something very large indeed has appeared overhead. Read aloud or paraphrase the following:

As you near the shores of the digestion pool, the light of Khnum's star appears to fade, and looking upwards you see the heavens eclipsed by a form so large that it blocks out the stars. As if in slow motion, a cluster of hideously writhing tendrils unwrap themselves, lowering inexorably through what remains of the atmosphere, appearing to move ever faster as they descend. At the last, the tendrils plunge into the centre of the vast lake of digestive fluid before you, throwing up great plumes of bio-acid as the pool begins to boil.

Now, you realise, is the moment to deliver your deadly, gene-keyed toxin.

Having reached the objective, however, the Battle-Brothers must face one final enemy. Just as the Battle-Brother carrying

MEANWHILE...

Magos Xenologis Klute explained to the Space Marines that the gene-keyed toxin would function as a slow-acting agent once introduced to the digestion pool, and that its effects might take days, weeks or even months to manifest. However, he was well aware that this assertion was based on very little evidence and he knew that the Hive Mind might in fact detect the toxin and react against it the instant it was introduced into the digestion pool.

Fearing that the Tyranids might be about to enter a new, previously unseen phase of planetary consumption that even the magma-warded bunker could not survive, Magos Xenologis Klute has put his contingency plan into action. An Adeptus Mechanicus transport vessel waits in orbit, secreted inside a shielded docking facility clamped to a small asteroid. The Magos and his key staff (ie the tech-priests and astropath, but none of the menials or servitors) are to teleport to the transport via a teleportarium hidden inside the most secret portion of the bunker complex. The evacuation begins almost as soon as the Space Marines depart, who have only two chances of detecting it during this phase of the mission. The first is if a player character is operating any sort of auspex gear (whether handheld or on the Stormraven) and can pass a Punishing (–50) Awareness Test (modified by the sensor gear in use). Success indicates that an anomalous return is detected, and it takes a successful Hard (–20) Evaluate Test to determine that the signal appears to be an energy spike caused by a teleportation device.

The other way in which the player characters might become aware of the evacuation at this stage is if they interacted favourably with Astropath Xhenek. When informed that the staff are leaving, the Astropath finally voices an objection to her fate and, if the Space Marines were not unkind to her, tries to beseech them for aid using her mind's voice to warn them of her master's treachery. A successful Very Hard (–30) Psyniscience Test establishes a tenuous link between the Astropath and a character, with the Degrees of Success by which the test is passed determining how much she is able to tell them before the communion abruptly cuts out as the teleportarium is activated.

the toxin cylinder approaches the shore, the ground trembles and the acid boils into a fountaining geyser! From out of the shallows rears a huge Mawloc (if they have faced one already in the adventure, it may be the same beast, having been resurrected by the raw power of the Hive Mind to pursue the Kill-team to its objective). The Mawloc's appearance from the shallows of the digestion pool means that it automatically Surprises the Battle-Brothers in the ensuing melee. However, for every combat round it spends at least part submerged in the digestive acid, it loses one point of Armour as its hardened chitin sloughs away in steaming runnels.

Any player character wishing to activate the toxin cylinder must make a **Challenging (–0) Tech Use Test**, before hurling it into the digestion pool. Because it takes an action to do so, it may be that the Battle-Brother carrying the cylinder must be covered by his brethren, or delay activating the toxin until the Mawloc is defeated.

If and when the cylinder is cast into the digestion pool, read aloud or paraphrase the following:

> *The cylinder arcs through the air, disappearing into the bubbling lake before sinking without a trace. Though you expected no immediate response, you can't help but be mildly disappointed when nothing appears to happen. Resolving yourself for the arduous return journey, you turn your back on the hideous spectacle of the grazer-vessel sucking up the digestive acid as well as the toxin. But then you pause, somehow aware that something isn't quite right…*
>
> *A gaseous expulsion bubbles up from the pool where the cylinder was cast into it, followed a moment later by a second, larger explosion of gas and acidic liquid. Then the ground starts to tremble and the feeder tubes of the grazer-vessel tremble. Soon they are jerking, then thrashing, and great gobbets of digestive acid are being cast in every direction. A rain of acid droplets is falls, leaving your armour pitted and smoking.*
>
> *As a mournful dirge echoes from the grazer-vessel overhead and the digestion pool explodes with motion, you know that if you don't get clear right away, your body will be put to rest on the blasted wastes of Khnum, your fate unknown and your deed unhallowed…*

EMERGENCY EXTRACTION

With the Tyranids reacting to the deployment of the gene-keyed toxin with such vigour, the Battle-Brothers have little choice but to get away before they are overwhelmed by a landscape driven into a wild paroxysm of death. Realistically, there are three options, but the GM should be ready for the players thinking up more.

CALLING IN THE GUNSHIP

If the Stormraven is on station, now is the time to call it in. If it's waiting in orbit, the Battle-Brothers must pass an **Arduous (–40) Tech Use Test** to establish contact. If it is waiting on the surface, they must make a **Hard (–20) Tech Use Test**. They can continue to make the test until it is passed, but each time it is failed some threat should present itself, such as a wave of ten or so Hormagaunts descending upon them. These assaults are intended to ramp up the pressure and to drive home the apocalyptic nature of the situation rather than to present a huge challenge.

AIRBORNE ACID SPORES AND VANISHING ATMOSPHERE

Should the GM wish to impart the sheer lethality of staying in the proximity of the now-seething digestion pool, he can apply some simple effects to represent the vanishing atmosphere and the acid rain coming down upon the Battle-Brothers. The simplest way to represent the acid droplets is to have each Battle-Brother sustain a 2d10+5 (Pen 4) damage hit every turn they remain in close proximity to the shore, reducing this to once per minute if they move away, and even less frequently if they make a serious effort to vacate the area whilst waiting for extraction. The Space Marines are able to weather the loss of the world's atmosphere so long as they are all wearing their helmets or are otherwise suitably equipped, but if they are not, it is suggested that, if the GM deems it necessary for the story, he uses the rules for Vacuum and Suffocation on page 261 of the **DEATHWATCH** Rulebook. At that point, it is likely the asphyxiated Battle-Brother's Sus-An Membrane Implant causes them to lapse into a protective coma until such time as he can be revived.

Once contact is established with the gunship, how long it takes to arrive depends on how far it is travelling, but there is no need to time the interval exactly. If it's travelling from orbit, the best way to represent the wait is to have several more individual or small groups of Tyranids harry the Kill-team, but once again, these are more an inconvenience, as the Battle-Brothers have already defeated the main enemies and completed their main objective.

When the gunship eventually arrives, the Battle-Brothers (and potentially any surviving native warriors) can board and depart. Read aloud or paraphrase the following:

> *As your armoured boots set foot upon the gunship's boarding ramp, you pause and take one last look at the world of Khnum. You can scarcely believe that mere weeks ago, the wastes before you were clad in dense forests teeming with animal life. How quickly and completely the Great Devourer has violated this world, and will do so to others, if it continues on its path.*
>
> *Without any of your number needing to voice it openly, you each swear that while you stand the Long Watch, the Great Devourer shall not be allowed to plunder the worlds of Mankind unopposed. This, by your Chapter and by your honour, you swear…*

RETURNING TO THE BUNKER

It is possible that, for whatever reason, the Kill-team might decide to return to Magos Klute's bunker. Perhaps they feel such a sense of duty to the occupants that they seek to aid them however they may. If this is the case, there is no need to roleplay the return journey, but it can be summarised by describing a world in its death throes, the Tyranids caught up in a frenzy of rage and confusion. When they eventually make it back to the Vale of Dreams, the Adeptus Mechanicus have of course departed, though this might not be immediately apparent. The Kill-team could at this point call in their gunship and extract (see Calling in the Gunship), or they could decide to weather the final stages of the death of Khnum inside the bunker and hope they are picked up by an investigation team once the Hive Fleet tendril has moved on. Should the players take this option, they are perfectly safe inside the bunker complex, its systems (in particular the magma-wards) functioning automatically for long enough to ensure their survival. Weeks later, once the planet is nothing more than a cold, dead, airless rock, a Deathwatch mission arrives and takes them back to their Watch Station.

HERESY REVEALED!

One last twist that the GM could throw at the players is to confront them with the truly heretical nature of the Circle Varnak, forcing a choice on them right at the very climax of the adventure. If the GM wishes to pursue this potential ending, then the message from Astropath Xhenek (see the "Meanwhile" box on page 231) should be made easier to detect, and a lot more urgent in content. It should in fact take the form of a desperate plea for aid, the Astropath having realised that in hiding the existence of the Teleportarium device, the Magos has shown himself as a traitor willing to send the Emperor's elite warriors to their deaths while he escapes unharmed. The message should arrive at the very moment of decision, such as when the Battle-Brothers are boarding their gunship or making their escape through the atmosphere. How they react is entirely up to the players

of course, but should they decide to heed the Astropath's warning and attempt to rescue her or confront Magos Klute, they have two choices as to how and where this can happen.

The first option is to have the confrontation take place inside the bunker, in the Teleportarium itself. The Space Marines must penetrate the bunker's defences and fight through its corridors against hordes menials and combat servitors despatched to slow them down while the senior staff escape (with the restrained Astropath). This option has the advantage of being fairly familiar ground to the PCs and the GM, making it simpler to describe and navigate. It is also an opportunity to reprise earlier themes, including the motivations of characters encountered earlier on. Ideally, the GM should engineer events so that the final confrontation takes place inside the Teleportarium just as the arcane device is powering up, the air filling with arcs of deadly energy. It could in fact continue on board Klute's vessel in orbit if the machine is not shut down in time (it would take a **Hard (–20) Tech-Use Test** to shut the system down in such circumstances), meaning that the gunship will have to extract the Kill-team from the landing bay under fire from the vessel's numerous combat servitors.

The second option is for the players to direct the Stormraven towards Klute's vessel in orbit, and to board it, forcing a confrontation on the landing deck. The ship has an effectively inexhaustible supply of combat servitors, so the Battle-Brothers have little hope of taking permanent control of the vessel. As such, this fight should concentrate on defeating the Heretek Magos, rescuing the Astropath, and escaping before the Kill-team is overwhelmed by reinforcements.

EPILOGUE

At length, the Battle-Brothers return to Watch Station Phaedas (see page 132) and are debriefed by Watch Captain Avincus (see page 138). This an opportunity to tie up any loose ends that remain, in particular regarding the fate of Magos Klute and of the effect his toxin had on the tendril of Hive Fleet Dagon that consumed Khnum. In the case of the former, unless the Battle-Brothers confronted Klute as he tried to evacuate, the Magos Xenologis escaped, but failed to return to the fold of the Adeptus Mechanicus. Klute and the entire Circle Varnak has been declared outcast by the Cult Mechanicus, ostensibly because of their delving into forbidden tech but also because they hid their activities and the results of their observations from their peers. The Inquisition has ratified its standing on the Circle, and announced its intention to hunt Klute down and bring him to justice. Already, the Chamber of Vigilance has received requests for aid in this matter, making it an ideal thread to pursue in future missions.

Despite Magos Klute's perfidy and heresy, the tendril of Hive Fleet Dagon that overran Khnum was actually halted, serving to compound his crime in not sharing his research with his peers. Having consumed Khnum, the tendril pressed onwards along the Salient, but several Deathwatch probe-drones trailing it then observed something very unusual indeed. Those Tyranid forces following on behind the tendril veered suddenly off course, intercepting the lead swarms of the tendril. What followed was an event never before witnessed or recorded—the new element fell upon that which had overrun Khnum and tore it apart, defeating in utterly in a huge space battle in the void some distance beyond Khnum. Inquisition xenosavants are only just beginning to study what observations were made of the battle, but some are already stating their belief that the tendril that was infected with Magos Klute's gene-keyed toxin was "rejected" by the Hive Mind. The tendril that destroyed it was acting as a creature's antibodies, cleansing the whole of a foreign body. The ramifications of these observations are great indeed, and the Kill-team is highly commended for the part they played in the incident.

REWARDS

The amount of XP points awarded should be based on a combination of how successfully each objective and goal was met, as well as how the players reacted to the shifting nature of the mission. Suggested rewards are as follow:

- Primary Objective Completed: 300 XP each.
- Secondary Objective Completed: 200 XP each.
- Tertiary/Personal Objectives Completed: 50 XP each.
- Delivering the gene-keyed toxin, while not an initial goal is a great challenge, and should garner each Battle-Brother 200 points instead of 50, as it was in effect a new, unanticipated Primary Objective.

In addition, players should be granted additional XPs for exceptional roleplaying and problem-solving.

FURTHER ADVENTURES

While Fall into Darkness works perfectly well as a stand-alone mission, it could serve as a jumping off point for several others. In addition, various characters introduced in the adventure might make appearances in the future, building up a familiar and ever-growing cast of "dramatis personae" unique to the campaign.

The following points might all prove worth pursuing over the course of future encounters. Some might form the basis of entire missions, while others might be ideal as personal goals, or encountered within the structure of other missions.

Hunt for Justice: The Kill-team is tasked with a mission to bring Magos Klute to justice. He might be hiding anywhere in the Jericho Reach, and while his hatred of the Great Devourer will undoubtedly endure, who knows what depths of heresy his expulsion from the Cult Mechanicus will cause him to plumb? Perhaps he sells his soul to Chaos and takes up with the corrupt Mechanicus of the twisted forge-world of Samech? Wherever the hunt takes the Kill-team, it might be accompanied by an Inquisitor or even a representative of the Adeptus Mechanicus, either of which might have their own agendas…

A Scream in the Dark: If Astropath Xhenek survived, one or more of the Kill-team might come across her psychic trace whilst engaged upon another mission, especially if the Battle-Brother is a Librarian. Do they follow the trace (perhaps going off-mission for a time) or do they return later and attempt to track it to its source?

Secrets the Outer Dark: If the Circle Varnak was able to construct such an advanced survival bunker on Khnum, might they have done so elsewhere too? Perhaps the Battle-Brothers are dispatched to a range of worlds in the path of Hive Fleet Dagon, in an attempt to track down the outcast Xenologis or others of his kind.

Return to Khnum: The Kill-team is sent back to Khnum, now a barren, lifeless rock, to recover any evidence of the gene-keyed toxin that Magos Klute synthesised, so that others might replicate it. Doubtless Klute left all manner of secrets behind, but are there other traps or silent sentinels still guarding the bunker that the Battle-Brothers know nothing of? In addition, what state might the magma-warding be in having been left unattended for any length of time? Perhaps the entire structure is on the point of collapse and the Kill-team's mission is a race against time to find any scraps of the gene-key formula before the raging mantle destroys the bunker and everything inside once and for all.

APPENDIX: NPCS AND ANTAGONISTS

MAGOS XENOLOGIS ERLAN KLUTE

Full background on Magos Klute may be found on page 222.

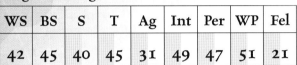

Magos Xenologis Klute Profile

WS	BS	S	T	Ag	Int	Per	WP	Fel
42	45	40	45	31	49	47	51	21

Move: 3/6/9/18   **Wounds:** 24

Skills: Awareness (Per), Chem-Use (Int), Ciphers (Biologis) (Int) +10, Common Lore (Imperium, Machine Cult, Tech) (Int) +10, Drive (Ground Vehicle, Skimmer/Hoverer, Walker), (Ag), Forbidden Lore (Adeptus Mechanicus, Xenos), (Int), Inquiry (Fel), Logic (Int) +10, Pilot (Civilian, Spacecraft) (Ag) +10, Scholastic Lore (Archaic, Chymistry, Numerology, Genecraft) (Int) +20, Speak Language (Low Gothic) (Int), Security (Ag) +20, Secret Tongue (Machine Cant) (Int) +20, Tech-Use (Int) +20.

Talents: Autosanguine, Binary Chatter, Concealed Cavity, Electrical Succour, Electro Graft Use, Energy Cache, Ferric Lure, Iron Jaw, Luminen Charge, Luminen Shock, Jaded, Maglev Grace, Mechadendrite Use (Gun, Manipulator, Utility), Meditation, Melee Weapon Training (Primitive, Power, Chain), Orthoproxy, Pistol Training (Bolt, Las, SP, Plasma, Primitive, Melta).

Traits: Touched by the Fates (3).

Implants: Bionic Arms (Superior Quality), Bionic Locomotion (Superior Quality), Bionic Respiratory System (Superior Quality), Auger Arrays (Superior Quality), Manipulator Mechadendrite, Utility Mechadentrite, Cybernetic Senses (all Superior Quality, incorporating Dark Sight, Photo-Visor, Recording Capacity, Microscopic Vision, Sonar Sense and a full vox system), MIU interface (Superior Quality).

Armour: Augmetic implanted armour (All 5).

Weapons: Concealed Hand Flamer built into right palm (Pistol; 10m; S/–/– E; Pen 3; Clip 4; Rld 2 Full; Flame), Concealed Plasma Pistol built into left palm (Pistol; 30m; S/2/– E; Pen 8; Clip 12; Rld 3 Full; Volatile).

Gear: Portable bio-auspex, respirator, personal cogitator.

ADEPT BHRAWK

Full background on Adept Bhrawk may be found on page 224.

Adept Bhrawk Profile

WS	BS	S	T	Ag	Int	Per	WP	Fel
30	38	33	36	28	46	43	45	10

Move: 2/4/6/12   **Wounds:** 24

Skills: Awareness (Per), Chem-Use (Int), Common Lore (Imperium, Machine Cult, Tech) (Int), Forbidden Lore (Adeptus Mechanicus, Xenos), (Int), Inquiry (Fel), Logic (Int) +10, Scholastic Lore (Archaic, Numerology) (Int) +20, Speak Language (Low Gothic) (Int), Secret Tongue (Machine Cant) (Int) +20, Tech-Use (Int) +20.

Talents: Autosanguine, Binary Chatter, Electrical Succour, Electro Graft Use, Energy Cache, Ferric Lure, Iron Jaw, Luminen Charge, Luminen Shock, Jaded, Maglev Grace, Meditation, Melee Weapon Training (Primitive, Power, Chain), Orthoproxy, Pistol Training (Bolt, Las, SP, Plasma, Primitive, Melta).

Traits: None.

Armour: Augmetic implanted armour (All 5).

Weapons: Las Pistol (Pistol; 30m; S/–/– E; Pen 0; Clip 30; Rld Full; Reliable).

Gear: Data slate, Combi Tool.

ASTROPATH XHENEK

Full background on Astropath Xhenek may be found on page 224.

Astropath Xhenek Profile

WS	BS	S	T	Ag	Int	Per	WP	Fel
25	25	22	30	40	43	39	50	40

Move: 4/8/12/24   **Wounds:** 10

Skills: Awareness (Per), Charm (Fel) +10, Common Lore (Adeptus Astra Telepathica) (Int), Invocation (WP), Psyniscience (Per) +10, Scholastic Lore (Cryptology) (Int), Speak Language (Low Gothic) (High Gothic) (Int).

Talents: Heightened Senses (Sound), Psy Rating (5), Resistance (Fear), Rite of Sanctioning.

Armour: None.

Weapons: None.

Gear: Astropath's green robes of office, staff, small bag containing minor personal effects.

Special Rules

Inner Voice: While full rules for an astropath's specialised psychic discipline are beyond the scope of this adventure, Astropath Xhenek does have the ability to cast her voice into the mind of others. Unlike many others, however, she is also capable of projecting her voice through the interference of the Shadow in the Warp. The target of her transmission should take a **Challenging (–0) Psyniscience Test**, with the Degrees of Success or Failure used to determine how clear her voice comes through and how much of her message the target understands.

NATIVE WARRIORS

These men and women are the last remnants of the human population of Khnum. The events they have witnessed over the last weeks have driven them beyond terror, yet they will fight alongside the Battle-Brothers if given the opportunity.

Native Warrior Profile								
WS	BS	S	T	Ag	Int	Per	WP	Fel
42	42	35	38	38	20	32	40	30

Move: 3/6/9/18 **Wounds:** 11
Skills: Awareness (Per), Climb (S), Concealment (Ag) +10, Dodge (Ag) +20, Silent Move (Ag) +10, Survival (Int) +20, Tracking (Int) +10.
Talents: Basic Weapon Training (Primitive), Melee Weapon Training (Primitive), Swift Attack.
Armour: Hides and chitin plates scavenged from slain foes (Body 2).
Weapons: Primitive weapons (1d10+3 R; Pen 0; Primitive). One in five are equipped with a bow (1d10+2 R; Pen 0; Clip 1; Rld half; Primitive, Reliable).
Gear: Tribal fetishes and ragged scraps of clothing.

TECH-PRIESTS

This profile can be used for any of the Adeptus Mechanicus staff serving under Magos Xenologis Klute, with additional skills added should any specialisations be deemed appropriate.

Tech-Priest Profile								
WS	BS	S	T	Ag	Int	Per	WP	Fel
32	31	32	37	30	41	33	35	21

Move: 3/6/9/18 **Wounds:** 12
Skills: Awareness (Per), Chem-Use (Int), Common Lore (Adeptus Mechanicus) (Int), Drive (Ground Vehicle) (Ag), Forbidden Lore (Adeptus Mechanicus) (Int), Logic (Int) +10, Speak Language (Low Gothic, Techna-Lingua) (Int), Tech-Use (Int) +10.
Talents: Binary Chatter, Chem Geld, Electrical Succour, Energy Cache, Gun Blessing, Luminem Charge, Meditation, Melee Weapon Training (Chain, Power, Primitive), Pistol Training (Bolt, Las, Plasma, SP), Mechadentrite Use.
Armour: Flak cloak (Arms 3, Body 3, Legs 3).
Weapons: Chain axe (1d10+7 R; Pen 2; Tearing), Laspistol (30m; S/–/–; 1d10+2 E; Pen 0; Clip 30; Rld Full; Reliable).
Gear: MIU Interface, auspex, mechadentrite (type appropriate to role), combi-tool, respirator, data-slate, personal cogitator, 2 laspistol clips, micro-bead.

MENIALS

To represent the numerous menials serving in Magos Klute's bunker complex, use the profile for Civilians given on page 374 of the **DEATHWATCH** rulebook.

RIPPER SWARM

The surface of Khnum is literally infested with these small, yet deadly Tyranid organisms. Rippers are essentially perambulatory mouths, their primary function being to overwhelm the target world and to attack and consume any form of prey that attempts to resist. When at last the creatures are engorged, they cast themselves into the nearest digestion pool, ensuring that their own bio-mass, and that of their prey is re-absorbed by the Hive Fleet. Rippers tend to move about the surface in great waves, and while individually they are dangerous (even to a fully armoured Space Marine) in large numbers they are truly lethal, well able to drag down even the largest opponent. These creatures can appear at any time, and while some burrow up from loose soil, others have wings upon which they swoop down upon the unsuspecting foe in a dark cloud of slavering, all-consuming mandibles.

Ripper Swarm (Troops)								
WS	BS	S	T	Ag	Int	Per	WP	Fel
35	—	25	30	40	10	30	30	—

Move: 2/4/6/12 **Wounds:** 10
Skills: Awareness (Per), Climb (S), Dodge (Ag), Silent Move (Ag), Swim (S), Tracking (Int) +10.
Talents: Fearless, Heightened Senses (Smell).
Traits: Burrower (1), Crawler, Dark Sight, Improved Natural Weapons (Mandibles), Instinctive Behaviour (Feed), Natural Armour (Exoskeleton), Size (Puny), Tyranid.
Armour: Exoskeleton (All 2, Horde 2).
Weapons: Mandibles (1d5+3 R; Pen 3).

SPECIAL RULES

Horde: Rippers can be used as a Horde (see page 359 of the **DEATHWATCH** rulebook for the rules for Hordes). While in a Horde, Rippers gain the Rampage, Relentless and Overwhelming Traits, the Swift Attack Talent, and their attacks gain the Tearing quality. A Horde of Rippers has the Fear 1 (Disturbing) Trait. Alter the Size Trait as appropriate for Horde magnitude.

Biomorphs: At the GM's discretion, Rippers may be given any of the following Traits: Toxic (1d10); Flyer (3); Unnatural Toughness (x2).

Spinespitter: +30 BS and gain ranged weapon (Pistol; 20m; –/3/–; 1d10+1 I; Pen 0; Clip –; Rld –; Living Ammunition).

Tenacious Grappler: Rippers drag down their prey by grappling with it so that others can latch on more easily. When attempting to grapple an opponent armed with a melee weapon, Rippers suffer –10 to their WS instead of the normal –20.

RELENTLESS TRAIT (HORDE)

The Relentless Trait makes a Horde nigh unstoppable and heedless of wounds, if not especially fast. A Horde with the Relentless Trait counts as having the Fearless Talent if it does not already have it (meaning it cannot be broken in combat by suffering 25% or 50% casualties and need never take a Willpower Test to avoid being broken). Such a Horde is slow however, so may never Run or Charge. Relentless Hordes are so difficult to stop with missile fire that they only ever suffer 1 point of Magnitude damage from ranged attacks, including those from weapons with the Blast quality. Melee attacks and attacks by weapons with the Flame quality damage the horde as normal.

RAMPAGE TRAIT (HORDE)

This Trait grants the Horde a chance to inflict additional hits on its enemies in melee combat. When a Horde with the Rampage Trait successfully hits a foe in melee combat, it may immediately make an additional melee attack against the same foe at –10 to hit. If this hit is also successful then may make another at –20, and so on with each additional attack suffering a cumulative –10 penalty. Note that these attacks do not need to inflict any damage to trigger an additional strike, only successfully hit. In all other respects, these attacks are worked out as normal. A Horde wielding two weapons or with either the Swift Attack or Lightning Attack Talents may use the Rampage Trait for each attack it makes.

GARGOYLES

In the initial stages of planetary consumption, vast flocks of Gargoyles roam ahead of the main assault waves, flushing out the enemy and cutting off isolated defenders. Later on in the process, they roam the skies on the look out for survivors or intruders, acting as the sentinels of the Hive Mind and alerting other Tyranids of the presence of prey or enemies.

| Gargoyle (Troops) | | | | | | | | |
WS	BS	S	T	Ag	Int	Per	WP	Fel
30	33	32	30	40	10	40	30	––

Move: 4/8/12/24   **Wounds:** 9
Skills: Acrobatics (Ag), Awareness (Per), Climb (S), Contortionist (Ag), Dodge (Ag).
Talents: Death from Above, Leap Up.
Traits: Dark Sight, Flyer (20), Natural Armour (Chitinous Carapace), Natural Weapons (Teeth and Claws), Instinctive Behaviour (Lurk), Tyranid.
Armour: Chitinous Carapace (All 3).
Weapons: Fleshborer (20m; S/–/–, 1d10+5 R; Pen 3; Clip –; Rld –; Living Ammunition, Tearing), Teeth and Claws (1d10+3 R; Pen 3, Primitive).

SPECIAL RULES

Biomorphs: At the GM's discretion, a Gargoyle may have Adrenal Glands (gaining the Furious Assault Talent) and/or Toxin Sacs (gaining the Toxic (1d10) Trait on all melee and ranged attacks.)

Blinding Venom: Attacks in melee from a Gargoyle have a chance of blinding its foe. If a blow from a Gargoyle with its teeth and claws strikes an opponent's head, he must make an **Easy (+20) Toughness Test** or become Blinded for 1d5 turns. Enclosed helmets (such as those on a suit of power armour) negate this ability.

Enclosed Space: Gargoyles are feral creatures and sometimes become trapped in places where they cannot fly, becoming crazed if their efforts to escape. A Gargoyle that becomes trapped in an enclosed space (i.e., where it cannot spread its wings or use its Flyer movement) gains the Frenzy and Furious Assault Talents until it escapes.

Gargoyle Hordes: Gargoyles often move and fight in vast flocks so dense that they darken the skies. They may be used as Hordes (see page 359 of the **DEATHWATCH** rulebook).

WARHAMMER 40,000
HORUS HERESY

WHERE DOES YOUR LOYALTY LIE?

Return to the 31st Millennium, when a golden age is shattered and demigods meet for one last apocalyptic battle!

Join in the *Horus Heresy*, a board game of monumental conflict for two players. Choose between the Holy Emperor of Mankind or the traitorous Warmaster Horus as they clash in a final battle for the fate of all humanity.

Horus Heresy is packed with over 120 detailed playing pieces, three dimensional terrain elements, and hundreds of components that will bring this saga to life on your table.

WWW.HORUSHERESY-BOARDGAME.COM

FANTASY FLIGHT GAMES

WARHAMMER 40,000

SPACE MARINE

I AM WAR

AVAILABLE NOW

ORDER AT SPACEMARINE.COM

MATURE 17+

M

Blood and Gore

Intense Violence

CONTENT RATED BY ESRB

relic ENTERTAINMENT

THQ